THE SOCIAL HISTORY OF AMERICAN AGRICULTURE

THE MACMILLAN COMPANY
NEW YORK · BOSTON · CHICAGO · DALLAS
ATLANTA · SAN FRANCISCO

MACMILLAN & CO., Limited
LONDON · BOMBAY · CALCUTTA
MELBOURNE

THE MACMILLAN COMPANY
OF CANADA, Limited
TORONTO

RELIEF

Over 8000 Feet
5000–8000 "
2000–5000 "
1000–2000 "
500–1000 "
Under 500 "

Reproduced from "The Atlas of Historical Geography of the United States" prepared by C. O. Paullin and J. K. Wright (1932). Published by the Carnegie Institution of Washington and the American Geographical Society.

THE SOCIAL HISTORY
OF
AMERICAN AGRICULTURE

BY

JOSEPH SCHAFER, Ph.D., LL.D.

SUPERINTENDENT OF THE STATE HISTORICAL SOCIETY OF
WISCONSIN; LECTURER, 2D TERM, 1935–1936, ON THE
COMMONWEALTH FOUNDATION, AT UNIVERSITY
COLLEGE, UNIVERSITY OF LONDON

NEW YORK
THE MACMILLAN COMPANY
1936

PRINTED IN THE UNITED STATES OF AMERICA
NORWOOD PRESS LINOTYPE, INC.
NORWOOD, MASS., U.S.A.

TO THE MEMORY

OF

FREDERICK JACKSON TURNER

PREFACE

THE several chapters of this book, written originally as successive offerings in a lecture course for University College, University of London, necessarily reflect some of the characteristics of spoken essays, each of which has to be relatively complete in its way. They were, however, so organized, in subject and in matter, as to tell the story implied by the general theme in a connected manner. The book, therefore, can be used either for topical study or for a comprehensive survey of the social history of agriculture. To fit it the better for class use, subtopics have been provided by way of analyses of the chapter contents.

It is pleasant to acknowledge the help given me by Professor B. H. Hibbard, of the University of Wisconsin, Department of Agricultural Economics, and author of *A History of the Public Land Policies,* who read chapters I and VIII; by Doctor H. L. Russell, late dean of the College of Agriculture, University of Wisconsin, and now director of the Alumni Research Foundation, who read chapter V; and by Professor John D. Hicks, of the History Department, author of *The Populist Revolt,* who read chapter VII. Each of these gentlemen offered valuable suggestions, some of which were embodied in a revision of the text. Doubtless errors and imperfections remain and for them the author is personally responsible.

The publishers and the author unite in acknowledging the courtesy of the Carnegie Institution of Washington and the American Geographical Society of New York who, as joint publishers of the *Atlas of the Historical Geography of the United States* (1932), prepared by C. O. Paullin and J. K. Wright, have kindly granted the use of the original drawings from which the illustrative maps in this volume have been made.

JOSEPH SCHAFER

State Historical Society of Wisconsin
Madison,
June 13, 1936

CONTENTS

CHAPTER I

LAND FOR FARMERS

The land supply. Farm lands in America, as compared with older countries, have always appeared to be superabundant. The few ship loads of English settlers who entered the Chesapeake region in the first quarter of the seventeenth century; the Pilgrims and Puritans of Massachusetts; the Dutch of New Netherlands; the Swedes of Delaware; and the other early groups, all thought of themselves as pioneering in a vacant continent. Nevertheless, among the earliest and most persistent social problems was that of making land available for ever-growing numbers. So eager and determined, at most times, was the quest for new lands that one would almost be justified in maintaining the exact opposite of the usual thesis that in America the supply of that commodity has always exceeded the demand.

Availability of land is a relative matter. Fertile soils were abundant in most districts, but sometimes the rights of the native Indian tribes stood in the way of their absorption by individuals, or perhaps the problem of clearing the forest seemed too arduous an undertaking. Distance from older settlements caused hesitancy always, and transportation

1

conditions were the most absolute of limitations. Movement into new areas was therefore spasmodic and, in a geological sense, catastrophic, rather than silently continuous.

The emigration of the Thomas Hooker congregation from Boston to the Connecticut valley was not complicated by Indian difficulties, yet it produced a powerful social disturbance in the Bay colony. Expansion in seventeenth century Virginia was marked by two bloody Indian wars, and a rebellion of the frontier settlers against the colonial government. And when, by the middle of the next century, tobacco planters had reached the headwaters of the Ohio, philosophers justified Britain's war with France as a means of breaking the barrier to expansion into much needed fresh tobacco lands beyond the mountains.[1] The attempt to interfere with the movement of population across the Alleghenies through the King's Proclamation of 1763 is reckoned among the causes of the American revolution.

Conditions of agricultural expansion. The military, political, and diplomatic history of America's territorial development makes a very general framework for her agricultural expansion. The wars of the nineteenth century with England, Spain, and Mexico had definite relation to the occupation of distinct regions, while within the greater areas a chronological map of Indian cessions might stand for a history

[1] John Mitchell, *The Contest in America between Great Britain and France,* London, 1751. Also his *Present State of England and the Colonies,* London, 1767. Also, *American Husbandry,* London, 1775.

of successive thrusts of a burgeoning people's colonizing impulse.

If all the good land with which the United States was endowed at the birth of the republic had been fully usable, there would have been no reason for Americans to cross the Mississippi prior to the middle of the nineteenth century, at the earliest. Such episodes as the settlement of Missouri, Texas, and Oregon cannot be explained on the theory of a redundant population in the older states. Yet, in all these cases the migrants were looking for land. The first large emigration to Oregon took place in May, 1843. At that very time occurred a land rush of settlers into the Sauk purchase of Iowa, while in the far-off Willamette valley the pioneers of the pioneering movement were framing a provisional government to guarantee the possession of their squatter claims.

Waterways and railroads. Men in the eastern states looked upon these events and marvelled. Horace Greeley thought the emigration of a thousand souls to Oregon wore "an aspect of insanity." In a burst of indignant eloquence he exclaimed: "Why do they brave the desert, the wilderness, the savage, the snowy precipes of the Rocky Mountains, the weary summer march, the storm-drenched bivouac, and the gnawings of hunger?" But the Oregon emigrants were not insane. They could give the editorial pundit a very sound answer, namely: "You say our wagon wheels in going to the Willamette carved ruts across millions of acres that are

fully as fertile as what we find here. True enough.
But what good is land if the means of getting its
products to market do not practically exist? In the
Willamette valley a navigable river flows by every
settler's door, and the ocean is only a short distance
away. Similar situations in the middle west were no
longer easy to find. Therefore, we headed for Oregon
to insure to ourselves and our children really valuable farm homes."

One cause of the Civil war was the spread of
slavery on the one hand, the progress of free-labor
settlements on the other. A cogent argument has
been made to show that, by 1860, slavery expansion
had reached its geographical barriers and could not
practically go farther.[2] Though vast areas in both
regions remained to be utilized, the South protested
every suggestion of preventing farther expansion of
slavery by law, and the North just as stubbornly
insisted on the principle of limitation. All this looks
strange now, but under conditions of the time it was
not unnatural. Dearth of land for farmers and for
planters was at that time a reality, not a fancy.
People were still under the psychological obsession
that areas a few miles from navigable water were
worthless for agricultural purposes.

This condition changed in startling fashion with
the progress of railway building. Whereas in the
earlier period only the river fringes had constituted
available farm land, the railways brought into use

---

[2] C. W. Ramsdell. *Mississippi Valley Historical Review*, XV,
151–171.

successive blocks of fertile soil lying at impracticable distances from water transportation. It would seem as if the railway should have been a permanent cure for the farm land shortage, and yet incidents like the great Oklahoma rush of April 22, 1889, when 50,000 persons, at the sound of a bugle, crossed the proclamation line in the hope of staking choice quarter sections for homesteads, or obtaining valuable lots in cities to be laid out and peopled the same day, throw serious doubt upon such a conclusion.

The king's grants-quitrents. The manner in which the soil of the New World passed into the hands of those who made farms is a matter of fundamental social importance. Under English law all land in the colonies belonged to the king who could grant it as he saw fit, and since custom is controlling in such matters, the method to be followed seemed preordained. The king would, of course, grant the lands in large tracts to companies or to his retainers who, in their turn, would lease them, for farming purposes, following the English practice. Colonies were needed for Britain's advantage, but they could not succeed without the guidance of leading men and these did not care for the terms of banishment implied in going to America, unless circumstances made staying at home unpleasant or removal very profitable. Land grants, therefore, were the travelers' checks with which migrating grandees were fitted out, and the investment comtemplated was settlers contracting to pay quitrents upon parcels of land.

Quitrents were supposed to fulfill two functions:

discharge the feudally derived obligation to the grantor; and satisfy the colonial government's claim upon landed property in the way of taxes. A rate of two shillings per one hundred acres, which was the rule in Virginia and not far from the average rate everywhere, does not seem like a burdensome tax. Yet it proved an enormously difficult levy to collect. Innumerable evasions occurred, stay laws were passed in the interest of grantees, as were laws permitting payment in products, usually at an overvaluation. After the Revolution, all the states abolished quitrents, thus changing holdings under grants that were so far conditional to strictly alodial or fee simple properties.[3]

Small-holdings of small people. While leaders of upper class derivation were necessary to the success of colonies, workers drawn from the poorer and needier social strata were indispensable. A voyage to the New World in the small seventeenth century ships was no holiday excursion. The percentage of deaths en route was high, and the period of acclimatizing also cost many lives. The plain people, in short, held the whip hand. They might refuse to leave home, and then all colonizing plans would fail. Or, they might agree to go if conditions were made sufficiently attractive for them. The assurance that a small area of land, usually fifty acres,

[3] For an excellent general treatment of the subject of quitrents, see L. C. Gray, *Agric. in the Southern U. S.,* I, 382–385. The New England colonies, however, did not adopt the quitrent system. For the whole subject of the land laws in Virginia colony, see P. A. Bruce, *Economic History of Virginia in the Seventeenth Century,* 1896, I, Chap. VIII, Macmillan.

would be given to every emigrant as a bonus for settling in an overseas colony was an irresistible temptation to landless people with means enough to pay their passage. And, when even the indigent could be carried to America and within three to five years each man receive for his mere labor,—which had meantime supplied his living,—a farm, some livestock and tools, one secret of the success of English colonies stands revealed.[4] Such "indentured servants" were the main reliance of Virginia and Maryland tobacco planters till toward the close of the seventeenth century, when negro slaves became plentiful enough to take their places and also to supply much of the farm labor in Pennsylvania and elsewhere in the colonies.[5]

Variety in colonial land laws. Land for farms was granted differently in the different colonies. Virginia and Maryland planters employed the so-called "head right." [6] This empowered one to locate fifty acres of land for every emigrant he brought to the colony. By transporting himself a man earned his fifty-acre grant. By introducing one hundred persons, he could claim five thousand acres. The headright was fearfully abused, claims being fraudulently created by hundreds and sold to be used as land scrip, the system ultimately breaking down and giving rise to the fee system of purchase; but

[4] W. E. Dodd, Emergence of Our First Social Order, *Am. Hist. Rev.*, XL, 2 (Jan. 1935).
[5] E. Channing, *History of the United States,* II, Chap. XIII, and notes.
[6] See P. A. Bruce, *supra.*

it yielded many of the great holdings that became the basis of the tobacco planting regime. Some dignitaries received grants as king's or proprietor's favorites, and set up what was intended to be the American equivalent of the English manor, though the jurisdictional features of the English nobleman's estate failed to mature and American manors remained practically great plantations.

In Pennsylvania, the proprietor granted lands, in tracts to suit settlers, at prices which were not always low compared with those later demanded by the United States government for wild land. The usual prices, in the eighteenth century, were from one shilling to three shillings per acre, equal to $1.00–$3.00 in our money. In New York, large grants were the rule and the Dutch patroons having early engrossed the district along the Hudson, agricultural settlement was retarded. It was not until western New York was opened up, after the Revolution, that farming development in that state came into its own.

Land law of New England. Of special interest was the system of grants in New England. Here we have what might be called controlled expansion. Men of prominence would associate together and ask for a grant of land. The general court would appoint viewers to help the applicants locate their tract, and to execute a survey, which came to be, frequently, in the form of a square six miles on each side. The grant made, the proprietors would divide it up into shares, and receive applicants for these fractional parts of the grant, to whom they conveyed title in fee simple. The settlers of the new tract would organize themselves into a town and hold town meetings, into a parish and maintain a church, into a school district and support a school. The proprietors would hold proprietors' meetings as long as any lands were left in their hands to dispose of. From early in the eighteenth century three shares were commonly reserved, one for the first settled minister, one for the ministry forever, and one for the school.[7] In this manner was the foundation laid for a full-fledged new community of the regulation Puritan type. Most of the private grants in New England were small, though a number of the leaders were favored with large areas, some of which became estates of the English type.[8] Rhode Island, small as she is, had some of the largest farms in New England, due to extensive early grants which were not divided up among heirs.

Squatting. One feature of colonial land settlement became very prominent later, namely, the custom of squatting. A squatter was a person who settled on a selected spot, built his cabin, cleared land and raised crops and cattle without bothering to secure in advance any kind of title to the tract he occupied. The land was there; he needed it. God meant the earth for man's use, so he used it. The forested character of most areas, and the ab-

[7] J. Schafer, *Land Grants in Aid of Education, U. of Wis. History Studies*, vol. 1, Madison, 1902.

[8] Bidwell and Falconer, *Agriculture in Northern United States*, 49.

sence of exact survey lines, made squatting easy and comparatively safe. At all events, it proved so difficult a problem to deal with legally, that proprietors of the back lands rarely attempted to eject squatters, or to collect rent from them for the use of the land. When surveys caught up with the squatter so his trespass became a matter of record, he was not punished, but was usually permitted to buy the land at the going knock down price. Thus the squatter in effect was treated as a pre-emptor. The farm of his own choosing became his after a period during which, with good luck, he might support his family from its products and also accumulate money to pay for the land itself.

Pennsylvania and Virginia were especially tender toward the squatter–pre-emptor. It was estimated that in the back parts of Pennsylvania, as early as 1726, were 100,000 squatters. "Improvement rights" were early bought and sold, like horses or any other kind of personal property. But by the middle of the eighteenth century "settlement rights" became the basis of a new kind of realty title. If a man had built a cabin, lived in it, and raised a crop on land he had cleared, he was a "settler" with rights protected by law.[9]

The pioneer who was bold enough to encounter Indian dangers on the western frontier cared little or nothing for the rights of landed proprietors

---

[9] J. C. Ballagh, *Am. Hist. Assn. Rept.*, 1897, p. 112. Of 670,000 acres of land "occupied between 1732 and 1740, 400,000 acres were settled for which no grants had been issued." That is, by squatters.

whether these were colonial governments, state governments, or great speculators. Pioneers carried a tomahawk for defense against the savage and as a camper's convenient tool and this they used to mark out on trees a claim to land they wished ultimately to settle upon, called, in consequence, "a Tomahawk claim." Then they would bring on their families, roll up logs for a cabin, deaden trees to open a clearing, and begin the crude process of subsistence farming. If someone came along who fancied the location and the land, they were ready to sell "improvements" and move on to begin again in some other spot. When the land came into the market, squatters were usually given preference over others who might wish to buy. In fact, during the post-revolutionary period a right of "pre-emption," which simply legalized squatting, became virtually universal though by no means uniform in the states which were to form the union.[10]

Washington's dealing with squatters. That the squatters of this period considered themselves all but invincible is demonstrated by their willingness to throw down the gage of battle to a speculator of such overmastering prestige as the military founder of American independence. The experience of George Washington in 1784 with a group of squat-

[10] This subject has been treated in detail by Henry Tatter in "The Preferential Treatment of the Actual Settler in the Primary disposition of the vacant lands in the United States to 1841." Ms. St. Hist. Library. Printed summary, Northwestern University, 1933. See also L. C. Gray, *Agric. in the Southern U. S.,* II, 621–629; and Bidwell and Falconer, *Agric. in Northern U. S.,* 75–76.

ters in western Pennsylvania is illuminating. Being a surveyor and an excellent judge of wild lands, Washington some years previously had become possessed of claims to many thousands of acres "over the mountains." One of these claims covering 2,813 acres of excellent land on a tributary of the Monongahela river (Millers Run), he had somewhat improved, by negro servants, as a means of holding the land; yet he found it now occupied in parts by fourteen squatters all of whom bore Scotch names.

These settlers believed that Washington's title was imperfect because his improvements had been very sketchy and so they determined to stand suit for ejectment rather than accept his offer to sell "the whole tract" at 25 shillings per acre (depreciated currency), to be paid in three annual installments, with interest, or to make them his tenants under leases running for 999 years, at £10 per 100 acres annually. The great man was successful in ejecting the settlers, due possibly to the care he had taken in perfecting his title but probably, in part, to the fact that he was George Washington whose name may have had a magic influence upon the high court before which the cases were tried.[11]

Pre-emption. The principle of pre-emption could not fail to grow out of the custom of squatting and both are normal products of the American frontier. Pre-emption did not become fixed in the national land laws till 1841, but frequent special acts of earlier dates had recognized its legitimacy. Wher-

[11] A. B. Hulbert, *Washington and the West*, pp. 49 ff.

ever, and for whatever purpose, men settled in the wilderness, they were sure to claim the right of buying, at minimum prices, the lands they occupied, including their improvements. Sporadic efforts of the federal administration to dislodge squatters from government lands or from Indian lands were so unpopular that eviction laws became virtually dead letters. Whole townships, future counties, even future states were once communities of squatters. It was reported in the United States Senate, in 1837, by no less a statesman than Jefferson Davis, that the newly created Territory of Wisconsin had a council, or legislative body, made up, in a large majority, of men who were squatters.[12] "Squatter sovereignty" became notorious politically in connection with Kansas. Yet many of these settlers were the very best type of American pioneers, emigrants from the New England states, western New York, Pennsylvania, Ohio, the border states and the South. They selected lands before they were for sale because in those regions were choice wheat lands or else reserved mineral lands, which were then specially attractive. They regarded themselves as pre-emptors, not as squatters.

During the nineteenth century, the pre-emption principle was not only made a part of the law controlling the disposition of government land, but was also inserted in all manner of special land grants.

---

[12] *Register of Debates,* XIII, 760–763 (February 1837). Davis' authority for the statement was Henry Hubbard, senator from New Hampshire, who was familiar with Wisconsin and was a large speculator in lands in that territory.

School lands might be bought at the minimum government price by those who had settled upon them. Companies receiving grants in aid of canal construction had to agree that settlers on their allotments would have the pre-emption privilege. And railroad companies, recipients of many millions of government land, were obliged to accept the same condition.

Professional squatters. Much has been said in condemnation of the pre-emption principle, and congressional debates on that subject were sometimes very bitter. Abuses in its operation were patent. One was the tendency to professionalize squatting. Men of a certain backwoods type actually preferred to move from place to place, keeping in the shadow of the forest, rather than to settle in a given spot and help reduce the land to a cultivated state. Being skilled axmen, these persons loved to open small clearings, to erect log cabins, and chop rails to enclose small fields. But that is as far as they cared to go in making improvements. At that point they were glad to sell out to a newcomer who wanted to make a farm and liked the location. The squatter packed up his few belongings, took down his trusty rifle, and traveling twenty, fifty, or a hundred miles, found another tract of land that suited him, and made similar improvements to be disposed of in the same way. Cases of squatters who repeated that operation a half dozen or more times were not rare. It was their method of making a living. Squatting was their trade.

Social effect of squatting. The squatter fulfilled, for his successor, two functions which otherwise were distinct: he "located" the land for him, a service always compensated at some customary rate when performed by a land-wise man, surveyor or other; and he contributed labor in making the first indispensable improvements. The locating function was speculative, but that was always the case. The man who could find choice tracts for incoming settlers, as the squatters did, was naturally able to command pay for his enterprise at a higher rate than one who offered them indifferent claims.[13]

The squatters' unrestricted wandering might, and often did, cause trouble with Indian tribes. This abuse, however, merely called for the more effective policing of Indian reservations which would have been desirable for other reasons. They were not the only white intruders upon Indian lands, and it is at least arguable that the dealer in fire-water, whom the law was designed to exclude but did not, was more often the instigator of Indian hostility than was the squatter. At worst, the squatters of the professional type were only the ragged fringe of the pioneering movement. The great body of new settlers, in any designated public land district, were honest householders seriously engaged in the laborious but hopeful business of making new farms. Such persons were squatters only in the technical

[13] Government surveyors were often charged with selling their information to settlers and especially to speculators.

sense of occupiers prior to purchase. By every moral standard they were pre-emptors.

Why pre-emption was opposed. The special laws granting the right of pre-emption were sometimes so faulty as to put a premium upon fraud, as for example, the "floating rights" provision in some of the early laws.[14] But fraud and corruption were not the only causes of complaint against the pre-emption principle. It contradicted the doctrine of free sale of public lands at the best prices obtainable, a policy inaugurated at the beginning of the national period and adhered to theoretically until adoption of the homestead law in 1862. The United States emerged from the Revolutionary war with a large public debt for the payment of which the government virtually pledged the public lands, their most available national resource. In order to make the most of this asset the lands must be sold for the best price they would fetch.

A plan for the disposal of the public lands was made in 1785, in the so-called land ordinance of that year, which applied to the country west and north of the Ohio river. The system of rectangular surveys was adopted, and ranges of six-miles square townships laid out on north and south lines. Alternate townships were to be sold entire, presumably to companies as was the custom in New England, or to speculators; the balance, in blocks of not less than one mile-square or 640 acres, at the price of

[14] Theodore Rodolf, Wis. Hist. Society *Collections*, XV, 357–358, gives an example of the way the floating right was used.

$1.00 per acre. Sales began in September, 1787, the auction being held in New York.[15]

Early federal land sales. The experiment failed to satisfy Congress. The demand was not keen. There was too much state land on the market, usually at a lower price and in locations both safer from Indian harassment and nearer the means of transportation.[16] Then, too, a Massachusetts aggregation had bought of Congress a vast area in southern Ohio on such favorable terms that they were able to undersell the government. Add to all this that hundreds of would-be settlers preferred to take possession of small tracts without the formality of buying them, especially if they had to travel long distances to land sales, and we have a situation that must have thrown considerable doubt upon the Congress plan to dispose of its public lands. The best chance appeared to be to let vast tracts go to companies or wealthy speculators which was done to the extent of several million acres in Ohio, the so-called Ohio company and John Cleves Symmes being the leading purchasers.[17]

In making these sales the government agreed to accept its own depreciated currency in payment. The rise in value of American money, after the adoption of the federal constitution, and particularly

[15] B. H. Hibbard, *History of Public Land Policies,* N. Y., 1924, 41.

[16] See, for example, O. Turner, *The Holland Purchase,* 363, 367, 368. Also, *Memoirs of the Historical Society of Pennsylvania,* IV, Pt. II, p. 114. J. F. Jameson, *The Am. Revolution: a Social Movement,* 64–65.

[17] For the conditions of these grants, see Hibbard, *Public Land Policies,* 43–45.

after Hamilton's financial plan went into operation, changed the whole aspect of the land business. For one thing, the deferred payments stipulated in the big contracts could not be made. For that reason the amount of land actually alienated to companies was greatly reduced from the original sale figures.

Hamilton's policy. Like the continental congress, Hamilton as secretary of the treasury under Washington, strongly favored the plan of large-scale sales to speculators and associations, and he was willing to accommodate the individual settler only incidentally. He suggested, indeed, a reduction of the price to thirty cents per acre, but since payment was to be either in specie or in securities of equal value, that was in reality a higher price than had been paid by the earlier large purchasers, but it was still very favorable to speculators. Hamilton made no real approach to the solution of the government's dealing with the actual settler. In fact, quite the contrary. Like many other public men, he believed that sales to settlers must be made mainly by speculators,[18] for he thought the government could not assume the responsibility of these petty transactions.

Problem of the land law. The other great secretary of the treasury of the early period, Albert Gallatin, being one of the apostles of Jeffersonian democracy, might be expected to deal with the public land question in a different spirit. That question,

[18] *The Works of Alexander Hamilton.* Lodge Edition, N. Y. 1886. Vol. XII. 47–54.

though much discussed in Congress session after session, seemed stubbornly insoluble. It had contradictory aspects, depending on whether it was regarded from the settler's point of view, from that of the government seeking revenue, from that of the states having lands to sell and settle, and from that of eastern communities loath to lose population through over-stimulated emigration.

An act of 1796, while incorporating most of the conservative post-revolutionary ideas, which were also those of Hamilton, diverged sharply from Hamilton on the subject of price. Congress may have hoped to discourage speculation by charging purchasers all that the lands were worth. Hamilton certainly did not want to limit speculation, and his proposed price had been thirty cents while that of the 1796 act was two dollars per acre. It did not work. Hardly any lands were sold under its terms. The stiff price, the virtual refusal of credit, and the size of the areas offered, not less than 640 acres, were blamed for its failure.

In 1800, under the leadership of William Henry Harrison, of Ohio, supported by Gallatin and other congressmen familiar with frontier conditions, the law was changed to permit minimum offerings of 320 acres, and also to give buyers a credit on three fourths of the purchase price, that balance to be paid in four equal annual installments. A settler could, therefore, become possessed of 320 acres on the payment of $160; and, if he made his subsequent payments promptly, the government waived its interest claim.[19] A very important provision of this law was its establishment of federal land offices in the districts in which lands were located. This became a permanent feature of the system and of course was in the interest of settlers who thenceforth could purchase land near home.

Democratizing the land law. Still, the competition of state lands kept down sales. Western New York and western Pennsylvania afforded many advantages to northern immigrants. Kentucky and Tennessee welcomed those from Maryland, Virginia, and the Carolinas. Settlers petitioned for the privilege of buying in such amounts as they could pay for. Gallatin believed that the price, $2.00, had had one desirable effect, of preventing large-scale speculation. Nevertheless, he recommended both a reduction of the price, and a reduction of the minimum acreage that could be bought by an individual. The latter point was exactly contrary to the views Hamilton had voiced a decade earlier; but Gallatin, being like his predecessor concerned about the state of the treasury, believed that receipts for public lands should build the fund for paying the nation's debt. He also foresaw that the evil of deferred payments must be avoided by selling for cash only.[20]

Gallatin's ideas were not fully met in the act of March 26, 1804, for the disposal of the public lands in Indiana territory. The minimum purchase, how-

---

[19] *Am. St. Papers,* Pub. Lands, I, 265. Gregg's Report from the Com. on Pub. Lands.
[20] Letter to Joseph H. Nicholson, Chm. &c., Jan. 2, 1804. *An. of Cong.* XIV, 1585–1589. Summary in Hibbard, *Pub. Land Policies,* 73–74.

ever, was reduced from 320 acres to 160 acres. Later laws permitted the purchase of as small an amount as 80 acres, and then, finally 40 acres became the unit in land selection and purchase. It was not till 1820 that the familiar one-dollar-twenty-five cents per acre price was established and coupled with it Gallatin's cash payment plan.[21]

Pre-emption again. In all of the discussions up to that time the demand from the West for a pre-emption privilege to the actual settler had been steadfastly resisted. It was felt to be incompatible with the policy of disposing of the lands so as to derive from them the maximum revenue. Pre-emptors—or squatters—would naturally pick the best lands in a given region, and for these they would, of course, pay the minimum price. That would discourage other buyers and there would be no enthusiastic bidding at the auctions. In short, it would demoralize the entire public land policy. This must be kept in mind if we are to understand the long and bitter struggle through which frontier states and territories secured the preferential treatment of actual settlers.

The architects of the American land policy were practical men, not logicians, and defended their system on a few simple principles. First among these was that the public lands belonged to the whole na-

---

[21] Readers of Eggleston's *Hoosier Schoolmaster* will recall how the old lady, who had a marriageable daughter, leered when telling the young schoolmaster about her husband's economic foresight in that "the six hundred dollars he got along o' me [was] all salted down in Flat Creek bottom land at a dollar and a quarter an acre."

tion. Hence, they must not be alienated in a way to benefit chiefly one part of the nation, namely the West; or so as to injure another part, the East, as would be the case if too many of its people were tempted to emigrate to the West. Congressional leaders, too, were as keenly interested in the doctrine of the "sufficient price" as was later Edward Gibbon Wakefield who gave that phrase currency. Like him they professed a desire to secure regularity in the settlement of the public domain, the exclusion of speculation, and the maximum benefit to the colonizing nation. But they were no nearer certainty as to what the sufficient price should be, or how it could be obtained, than Wakefield himself.[22] Besides, so many public men were engaged in land speculation that professions cannot always be taken at face value.

When in 1820 Congress abolished the credit principle they coupled with that change the reduction of price from what had been nominally two dollars but actually somewhat less, to one dollar and twenty-five cents per acre where it remained.[23] The theory was that any land that was wanted at all should be worth that much, and that competitive bidding would bring up the sale price of the rest to about what it was worth. Lands once offered for sale which were not bid off, were then to be offered, by the land office, at private sale at the minimum price.

[22] See his *Art of Colonization* and his *England in America*. Also, Hibbard, *Public Lands,* 551–554.
[23] The graduation principle, passed in 1854, applied only to lands once offered at public sale and passed over.

Direct action of settlers against speculators. Such was the theory; the practice was far different, due mainly to the conflicting interests of speculators and squatters. For, despite the views of Gallatin and others that the prevailing knock down price would prevent speculation, it actually failed to do so for several reasons. In the first place, men with money could usually assemble certain kinds of scrip, or warrants which empowered the holder to locate and enter definite amounts of land, as Virginia colonists did with headright certificates. The first of the series of soldiers' warrants were those representing the claims of revolutionary soldiers and officers. It was those warrants that Washington used so largely in his land speculating.[24] Next, the soldiers of the War of 1812 received land warrants; then those of the Mexican war; and finally the northern soldiers of the Civil war. Such warrants not only guaranteed their possessor a price as low as the minimum, but generally lower than the minimum. Hence speculators were eager purchasers of soldiers' land warrants which had a definite place in market quotations.

Then, too, men of means and social position like many of the speculators, could exert influence in various ways that gave them advantages over the common man who tried to buy land for a farm. One method was to court the surveyors who, of all men, knew most about the lands that were up for sale at the land offices. By commanding the sur-

[24] Virginia soldiers' warrants could be assigned. See *Am. State Papers,* Pub. Lands, I, 13.

veyor's co-operation by whatever means (and charges of actual corruption freely launched were probably not always fallacious) the speculator would know exactly what lands to place scrip on without personally inspecting them. If, then, certain of the tracts he coveted were actually occupied by a squatter who had made improvements but had not the means of purchasing, the speculator could take the improved claim out from under him. And he had other tricks in his bag. One was to bid high enough for desirable lands to have the tract knocked down to him, and then forfeit the purchase by refraining from reporting at the receiver's desk and paying over the money for it. In that case the same tract would be open to private purchase after the auction closed. He would then go around to the land office and buy it of complaisant officers at the minimum price.

Speculation, when profitable. Of course, there were frequent occasions when more than the minimum price could be safely paid in the expectation that the lands would increase rapidly in value. That was true when the speculator himself was able to set in motion a current of immigration to the neighborhood of his selections, as when he controlled the local water power and built a grist mill, or the natural townsite and established a local trading center, or the best steamboat landing which would determine a townsite; or if he had influence in an eastern community from which many emigrants were heading west, so that his personal appeal would bring in numbers sufficient to absorb the remaining public lands and also his private holdings.[25]

All of the above situations were illustrated in the settlement of every one of the western states, and besides there were not wanting speculators whose appeal to special foreign immigrant groups was peculiarly effective. For example, Morris Birkbeck and George Flower, two Englishmen of means, established an English colony in Edwards county, Illinois, by bringing over a hundred and fifty English farm laborers as purchasers of their lands. Montgomery county, New York, in the last decade of the eighteenth century, received a large Scotch colony, appropriately named Caledonia. They came from the Highlands of Perthshire and were attracted to America by the representations of Charles Williamson, a Scotch or English speculator who sold them land at $3.00 per acre, on a credit of ten years, supplied them with provisions for a year, with teams, cows, etc. This case reveals some of the services which the large speculators were able to perform for their clients.[26] Sometimes they built roads, as in the Genesee country of New York, obtained public favors for their communities from state legislatures or from Congress, and generally played the role of patron or laird till the community arrived at the stage of self-helpfulness when the great man often fell into disfavor.

[25] An admirable account of one of the greatest land speculations is in Paul W. Gates, *The Illinois Central Railroad and Its Colonization Work,* Cambridge, Harvard University Press, 1934.
[26] O. Turner, *Holland Land Purchase,* 380 ff.

The question as to speculators' profits cannot be answered in a word, for these necessarily varied with circumstances. Where a rapid flow of settlement filled up the area in which speculators' lands lay, they were apt to reap sure and generous rewards, provided they were not too greedy. If they held their lands at too high a valuation, as compared with comparable lands not too far removed, settlers would pass them by. Then taxes, interest, and possibly a financial depression would be likely to cause losses instead of gains.

The years 1835 and 1836 were one heyday of speculation in government lands. The panic of 1837 and the resulting financial depression ruined many speculators as well as more legitimate business men. Among holders of Wisconsin lands who felt this pinch was Daniel Webster of Massachusetts. He, as well as Edward Everett, Ralph Waldo Emerson, and Caleb Cushing, owned considerable western land bought at the minimum government price. Slow sales, annual tax demands, and interest charges proved too much for Webster who was forced to relinquish his Wisconsin holdings to Cushing.

Soft snaps for speculators. Some shrewd Yankees speculated in ways that almost guaranteed profits. There were state lands to be had at times. In Wisconsin the so-called "500,000 acres" given to the state under an act of 1841, by the United States for an internal improvements fund, was choice tracts, selected by state officers out of the aggregate of unclaimed government land. It was located in the

most promising situations, and of course only lands
of good quality were chosen. Having made its selections, the state proceeded to sell them at the
government's minimum of $1.25 per acre; and this
it did on a thirty years' credit, the interest only at
seven per cent being collected each year in advance!
Here was a chance for speculators, it almost looks as
if it had been made for them. They hurried to buy
up the several parcels of the 500,000 acre land in
certain counties, paid the interest on the purchase
price, and quickly found purchasers at about double
the state's price only a few cents of which they had
as yet paid in.[27]

Settlers' grievance settled. It was the actual or
suspected partiality shown by officials to wealthy
speculators which, by a natural reaction, brought
about co-operation among the squatters or settlers
to render a portion of the land law inoperative. The
law was clearly designed to bring about a free sale
of the public lands for the highest price to be had
among competing bidders. Since speculators, by
their chicanery, tended to make free bidding impossible or abortive, the settlers combined to abolish
the practice entirely. So far as they were concerned,
there would be but a single bid for each tract
claimed by a settler and that bid would be "one
dollar and twenty-five cents." Should any moneyed
man, or his legal representative, attempt to bid
after "settler," something was sure to happen to him

[27] Joseph Schafer, Wis. Hist. Society *Proceedings,* 1920, 156–
181.

and he was likely to recover consciousness only to learn that "settler" had paid for the land and carried away with him the register's receipt which was a good title. After a time speculators carefully refrained from bidding on claimed lands. The frontiersmen, by direct action, had democratized the system of land sales at the cost of government income.

It would be a mistake to suppose, however, that they had eliminated speculation, or that dishonesty was wholly foreign to the character of pioneer settlers themselves. Money not only continued to "talk" but also to beckon. In Wisconsin, the effects of the 1837 panic and depression were so severe that it was known hundreds of claimants would not be able to raise the money to pay for their lands. President Jackson, acting on petitions from the settlers and from the territorial government, postponed the sale several times. Finally Van Buren set it for late February and early March, 1839. At that time so much government land was on the market in several public land states, approximately 12,000,000 acres in the aggregate, that a money famine seemed inevitable. Therefore, thought one of the local speculators, "opportunity will be afforded, to those who have money, of entering one half of a pre-emptor's farm which is improved by paying for his half; that is, the pre-emptors will be willing to let you bid off their lands at the sales and deed one half to them. My opinion is that as much money can be made at the land sales to take place this fall as at

any former period, by purchasing only such lands
as have been improved, with the settler's consent." [28]
That plan was carried out by half a dozen speculators, some of whom secured in this way a few
thousand acres of good land. Some, however, were
over-reached by the settlers who turned over to the
speculator the part of their claim that was swampy
or otherwise worthless.[29]

Settlers become speculators. But settlers were
speculators on a small scale just as truly as the
moneyed men were on the large scale. It was the
common practice, especially of Yankees, to enter
more land than they expected to use for farming
purposes in order to have a tract for future resale
at a high price. The rules of the Milwaukee county
settler's association permitted the claiming of a
maximum area of 640 acres though the normal claim
was 160 acres. Evidently most of the largest were
intended to be divided later, and probably some of
the smaller holders expected to get along with 80
acres, speculating on a good price for the balance.
Besides, all sorts of small business and professional
people became "settlers" in the beginnings of new
communities for the sake of acquiring settler's rights
to good land in which they would then be protected
by the settler's association. Once entered at the land
office their tracts were held for a speculative rise in
price.

[28] John Catlin to Moses M. Strong, Aug. 2, 1838. With
Strong Mss. in Wis. State Hist. Library. When this was written
the sale had been proclaimed for November, 1838.
[29] J. Schafer, *Four Wisconsin Counties,* chap. V.

Foreign immigrants not speculators. Here, however, a distinction should be drawn between settlers who were normally of a speculative turn, like the American Yankees, and such persons, mostly foreigners, as were only too glad to obtain possession of a small tract of land out of which to make a farm. The best examples of the latter class were, of course, the peasant type which constituted so large a proportion of the immigrants from every foreign country. Never having owned any land, or if any merely a Liliputian area, such persons rejoiced exceedingly if, through the expenditure of $100 they could acquire title to eighty acres, or for fifty dollars even as little as forty acres. And having gained it, unlike the mobile Yankees, they stuck to it, through good and evil report, making farms which in due time were frequently used to finance the purchase of other tracts relinquished by American neighbors anxious to "go west," and raise wheat or cattle on a larger scale.[30]

But both the modesty and the immobility of foreign stocks disappeared after the lapse of a single generation in America, and the children of Irish, German, English, Scandinavian, Polish, and Bohemian parents became quite as land hungry as Americans of the older lineage. The later phases of the public land history would have a character distinct from the earlier on that account alone—the

---

[30] See Letters and Diary of Fr. Diederichs (trans.), *Wis. Mag. of Hist.*, VII, 218–237, 350–368. Also, J. Schafer, *Winnebago-Horicon Basin* (in press), chaps. VIII–XIII, especially chap. IX. And J. Schafer, Yankee and Teuton in Wisconsin, Characteristic Attitudes toward the Land, *Wis. Mag. of Hist.*, VI, 125–145.

universal grim determination to secure the very largest portion of land to be obtained on the minimum government terms. There were, however, other concurrent circumstances affecting that history. We are dealing, in this late phase, with the immense non-forested areas of the great plains, with the heavily timbered western mountains, or the dry grass-covered plateaus. From the point of view of land utilization each one of these characteristic land types invited to exploitation on a scale greatly enlarged from the earlier farm-making practice.

Homesteading. The original homestead law, offspring of the earlier pre-emption policy, which in its turn sprang from the custom of squatting on the public lands, required a five year residence on the quarter section homesteaded as a condition of receiving patent free of cost save a small entrance fee. But later a commutation amendment was adopted whereby purchase could be made at the minimum price after fourteen months. Later still the residence requirement for a free homestead was reduced to three years. A homestead entry could be treated as a pre-emption. Also the person who had "proved up" on a pre-emption, settled upon perhaps before the land was surveyed or ready for entrymen, had no need to live on it longer and he could then take up a homestead. A timber-culture law of 1873 provided a way of obtaining another quarter section by cultivating one fourth of it—later one sixteenth of it—in trees.[31]

---

[31] In 1878 this law was changed by requiring only ten acres to be planted and cultivated in trees.

A very present help to the eager seeker of a mile square farm was the Civil war soldier's land warrant, issued under a law which was designed to encourage the ex-soldier holders to select farms for themselves and thus obtain the full benefit of the government's bounty. Did they do it? In 1868 the commissioner of the General Land Office wrote: "It is believed that not more than 1 in 500 . . . have located their warrants . . . the greater part of such warrants having been sold and assigned, the soldier having received in cash probably an average of 75 per cent of the minimum price of the land." [32] Various other kinds of land scrip could be had to supplement soldiers' warrants, such as agricultural college land certificates issued to states having no public lands and sold by them for cash; common school fund claims; railroad land-grant scrip, etc. These were on the market, as well as the lands owned by railroads and other organizations under federal grants, which sometimes were sold to individual farm-makers at not much above the government's price.

Acquiring large prairie farms. In some or all of these ways, in addition to purchase from private holders, the makers of prairie farms, on which full advantage could be taken of the newest labor saving machinery, succeeded in gaining farm areas distinctly larger than settlers had secured in more easterly localities. The census reveals the result. North Dakota farms, for example, according to the

[32] Commr. Joseph S. Wilson, Report for 1868, p. 106.

1910 census, averaged 382 acres while the census of 1920 makes that average 466 acres. For corresponding dates, Wisconsin's average was 85 acres and 117 acres respectively.

The great plains of North America stretch from about the western limits of the first tier of states beyond the Mississippi, that is, Arkansas, Missouri, Iowa, and Minnesota, through an average of more than ten degrees of longitude, to the high Rockies. In that broad sweep the terrain changes in character both from the effects of increasing altitude and increasing aridity. It comprises what travelers and geographers, from the time of Long's expedition to the Rocky Mountains in 1819, called the great American desert. Emigrants to Oregon, California, and Utah, crossing it summer after summer with large numbers of livestock, demonstrated the falsity of that description, for a land which would graze cattle all summer and, as was proved incidentally, all winter too, and sometimes bring the beasts out in spring fat enough for the slaughter pens, is not properly a desert.

The railroads crossed the great plains from east to west, as did the main emigrant trails. Farming settlers crowded along all communication lines, especially the railroads, taking homesteads as near to transportation service as possible, which means anywhere along the entire line at distances north or south within a practicable hauling distance from the road. Geographers, public men, even land office commissioners warned against the danger of entering

land beyond the 100th meridian for ordinary farming purposes.

At that time no settlement, practically, had broken
into the vast buffalo range of the semi-arid plateaus,
the big herds of Texas cattle ranging freely from
the staked plains to the Canada boundary. As late
as 1882, when Dugald Campbell, an Argyleshire
sheep specialist, took up his homestead and timber-
culture claim in the valley of the Cannonball river,
North Dakota, he was at the edge of settlement, the
land adjacent to his being unsurveyed. He says: "I
camped in my covered wagon beside some twenty
thousand square miles of unoccupied land; devoid
of animal life, except the ubiquitous jack-rabbit, a
few packs of devilish wolves, and at times a welcome
band of the shy and graceful antelope." The next
summer, driving across the waste of "bad lands"
into southern Wyoming Campbell, aided by a Scotch
shepherd lad and a collie dog, grazed a flock of
sheep, purchased in southern Wyoming, a distance
of 600 miles to his Dakota ranch home, never getting out of the public lands area. Twenty years
later this sheep rancher abandoned his business,
which had been rendered impossible by the incursion
of agricultural settlers, and removed to the Willamette valley of Oregon where he started a fruit
farm.[33]

Tempted by the opportunity to obtain fine appearing lands near the railroad, and deceived by the

[33] Dugald Campbell, *Sheep and Shepherds Here and Elsewhere,*
Ms. in State Hist. Library.

exceptional precipitation of a few abnormal seasons into believing those lands fit for agriculture, the thousands rushed in with results which in a large proportion of cases were tragic. Those who wanted the lands for grazing, the purpose for which they were adapted, were unable to obtain them at economic prices. So farmers and graziers mingled belligerently on the high plateau, to the ruin of both classes and of the grasslands. The government's inflexible land laws made criminals of some ranchers, as it did of some lumbermen, together with their thousands of perjured aiders and abettors.

Violating the land laws. Cattlemen boldly fenced public land, or in some cases where certain tracts would control a water privilege for them, or where land designated as swamp land was cheap enough, they hired persons to locate upon quarter sections and enter them for the cattlemen's benefit, as lumbermen were doing in the forested areas in order to control adequate areas of timber to make the basis for successful milling.

It must not be assumed, however, that large-scale adventurers, like the cattle kings and the lumber barons, were the only offenders against the land laws during the later phase of settlement. Just as in the earlier phase, farming pioneers were quite as ready to stretch the law to the breaking point as were the big operators. On making his entry under the homestead act the homesteader swore that he was taking the land "for his exclusive use and benefit, and not either directly or indirectly for the use or benefit of any other person or persons whatsoever." Yet in thousands of cases understandings were entered into and finally executed which gave the patented land to farmers exactly as was done in behalf of lumbermen and big ranchers. The ethical question involved was simply never raised—at least not until the time, about 1903, when President Theodore Roosevelt began to enforce the conservation principle by bringing some of the timber barons into the courts on charges of fraud. Then farmers and others also began to reflect upon the process by which they had acquired their large holdings.

About that time a certain highly ethical and deeply religious retired farmer was heard explaining to his somewhat puzzled but frankly honest wife, how wicked the timber men had been in promising to pay entrymen certain amounts for their claim when it should be proved up. "Why," said the good woman, harking back to a time twenty years earlier when her husband and eldest son took contiguous homesteads in the Jim river valley of Dakota: "Isn't that what you done with Byron?" "Oh," said the husband, coloring deeply, "that was a wholly different matter."

Chapter II

PRIMITIVE SUBSISTENCE FARMING

VIRGINIA, "Earth's only Paradise" as viewed from afar by the imaginative poet Michael Drayton, at close range wrought magically also upon the practical mind of Sir Thomas Dale. After surveying the country with care, Dale assured his employers in London: "take four of the best kingdoms in Christiandom and put them all together, they may in no way compare with this countrie either for commodities or goodnesse of soile." [1]

Colonizing motives. Britain's colonization of North America was motivated by the hope of deriving therefrom certain national advantages. Among these was the production of staples like wine, silk, flax, hemp, tar, and soap ashes. Also the opportunity to secure a supply of ship timber, to promote shipping, and to create a great new market for English manufactures, such as woolens. Another advantage was that colonies would relieve the mother country of her redundant population, especially the poorer sort.

The character of the establishments which were to be erected in America was implicit in the national

[1] Brown's *Genesis,* I, 494.

objects that should be promoted by them: they were destined to be agricultural colonies. Other objects there were, to be sure, inspired by the history of Spanish colonization in the two Americas. Most engrossing was the hope of finding mines of the precious metals and hardly second that of discovering a waterway which should open a passage for English ships from the Atlantic to the Pacific. And in the first thrill of excitement over Virginia the latter objects were pursued to the partial neglect of the more legitimate ones. But this condition rectified itself in the course of a few years and Virginia became the first of the long series of English agricultural colonies in North America.

Beginnings of agriculture. The great river valleys of eastern Virginia, before the coming of white settlers, were occupied by an Indian population variously estimated at from 5,000 to 10,000, who obtained their living to a large extent by cultivating the soil. Their method of clearing away groves of heavy timber was by girdling the trees in early spring, to prevent the sap from rising. Through this means the trees died, decayed, and either rotted away or were consumed by fire. To such an extent had clearing and planting proceeded that many hundred acres of open land existed in 1607, but such tracts along James river, where the colony was begun, were all cultivated by the Indians themselves. The colony for strategic reasons took possession of Jamestown Island which was heavily forested.

The English did not understand the labor-saving

methods of the natives, but followed the more laborious mode of land clearing by physically removing all trees and the undergrowth from the soil. Having quickly done this on the small tract immediately around their fort, they sowed about four acres of wheat the first season. Meantime they learned, in the course of their explorations, how largely the Indians depended upon maize or corn for food and saw how it grew in the open fields. Much corn was secured from the natives in trade. When Captain John Smith in the spring of 1609 had about forty acres cleared for the purpose, and also had two Indian captives to teach the whites how to prepare the ground and set the seed, a large field was planted to that cereal.

Capt. John Smith and Sir Thomas Dale. Smith's removal from the governorship, the neglect of the corn crop by the settlers, the failure to secure supplies from the natives, and the arrival of more mouths to be fed, resulted in the "starving time" of 1609–10. It was not till the arrival of Sir Thomas Dale a year later that the colony took on the characteristics of a permanent agricultural community.

The original colonists, like their promoters and leaders—except Captain John Smith—were far more intent on adventure, such as gold-hunting and geographical exploration, than on producing food in the sweat of their faces. The company in London, they hoped, might send adequate supplies of food; or, failing this, they could perhaps obtain it from the Indians in trade. So reckless were they that, as was reported, many of them exchanged their axes, hoes, mattocks, and other tools—even their fire-arms—with the Indians for supplies. Since no one had personal property in these things, and all were expected through their labor to contribute to a common store, the sense of personal responsibility was weak, and only a relentless master could overcome their indolence.

Such a master they had in Smith, and such a one they received again in Sir Thomas Dale. On his arrival, May 12, 1611, at Old Point Comfort, Dale lost no time but with all available hands, "fell to digging and cleaning the ground and setting of corn and in 4 or 5 days we had set more ground about Fort Henry than Sir Thomas Gates found sett by the Indians in the year before." He utilized fully the Indian cleared lands about the lower forts, then sought out more Indian lands up the river toward the falls. Most important he saw the need of assigning "farms" (limited for the moment to 3 acres) to a number of the most worthy settlers on a lease-hold basis, which went far to insure the growing of adequate food supplies. But he also caused the balance to labor regularly in the "common garden."

Tobacco planting begun. Sir George Yeardley, Dale's successor, extended the system of individual holdings, introducing for the company the custom of granting freehold tenures, with a reservation of quitrent. Settlements were extended, many new homes built, the stock of cattle, goats and hogs multiplied rapidly notwithstanding Indian depredations. In a word, to use the language of one of the old school histories, "Industry and good habits spread among the people."

Virginia, however, quickly passed out of the phase of subsistence farming. Or, perhaps it would be more accurate to say that a different type of farming developed promptly alongside of the subsistence type, which threw the latter into the background. In Virginia's great valleys, served by navigable tide-water rivers with their numerous excellent ports, agriculture leaped from the subsistence plane to the business plane with no intermediate steps. Yet, not far off, on the uplands between the parallel streams, and in the valleys themselves above the fall line, were both subsistence farmers and general farmers.

The reason for this peculiarity of her agricultural history is tobacco. Tobacco was not one of the staples that the colony had been designed to produce, and for several years persistent efforts were made to promote wine growing and silk growing. Exceptionally fine native grapes, and a great abundance of mulberry trees seemed to favor these industries which if once competently advanced, would have freed England from a costly and precarious dependence upon France and Italy for supplies of these luxuries. Some wine was made and also some silk, but the results were negligible. On the other hand, the colonists found the Indians growing tobacco, they promptly began planting it themselves, looking to the Spanish West Indies for seed and for

instruction in the best methods for its management.
Since England required a very large supply, the
custom of smoking having expanded rapidly since
the days of Sir Walter Raleigh and of King James's
"counterblast against tobacco," an assured market
was at hand. This is why, in the short space of seventeen years, Virginia had passed from the condition
of a struggling colony, worried about how its people
were to be fed, to a community fired with an ambition to grow rich through the production of a great
marketable staple.

Not that riches were attained too quickly and
easily. Questions of adequate lands for expansion,
questions of a labor supply, questions of the best
methods to pursue in order to guarantee the sala-
bility of the product: all of these had to be worked
out. But the outcome was the planting system, one
of the most characteristic forms of business agriculture. The typical early subsistence farming region lay far to the north.

Captain Smith describes New England. "Who
can desire more content, that hath small means,
or but only his merit to advance his fortune,
than to tread and plant that ground he hath purchased by the hazard of his life. If he have but the
taste of virtue and magnanimitie, what to such a
mind can be more pleasant than planting and building for his Posterite, gotte from the rude earth, by
Gods blessing and his own industrie, without prejudice to any?" ". . . And what sport doth Yeeld
a more pleasing content, and less hurt or charge than

angling with a hooke, and crossing the sweete ayre from Ile to Ile, over the silent streames of a calme sea?" Thus mused the redoubtable Captain John Smith, sometime colonizer of Virginia, in his *Description of New England,* written before the Pilgrims came thither to test the austerities of his prescription for obtaining earthly happiness.[2]

Location of Plymouth colony. When the Pilgrims arrived, after devoting about five weeks to exploration, during which time they had the luck to find a cache of Indian corn ears for seed, "some yellow and some red, and others mixed with blue—a very goodly sight," they "came to a conclusion, by most voices, to set on the main land—on a high ground, where there is a great deal of land cleared, and hath been planted with corn three or four years ago; and there is a very sweet brook runs under the hillside and many delicate springs of as good water as can be drunk, and where we may harbour our shallops and boats exceeding well; and in this brook much good fish in their seasons; on the further side of the river also much corn-ground cleared. In one field is a great hill, on which we point to make a platform and plant our ordnance, which will command all round about. . . . Our greatest labor will be fetching of our wood, which is half a quarter of

---

[2] The writer of A Perfect Description of Virginia, 1649 (see Force's *Historical Tracts,* II, No. 8, p. 12), says: "That New England is in a good condition for livelihood. But for matter of any great hopes but fishing, there is not much in the land; for it is as Scotland is to England— There is much cold, frost and snow, and their land so barren except a herring be put into the hole that you set the corne or maize in, it will not come up—"

an English mile; but there is enough so far off." [3]

Having a situation commodious in all respects
for the beginning of a colony, when the leaves on
the white oaks were the size of a mouse's ears, as
the rules of Indian husbandry prescribed, they began to plant their corn. Squanto, the much-traveled
native, sole survivor of the tribe or clan which had
inhabited that site, taught them how to set it,
fertilize the soil with fish, and cultivate the corn;
with the result that they obtained a crop of that
indispensable food grain. Their English seed, "wheat
and pease . . . came not to good, eather by ye
badness of ye seed or lateness of ye season, or both,
or some other defects." [4] Their corn supply, small
as it was, when supplemented with a store of water-
fowl and other game and with fish, roots, and vegetables, made a kind of relative momentary plenty
for which the thankful Pilgrims celebrated. But it
was not until the third season, when, as Bradford
puts it: "after much debate of things, the Govr gave
way that they should set corne every man for his
own particular," that famine was permanently
routed and subsistence farming for the first time
actually guaranteed subsistence. In two years they
had corn for trade with the Indians. [5]

Subsistence farming and farms. It is worth while
to consider the ground plan of Plymouth colony in

[3] Bradford and Winslow's *Journal.*
[4] Bradford's *History of Plymouth Plantation, Boston,* 1898,
121.
[5] Bradford, *History,* 246–247. A cargo sent to the Kennebec
brought as return 700 of beaver.

its commencement. The basis, Indian corn land along both sides of the estuary, has already been referred to. The granting of one acre to each "particular" took place in 1623. Then, in 1627, after agreeing upon shares in the general venture, the livestock was divided, a cow to six shares or families, two goats to the same, and the larger number of swine in the like proportion. Most significant was the division of the land, the tillable portion of which was bestowed twenty acres to each family or share. This arable lot stretched five acres in length along the waterside and extended back four acres in breadth. The balance of the land they passed by "as refuse or common." "But no meadows were to be laid out at all, nor were not of many years after, because they were but streight in meadow grounds; and if they had been now given out it would have hindered all additions to them afterwards; but every season all were appointed where they should mowe according to ye proportion of cattle they had. This distribution gave generally good content and settled men's minds." [6]

Differences between the Plymouth situation and that of early Virginia are striking. While the Virginians settled in the midst of a numerous and powerful Indian population, the Pilgrims chanced upon, or as they believed, were providentially guided to a spot from which and its neighborhood all the native inhabitants had been recently removed by a deadly contagion. Their extensive corn lands, therefore,

[6] Bradford, *History,* 259–261.

were a free gift to the pious immigrants who, unlike their southern friends, were not compelled to clear away the forest in order to secure ground on which to raise food, or to make enemies of the natives by driving them away from their cleared lands.

Moreover, the Pilgrims enjoyed the advantage of the colonizing experience had in Virginia. Echoes of Virginia's "starving time," however, and the severity of the northern winter, warned them never to relax their diligence in producing food, at the same time that they redeemed their obligations to the London merchants who stood financial sponsors for the colony. The second object called into requisition the best business talent the colony possessed and in this respect the leadership of Edward Winslow stands out in their early annals. Some of their labor force was largely engaged in navigation, fishing, trading, and woods work. But the major portion all of the time, and the entire population part of the time, was occupied with the tillage of their twenty-acre fields and their one-acre gardens, besides utilizing the wood commons, the hay commons, and the pasture commons.

Methods of cultivation. It should be understood that hand cultivation prevailed during the first years. The Pilgrims grew maize precisely after the Indian fashion, save for the possession of better hoes and the labor of men as well as women. In preparing for the corn crop, strips of ground of a hoe's width were loosened up several inches deep and several kernels covered therein. By Squanto's direction, a fish or two was deposited in the soil near the seed. These plantings were made from four to six feet apart each way and as the plants grew, the intervening ground was hoed over to kill the weeds, also the soil around the growing corn was kept loose. Later the corn was "laid by" through the process of hilling—just as the Indians made their corn hills.

When plows and animal power came into use the system was changed. The field was furrowed out in squares of five or six feet. The seed being dropped at the intersections was then either covered with a hoe or with the loose soil of a second furrow. As the young corn grew, the space between the rows was plowed, and the weeds within the rows hoed out. The final hilling up was generally done with the plow.

In a rough way, the above describes the husbandry not only of Plymouth colony, but of all New England, so far as growing their principal food crop was concerned. Wheat, after corn, succeeded fairly well for some years, but by the end of the seventeenth century it was understood that southern New England could not grow that grain successfully on account of the "blast," a mildew or smut which damaged the crop seriously. Rye was a more dependable bread grain and it continued to be grown even beyond the colonial period. Mixed with corn-meal, its flour made New England's staff of life, proverbially described as "rye and Injun."

Fish and meat food; wool. Contemporaries of Izaak Walton, Pilgrims and Puritans were not only lusty commercial fishermen, but devoted anglers as well, particularly when they had the valid excuse that fish were needed for food. Since the early settlements were almost exclusively along the seacoast, its inlets and the principal rivers, fish was always an important element in the people's diet. Of animal food, pork was the most plentiful, the swine running in the woods and becoming conditioned on nuts, acorns and roots. A little corn finished them off. Cattle also ran in the woods and over the rough grounds, which were the cow commons. They received very little attention, frequently living all winter on browse, dry corn stalks, a little hay and straw, without artificial shelter of any kind, the contemporary English custom of wintering stock in the open being too strong to break despite the difference in the winter climate between the old England and the new. The result was lean kine always in spring, and a very high death rate among the herds. When animals were stabled, the shelter provided was extremely meagre.[7]

Sheep flourished on islands, or where they had some defense against predatory wild animals like wolves, wild cats, panthers and bears. Like the neat cattle, they were liable to be sadly neglected. Yet

[7] Samuel Pickard, *Life and Letters of John Greenleaf Whittier*, Boston, 1894, I, 17. Whittier told his biographer that the "old barn" on his home farm, used till 1821 had no doors; that "the winter winds whistled through it, and snow drifted upon its floors for more than a century. The horses and cattle were but slightly protected in their stalls and 'tie-ups.' This was the early practise throughout New England. Our fathers, coming from the milder climate of Eng., had the traditional English slowness in adapting themselves to changed climatic conditions."

they were kept in small numbers almost everywhere for a home supply of wool.

Home industries. What with field crops, like corn and rye, a variety of farm livestock, and the products of the gun, trap, and rod, the New England farmers could supply themselves with food, and this in spite of the crudeness and wastefulness of their agriculture. But in order to procure those necessaries which the soil did not yield—salt, sugar, tea, coffee; also clothing, footwear, hats; iron and tinware; leather goods; tools and implements; and the small change required annually by church' and commonwealth, all manner of shifts were resorted to. Whatever it was possible to make, even though the expenditure of labor upon it was excessive, they made at home. Rough furniture was fashioned from surplus timber, garments and harness from leather made by tanning the hides of animals that died of winter exposure and starvation, or of deer killed in hunting; and shoes and boots from the same. Clothing was wrought from home-grown wool, or flax. The wooden parts of plows and harrows, tool-handles, cart tongues, ox-bows and yokes, often cart wheels, were made on the farm mostly in winter.

The cash absolutely indispensable might be derived from forest products which were incidents of land clearing, like pot and pearl ashes, charcoal, firewood, or other more valuable timber, especially such as could be used in shipbuilding or for lumber. The farmers also manufactured for sale shingles or "shakes," barrel staves, hoops and heading, sugar molds for the West Indies, treenails for ship builders, wagon wheel spokes, bowls, and in fact all articles made of wood for which a market could be found. Sometimes they could turn off a barrel of salt pork, some smoked hams, or some dressed fowls. And, in many places, where the hard maple tree prevailed, the spring sugar making supplied the home with sweets and often left a surplus for the market. The planting of orchards was common, apples being the favorite fruit. Out of a portion of the apple crop the farmers made cider and if a barrel of cider became "hard" it might perchance be sold as vinegar. Possibly, during the prevalence of the winter snows —after the New Englanders began using sleds, which they learned from the Dutch [8]—interior farmers might manage a trip to Boston, New Haven, or New York, carrying the summer's surplus of butter and cheese, the frozen carcass of a slaughtered hog, or a quarter of beef.

Farming defects. The New Englander in American cultural history symbolizes the qualities of canniness, thriftiness, industriousness, and efficiency. There can be no doubt about the subsistence farmer of that region representing the second and third of those four virtues; he frequently illustrated the first, also, as the saga of horse trading proves; but much more rarely the last. Good farmers were probably as scarce in New England, at the close of the eighteenth century, as they had been in Old Eng-

[8] The use of the sled was copied from the Dutch in New York. England, nearly snowless, did not use them, hence New Englanders had to learn their utility.

land at its beginning. Custom, it must be repeated, is the determining factor in the transmission of institutions from an older to a newer land. And does not Lord Ernle tell us, what later writers confirm, that in England, "From the reign of Henry III to that of George III the trinity fields received the unvarying triennial succession of wheat or rye, spring crops such as barley, oats, beans or pease, and fallow." [9]

The uneconomical open field system, long under condemnation in England, was not reproduced in the New World, except sporadically, but the rotation it implied, or the lack of it, was followed roughly for generations, as if it were a sacred tradition. The weedy fallow was grazed by livestock, just as it was in England, the tillage of the planted fields was equally shallow and ineffective, and similarly the kine "only survived the winter in a state of semi-starvation." Seventeenth century English agriculture, as yet only mildly tinged by a spirit of improvement, save as it had been affected by the market for wool, which made arable land scarce and grain foods dear, was reproduced in New England with but few modifications or adaptations to the different conditions and without the stimulus of high prices for farm products.

Habit was the basis of agricultural practice up to the time when the revamping of general economic conditions compelled its transformation. In Eng-

[9] R. E. Prothero, The Pioneers and Prospects of English Agriculture, *Quarterly Rev.,* 159 (1885), 325.

land that time came with the onset of the industrial revolution and the urban growth and trade expansion accompanying it in the eighteenth century. In America it was deferred till in the early years of the nineteenth century a somewhat similar economic upheaval broke the "cake of custom" letting in new ideas from all sources and new practices which were partly of indigenous growth but largely borrowed from older countries.

Yankee handyman a poor farmer. The New England farmer rather prided himself on his ability to turn a hand to almost any necessary work. He was an expert axman, and he wrought so persistently in wood as to become more or less skilled in carpentry, joinery, and cabinet making,—sometimes also in wood carving. But he was likely to be in addition a cobbler, harness maker, and perhaps a blacksmith, all on the same plane of imperfect training and incomplete equipment, a true "jack-of-all-trades" and master of none. There is no question that all of these experiences made him a more resourceful man than his farmer contemporary in the Old World. But just as certainly it made him an inferior farmer.

The farm, in its most amiable mood, is a jealous mistress. As Jeremy Belknap of New Hampshire wrote, late in the eighteenth century, "so sudden is the succession of labors that upon any irregularity in the weather they run into one another; and if help be scarce, one cannot be completed before the other suffers for the want of being done." He felt that "It is partly for this cause . . . and partly from a want of education, that no spirit of improvement is seen . . . but everyone pursues the business of sowing, planting, mowing, and raising cattle with unremitting labor and undeviating uniformity." [10]

These observations are keen and eminently just. Farm operations themselves were always, save in winter, pressing on one another's heels. But when the farmer's attention to his inevitable routine was distracted daily or hourly by duties which were quite alien to the function of tillage, like mending harness, shoeing oxen, tightening cart wheel tires, cobbling children's shoes or fashioning an ax or hoe handle, there was no time even to think of possible improvements in his farming. The only way to get along at all was to let habit substitute for thought.

Social arrangements. New England life centered in the "Town." This was part village and part scattered farmsteads. As late as 1810 more than two-thirds of the people in the states of Connecticut, Massachusetts, and Rhode Island lived in towns having from 1,000 to 3,000 inhabitants. Most of the villagers were farmers as well as the dwellers around the village. The villages contained perhaps one hundred houses, though the majority rarely exceeded fifty. Each family had its lot, and its outlying field.[11] But some were clergymen, lawyers, physicians, craftsmen, tradesmen, taverners, mill-

---

[10] *History of New Hampshire* (Boston, 1792), III, 137–138.
[11] Percy Wells Bidwell, *Rural Economy in New England,* New Haven, 1916. (Trans. Conn. Soc. Arts & Sciences, v. 20.) 253.

ers, sawyers, tanners, etc., in addition to owning
and operating farms. Naturally, the intensity of
interest in farming varied inversely as that in the
profession or trade pursued. Yet it was perhaps the
relative leisure insured by the professional man,
and especially his superior intellectual training, that
gave the earliest impulse to improvement in the
methods of New England farming. Jared Eliot, the
earliest writer on agriculture, was minister and physician as well as farmer.[12] In this respect we have a
rough correspondence with early English agricultural improvement, which began not on the petty
and ragged holdings of peasants but on the estates
of the leisured class. For example, it was long before
clover emerged "from the fields of gentlemen into
common use." [13]

How the land was used. The farms of the towns-
men might contain fifty, one hundred, or even two
hundred acres, but the amount of arable was commonly an insignificant fraction of the whole. Ten
or fifteen acres was the rule, the balance being forest,
native pasture, and meadow land. Most of the arable
was always set to corn, their most useful cereal.
It provided—mixed with rye of which a couple of
acres were grown—the bread of the family; it fed
and fattened livestock and poultry; the stalks when
cured served for winter feeding in barns and sheds
or, left standing in the field above the snow, at-

[12] Jared Eliot, Minister, Physician, and Farmer, *Agric. Hist.*,
2, 185–212.
[13] *Qtly. Rev.*, 159, p. 333.

tracted the hungry, browsing cattle till plowed under in the spring. The husks of the corn ears made mattresses for the beds; the cobs kindled fires and were an ever ready resource to the tobacco smoking householder who frequently needed a new pipe bowl. The New Englander's heart throbbed in unison with that of her poet, Whittier, when he sang the "Corn Song":

> Heap high the farmer's wintry hoard
> Heap high the golden corn!
> No richer gift has autumn poured
> From out her lavish horn!

> Let other lands, exulting, glean
> The apple from the pine,
> The orange from its glossy green
> The cluster from the vine;

> We better love the hardy gift
> Our rugged vales bestow,
> To cheer us when the storms shall drift
> Our harvest fields with snow.

Some flax was grown for fiber, and a little for seed. There were no regular root crops, though most farms provided a few garden vegetables. Rotation of crops was irregular. The same ground might be planted to corn, or sowed to flax and oats, year after year till "it ran out," then be left to weeds and grass for a few years before being broken up again. Pasture and hay were more important, in general, than cultivated crops, livestock pretty much caring for itself with some slight attention in the coldest weather. The best New England farmers, particularly those near market towns, as we shall see, farmed differently but the great majority were still, at the end of the eighteenth century, subsistence farmers.

There are, however, various levels of subsistence and the testimony shows that, on the whole, New Englanders lived well. By the middle of the eighteenth century primitive housing had been replaced with decent, fairly commodious and well-appearing structures—the classic white painted wooden houses with green window shutters, surrounded by a neat picket fence also painted white. Clothing and food agreed with the housing. Here we have a sharp contrast to what could be seen in other subsistence farming regions and the reason for the difference is partly in the character of the Puritan founders, but more largely in their organization of church life, education, and local government. The sometimes nagging, but effective social habit of looking after each other's private affairs tended to generalize the best social ideas.

Another powerful influence was the economies these industrious farmers were able to make both on and off of their farms, in non-agricultural ways. By manufacturing woodenware to sell, sending a son into the pinery for a winter in a logging camp, participating in coastal trade, in fisheries, in the adventurous whaling voyages, in peddling goods through the South and West, or becoming drovers, they kept themselves alive and alert, maintaining a rural morale which was prepared at the proper time for the more profitable farming that was to come.

Appalachia. "To a person who has witnessed all the changes which have taken place in the western country since its first settlement, its former appearance is like a dream, or romance." [14] Thus wrote Joseph Doddridge, in 1824, from the valley of Virginia. Doddridge's father had settled in the western district which was then still disputed between Virginia and the Quaker colony, in 1773.

The geographical region should be known inclusively as Appalachia. From the eastern slopes of the Alleghany mountains in Pennsylvania the so-called Great Valley sweeps southwest across Virginia and West Virginia, embraces parts of eastern Kentucky and of Tennessee, and communicates with the Piedmont or lands east of the Blue Ridge in southern Virginia, the two Carolinas, and Georgia. Included in the area are the loftiest of the eastern mountain ranges, high, narrow and steep intermountain valleys, deep river gorges and beetling cliffs. In general the mountain slopes were heavily forested, with big timber and dense undergrowth. This is the mediating section between the seaboard states and the Mississippi valley, the transitional terrain, joining the East and the West. In Turner's nomenclature, it constitutes "The Old West." He

[14] This is the opening sentence in Joseph Doddridge's *Notes on the Settlement and Indian Wars of the Western Parts of Virginia and Pennsylvania.*

found it was peculiarly the theater of pioneer state making during the Revolutionary era, and that it holds a most important relation to the development of the New West, as well as to the expansion of the seaboard colonies.[15]

A frontier farming region. In another aspect this mediating land was America's western battle front in the age-long contest of her people with the hostile Indian tribes of the interior. That warfare began early in the history of the colonies, it was intensified by the rivalry of English, French, and Spanish, and later by the pressure of settlement toward and through the Ohio river gateway and Tennessee river gateway to the West. The new American republic found herself forced to conquer the country from the Indian allies of the English and the Spaniards. It is not surprising, therefore, that for a hundred years after the Revolution the area was known as the western border, much as in Great Britain the Grampian Hills and the Cheviots for ages marked a borderland between England and Scotland, or the Rhineland between France and Germany. And if Appalachia lacked in border poetry, it was not deficient in more homely forms of the literature of romance. The stories of its heroic pioneers and Indian fighters—its Boones, Kentons, Bradys and Wetzels—stimulated to historical writing if not to balladry. Up to the time the sons and grandsons of those pioneers began going to Oregon and Cali-

[15] See his *The Old West,* which is Chap. III in the *Frontier in American History,* New York, 1921, especially pp. 85–100.

fornia, thereby inditing the new and greater drama of Pacific coast pioneering, the Appalachian frontier continued to be the favored land of the romantic historian.[16]

The Piedmont in Virginia was settled early, and largely from the tidewater and middle sections, the frontiers above the fall line on the rivers being defended by what Virginia lawmakers quaintly called "Warlike Christian men" maintained at colony expense, under the leadership of some distinguished or able commander combining the character of colonizer or trading speculator.[17] Later, with the enormous drift of Scotch-Irish and German settlers south from Pennsylvania, the Piedmont of Virginia, the Carolinas, and Georgia, as well as the Great Valley, became largely settled by people of those derivations who generally could be described as being in poor or middling circumstances. Many were squatters taking advantage of the liberal land laws of Pennsylvania and Virginia to obtain farms in the back country.[18]

A greater New England. It must be clear to the student of American geography that Appalachia,

[16] Doctor Lyman C. Draper, for example, devoted a lifetime to collecting the manuscript memoirs of descendants of the Appalachian pioneers; wrote sketches of many of them, and an elaborate history of their greatest collective achievement, the triumphant defense of the border at King's Mountain against seasoned British troops. The Draper Collections, bound in 565 volumes, are in the Wis. State Hist. Library. They formed one of the bases of the significant work of Prof. Frederick J. Turner.

[17] *Cf.* Alvord and Bidgood, *First Explorations of the Trans-Alleghany Region,* Cleveland, 1912. Introd.

[18] The best summary of this history is in F. J. Turner, *The Old West.*

from the standpoint of the kind of farming which prevailed there in pioneer times, was essentially a greater New England. Western New York and northern Pennsylvania could well be added to the enormous block of the subsistence farming area occupied by Americans in the closing years of the eighteenth century, though the period of transition to general and business farming was in each of those districts exceptionally brief. The Piedmont, the valley of Virginia, and connecting valleys constituted for an entire generation the most characteristic subsistence farming area outside of New England.

Character of the country. Our instinctive belief, however, that the farms of that great region all had to be hewed out of the forest is a mistake. The Piedmont "was a rare combination of woodland and pasture with clear running streams and mild climate." [19] The same remark would describe the Great Valley as it was in the period of its settlement. At an earlier time it seems to have been more densely forested, but the Indians gradually burned so much of the woods that large open spaces, richly covered with grass and peavine, were accessible to the cultivator and grazier. This, taken in connection with the deficiency of good grassland in eastern Virginia, helps to explain the trend toward cattle raising on the frontier where the "cowpens" or stock corrals marked off distances along the north and south

[19] Turner, *The Old West.* See also Alvord and Bidgood, *First Explorations of the Trans-Alleghany Region,* Cleveland, 1912, p. 48 ff.

trails. Small farmers, however, were much more numerous than the owners of large herds. Redemptioners from England, on completing their term of service, went west to take up the small tracts to which they were entitled, adding of course squatter's claims; those from Germany who spent their contract period in eastern Pennsylvania, in Jersey, or "York State," moved west and south; while thousands of Palatines and other Rhinelanders, instead of remaining to swell the number of "Pennsylvania Dutch," formed little colonies in the valley of Virginia, or in the Virginia, Carolina, or Georgia Piedmont where they met and mingled with a double stream of Scotch-Irish, from Philadelphia and from Charleston.

Crops and markets. The large-scale cattle growers must be classed as business farmers to be discussed later. All the balance for a time were subsistence farmers. They produced on their lands all the food required for their families, and for the rest they made out in a variety of ways, some of them laborious enough, to obtain the essential outside supplies. Some raised small fields of tobacco as a first crop on their newly opened lands, and either "rolled" it in hogsheads to a tidewater market, attaching thills to the cask and driving an ox hitched thereto; or they worked their little crop down the stream in small boats. After roads were built into the interior upland, wheat, or the flour from it, made in the numerous little frontier water-driven mills, could sometimes be wagoned to tidewater when prices were very high, as during the Napoleonic wars. Generally, however, grain would not bear the cost of transportation for which reason the whisky distilled from it often became the sole resource of the westerners as a means of exchange for necessaries to be bought in the seaports. Of this the tragedy of the Whisky Rebellion is the permanent but sad memorial.

The marts of trade were Philadelphia and Baltimore for the Pennsylvania, Maryland, and Virginia frontier; [20] and Charleston or Savannah for the up-country of the Carolinas and Georgia. The actual pioneers in the several communities were in the habit of making up a train once a year for going to market. All travel was on horseback, and pack horses carried out the furs, the bacon, linen, linsey-woolsey, or whisky to be used in making purchases, while at times livestock was driven along for the same purpose. Salt was one of the most indispensable articles to be carried back, and it cost, in the early period, a good cow and calf per bushel. A pack horse could carry back a two-bushel bag of it. Iron was another prime necessity, also very dear; and gradually, as the settlers' resources of livestock and other products increased, the ever expanding wants of the people gratified themselves with imported stuffs for making their company clothes, buckle shoes, wigs, tea, coffee, and other articles once considered luxuries.

Rapidity of change. But when that stage was

[20] But see "Falmouth and the Shenandoah Trade before the Revolution," *Am. Hist. Rev.*, July, 1935, 693 ff.

reached, it was no longer necessary to join the annual brigade for market. The market had come to their towns and villages, the merchant buying such farm produce and household manufactures as he could resell, and exchanging for them the goods individual farmers required. Furs and skins continued for a long time as an element in this trade, but pork, beef, homecured hams and bacon, honey, butter, cheese, and eggs, gradually dwarfed their significance. At last the extent and variety of farm products that could be sold was such that, while the actual mountaineers lagged permanently behind, the farmers in the more favored districts of Appalachia had clearly passed out of the subsistence and into the general farming stage of development.

How early did this take place? Hear Doddridge, as he describes the region in 1824, representing one (himself) who was brought up there: "The little cabin of his father no longer exists: the little field and truck patch, which gave him a scanty supply of coarse bread and vegetables, have been swallowed up in the extended meadow, orchard, or grain field. The rude fort in which his people had resided so many painful summers, has vanished. . . . Large farms, with splendid mansion houses and well-filled barns, hamlets, villages, and even cities, now occupy the scenes of his youthful sports, hunting or military excursions." [21] Doddridge, who lived near the one great national highway, wrote pridefully of

[21] Joseph Doddridge, *Early Settlements,* Albany, 1879, 59. *Cf.* Buck, S. J., "Frontier Economy in Southwestern Pennsylvania," *Agric. Hist.,* X, No. 1 (Jan. 1936).

the fine roads which had taken the place of the
pioneer horse trails, and of the extensive wagon
freighting over them; he dilated upon the improvement in housing which, in his view, changed the
psychology of the people and, being a clergyman as
well as a historian, he emphasized the profound
alteration which the progressive amelioration of
living conditions, coupled with general education
and the influence of organized religion, had produced
in the manners and social character of the people.
He tells us that when, as a boy of seven, he was
sent east from the frontier to attend school, his
astonishment was great on finding there were houses
in the world not built of logs. Forty years later he
is environed with "splendid mansions."

The New West. West of Appalachia lay the vast
new agricultural world of the Southwest and the
Middle West. Whoever has experienced the thrill
of passing the Alleghanies from the East, whether
to emerge upon the lowlands of Ohio, Kentucky,
Tennessee, or Alabama, will appreciate the difference between the farming opportunity in those fertile, horizon-bounded plains and that of the country
to the eastward.

Also, in that region, fruitfulness was but one of
many favors conferred by a bountiful nature. Splendid forests alternated with open lands, or neighbored
with far stretching praires; tree clad hills and
wooded vales diversified the general landscape;
springs and streamlets, lakes and rivers guaranteed
an abundance of good water. But most important,

in the eyes of the eager homeseeker, the Mississippi river, its principal branches, and the Great Lakes with their eastern connections provided natural systems of transportation always available to those who prudently settled near their borders.

Its abounding resources. And if "angling with a hooke" yielded "a pleasing content" to the maritime New Englander, how much more suitable to the pioneer rangers of a continent was the experience of hunting in the trans-Appalachian West! Buffalo, deer, and bear they had for big game possessing food value as well as a secondary value for pelts. Turkeys, prairie chickens, pheasants, water fowl, and myriads of passenger pigeons enticed the less ambitious sportsman. Streams and lakes teemed with fish, while the fur-bearing animals—beaver, otter, mink, muskrat—excited the trapper's cupidity. Even as Daniel Boone, that mighty hunter, in taking his long look westward from the Alleghanies, pronounced Kentucky "an earthly paradise," so the pioneers who were prospecting for ideal farming situations exulted in the promise of the new land.

Variety in the Southwest. The Southwest was destined to be exploited mainly by the class of business farmers under the resistless impulse of cotton, tobacco, and sugar planting, with negro slave labor. Nevertheless, it too, like New England, Appalachia, and the Middle West, had its subsistence farming stage of pioneering, and there were likewise permanent subsistence farming eddies in the great onsweeping current of planting history. The squatter erected his rude cabin, or his log house, in the valley of the Tombigbee, the Big Bend of Tennessee river, and the Pearl, just as his forebears had done by the waters of the Yadkin, the Roanoke, or Miller's Run. His patch of corn, his cow, and razor back brood sow were there, as they had been yonder, and as they were to be in all the region north and west of the Ohio, the economic basis of his existence. But, when the claim he located was wanted for cotton growing, by men who felt able to pay ten, twenty, even a hundred times the government price for the rich "buckshot" lands so famous for their cotton, no squatter could withstand the pressure. He either passed on to the farther Southwest—say Missouri, Arkansas, or Texas—moved across the Ohio to get wholly away from the competition with slavery, or slunk back onto the rougher, stonier and thinner soils to persist as a small farmer or as "poor white trash" in a planter dominated world.[22]

The Middle West. The Old Northwest, and its neighbors on the western side of the Mississippi, make up the imperial domain for which the descriptive name Middle West is now the accepted designation. Large enough to embrace the combined areas of France, Germany, Italy, and the historic Austria-Hungary, with something to spare, this country was destined to become the world's greatest single food-producing region through the development within its dozen states of a varied and pro-

[22] Compare F. J. Turner, *The New West,* especially pp. 71–78.

gressive agriculture representing something new and distinctive in rural sociology.

Throughout the region, however, the beginnings of farming were everywhere essentially the same, save in cases where control of capital permitted a deviation from the normal. The man of means could select and buy the land he wanted, build a good home, clear, fence, and break up ground for fields, assemble livestock: in short, make a farm with all its appurtenances, while maintaining himself and family out of previously accumulated funds. To him there was no need of eking out a bare living from the soil, the forest, and the stream. He could begin and continue as a business farmer; and that is what a certain small proportion of the settlers on each successive frontier did, that proportion growing larger as farming encountered the great open prairie.

Its typical settler. The average settler, however, was a poor man. If he had the wherewithal to pay for his land, and buy the barest necessaries for taking possession, he was fortunate. Beyond that everything depended upon the vigor and intelligence with which he attacked his problem of living and farm-making; upon his credit with friends in the old home, his business ability, and his "luck." The first couple of years at least were bound to be a time of privation, sometimes of temporary want and of struggle for the elementary requirements, food, shelter, and clothing, without which life on a civilized plane is impossible. But how far beyond those initial seasons the subsistence farming would have to continue depended on outside help the farmer could command to speed up the process of farm-making, the kind of land he happened to secure, whether open land or forest, and the accessibility of a market for what he could raise on his newly broken-up soil.

Some fortunate districts, of which examples are southern Michigan and southern Wisconsin, northern Illinois, eastern Iowa and eastern Minnesota, favored by both soil and transportation facilities, passed from the primitive to the general farming stage almost unconsciously. In other districts the people experienced long and bitter struggles merely to survive. Except on the poor soils, however, or in out-of-the-way places where they were quite cut off from markets, the transition period to farming for profit was relatively very brief.

The plains and far West farmers. The pioneer on the Great Plains differed from the settler of the nearer West in being wholly dependent upon artificial means of transportation, especially the railroad. Generally, also, he required more capital to make a safe beginning, having to buy many things which older pioneers made from the timber on their claims. Nevertheless, the sod house and sod stable often took the place of the more easterly log structures, thus deferring the expense of permanent building till crops could be raised to pay for materials and labor.

Since, however, the plains farmer operated on a

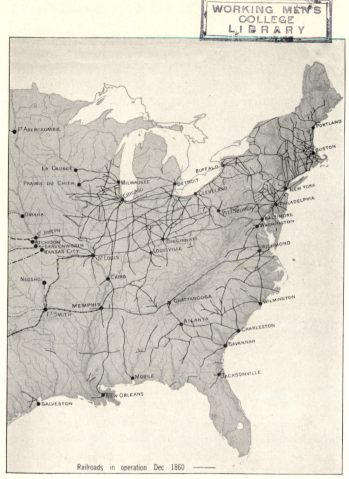

Railroads in operation Dec. 1860 ———

Reproduced from "The Atlas of Historical Geography of the United States" prepared by C. O. Paullin and J. K. Wright (1932). Published by the Carnegie Institution of Washington and the American Geographical Society.

larger scale than his ancestors farther east had done, he required more and more expensive equipment, and more stock. The plains, it has been well said, were mastered as an outgrowth of the industrial revolution which gave man the revolving pistol with which to fight the mounted Indian, barbwire to fence the fields, the windmill to pump water, and the self-binder to reap their crops.[23] All of these cost money. But the pioneer of the Great Plains was apt to be an individual who had already gained either property or credit on an older frontier. If not, he was sure to suffer severe privation, or perhaps fail entirely.

Primitive farming in the far western highlands, and in the valleys along the Pacific, varied little from that already described, though the high plateaus were at first occupied by graziers rather than farmers and life in many mountain areas began with mining which provided local markets for farm products, thus enabling farmers to work their way rapidly out of the primitive and into an improved state of agriculture. It is hardly necessary to point out that the American frontier which, through the seeing eye of a Turner, has taught us such important historical lessons, passed away along with the primitive subsistence farming that characterized it.

[23] Walter Prescott Webb, *The Great Plains*. Boston (Ginn) 1931.

Chapter III

BIG BUSINESS FARMING

Woodlands and tobacco. "Woodlands are to a planter in North America what a dunghill is to a farmer in Britain." In such homely phrase does Doctor John Mitchell, whose writings are generally wanting in epigrammatic piquancy, provide the true key to the history of tobacco planting expansion.

When the Virginia or Maryland owner of a hundred head-rights could select 5,000 acres in any of the favored parallel valleys, and many engrossed several times that amount, it followed that the best lands accessible to ports on tidewater were quickly occupied and tobacco growers began looking beyond those limits for fresh planting opportunities.

Passing the fall line into the upper reaches of the valleys, spreading out along the Piedmont, penetrating the so-called Great Valley, a few more decades brought them to that over-mountain region of surpassing fertility and indefinite extent which, unfortunately, was dominated by French forts as a means of controlling the fur trade.

Mitchell's plea for the expulsion of the French from the Ohio and Mississippi country was supported by ample, even verbose, argumentation. It is, however, epitomized in the words quoted above. Tobacco had proved a profitable staple to Great Britain, justifying her continental colonizing enterprise much as did the production of sugar in the West Indies, rice and indigo in the Carolinas and Georgia. On the other hand, the general farming middle colonies were of comparatively slight utility to the mother country, while fishing and trading New England was a positive detriment except as a source of ship-timber. Tobacco lands east of the mountains had been so largely exhausted, the old planters being forced to adopt an economy dominated by grain raising and livestock, that, from the national point of view, expansion into the farther West appeared imperative.

Land, capital, and labor. A fateful union of woodlands, capital and labor, in the hands of men endowed with business talent, coupled with the guaranteed market in England, made tobacco planting for nearly a century an almost certain road to fortune. The land was cheaply acquired, while capital was of course derived originally from accumulations in England. Labor at first was supplied, in fairly adequate amounts, by indentured white servants, but in the course of the seventeenth century these were gradually superseded by African negro slaves.

Negro slavery was considered more favorable to the planter than contract labor for several reasons. First costs were of course much greater, and insurance against loss during acclimatization, always a precarious period, was heavy. But once past this danger a likely young negro could be counted on to render uninterrupted service for many years. And such service freed the planter from all the usual vexations involved in contract labor. There were no appearances before county officers to record contracts or their termination, no violations of contract to be investigated by officious magistrates, no hampering restraints on discipline, no expensive settlements with departing servants. Slave labor made all plain sailing provided the slave continued in health and the master could train him to work effectively and docilely.

Some, however, were incapable of learning, some were intractable, some incorrigibly lazy. Besides, there was always the danger that an active field hand might sicken and die, and the equally disturbing prospect that the useless aged might live on indefinitely as their owner's pensioners.[1] So, even when capital owned its labor all was not unalloyed satisfaction on the tobacco plantations from day to day, while the occasional depressions due to falling prices created temporary crises,[2] and epidemics of disease like smallpox or cholera could ruin planters in a few weeks.

Big-business farming results.   Tobacco culture,

[1] Philipps, *Life and Labor*, 174–176.

[2] Philipps, *Life and Labor*, Chap. X; Gray, *Southern Agriculture*, I, 474. Jernegan, *Laboring and Dependent Classes*, Chap. I, discusses the effect of low prices for staples in causing diversification in production, the training of slaves along mechanical and industrial lines, and their employment in manufactures.

which was the characteristic planting industry of the
seventeenth century, and continued to be the leading
type in Virginia and Maryland, save as it was modified by grain farming, was flanked during the eighteenth century by rice planting in the coastal region
of the Carolinas and Georgia. This connoted a more
intensive system of tillage than that involved in
tobacco production. Rice could be grown successfully only on swampy soils, susceptible of being
flooded, which at the outset fixed a sharp geographical limitation for that form of planting. Also,
the closeness of supervision required emphasized
the overseer relationship as it was not emphasized
in the tobacco regions, and this, in turn, combined
with the malarial character of the terrain, gave rise
to absenteeism on the part of owners and their
families, who either sought health in the mountains
during the hot months and social recreation in the
cities, especially Charleston, during the winters, or
else fixed their principal residence in the city permanently. In either case the slaves, engaged in the
most laborious cultivation, most of the time in water
and slime, under the hardest conditions to be encountered in the entire South, were subject to a
hired overseer whose leading motive was to show
the master a favorable balance sheet.[3]

Indigo planting, introduced by Eliza Lucas, the
later Mrs. Charles Pinckney, in the forties of the
eighteenth century, was often carried on in con-

[3] Fanny Kemble, *Journal of a Residence on a Georgia Plantation,* 1833.

nection with rice culture. While the latter utilized the swamps, the former might employ the strips of oak land adjacent to the swamps. Slave labor could usually be employed more profitably in a combination of the two than in either form of planting by itself, except where the best uplands favored indigo as a single crop. However, indigo planting declined seriously before the end of the eighteenth century, due to the competition with the East Indies and to the ravages of insect pests,[4] leaving rice the dominant staple of the far South.

Rice and indigo in the South. It was considered, in the eighteenth century, that thirty slaves could be worked to advantage, under a single overseer, on a rice plantation.[5] Thus, the owner of 500 or more slaves, of whom there were examples,[6] could cause them to be distributed among a score of distinct plantations, some of which he might not so much as set eyes upon from one year's end to the other. Indigo planting could be made profitable with a few slaves, the overhead costs being very light, and where carried on separately from rice planting might be under the direct supervision of the owner.[7] But the opposite condition prevailed so frequently that the slavery regime in the lower South as a whole gained an evil repute for harshness as compared with the patriarchal system of Virginia and Maryland.

[4] Philipps, *Life and Labor*, 118–119. *American Husbandry* (by an American), two vols., London, 1775, II, 400 ff.
[5] *Am. Husbandry*, 395.
[6] *Ibid*, 425.
[7] *Am. Husbandry*, 432.

Up to this point we have considered merely the beginnings of the planting type of agriculture, if looked upon from the standpoint of its physical extension, for it was cotton that explains the planting and slave systems of the historic pre-Civil war South. As Dixieland would have it in the days of tension between the sections: "Cotton, not corn, was King." So far as that slogan was true, the development making it so practically all took place in the post-Revolutionary era. A little cotton had been grown earlier, even from the beginnings of colonization, and attention was often drawn to it by the promoters of the doctrine that a diversity of staples would be better than a few, both for the colonies and for England. Cotton usually came into the list of desirable products along with silk, wine, hemp, and flax. But prior to the Revolution it was grown only for the consumption of the home in certain sections, especially the Carolinas.[8]

The cotton which served these domestic purposes was the short staple variety, with clinging green seeds from which the lint could be separated only with a large expenditure of hand labor. It throve both on rich bottom lands and on the uplands, in the appropriate climatic zone, but was economically unfitted to be the basis of a planting regime unless invention should solve the problem of cheaply separating the fiber from the seed.

Sea-island cotton. On the other hand, there was

[8] Philipps, *Life and Labor,* 410. "Cotton will hereafter be a valuable staple."

a long-staple, black-seeded variety of cotton, grown
in the West Indies, the fiber of which was easily
saved and was also very much more valuable in the
market. Seed of that cotton was sent to Georgia
in 1787 with the result that a very few years saw it
in possession of the coasts and islands of that state
and Carolina where it grew to perfection, gaining
thereby a commercial status under the name of sea-
island cotton. The light sandy soil, long growing
season, and salt air of the islands are believed to
have been the explanation of the marvellous crops
produced, conditions not fully duplicated anywhere
else, wherefore the sea-islanders enjoyed a monopoly
like that maintained for ages by some of the owners
of favored European vineyard lands.

A cotton craze. The profits derived from this
aristocrat among the cotton plants [9] in a restricted
area, fanned the desire for a cotton-growing regime
of unlimited extension through the successful cultivation of the short staple on the uplands of the
Old South. Fortunately, at the proper time, the
ingenuity of the Connecticut Yankee, Eli Whitney,
with the encouragement of General Nathanael
Greene's widow, who owned a plantation in Georgia,
gave the world the saw-tooth cotton-gin and the
revolution was on. The sudden up-curve in cotton
production, after the Whitney invention had been
perfected and generally employed, marks the be-

[9] Philipps, *Life and Labor,* 92, describes life on the island of
Edisto, showing a uniquely prosperous society where, in a good
year, the proceeds from the cotton crop amounted to $8,683 per
white family.

ginning of an expansion movement which swept first over the southern uplands, then entered the trans-Alleghany and the Gulf plains and, crossing the Mississippi, assimilated the more southern states along the river and the enormous spread of Texas. In the period following the close of the War of 1812, when cotton prices were at the peak, this movement assumed the intensity of a craze, men paying many times the minimum government price for choice cotton lands, and paying likewise prices for negro slaves which were predicated both on their growing scarcity, due to the prohibition of further importations, and on their new economic value as cotton planting hands.

Where the best cotton lands were, there was the largest proportionate slave population, as along the Mississippi river, in the Alabama and Tombigbee peninsula, the Huntsville or Big Bend district on the Tennessee, portions of Texas, Arkansas, and Louisiana. The concentration of slaves, combined with the extent and intensity of the planting business, under overseer dominance, made these the darkest regions of slavery, superseding in that respect the older Carolina and Georgia lowland plantations. Slaves sold "down the river" felt themselves doomed to severest labor, harshest treatment, and most utter helplessness. Nevertheless, economic compulsion caused the benevolent Virginia and Maryland planters to make generous use of that great market for surplus hands.

Sugar planting. Beginning almost coincidentally

with the revolution in cotton growing, there developed, in the gulf lowlands, especially the delta country in Louisiana, a regime of sugar planting which more definitely even than tobacco, indigo, and cotton, was inspired by the planting economy of the West India Islands. It was probably emigrants from San Domingo, expelled by the black rebellion against the French, who began to raise cane sugar in Louisiana, but the origins of the industry are obscure. Though natural conditions, length of the growing season, security against frost, and the relative permanence of the cane plant, are all in favor of the Islands as against Louisiana, yet the richness of the delta soil, and consequent abundance of the yield, with some artificial tariff stimulation, has caused sugar planting to persist and to expand. It is a capitalistic business, more allied to manufacturing than to agriculture, and is carried on under corporate management for the most part.[10]

The foregoing summarizes the principal kinds of business farming which are characteristic of America's southern states. Much remains to be said about the social outgrowths of the planting system and still more about the influence of planting and of slave labor upon the political history of the country. We will find, also, that both the stage of general farming, already adverted to, and that of scientific or professional farming, find illustrations

[10] L. C. Gray, *Southern Agric.*, II, 739–751; Philipps, *Life and Labor,* 119–123; Judah P. Benjamin in Debow's *Rev.*, II (Nov. 1846) 322–345; Dept. of Agric. *Yearbook,* 1923, 151–228.

within the system which began as a purely exploitative enterprise.[11]

Large scale grain cropping. Wheat, the "corn" of Old World commerce, was brought to America by the first colonists and has always been grown for subsistence and for market. As already noted, it did not flourish permanently in southern New England, though in Maine, New Hampshire, and Vermont it was grown successfully, on a moderate scale, till well into the nineteenth century. In the small fenced fields of southern New England and even in the large fields of the three northern states, the wheat crop—or the substitute crop of rye— could be harvested with the average family's labor supply. This was true, particularly after the sickle, reminiscent of the Bible story of Ruth, had been replaced by the grain cradle. With the cradle (a scythe blade in a frame with several parallel wooden fingers), a strong man could reap two acres per day, many experts could reap four acres, and an occasional champion was good for as much as eight acres. The binding was done by a couple of men, boys, or women, who followed the reaper armed with hand-rakes to arrange the grain in bundles, an easy matter, the cradle having laid it straight with heads all one way. Threshing was still as primitive a process as it was when the humane Scripture writer admonished the ancient Hebrews: "Muzzle not the ox when he treadeth out the grain."

[11] For pictorial illustrations see *Yearbook of Agriculture* (1926), 264 ff.

The early failure of wheat crops in eastern Massachusetts, Connecticut, and Rhode Island was ascribed to the black rust or "blast," supposed to have been an infection derived from the barberry bush. However, soil exhaustion and bad tillage seem to have been coincident causes and the cry of the wheat growers, like that of tobacco planters, was always for fresh lands on which wheat grew to better advantage. As early as 1757 the complaint arose in eastern Connecticut: "Many are inclined to remove to new places that they may raise wheat." [12] It was a perfectly normal ambition for free cultivators in a country possessing fresh and fertile lands that could be had for little or nothing. Why labor to restore partly worn out soils in stony New England, when fatter new land on Long Island, in West Jersey, or Pennsylvania was to be had, in more ample tracts, and quite or almost as advantageously located with reference to marketing?

Migrating wheat growers. The American wheat grower, from colonial times, has been a migrant. From southern New England he went to the Delaware or Susquehanna valleys, from there perhaps to western New York. Again the wheat crop failed and a new remove carried him to northern Ohio, Indiana, Illinois, and to southern Michigan and southern Wisconsin. It was a western movement of wheat-growers that largely accounts for the tremendous expansion of northern population taking

[12] Bidwell and Falconer, *Agriculture in Northern United States,* 92, quoting Dr. Jared Eliot.

place between the completion of the Erie canal in 1825, and the beginning of the Civil war. But many of those farmers merely paused to exploit the rich soils for a few years, then passed on into western Iowa, Minnesota, Kansas, Nebraska, the Dakotas. A final trek brought them to the "wheat hills" of the Palouse country of Washington, the Grand Ronde and Wallowa valleys of Oregon. In the 1790's the center of the American flour milling industry was at Wilmington on the Delaware; thirty years later it was at Rochester on the Genesee, with a subsidiary center at Louisville on the Ohio; Milwaukee and Neenah-Menasha rivalled Rochester in the seventies of last century; for many years Minneapolis and Spokane have shared the honors of leadership in the widely severed premier wheat regions of the great plains and the Pacific slope.

It is in no sense fanciful to affirm that the grandsons of men who cradled wheat from twenty-acre Vermont fields in 1835, or from forty or eighty acres on the Genesee, were last year gathering their crops with tractor-drawn combines from five hundred or five thousand acres in the Red river valley, on the upper Missouri, the Walla Walla, or the Umatilla. Since wheat growing meant mining the fresh soils, just as did also tobacco and cotton growing, persistent movement at intervals of a generation or less was a characteristic of the industry.

Early harvesting methods. In its early stages wheat growing was merely a factor in subsistence farming and when that stage had been passed it might persist as a feature of the mixed or general farming which so commonly supplanted that phase. In such cases the opening of new land on farms long occupied, or the adoption of better methods of tillage such as a rotation including wheat after clover, explain the comparative permanence of the crop. Farmers on the heavily forested lands in southern Wisconsin continued to grow wheat successfully as late as the eighteen nineties, but those on the open lands who made the big wheat crops in the early days because all the good land could be broken up in a few years, were out of the game by 1875. The woods farmers cleared a few acres each year and by the time the new soils were all under cultivation they had learned how to restore the productivity of their partly exhausted lands through fertilization and proper rotation of crops.

We have seen that tobacco and other planters could become business farmers, exploiting the fresh woodlands of the southern states, only because circumstances favored that mode of capitalistic production. The principal items operating to their advantage were cheap land, a labor supply, and a market. Of these the northern wheat grower could also count on the first and the last, but not on the second. The critical stage in wheat production as in wine-making, comes at harvest time. Preparation of the soil can be carried out during a protracted season, the planting of the seed is a process requiring skill but is of comparatively short duration. The growing season, say from April to August, is a holiday for the one-crop farmer. But when the fields are "white to harvest," then let him beware of slothfulness, indifference, or faulty management.

A woodland farmer in eastern Wisconsin in 1857, who happened to be a diarist, gives us a full day-to-day account of his harvesting operations. He commenced August 18, "went to cradling with good cheer" but sprained his back and had to quit. However, he was able to obtain help from two neighbors, one to cradle, the other to bind. The third day he had three men at work. The fourth day "rained out" as radio announcers say of ball games. Fifth day, rained out. Sixth day, the cradling went hard for him, but he had two men binding up. Seventh day, it went fine, and two men bound up. Tally, 3595 sheaves. Eighth day, he and another cradled. Two hands bound. All went well. Ninth day, he records, "Finished cutting this morning 10 o'clock. Have now harvested 5365 sheaves of wheat all together. After we got done cutting we commenced hauling in—got in 13 shocks when it commenced raining hard." In three later days he hauled in the balance of his wheat and estimated the crop at 198.80 bushels. Of course it still had to be threshed but that year he bought a four-horse threshing machine for $145 and made a quick job of this process.

Due to the panic, prices broke and at Milwaukee, to which place our farmer had a six-mile haul over execrable roads, he could get only from fifty-five to sixty cents per bushel for his wheat. Such was the wheat farming of one who as yet was a subsistence farmer with a side line of surveying which brought in a few dollars extra.[13]

A very few wheat growers in early Wisconsin grew a large enough acreage and volume of wheat to be ranked as small business farmers. We have accounts of a few Yankee pioneers who came prepared with the financial means to buy outright, at the land office, four or five hundred acres of open land. On this they set their breaking outfits to work, preparing in a single season from 100 to 200 acres which in the fall or the following spring was seeded to wheat. The harvesting in some cases could be done with the aid of impecunious pioneer neighbors who needed the opportunity to earn some money. The process, however, was expensive, the profits very small. Fortunately, the means of reducing cost of production was already at hand.

In the summer of 1844 two neighbors whose lands adjoined, with ten yoke of oxen and a couple of boys to drive, broke up in a few weeks 200 acres of Rock county prairie which they sowed that fall to wheat. The next year they harvested their crop with a machine in 12½ days and secured 5,000 bushels, a part of which was sold at Racine at 62½ cents per bushel.[14] The entire crop was estimated to be worth, on the farm, $2,500, giving each of the associates $1,250, a very fine income for pioneer farmers.

[13] Diary of Anson Buttles. St. Hist. Library MS.
[14] U. S. 29 Cong. 1 Sess. Sen. Doc. 307 (Ser. No. 475), p. 138. (Patent office report, 1845–46.)

Reaper and twine-binder. The machine these men used was probably that which had been invented by Cyrus Hall McCormick in the middle 1830's and which began to have some vogue in the West a few years later. It was a reaping machine, designed to cut the standing grain near the ground, assemble it on a platform, and allow a man to rake it off in bundles ready to be bound into sheaves. It performed the work of cradler and raker. Later a "self-rake" was invented, and still later, John F. Appleby's twine-binder was attached to most of the reaping machines employed in the Middle West. It was the self-binder which served the bonanza wheat farmers of the Red river valley in the 1870's and 1880's. On the Dalrymple farm, at Casselton, N. D., might have been seen during some harvest periods, sixty self-binders following one another around a seemingly boundless area of wheat.

The combine. But that useful invention, too, was destined to be superseded. J. Fenimore Cooper, on a visit to Prairie Ronde in southern Michigan, in 1847, witnessed the performance of a huge machine, drawn by sixteen or eighteen horses, which attacked the standing grain, severed the heads, threshed, cleaned, and sacked the seed ready for the mill.[15] This was the *combine,* invented by Hiram Moore about 1836, almost contemporaneously with the reaper inventions of McCormick and of Hussey. The combine, though it gathered the cleaned grain of from twenty to thirty acres in a single day, as

[15] Cooper, *The Oak Openings,* first published in 1848.

Cooper tells us, proved not wholly successful in Michigan or in Wisconsin, doubtless because the climatic conditions were unfavorable and also because farms were comparatively small. One of Moore's machines, however, was taken around Cape Horn to California and there in San Jose valley in 1854 it sacked its twenty acres per day. In that dry region of large-scale wheat farming where straw was no object, the combine was appreciated. Various modifications of it were later invented, and for many years it has been the mechanical basis of the business farming whose staple product is wheat.[16]

The combine moved from the West eastward. Having proved its superior economy in California, Oregon, and Washington, it invaded the great plains, displacing the self-binder wherever the wheat farms are of a proper size. It has even done much to revolutionize the size of farms. In the wheat belt the cost of equipment, which means the combine as a unit, together with the plows, harrows, drills, wagons, and—formerly teams, now tractors—was so large that a scope of activities guaranteeing their economical use had to be acquired. At the same time petty wheat farming did not pay in comparison. Low prices destroyed the small grower while the larger grower could survive them. Hence, those in command of the machinery and a reasonable parcel of land always bought out small-scale neighbors till

[16] Moore's invention is described in *Wis. Mag. of History*, XV, 234–243.

they owned as much as their unit of machinery could handle. The quarter section homesteads, in the wheat belts, are no more. But often the pioneer homes, schoolhouses, churches, and even hamlets, are now decaying in an otherwise unbroken expanse of wheat. Farms of one thousand acres or more have been increasing in numbers, despite the steady multiplication of small holdings.

Westward movement of wheat growers. The relation of older wheat growers to the newer generations is nicely illustrated by the case of a Wisconsin farmer who was a very successful wheat grower on a 360 acre farm, producing, however, as his maximum crop, 921 bushels in 1874. To be sure, he was a general farmer, raising wheat as a feature in a well balanced rotation. This farmer's eldest son emigrated in the late 1870's to eastern Kansas where he took up a homestead and afterwards added to his farm by the purchase of adjoining land. According to his father's diary, the Kansas farmer produced in some years 10,000 bushels of wheat.[17] Of course that was a bagatelle as compared with the output of the bonanza farms, but this man was an ordinary farmer not a capitalistic farmer. Multiplying his case by 25,000, which would probably not distort the facts, and we would have a basis for 250,000,000 bushels from that single class of moderate sized, personally conducted farms. Those of two other classes, smaller and larger, could readily have duplicated that figure. As early as 1878 the country produced 420,000,000

[17] Diary of Jacob Baumgartner, MS. St. Hist. Library.

bushels, in 1892 the figure was 516,000,000 bushels, and in 1904 it stood at 552,000,000 bushels.

The wheat harvest under earlier conditions, when self-raking reapers were employed for cutting, called for a large investment in labor. Four persons were usually required to bind after every machine, and in heavy grain an additional person to help in setting up or "shocking" the sheaves, a work to which the binders contributed in spare moments and often in overtime. The twine-binder eliminated the hand-binders, but men were still needed in the field for shocking up after the machine and, inasmuch as the threshing could be most economically done at once on completion of the reaping, the harvest hands of a given locality were to be found following the threshers.

Seasonal labor was relied upon for harvest help. A class of persons of no special training or occupation made a business of following the harvest from the southern grain states to the Canadian border, thereby providing themselves with paying jobs for two or three months. Many of these men were of the "hobo" type, wholly undesirable as house guests on the farms, and yet they had to be fed and cared for by the women of the households except on the bonanza farms where barrack life was the rule.

This constituted a social reason for the introduction of the combine in addition to the economic reasons. With that great machine and plenty of horse or mule power, a very few men could handle an enormous harvest. And, since the forty-horse

combine was too costly for the moderate sized wheat
farm, the more recent invention of a truck-borne
and tractor-drawn small combine has come in to fill
the gap. Now the average wheat-growing family can
manage its own harvest, the women hauling the
sacked grain to the elevator in preference to caring
for strange men in the home. Thus, through invention, have we returned socially to conditions
like those of pioneer life, when the farmer, his
children and wife might gather the crop from his
few arable acres. Machines are the slaves of the
wheat farmer.

Future of wheat farming. The question as to the
permanence of successful wheat growing on the
great plains and the other wheat belts is not a
simple one. Certainly the lands of the Red river
valley and the Palouse country have shown remarkable staying qualities under the one-crop wheat
regime. Also, the better tillage incident to modern
business farming on the cheap lands of many districts formerly used for grazing has at least tempo-
rarily brought profits. In the depression years,
when wheat prices dropped below thirty-five cents
per bushel, big operators could still figure a narrow
margin of profit whereas the ordinary farmer was
sunk. Whether or not the system can maintain itself by rotation, the use of artificial fertilizers, and
superior management remains to be determined.

Wheat breeding and the selection of resistant
varieties in other lands has brought into the belt of
safety vast aggregations of land formerly believed

to be too dry, to lie too far north or at too high an elevation for wheat growing.[18]

Sir William Crookes, who had warned the world of the possibility of a wheat shortage within a few years unless the wasteful system of cultivation were promptly changed to a better one, especially in the wheat producing regions of the United States, left us the following challenge in 1899. He then said: "If at the end of another generation of wasteful culture my forecast is invalidated by the unforeseen I cheerfully invite friends and critics to stone me as a false prophet." [19] The time limit is up, the prophecy invalidated, but the distinguished scientist is out of the range of any stone that might be heaved at him. Those whose ears are properly attuned to the supersensual may perhaps hear him laughing at his foiled critics. If we are to judge of the future in America from what has taken place in older countries, wheat growing will steadily be made more scientific, which means it will cease to be a single crop industry and become, as in France and England, a feature of a well planned rotation. Thus will the acreage be greatly reduced, the yield greatly increased, and doubtless the national needs at least met on a permanent agricultural basis.

Cattle ranching. Primitive subsistence farming, save as it involves the element of migration to new and newer frontiers, has in it little of the romantic,

---

[18] Paul de Kruif in *Hunger Fighters* describes the great work of Mark Alfred Carleton in finding wheat for America in Russia.
[19] William Crookes, *The Wheat Problem,* London, 1900, XIII.

and the same is true of general farming. In both, the obtruding ideas are of seldom relieved hard work, the daily grind, meager profits, and a dearth of opportunities for relaxation. The business farming so far described affords to persons at the head of the various establishments the satisfactions of controlling their own time and means of gratifying inclinations and desires. But the "hands" on cotton or other plantations, or on the wheat ranch large or small, savored little of the good times their bosses made for themselves.

Cattle ranching is distinguished from other forms of business farming by the fact that it combines fun with work for all concerned, man as well as ranch boss and—rarest of agricultural social phenomena— even for the women of the household.

Early phases. It is a historical axiom that migrating peoples take their domestic animals with them. The Spaniards did so when, under Columbus' leadership, they colonized Hispaniola. Later, spreading over Mexico, Central and South America, Florida, Texas, New Mexico, and California, the herds of Andalusian cattle everywhere outran the rate of population increase, multiplying apace whether on the pampas of Argentina, the mountain pastures of Mexico, the cane-meadows of Texas, or the dry-land ranges of California and New Mexico.

The English colonists, hoping to sustain themselves partly from the spontaneous products of the soil, brought over cattle, sheep, goats, hogs, and horses at the outset of their colonizing enterprizes.

The French likewise, in Canada, Acadia, and the sporadic settlements marking the course and extension of the fur-trade, were always sustained by a variety of livestock. The Dutch in New York, the Swedes in Delaware and New Jersey, were no laggards in their devotion to animal husbandry. Even the Icelandic sagas testify to the bringing of kine to North America by the Scandinavian discoverers of the continent about the year one thousand A.D.

Common sense and common observation suggest that cattle can flourish with no help from man in some situations while in others they will quickly die out. If the coast reached by Leif Ericson had been as favorable climatically and otherwise for cattle as the lands occupied by Spaniards, North America would have been crowded with wild cattle on the arrival of the later European immigrants. If Mexico, Florida and Texas had had as rigorous winters as Acadia or Canada, where would have been the millions of longhorns and the great bands of wild horses that ranged over the American South and Southwest in historic times?

Another general observation is that every favorably conditioned frontier is apt to have a livestock surplus before it can have a surplus of the productions of tillage. We have already seen that even the severe New England winters, while they limited the multiplication of cattle by killing off each year a large proportion of the animals, nevertheless yielded to the ubiquitous subsistence farmer of that region, with slight effort on his part, a certain resource for leather, for meat, and for merchantable beeves. The business was both small and precarious, and yet, as Whittier tells us, the drovers of New England found limited supplies of animals that differed markedly from "Pharaoh's evil cattle." [20]

When New Englanders drifted west into the milder and more fertile valleys of Ohio, Indiana, and Illinois, cultivating the borders of an almost limitless common, they soon found their herds multiplying naturally to such an extent that cattle driving to the eastern market, to military posts, and to the newer settlements became a feature in what might be called the adventure element in farm life.[21]

But the region of spontaneous livestock development lay in the South rather than in the New England states and their western neighbors. From Maryland to Florida the climate was so genial that, with abundance of land for the growth of pasturage and winter browse, cattle could multiply to any extent with practically no attention from man except such as would insure their safety against wild beasts and piratical men.

The cattle business in those colonies and states was of two kinds, plantation herding and frontier herding. Many of the plantations had attached to them areas of pasture and woodlands—swampy

[20] Whittier, *The Drovers.*
[21] When Wisconsin and southern Michigan were settled by eastern farmers who needed cattle, drovers from southern Indiana, Ohio, and Illinois supplied the deficiency. Cattle, sheep, and horses were "peddled" through the new settlements.

grounds rich in grass, or woods that were open through repeated burnings, where also excellent pasturage was found for cattle and great store of nuts and acorns for hogs. Since only the actual planted areas were fenced, cattle and hogs ranged all the balance of the lands as commons where were found the intermingled herds of several neighbors. This was the beginning of a livestock economy which ultimately became systematized under more or less scientific principles of animal husbandry. Some of the tidewater plantations are said to have maintained herds of 1,000 or over.

The frontier type of cattle raising, however, is of special interest as the parent of the glamorous ranching business of the nineteenth century. Its origins are not known in detail, but no doubt it was similar to the origin of the cattle ranching of the great plains and that on the Pacific coast, both of which grew up in the white light of the nineteenth century. Settlers in the Willamette valley of Oregon in the 1840's, if their claims adjoined the unoccupied lands along the Cascade mountains, or the low grounds along the river, kept cattle which fed on unappropriated pastures and with little or no attention multiplied apace. But, for a start, since it had been impossible to bring enough breeding stock from the states, enterprising settlers had joined together to buy California cattle which were driven north through the mountains. The reservoir of livestock on the California "ranchos," of Spanish creation, was so vast that any desired number could be had for the northern ranges provided they could be safely transferred through the intervening wilderness. In a few years the mountain valleys swarmed with the wild black longhorns which, when wanted for beef, could be best secured by shooting. They were a menace to travelers, more feared than any of the beasts of the forest except the grizzly bear and, in fact, a famous English botanist, David Douglass, was killed in the Oregon mountains by a bull of that lineage.

Cow-hunts in Virginia and Maryland. In Virginia and Maryland colonies cattle ran wild to such an extent that rules for hunting them during certain open seasons were enforced by law. The chief hunter and his assistant divided the meat, the hide and tallow belonged to the governor or to the king. It was from this large surplus of plantation cattle that were recruited the herds for the distinctively "cow-country" above the tidewater settlements. The use of brands or earmarks as evidence of ownership became universal under legal compulsion, and the annual roundup for branding calves and selecting marketable animals necessitated the erection of "cowpens" which, as soon as the herds began to be driven inland, became a feature of the frontier cattle trails.

The entire southern Piedmont as well as the Great Valley and the valleys opening toward the Ohio were favorite herding regions. The numerous meadows, and the intra-forest peavine openings, afforded luxuriant pasturage where animals could grow and fatten to an all but unlimited extent. The pioneers of the industry may have established temporary camps for their "cowboys," already so-called in the eighteenth century, but the attractiveness of the country, its excellent farming lands, charming scenery, healthfulness, and the sure and easy profits of the cattle business caused the early creation of regular settlements throughout this upper country. During the Revolutionary war great herds of fat cattle were driven from these choice pasture lands to the markets at Charleston, Baltimore, and New York. Charleston, indeed, had long enjoyed an extensive trade in cattle shipped to the British West Indies.

Piedmont ranchers. There is evidence that many tidewater planters, having learned to depend upon the livestock industry as an essential creator of profits, when their local pasturage resources became restricted sold their plantations and moved to the frontier where their herds could make them wealthy while they prepared new plantations on cheaper lands. This process similarly finds illustration in the far West, for some of the big farmers and cattle raisers of the Willamette, Umpqua and Rogue river valleys, in the sixties and seventies of last century migrated to the high plateaus of eastern Oregon, Washington, and Idaho to become the greatest ranchers in those regions.[22]

[22] William Hanley, for example, went to the Klamath region from Josephine county, where the old Hanley homestead still stands near Jacksonville in the Rogue river valley.

Also, as in the far West, the cattle ranching activity of the Southeast was enlivened and often rendered critical by the incursion of wandering herds of wild horses. These, of course, were of Spanish origin. They had drifted north from Florida just as in the far West Mexico was their point of departure. Hunting, lassoing, and "breaking" wild horses was a feature of frontier adventure generations before Philip Nolan excited the world with his stories of the wild horse bands of Texas.[23]

Virginian "cowboys." That the cowboy of romance should be a Virginian accords with the proprieties of history, for Virginia herders were pasturing the peavine uplands from the last quarter of the seventeenth century. They were driving their herds south to the Carolinas and Georgia along the great cattle trail near the heads of the east-flowing rivers. They were also fighting and "regulating" cattle thieves as they would continue to do for two centuries. Doubtless the early Virginian cowboy was the same clever, charming, resourceful, and at times daredevil rider of the range, who has been depicted with such faithful artistry by Owen Wister.[24]

Ranching regions south and west. We have seen how the southern fringe of the continent—Florida, Texas, New Mexico—became stocked and saturated with Spanish cattle. So great was that surplus it was steadily penetrating new lands, Texans drifting

[23] *Dict. Am. Biog.*, Philip Nolan.
[24] Owen Wister, *The Virginian, a Horseman of the Plains.*

into Louisiana where some of the Acadians became famous herdsmen and cow-operators, spreading into the Indian country of New Mexico, and upward toward the great plains. From California, whose mission herds and Spanish ranchos supplied both Boston traders and English traders with cargoes of hides and tallow,[25] and the Oregon pastures with abundant breeding stock, the American drovers were soon to provide the mining region of the Sierras with beef, and cattle operators of the great basin with the beginnings of a new and far-flung ranching business which was spreading in like manner from Oregon over the inland empire in response to the opening of mining centers in eastern Oregon, Washington, Idaho, Montana, Wyoming, and Colorado.

The day of the cattleman. Thus, when "the day of the cattleman,"[26] as the last third of the nineteenth century has been called, opened up, the theater on which he was destined to play his dramatic rôle in American agriculture was already roughly defined. The farming frontier was in that tier of new states west of the Mississippi which were in turn restricted westward at certain points by Indian reservations, and in the beginnings of recently formed settlements in Kansas, Nebraska, and Dakota. However, the major part of the enor-

[25] The classic source for that business is Richard H. Dana's *Two Years before the Mast.*
[26] The book under this title by Ernest Staples Osgood, Univ. of Minn. Press, 1929, is one of the best and most comprehensive treatments of the ranching business.

mous spread of the great plains, or the sub-marginal
grassy upland of the far West, extending into and
across the Rocky mountains, was open for pastoral
exploitation.

Long before the outbreak of the Civil war the
great plains and Rocky mountains witnessed the
incursion of neat cattle into restricted areas of the
buffalo country. Emigrants to Oregon, beginning as
early as 1843, drove annually several thousand head,
mostly as draft oxen but partly as loose cattle. Of
both classes some gave out through worn feet or
weakness and had to be left along the trail where
soon the occasional trader recruited a herd from
which later trains could be supplied both with food
and fresh draft animals. The mining centers to a
large extent were supplied from near-by ranges
where either eastern cattle, western cattle or Texas
cattle had been brought to start the herds. From
the borders of the farming frontier the herds of range
cattle grazed stragglingly out upon the grassy great
plains, much as the herds of tidewater Virginia
penetrated the Piedmont two centuries earlier. It
was the great zone of uplands lying between the
settled states of the West and the Rockies.

Texas cattle supply the great plains. The greatest
reservoir of cattle for ranching purposes being in
Texas, where cow-hunts occurred every spring as
the sole means of keeping even a general oversight
of their rapidly growing numbers, and Texas experiencing extreme hard times following the war, it
was inevitable that cattle from that region should

be drawn upon to stock the more northerly ranges. Railway building into the great plains along the lines of the Union Pacific and the Northern Pacific (later also the Kansas–Pacific) encouraged the hope of a future permanent market for beef cattle, only a few herds of which had theretofore been driven from Texas to Iowa and Illinois. The experience of successive winters, in widely separated districts of the northern grasslands, seemed to prove their availability both for the summer fattening and winter subsistence of range cattle. The "buffalo grass," with which the uplands were covered, had the nutritive qualities of a respectable kind of tame hay. The buffalo herds being destroyed, by keeping stock off a portion of their range in summer that area would provide good winter feed, the entire growth of the season awaiting the cattle, provided it were not covered too deeply with snow, which was seldom the case especially on the higher ridges from which snow was apt to be blown away by the wind.

Thus open-range cattle ranching was seen to be the simplest way to exploit the spontaneous growth of the vast continental uplands. Government owned the land, which made the pastures free. Government was ready to give the rancher a "home-place" for his house, horse-barn, paddocks, and such slight cultivation as would be required. For the rest, he could invest his money in cattle which Texas drovers, or northern buyers of Texas stock, were prepared to sell him. Beginning with a small herd of cows, the poor man could watch his wealth grow year by year until, if he wished, he could gratify his ambition to cut a figure in finance or commerce. It was not so much a way to get rich quickly as to get rich surely. No ordinary business could compare in profitableness with the open-range cattle business in its halcyon days, say from 1866 to 1885.

The open-range ranching business. During most of that period the ranges were not crowded save in a few localities. The spirit of Abraham in his relations with Lot dominated. When two men found themselves with herds in the identical area they would agree to take either the right hand direction or the left hand direction. The one would graze this river valley, or mountain glen, the other that. The doctrine of "customary range" was widely prevalent. Close herding was not practiced. The range cattle fed where they pleased but came to a definite stream—often a certain place on a certain stream—to drink. Their pasturing range was limited by the distance from water, which could hardly ever exceed ten miles. Commonly it was not over five miles.

Under such conditions three or four well-mounted cowboys could "ride herd" on ten thousand cattle. This meant simply that they circled the range occasionally, prevented small groups of animals from drifting to other ranges, eliminated groups bearing other brands, watched for signs of destructive wild beasts, or of the onset of cattle diseases. Such was the cowboys' work in quiet times. When the spring roundup was on, in May, the story was a different one. Then the cow hands of associated ranges brought all stock together in an agreed upon area, where those belonging to each outfit concerned caught and branded all calves, identified through their mothers, distributed the "mavericks" or motherless according to established rules, castrated young males, and cut out marketable steers and cows. The roundup cost days of gruelling work, relieved, however, by its social features, which included feasting, frolicking, visiting, racing, lassooing, bronco-busting, hog-tying bulls, and all the rest of the stunts which frontier dramatists have labored assiduously to perpetuate under artificial conditions. Driving the fat cattle to the railroad for shipment brought another period of heavy service for the cowboy, but most of the year, both winter and summer, was marked by an easy riding schedule.

Changes in ranching methods. We have, however, described only one phase of the range business, whose aspects changed with almost kaleidoscopic suddenness. Despite the colossal amplitude of the range country, its area was being contracted by the stupendous post-Civil war movement of farming immigrants into the West, the rapid settlement of Kansas, Nebraska, the Dakotas; and the expansion of agricultural settlement about the mining centers in the Rocky mountains.

The profits of ranching had made of that business a world craze, like the earlier cotton planting, in which Scotch and English financiers vied with Americans for the stakes of success. It was then the New York Roosevelt and the English Frewens became ranchers. Cattle companies, heavily capitalized, sprang up like mushrooms after a spring rain. The Texas drivers delivered millions of cattle to the northern ranges; other millions of so-called "pilgrims" were brought in by rail from the middle-western farmlands. By 1880 cattle supplies for the newly created or enlarging outfits were becoming scarce, and prices took a sharp advance.

The cattle craze—its explosion. The cumulating difficulty of segregating customary ranges, joined to the invention and cheapening of barbed wire fencing, led to the widespread custom of fencing the adjacent public lands along with the privately owned water rights which reduced the cost of herding and permitted breeding for improvement. Then, in the winter of 1885–1886 came the most memorable disaster of ranching history in a series of snowfalls and blizzards which decimated the ranges and caused an almost universal financial crash among the cattle companies.

The government about that time stepped in to abolish illegal fencing of the range and to protect the increasing number of farmer homesteaders in the range country. The cattle business was again reorganized. Now the ranchers, and ranching companies, were disposed to buy or lease range lands. Wholesale frauds were committed in the process whereby government lands were transferred to private ownership, a story quite on a par with the monopolization of the country's timber lands by a few great operators. At the same time the ranching regime was changed to respond to the lesson of the terrible winter. The growing of hay, on natural meadow or on irrigated land, and the winter feeding—sometimes also shedding of stock—became a normal practice. Another change was in the more rapid improvement of the range animals. The lanky Texas longhorn now rapidly disappeared and in his place the white faced Hereford became the ubiquitous tenant of the ranges, though the famous "101" still breeds the longhorn for Hollywood's benefit.

More recent stock-ranching. In effect, therefore, the cattle ranch and its picturesque life, with its colorful hero the cowboy, are no more. The ranch has become the large-scale cattle farm, but its owner is still the nabob of the American uplands. He has not forgotten the traditions of the cattle baron. He is still contemptuous of the "hayseed farmer," still mingles on terms of equality with packers, bankers, exporters, and statesmen. His business has made him a type quite as distinctive as the cotton-planter or the bonanza wheat grower. For purposes of drama, indeed, the western cattleman not only tops the cinema market, but he is the theme of the novelist and playwright to a greater extent than any other class of agricultural producer. He is the possibly crude, but free, fearless and self-satisfied continental aristocrat.

Fate of the grasslands. It is today by no means a settled question whether the cattle business is to shrink further or to expand. The terrible droughts of recent years have induced a reflux of the tide of sub-marginal farmers, latterly aided by government. The sentiment just now—which may prove temporary—would seem to favor restoring the upland grass country to the ranchman. Unfortunately, the grass prospects have been much impaired by the overstocking of the ranges in the past, by cultivation which destroys the native buffalo grass, and by the disastrous dust storms to which widespread cultivation has been contributory. There is some doubt whether range conditions could be effectively restored should all farmers abandon the high, drought-scourged plains, though it is evident that at least the remaining grazing lands are now more apt to be left undisturbed by intruding farmers.

Two generations ago scientists, including the celebrated geologist, John Wesley Powell, who was intimately acquainted with far West conditions, warned solemnly against the agricultural occupation of the plateau country lying west of the one hundredth meridian. The high plains, these men agreed, should remain to the operator in live-stock. The advice went unheeded; but of late its echoes are heard on every side so that, in the long run, the scientists may have the satisfaction of being listened to with respect on that subject.

Sheep. But, even if the high plains shall once more be restored to the pastoral interest, it does not follow that they will be turned over wholly to the cattleman. From the early ranching period the sheep man has disputed the range with the cattle baron and, owing to the natural repugnance of horned cattle to sheep and the grazing habits of the latter, the contact between the two has usually been hostile. On the whole, it must be recorded, the sheep men have gained the advantage partly because sheep are better adapted to exploit the mountain terrain than cattle.

Great fortunes were made, in the eighties, the nineties, and even later by men who ranged sheep in the mountains of Wyoming, Montana, and Colorado by the herding system. A single herder would be put in charge of a band of several thousand animals destined to a definite general grazing region. The herder lived in a wagon, watched his charges' outward movements during the earlier part of the day, let them return of their own accord to the bedding ground toward evening, and kept a sensitive ear for sounds of disturbance at night. The lambing season, the shearing season, the marketing drive, were the periods of excessive labor for herder, assistants, and owner. For the rest, an occasional change of camping ground relieved the tedium of herding, as did the winter at the ranch house when the sheep were being fed at the sheds.[27]

The increase of the sheep population has been so largely at the expense of cattle that one might be justified in the prophesy that the day of the cattleman is about over, whatever fate may be in store for the natural pasture lands of the West.

[27] Archer Butler Gilfillan, *Sheep,* Boston, Little, Brown, & Co., 1929, is an intimate literary portrayal, by an actual sheep herder, of the sheep business as viewed from the herders' standpoint.

CHAPTER IV

IMPROVED FARMING

A MILLION independent farm-owning and farm-operating cultivators, scattered over four and twenty states of varying contours, climates, social complexes, and rural traditions, cannot be "hustled." When, therefore, the need of agricultural improvement became acute in the older sections of the country, about 1830, the leaders recognized that there was no royal road to its realization.

Each farmer a distinct problem. In countries whose farmlands are owned by a few score landlords, and by them leased to farmers as in England, East Prussia, and some other European states, the problem of introducing changes in cultivation as they may be needed is far simpler. "In the great days of agricultural progress," says Lord Ernle, "English landlords were the pioneers of improvements or missionaries of science." [1] Such characters practically did not exist in northern America. Instead of reaching a hundred wealthy, intelligent, business-trained persons with their propaganda of better farming and letting them, through the terms of leases, through managerial oversight and the

[1] *English Farming, Past and Present,* 418.

steady exertion of landlord prestige, put the ideas in operation on thousands of farms at a stroke, the American reformers had the task of educating the individual cultivator directly. Here was a challenge. How could it be met?

Robbers and conservers of the soil. It is axiomatic that whatever mitigates the sure disaster implicit in soil exhaustion is an agricultural improvement, but just so long as money was made most rapidly by robbing the soil, exploiters could not be persuaded to become conservators. In the latest settlements, while fields were new and cheap fresh lands still available, interest in improvement was virtually nil. Not until soil exhaustion had gone far enough to threaten the owner's impoverishment would he pause to consider ways of restoring its productive powers. But that condition was always common to large numbers at any given time, and therefore, propaganda was fortunately able to utilize social instrumentalities in operating upon individuals.

An impression has prevailed rather widely that the soil-robber and the soil-conserver were usually distinct types. Sometimes that was true, as the prominence of the professional squatter in some sections of the West attests. James Flint's three grades, however, the backwoodsman, the subsistence farmer, and the capitalist,[2] were not characteristic

[2] *Flint's Letters from America.* Thwaites Ed. 233–234. *Cf.* also J. F. W. Johnston, *Notes on North America,* Boston and Edinborough, 1851, I, 163. And Toqueville, as quoted in E. L. Bogart, *Econ. Hist. of Am. Agriculture,* N. Y., 1923, p. 91.

of all frontiers. That discerning Scotchman was reporting what he saw, and especially what he was told, of the situation in southern Ohio and southern Indiana, a region occupied largely by the Hoosier or Appalachian mountain type. Had he visited the West of thirty or forty years later, he would have seen that a large proportion of the first settlers remained on the land and passed all his grades in succession, beginning as squatters and becoming at last sound, progressive cultivators.

"Men," says Craven, "produce what they can sell and, in the long run, use those methods which yield them the greatest returns." [3] This is not only a correct summary, applicable to every type of farmer, but a wary statement as well. "In the long run" is a phrase which preserves to the "improving" class large numbers whose progressiveness might not otherwise be authenticated.

Types of improving farmers. Taken by and large that class has been composed of what have been called "general farmers," as those seeking profit through diversification, as opposed to the big and little exploiters heretofore described, and it has been recruited from the ranks of the exploiters. The propaganda of farming betterment carried on by agricultural societies, an agricultural press, county and state fairs, farmers' clubs, has been addressed

[3] Avery O. Craven, *Soil Exhaustion in Virginia and Maryland, 1606–1860,* 12. Professor Craven's monograph is one of the best sources upon which to base a history of agricultural improvement in the United States. L. C. Gray, *Agriculture in the Southern U. S.,* and Bidwell and Falconer, *Agriculture in the Northern U. S.* are likewise exceedingly valuable.

on the whole to those who were or were becoming general farmers. Fundamentally, the method was that of exhortation. Farms in the older states were so generally "run down" through generations of soil robbery that community as well as individual solvency depended upon persuading men to farm more intelligently. Of course conversions could not take place till market conditions permitted something other than a subsistence type of farming.

English precedents and preachers of better farming. Early advocates of better farming in this country held up English practices to the emulation of American cultivators. Benjamin Franklin's grandson, for example, took a newly arrived English farmer as his associate and teacher in managing his new six-hundred acre farm near Philadelphia.[4] It was not accidental that a large proportion of the limited space in the first volume of *The American Farmer*[5] was given over to a detailed account of the ruta baga by that fluent and expansive writer the Englishman William Cobbett; that the Englishman John Barney of Port Penn, Delaware, was hailed as the best cattle feeder in the country; that long quotations from Arthur Young were scattered through the various numbers; or that an extended report of the English board of agriculture should provide the first serious discussion of improved dairying.

[4] Bigelow Ed., Franklin's *Works,* IX, 296.
[5] Edited by John S. Skinner, Baltimore, 1819.

With the exception of Jared Eliot, who wrote in the decade 1749 to 1759,[6] employing largely the methodology and the ideas of the English agricultural improvers, the principal writers who influenced American agriculture in the later eighteenth and early nineteenth century were Englishmen.

The most thoroughgoing of these was the anonymous author of *American Husbandry,* published at London in 1775, but written perhaps a decade earlier. This book has been ascribed to Dr. John Mitchell who, though he had lived some years in Virginia, died in London in 1768. There is a possibility that the work as written by Mitchell was actually published under the editorship of Arthur Young.[7] George Washington and Thomas Jefferson both corresponded with Young in the hope of obtaining helpful suggestions, and other contacts between the improvers of the two countries were not lacking. Briefly, American advance in husbandry, conditioned at it was on the one hand by the market for products, on the other was inspired mainly by English examples. Also, as in the older society, the most hopeful contributions toward a better type of farming came at first from the larger and economically abler operators.[8]

John Taylor and Edmund Ruffin. The leading cause of prosperity in the tobacco-growing colonies for about a hundred years had been the excellent

[6] Essays on Field Husbandry in New England.
[7] Letter of Lyman Carrier, 1935.
[8] See Craven, *Soil Exhaustion,* etc. 92 ff. especially 104–105.

market for tobacco in England. The main cause of
agricultural decline in the same colonies, during the
greater part of the eighteenth century, was the excessively low price of tobacco, together with the
import, export, and other charges upon the crop.
Planting prosperity meant coining the riches of the
soil into money rapidly; loss of prosperity for a
time caused still more rapid exploitation of soils
in the feverish hope that something might be saved
through such processes. It was the drowning man
clutching at the proverbial straw.

Only when the decline struck bedrock did improvement begin, because then bankruptcy was the
obvious alternative. The advance movement took
the form of better tillage, diversification of crops,
and closer attention to the business end of farming.
Grain raising, especially wheat, was largely substituted for tobacco, deeper and more careful plowing
prevented erosion, cattle yarding, with winter feed
provided manure which brought up the productivity
of the fields.[9]

The sale of lands and slaves reduced many to-
bacco-planters' holdings to more manageable proportions for supervision. Attention to breeding im-

[9] The prophet and most scientific exponent of the new southern
agriculture was John Taylor of Caroline who wrote his *Arator*
articles in 1803, the year in which Sir Humphrey Davy delivered
his first series of lectures on agricultural chemistry. Taylor apparently knew little or nothing of Davy's subject; but from
conversation, reflection and experimentation he learned and
taught much about the production and use of manures, about
clover as a fertilizer, about careful cultivation and good farm
management. He may stand as the type of the earliest scientific
or professional farmer in the South.

proved the herds and flocks.[10] A period of good prices for grain during the Napoleonic wars gave a strong impulse to progressive, diversified agriculture which was later interrupted. Around 1820 to 1830 most of the large farmers of Virginia went into bankruptcy. Jefferson did so, Monroe and Madison fared little better. It was the age of the Virginia slaveholder's despair.

Fortunately, thereafter surplus slaves, otherwise a ruinous expense, were rapidly drawn off to the new cotton planting districts and the farms were steadily reduced in area; new transportation facilities, canals, railroads, and wagon roads, cheapened the cost of getting crops to market, thereby compensating for the somewhat low prices. Persistent preaching of better farming methods, and significant new experiments like that of Edmund Ruffin with marl, the use of clover and commercial fertilizers, the importation of blooded stock—all worked together to make the farming of Maryland and Virginia in the twenty years before the Civil war among the best in the United States.[11]

Sporadic improvers in New England. But the surest approach to improved agriculture, for the average farmer, is through better livestock, and in that fundamental department the small farmers

[10] Which, however, were still of inferior quality as late as 1817 if Birkberk's observations are to be regarded as evidence. Morris Birkbeck, *Notes on a Journey in America. Passim.*

[11] This is according to the testimony summarized by Craven in Chapter IV, the Agricultural Revival, 1820–1860 of *Soil Exhaustion,* etc. See also *Georgia Historical Quarterly,* Dec. 1935, article "Agriculture in the Interior."

of New England and the middle states unquestionably took the lead. The farm journals celebrated the
achievements of northern feeders of cattle and swine.
The editor of the *American Farmer* found that some
of the New Englanders raised pigs that would dress
150 pounds at six months, as against the average in
Maryland which did not exceed that weight at
sixteen months.[12] Some of the best cattle feeders,
for many years, were located in the Connecticut
valley of Massachusetts where was produced an
abundance of hay, corn, peas, oats, and roots for
fattening.[13]

The improvement in all lines of agricultural activity in New England followed the development of
town and city markets. Commerce carried on from
Boston, Providence, New Haven and New York
with the West Indian islands during the colonial
period had called for the shipment of much meat,
wheat and flour, feed grains, potatoes, lumber, and
horses. The famous Narragansett pacer stock was
actually depleted through the intensity of this export trade.

Magic of the market. But after all, the West
India market was distant and the human imagination is weak. Farmers require market benefits that
are near and obvious as a stimulus to best endeavor.
As the cities grew through commerce and especially
through the new manufacturing industry, multiplying their demand for "victuallers" supplies, farmers

[12] *Am. Farmer,* I, 47. See also same, page **23** and **48**.
[13] Bidwell and Falconer, 224–225. Also, *Am. Farmer,* I, **197**.

accustomed to visit the markets learned the best methods of satisfying that demand with profit to themselves. They supplied pigs fatted in the way that brought the best prices, and they gradually learned to raise the breed of swine that could be grown and fattened at least expense.[14] And, as with hogs, so with cattle. The Brighton market near Boston was visited by farmers and drovers from all sections of New England, giving the same currency to knowledge of preferred types of animals that the modern cattlemen derive from visiting the packing centers of Chicago, Omaha and Kansas City.

A certain degree of specialization was caused by the popularity of active oxen fitted for farm work and woods work. Since the red Devons were preferred for the yoke, and also were good milkers, New England farmers generally stuck to that breed, raised steers, and trained them for service. "New England broke oxen" were auctioned off near Lancaster, Pennsylvania, to the number of forty pair, in August, 1797.[15] Large numbers were employed in the Maine and New Hampshire lumber camps, and thousands of ox-teams bore emigrating families, with sled or with wagon, into western New York, western Pennsylvania, and Ohio. Rhode Island, the lower Connecticut valley, and the towns of northwestern Connecticut excelled in dairying.

[14] *Am. Farmer*, I, 23. The Byfield breed was a New England favorite about 1819. *Ibid*, 48.

[15] B. J. Andrew Frantz, Lancaster Co. Hist. Soc. Papers, 28, 44.

Pennsylvania's good farmers. Perhaps the best general farming of the Revolutionary period was in the neighborhood of Philadelphia, which was an exceptionally good market. An ox weighing 2,884 pounds was reported in Elizabethtown in 1796. The big Pennsylvania barns were used for stabling cattle as well as horses, and all beasts therein were well fed.[16] Cattle feeding as a business was carried on in Lancaster county during the Revolution, the stock cattle coming from Virginia and being destined, when fat, for the American army. Arable lands sown to tame grasses were used for pasturing before the end of the eighteenth century, and during many years of the nineteenth century that district fattened cattle brought in by drovers from Ohio, Kentucky, northern Pennsylvania and western New York, supplying the eastern market.[17] Southeastern Pennsylvania also developed the famous Conestoga horse and the very popular Chester White hog.

The kind of farming which distinguished that and some other eastern areas favored with good markets, at the close of the first quarter of the nineteenth century, was not widely prevalent through the country at large, though the construction of the Erie canal, completed in 1825, opened such enviable prospects to the people of western

[16] "On June 2, 1798, in the Lancaster Journal there appears an advertisement for the sale of a tract of land, adjoining the borough of Lancaster, with a barn containing stabling for a number of cattle." *Supra*, p. 45.

[17] B. J. Andrew Frantz, Lancaster Co. Hist. Soc. Papers, 42, 44, 45.

New York that very rapid improvement, both in tillage and in animal husbandry, took place among them. This so-called Genesee country had long been noted for its wheat crops, which had been marketed at Montreal, Baltimore, or New York. With the opening of the canal New York became a perfect market for that area, and soon western New York gave to the new agriculture some of the proudest and most intelligent farmers of all America.[18]

The Erie canal's influence. But the Erie canal's influence did not end at Buffalo. That work, as its chief architect, Governor De Witt Clinton proclaimed, "married the Lakes and the Ocean," joining the far-extended waters of America's great inland seas to the magnificent harbor at the mouth of the Hudson, so that from Cleveland, Detroit, Mackinac, the later Chicago, Milwaukee, Duluth, and Superior— with scores of lesser lake ports—commerce was attracted eastward to the great and growing Manhattan city.

When Morris Birkbeck, an English farmer, visited America in 1817, traveling through Virginia and by the national turnpike to Ohio, Indiana, and Illinois, he made a shrewd observation about the future of western trade and travel in the remark: "We approximate to Europe as we proceed to the West. The upward navigation of these [western] streams is already coming under the control of

---

[18] New York ranked first as a producer of beef cattle in 1840. Russell H. Anderson, *Wis. Hist. Mag.,* XVI, 173.

steam, an invention which promises to be of incalculable importance to this new world." [19]

Birkbeck was right in supposing the Mississippi route to Europe would be popularized by the steamboat. Yet, had he passed through New York state instead of through Virginia, and witnessed the active beginnings of canal construction, at the same time studying northern geography, he would not have failed to see a future rival to the Mississippi in this partly artificial transportation system. Moreover, the Erie canal was the effective cause of the era of railway building from the eastern harbors to the West, which in time rivaled both the Mississippi and the Erie canal transportation systems.

Forty years after Birkbeck an Englishman of greater prominence than he, the Hon. James Caird, M.P., examined the prairies of Illinois with an eye to favorable opportunities for agricultural emigrants from Britain. He found Illinois a state "traversed by a most perfect system of railroads, where no settler need be more than ten miles from a station, whose shore is washed by one of those great lakes through which an outlet is found to the Atlantic, and which possesses in the Mississippi itself a vast artery of commerce navigable by steamboats for thousands of miles." [20]

The interval between Birkbeck and Caird wit-

[19] Morris Birkberk, *Notes on a Journey in America*, Phila., 1817.
[20] James Caird, *Prairie Farming in America*, N. Y., 1859. See also P. W. Gates, *The Illinois Central Railroad and Its Colonization Work*, Cambridge, Harvard Univ. Press, 1934, on Caird, 215 ff.

nessed the first transitionary period in American agriculture of the nineteenth century. It was the age of developing industry in the eastern states, the upleap of urban population, the conquest of the rivers by the steamboat, and the opening of the prairies to the farmers by means of the railroad. The population maps of 1820 and 1860 tell the story better than many pages of narrative and description.

Railroads promote marketing. Caird says, what becomes doubly apparent to the student of American geography of that period: "There is a complete organization of markets throughout the country." [21] Indeed, so powerfully had the growth of the older cities and the multiplication of new ones wrought upon the popular mind that Henry Clay was able to preach to an interested constituency the policy and opportunity of providing an adequate "home market" for the products of American agriculture. Nevertheless, the ports opened freely outward, and foreign demand for American breadstuffs was not likely to be cut off so long as only ten to sixteen percent of England's adult population was engaged in agricultural production,[22] and the United States remained the cheapest source of supply.[23]

---

[21] The remark applied especially to Illinois but was equally true of more easterly states.

[22] Caird, 9.

[23] From the late 1840's, the English food market had been open to Mississippi valley farmers, and in a few years a reciprocal trade in English manufactured goods had developed. See Martin, Thomas P., "Cotton and Wheat, 1846–1852," *Jour. of Southern History,* I, No. 3, p. 292 ff.

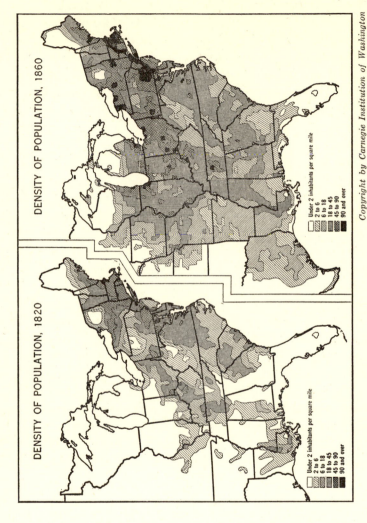

DENSITY OF POPULATION, 1820

DENSITY OF POPULATION, 1860

Under 2 inhabitants per square mile
2 to 6
6 to 18
18 to 45
45 to 90
90 and over

Reproduced from "The Atlas of Historical Geography of the United States," prepared by C. O. Paullin and J. K. Wright (1932). Published by the Carnegie Institution of Washington and the American Geographical Society of New York

We have reached a time when many thousands of American farmers, widely distributed over the country, were in a condition approximating that enjoyed at an earlier period only by those living near a few of the eastern cities. Since nearly all could reach markets of some kind, farming for profit, in the spirit of business, became a normal substitute for subsistence farming.

Journals, societies, and fairs. The generation 1820 to 1860 was fruitful in means for promoting agricultural improvement, among which one of the most effective was an active agricultural press. The *American Farmer*, edited by John S. Skinner in Baltimore dates from the early months of 1819. The *New England Farmer* followed in 1822, the *New York Farmer,* and the *Albany Cultivator* in the first years of the next decade. In 1840 the *Prairie Farmer* opened its better farming campaign in Chicago, and in 1843 was begun in New York one of the greatest journals of the series, the *American Agriculturist,* rendered famous by the scholarship and the practical farmer-sense of Orange Judd. Before the period closed nearly every state and certainly every distinct farming region had its agricultural journal which appealed to farmers for local reasons, many of them reading also the more general farm periodicals. With practical unanimity the states organized agricultural societies.

Another educational agency of a still more practical kind, fostered by the state societies, was the county and state fairs. These, in the form that now became prevalent, originated at Pittsfield, Massachusetts, in the exhibition by Elkanah Watson in 1807, of the two Merino sheep he had acquired from Chancellor Livingston. Other shows, featuring all types of farm livestock, also field and garden products and household arts and industries, followed under Watson's inspiration and finally the state of New York made provision for county fairs throughout that state and also a great state fair. The movement spread because times were ripe for it, and so the county fair came to be an all but universal interest of American rural life, a "harvest home" festival attended by careful farmers and careless alike, and teaching through the interest of its diverse exhibits many a lesson which would not have been derived from books and magazines.

Federal and state promotion agencies. It was now, also, that the federal government began to exert itself in behalf of agricultural improvement. The states had already done something, the local communities and private associations still more when, in 1839, the United States Congress voted $1,000 to the patent office for "the collection of agricultural statistics, investigations for promoting agriculture and rural economy." Thereafter, until 1862, the patent office report carried a section relating to farming which afterwards was more adequately represented by reports of the separate department of agriculture. Other agencies, destined also to become institutionalized during the Civil war, were the special schools of agricultural science so powerfully stimulated through the passage by Congress in 1862 of the Morrill act.[24]

Improved livestock. It was in the years 1818 to 1840 that this country acquired from England the foundation animals of those herds, of choicest strains, which made some of the breeders in New York, Pennsylvania, New Jersey, Kentucky, Ohio, and Illinois almost as celebrated for their Shorthorns as were formerly the Collings brothers, Rev. Henry Berry, and Thomas Bates in England. Pure-bred Devons were imported by Patterson about 1817. Later came the interest in other beef breeds like the Herefords, which captured the open ranges, the Polled Angus, and Red Polled. Also the breeds developed especially for milk, Ayrshires, Jerseys, and Guernseys. Still later came the now universally popular Holstein-Friesian, brought in from the continent. It is noteworthy that importations during the period we are now studying took hold and flourished, whereas those of earlier dates, of which there were several, especially of Devon cattle, attracted only passing attention.

Sheep and wool industry. A wooded country is notoriously unfavorable for sheep. During the entire period of colonial history little emphasis was placed upon the production of wool except as an element in the prevailing subsistence farming. The household needed a small supply of yarn and for

---

[24] The service of the Illinois Central Railroad Company in promoting agricultural improvement is brought out in Gates, *op. cit.,* chap. 13.

that reason a few poor or indifferent sheep were usually kept about the farm. There was no such reliance for occasional market surplus upon these animals as there was upon cattle and hogs, though as the West settled up flocks were driven from older to newer regions to be sold for breeding stock to beginning farmers. For meat food the sheep was despised by Yankees though favored by Virginians. Cattle and hogs, in great numbers, were regularly driven several hundred miles to market, sheep were rarely seen on the highways except when they were being "peddled" through new settlements.

It happened, however, that during the Napoleonic regime, Spain was compelled to give up her monopoly in fine-wooled Merino sheep, and from the large importations of Consul William Jarvis in the years 1809, 1810, and 1811 the flock-masters of Vermont, New York, and other states supplied themselves with breeding stock. A few Merinos had previously reached the United States from France, through the efforts of Chancellor Livingston, and a few from Spain by way of Portugal, but the Jarvis Merinos were the founders of the later great flocks. Improved Leicesters, Cotswolds, Southdows, and Shropshires, all English breeds, followed rather than preceded the Merinos, which may be regarded as primary improvers of the American sheep stock.

Woolen mills and Merinos. The sheep industry rested upon the demand for fine wools created by the erection of woolen factories in the years of partial or complete blockade prior to and during the War of 1812, another illustration of the relation of agriculture to the market. Prices of fine wool skyrocketed, and so did prices of the purebred Merinos. When Livingston could sell his rams at $1,000 apiece, as he did in 1810, a craze is indicated, and that craze went to the usual extremes. Of course, it was the re-establishment of trade with England, and the "dumping" of English manufactured goods at United States ports, which broke the market for fine wool. Merinos, considered wholly unfit for mutton, now became a drug on the market. Mothers no longer named their newborn sons Merino as they did earlier in some instances. Farmers sold their stock at a great sacrifice. Nevertheless, the wool clip of the common sheep of the country had been somewhat benefited by the infusion of Merino blood, and now entered the English breeds to improve further both wool and mutton.

With the firm establishment of American woolen manufactures, under the principle of tariff protection, which was achieved by 1830, the wool industry recovered and within a few years expanded mightily. The region of Vermont and the Berkshires, composed largely of rough pasture lands, was a famous sheep country and long after the heyday of the business had passed, Vermont sheep fanciers were still selling breeding stock to farmers in the western states. Merinos gained a new and more secure popularity in the course of expansion into Kentucky, Ohio, Indiana, Illinois, Michigan, and elsewhere.

As late as 1851, the first state fair of Wisconsin offered prizes for Merino, Saxon, Paular Merino, and cross-breed sheep, as well as for long wools, and middlewools.[25]

The Ohio wool center. In the region just defined, Ohio was the leading wool producer. One half the aggregate number of sheep belonging to the north central states in 1850 were to be found in Ohio and, most intensively, in the eastern portion of that state. The westerners' argument for producing wool instead of grain turned upon the cheapness with which it could be raised, and its lightness and consequent cheapness, in relation to its value, as an article of transport. Naturally, their interest in stabilizing wool prices went far toward making north central farmers tariff protectionists. As showing how effective was western competition in wool growing, it may be pointed out that in the decade 1840 to 1850 the north central states increased their aggregate sheep population more than one hundred percent, while New England and the middle states lost more than three million head in the same period.

Sheep farmers in the West, as in the East, fought shy of the woods. Heavy forests in Wisconsin harbored bears, lynxes, wildcats, and most dangerous of all, timber wolves. All of these were deadly enemies of sheep, wolves being capable of decimating flocks with frightful celerity. Accordingly, the towns or districts where much forest remained had few sheep. The open towns, especially if they contained

[25] *Cf.* Turner, *United States,* 1830–1850, p. 303–304.

high and rough lands, sometimes had many.[26] The
high, dry prairies too, were favored by sheep raisers
as long as the land was not required for more intensive farming.[27] In the long run, as in England
and Scotland, sheep ultimately claimed the rough
mountain slopes because they are the most economical exploiters of the grass on such a terrain.
Sheep will be found today grazing the steep, grassy
"buttes" in Oregon, just as they graze the Eildon
Hills above Melrose Abbey in Berwickshire. America's wool supply at present comes largely from the
mountain areas, while near the great cities mutton
and lamb are in request. Diversification in the
sheep industry, to meet varied demands, has long
been a powerful stimulus to agricultural improvement.

Swine as mortgage lifters. In addition to sheep,
the general farmer gained great advantage from
raising swine. Pork and maize, in the form of
"hog and hominy," had been the staff-of-life for
most families that lived on the subsistence farming
plane. The American woods, in partly settled areas,
were alive with half-wild "razor-back" hogs which,
in many cases, could be secured only with rifle and
ball. The forest was as favorable for hogs as it was
unfavorable for sheep. Naturally, the general farmer
stood for improvement in the stock of swine, though
in most parts of the West he began with the rough,

[26] *Wisconsin Domesday Book, Town Studies* (Whitewater
Town): also *Winnebago-Horicon Basin* (in press), Chap. XII.
[27] See Caird, *Prairie Farming,* etc., 62–64. Also Schafer, *Agriculture in Wisconsin,* 103.

bony, ill-formed woods creatures, which could be quickly modified by good feeding and judicious breeding. Crossed with the Suffolk, Cheshire, Berkshire, Poland China, Essex or Chester White and kept under favorable farm conditions, a few years served to work a complete transformation in the stock. The rapidity with which pigs multiply made the process of improvement cheap, easy, and rapid. A few dollars would usually buy a well-bred male pig and in a single year the results of the investment would appear. For this reason the propaganda of the farm journals in the interest of improved livestock obtained a quicker response from pork-raisers than from cattle, horse, and sheep raisers.[28]

Hog raising on a business scale, however, like the earlier sheep raising, was one answer to the economic requirement of diversification. When the persistent cropping of the land with wheat became unprofitable, as it always did sooner or later, the farmer either changed his habits, making wheat an occasional crop in a rotation, or else sold to someone who would farm in that better way while he himself went west to exploit another piece of rich virgin soil. A certain proportion always took the second alternative. For example, it was computed that 140,000 persons had emigrated from Ohio, under these circumstances, between 1850 and 1857, and in some of the best wheat growing areas the actual

---

[28] This was the opinion of Joseph Harris, famed pig-breeder of Rochester, N. Y. See *Harris on the Pig,* 2d Edition, New York, 1889. 247–248.

decline of the agricultural population amounted to six percent, small farmers selling to larger land-holders and going west.[29]

It was a process which was repeated on every maturing frontier, but the modification of farm practice which accompanied it varied with the times and conditions. When Vermont Yankees gave up wheat as their main crop, and went by thousands to Ohio, Michigan, Illinois, and Wisconsin, those who remained behind enlarged their farms in order the more successfully to raise cattle, horses, and sheep. When the Genesee country farmers grew restive for the same reason and some followed the same course, the home-staying remnant raised cattle and finally went into co-operative cheese dairying. Eastern Pennsylvanians diversified their crops, raised hay and corn, and fattened cattle bought from western drovers. Ohioans, and other north central farmers, became largely wool growers where practicable until about 1870, when wool growing as a farming interest ceased to be profitable, but the farmers in Illinois and Indiana, also parts of Ohio, fed cattle and hogs, or hogs along with cattle, marketing beef and pork as a substitute for the wheat crop. After about 1870 most districts east of the Mississippi which until then had depended mainly on wheat, by reason of the rust, the ravages of the chinch-bug, and the increasing repugnance of the soil to the wheat plant, were forced to revise their

[29] Caird, *Prairie Farming*, 119. Quoting Ohio State Agricultural Report.

farming practices which had already tended toward diversification.

Beef and pork farming. It was then that beef and pork became major crops on the better western farms. The average subsistence farmer's "cow-brute" herd usually included a few steers that could be sold at a low price to drovers who in turn sold to the cattle feeding farmers farther east. The larger pioneer farmers might have large herds. The improvement of the beef stock on the farms waited on the general introduction of Shorthorn, Devon, Hereford, Angus or Galloway foundation animals, a process which went forward at a rapid rate, after the railroads had opened a western market for fat beeves, particularly in the corn-belt states of Illinois, Missouri, Iowa, Kansas and Nebraska.

There were two ways in which the corn-belt farmer could utilize his crop for the improvement of his land, by buying cattle to feed or by raising the animals on his own farm. The decision as to which method would be followed often turned on whether or not the farm afforded cheap pasturage to a sufficient extent. If it did, the farmer was likely to become a breeder. If not, cattle could be bought and fed in winter only. In either case the farm would benefit from the manure resulting from a winter's feeding.

Whether as feeder or as breeder, the good farmer possesses a distinct and often decisive advantage over the one who is careless or indifferent. If he buys stock cattle he knows the types that can be fed profitably, and refuses offers of others. As a breeder he insists on foundation animals that will be least liable to produce inferior individuals. His feeding arrangements, shelters, rations, manure conservation are all attended to with care as factors in what is often a business dependent upon close margins. If he makes a money profit however small, his enterprise succeeds because, by husbanding the manure and applying it to his corn and hay lands, he is steadily enriching his farm.[30]

Pigs with cattle. The feeding of hogs along with cattle, a practice as old as American agriculture, continues to be followed by corn-belt farmers. Hogs being good scavengers, they save what cattle would waste. Besides, on the farms that produce much corn, a field can usually be set aside to be "hogged down" when ripe by pigs that are being conditioned for the market, thus saving the expense of harvesting the crop and also the expense of pen feeding. Hogs and cattle, too, will pasture amicably together which is not true of cattle and sheep.

The decade 1880 to 1890 witnessed the phenomenal increase of swine for the country from 47,681,790 to 57,409,583 and of that total, 37,624,632 were in the north central division which included the five states of the Old Northwest together with Minnesota, the two Dakotas, Iowa, Nebraska, and Kansas. The census of 1890 showed an increase in

[30] An admirable survey of the beef-cattle farming of America is by E. W. Sheets, O. E. Baker, C. E. Gibbons, O. C. Stine and R. H. Wilcox in *Agricultural Department Yearbook* for 1921, pp. 227–322.

Illinois since 1870 from 2,703,000 to 5,925,000; in Iowa from 1,354,000 to 8,267,000; in Kansas from 206,000 to 4,023,000; and in Nebraska from 59,500 to 3,815,000. This indicates how the corn-belt states were finding their profit from turning corn into pork, partly in order to save in the freight bill. But even Wisconsin, which is not in the corn-belt, yet was raising considerable of that food cereal, as well as barley and oats, advanced her hog population from 513,000 to 1,348,000.

Markets for pork. For many years, beginning at least as early as 1820, Cincinnati was the "Porkopolis" of the Mississippi valley. Chicago gradually forged ahead, and Indianapolis, Louisville, St. Louis, Kansas City, and Milwaukee shared in the business. Recently many additional pork-packing centers have been created. "Improved farming," as already indicated, was more generally illustrated in the care and breeding of swine than in any other department of farm livestock activity. The agricultural journals multiplied their warnings against slow-maturing breeds, the fairs emphasized the quick growers and easy fatteners. The extra expense and inconvenience of wintering, in the cold northern states, also stressed the economy of early fattening. Farmers could not resist that propaganda. They accordingly competed everywhere for recognition as successful producers of six-months old, or eight-months old swine, the kind that was universally hailed as the "mortgage lifters."

Leasing corn lands. The profits of farming the

corn-belt farms, over a series of years, especially the period from 1900 to 1920, were exceptionally large. Thousands of owners received incomes from their acres which enabled them to live away from the land as retired farmers, entrusting the actual operations to renters or hired managers. The extraordinarily high prices at which corn lands sold is a testimony both to their fruitfulness and to the advanced state of tillage under which they had long been kept. The custom of leasing has in many sections unfortunately marred the outward evidence of the corn farmers' prosperity, yet it is undeniable that much of the improved farming up to the present time is to be found among corn-belt farmers.[31]

The cattle-feeding farmers have always been recognized as exceptional men on account of their adventuresomeness. Purchasing, fattening, and marketing cattle calls for unusual business qualities. The purchasing requires a large credit, shrewd judgment, and good bargaining ability; the marketing, forethought and decision. Feeding calls for the most careful cost accounting. The farmer who can succeed in all of these respects is not apt to fail in his more general farm improvement plans.

Horses. An exciting chapter could be written on the American farmers' activity in raising horses and mules, especially the former. The business was important from several points of view, some of them economic, like the production of farm work horses,

---

[31] J. Schafer, *The Wisconsin Lead Region*, Chap. XII; Dept. of Agriculture *Handbook*, 1921, 227 ff.

cavalry horses, and draft animals, and others chiefly social like the interest in race horses which began in Virginia during colonial times,[32] extending thence to other southern states, to Kentucky, and finally to the rest of the country. On the whole, however, the raising of horses was either an incidental activity of common farmers, with no special influence upon the quality of the farming pursued; or else of wealthy patrons of the turf or mere horse-fanciers.[33] Horses, indeed, rescued northern agriculture from the slow tempo of ox tillage and travel, the mule performing the like service for the southern planter. As an item in the average farmer's budget, the sale of a young horse or team of horses not infrequently represented most of the year's profits.

The dairying interest. A livestock farming economy which is not only responsible for much of the agricultural improvement in the United States, especially in the past eighty years, but which has given rise to a vast manufacturing and distributing industry, is dairying. Economic revolutions have occurred in many lines since early colonial times, but nothing could be more startling than to compare the Pilgrim's division of the cows, one to every six families, and the present elaborate and complicated arrangements for supplying fresh pasteurized milk to the millions residing in cities from which cows are rigorously barred.

[32] Fairfax Harrison has given us a charming account of the origins of the Virginia racing stock, *Va. Mag. of Hist. and Biography*, XXXV, 329–370 (Oct. 1927).

[33] J. Schafer, *Agriculture in Wisconsin*, 117–121.

The subsistence farmer—or rather his wife or daughter—milked a cow, or several cows, in order to have milk for family use, also butter for the table and possibly a little butter or cheese to exchange for groceries. Pioneer dairy products were prevailingly poor and unappetizing partly because of imperfect equipment, partly by reason of the summer heat which was unfavorable, but largely on account of ignorance on the part of household dairy managers. Nevertheless, certain districts like the Connecticut valley, parts of Rhode Island, and northwestern Connecticut early became famous for the excellent butter and cheese their farmers made and marketed in nearby cities. Where cold springs could be used for refrigeration, butter made during the summer might be salted and packed in firkins, or kegs, and kept sweet until winter when it could be sold at an extra high price, winter dairying being almost non-existent. It was in this way, apparently, that the first real advance was made in dairying.

Origin of farm dairying. A "spring-house," too, made possible the production of a superior quality of butter, from sweet cream, to be sold to discriminating customers during the summer at much above store prices. Many a careful housewife proudly bore her stated weekly supply of golden butter to the homes of prominent villagers—the doctor, judge, banker, etc.—receiving her twenty-five cents a pound cash when the grocer was paying eight or ten cents "in trade." These are illustrations of the ways in which the idea of a definite and dependable income from dairying may have arisen and caused attention to be paid to the care of cows as an important part of the farm business.

Gradually, dairying on a more or less systematic business basis spread throughout New England, New York, Pennsylvania, New Jersey and in general all farming sections accessible to city markets for butter and cheese. The fresh milk needed by the cities was at first provided by nearby dairies from which delivery could be made once or twice daily. Obviously, the enormous growth of the cities multiplied the demand both for fresh fluid milk and for milk products, with the result that dairying received a stimulation similar to that which affected wheat-farming and meat-farming.

Dairy organization. Dairying, however, lends itself to organization more than most kinds of farming. Without considering the huge milk distribution concerns that now focalize the activities of thousands of farm dairymen, we may remind ourselves of how cheese manufacturing and butter manufacturing have almost abolished the kitchen arts of cheese and butter making.

Cheese factories had their rise in western New York shortly after 1850. They spread rapidly, due to their high utility, soon being found throughout the northern states from New York and Pennsylvania west to the Mississippi. Northern Ohio and Wisconsin, however, and more recently Minnesota, became the chief rivals of New York as a producer of cheese. For many years Wisconsin has stood first in that industry. The creamery or butter factory, the milk condensing factory, the milk powder or evaporating plant, the ice-cream factory, the chocolate factory are other institutions for drawing to a single center the daily milk product of many farmers and all of the above operate over larger areas than does the neighborhood cheese factory.

Dairy farm incomes. Whatever processing concern or distributing agency takes his milk, the farmer has a definite idea of the gross income he derives from his cows, and a little care will show him which animals are profitable or the reverse. He usually has some notion of the profit he obtains from the business as a whole and has a daily reminder that poor cows do not pay, that good ones do pay; that good care, wise feeding, and gentle treatment will yield a money value, and that foresight in breeding brings exceptional rewards. Questions of forage feeds, silage, pasturage, the kinds of concentrates to use—all must be settled on a sound common-sense basis, or upon the basis of science, if the best returns are to be expected.

Influence on farmers. The dairy farmer receives his pay checks weekly or monthly, thereby freeing himself from the primitive farmer's costly method of credit purchasing. The necessity of a strict attention to his affairs, every day in the year, as William D. Hoard pointed out, reduces his farming to "the same law of success" as any other business. The co-operative phases of butter and cheese manufacturing and of milk marketing impart an important social relationship to his activities, while science comes into play variously in connection with milk handling. On the whole, dairying is a branch of farming which improves the farmer as well as the farm.

Spread of dairying. Dairying expansion since the beginning of factory cheese making in the eighteen-fifties has been stupendous. Not only has it come to dominate agriculture in most eastern farming sections, due to the enormous demand for wholesome fluid milk, but cheese and butter manufacture or milk production for cities have taken complete possession of several middle western states and flourish sporadically throughout the West. In recent years considerable dairying development has occurred in the cotton-raising South also.

At the present time there are about 25,000,000 cows in the United States, distributed among 4,600,000 farms. These cows are supposed to produce not less than 12,500,000,000 gallons of milk per year. This explains why "The production and distribution of milk and dairy products form the largest industry in the country," and why dairying "is far and away our largest agricultural enterprise." [34]

Dairying therefore has a significant relationship to general business, as well as to the problems of employment, of nutrition, particularly the feeding of infants, and the public health. On the mechanical side modern milk plants reveal in striking fashion

[34] Arthur Pound, *The Atlantic,* November, 1935.

the results of invention. But, after all, the most important incidental result of the spread of dairying over the country is in connection with the conservation and improvement of the soil. It is helping to guarantee the permanence of American agriculture.[35]

Cotton farming—its extent. Since cotton is, and long has been, the greatest commercial crop produced in the United States, one naturally expects to find that much good farming is associated with the business of cotton growing. Unfortunately, the aspect of cotton farming which obtrudes itself is the share-cropping system, one of the social sore spots of American life. Share-cropping accounts for something like twenty-five percent of all American farmers and the characteristically share-cropping districts are the slums of rural America, with a population ill-fed, worse housed, ignorant, diseased and hopeless. A large proportion of the share-croppers are negroes who have exchanged a legal slavery for a type of peonage which is freer but less secure. Owing to the conditions under which they occupy land, they are practically forced to produce cotton almost exclusively, which is the worst possible use of land in the cotton-belt.

However, cotton is produced also by thousands of upstanding American free farmers and it is they who have developed an improved agriculture in

[35] Russell H. Anderson, New York Agriculture Meets the West, *Wis. Hist. Mag.,* XVI, 163–198 and 285–296. Joseph Schafer, *Agriculture in Wisconsin,* Chap. IX. *The Winnebago-Horicon Basin* (in press) Chap. XII.

connection with cotton growing. If, as stated previously, it is axiomatic that soil depletion spells poverty for the farmer, logic requires that farms be managed in such a way as to conserve the soil and its fertility. This cannot be done by growing cotton on the same land year after year without special attention to its fertilization. Besides, from the strictly business end of farming, it is necessary to so plan production as to make the net annual income of the farm as large as may be, consistently with the steady improvement of the land.[36]

Improved cotton farming. Good farmers have solved that problem. They provide for such crops as may be needed to feed livestock and people, and keep the land in good heart—by means of legumes, pasturing and manuring—and after that determine what proportion of the cultivable area can be used economically for the marketable crop. These farmers use vast quantities of commercial fertilizer on their cotton land, grow corn, peanuts, cow-peas and soy-beans, clover and grasses; feed pigs and cattle as well as working horses or mules. Briefly, instead of the single staple they diversify in order to render the growing of the commercial crop most profitable in a permanent agriculture. Their practice is similar to that of the successful general farmer's plan of growing wheat.

Agricultural specialties—tobacco. Thus far the course of agricultural improvement has been de-

[36] See *Agricultural Yearbook* for 1921, 323–406 for a good discussion of the cotton-farming situation.

scribed as connected mainly with what could be called general farming. Cotton culture, to be sure, is an exception to that rule, though as we have seen, the best farming in the cotton area is done by farmers who diversify production to a considerable extent. The same has been true, since early times, in tobacco culture. That business, however, has broken out of its former geographical bounds and is now carried on in several northern states, notably Connecticut in the East and Wisconsin in the Middle West, usually in connection with dairying. A dairy farm of 160 acres, for example, may have growing upon it every season say ten or fifteen acres of tobacco. In such cases the farm livestock supplies the necessary fertilizer. In the specially favorable tobacco regions, however, tobacco is grown much more intensively with the use of commercial fertilizers.

Fruit farming. When we come to fruit growing as a business, or market gardening, not only good farming practice is implied but also the command of a certain amount of science. Co-operation is often resorted to as a means of obtaining the services of scientifically trained supervisors of entire orcharding regions, and to compel all individual orchardists to comply with the supervisor's instructions. Marketing, also, is taken out of the hands of the individual and handled collectively, as is in some instances the actual cultivation of the orchards. On the whole, therefore, these specialties have helped powerfully to educate selected groups of general farmers to be well-informed and highly skilled representatives of their calling. In fact, so sharply demanding is fruit culture as a business, that only those of somewhat exceptional aptitudes have been able to master its intricacies. The average wheat farmer requires a period of apprenticeship and a large amount of instruction before he is ready to manage a fruit farm. The spread of fruit growing, like that of dairying, has notably advanced farmer-training.

CHAPTER V

PROFESSIONAL FARMING

THE farmer equipped with science wields a practical kind of magic. For thousands of years the cultivation of the soil was a purely empirical activity. "Behold, a sower went forth to sow, and when he sowed some seeds fell by the wayside, and the fowls came and devoured them up; some fell upon stony places, where they had not much earth: and forthwith they sprung up because they had no deepness of earth. And when the sun was up they were scorched, and because they had no root they withered away. And some fell among thorns, and the thorns sprung up and choked them. But other fell into good ground and brought forth, some an hundred-fold, some sixty-fold, some thirty-fold. Who hath ears to hear let him hear."

Scientific magic vs. *tradition.* Disregarding the hazard of birds, the hazard of drought, and the hazard of thorns, all of which are as baleful today as they were when Jesus spoke his fadeless parable, what is to be said of the range of production from seed falling into "good ground?" His "hundred-fold" is seventy percent more than the "thirty-

143

fold," and forty percent above the "sixty-fold"—
why?

Is it that the cut-worms were more destructive
in some spots than in others; that the moles traversed a part of the field only; that shade from
neighboring woods robbed of sunlight a strip of
the growing grain; that some ground was steeper
than the rest and lost its humus under the pelting
of the "latter rain"; that the lower ground was too
wet; the higher too dry; that a fraction of the field
had been summer-fallowed, the balance not; that a
part had been recently broken up, the rest older
cultivation; that some of the soil was clay loam, the
rest sandy loam; that a part had too little lime in
solution; another part deficient in nitrogen; that
some was in want of phosphates? It is astounding
how many possible reasons could have existed for the
wide divergence in production from ground that was
well prepared for receiving the seed.

Chemistry basic in agriculture. To the solution
of this latter problem especially, not so much to
that of ravenous birds, quick-growing thorns, or
blasting heat, science makes its amazing contribu-
tion. If agriculture has finally attained a professional status, that happy result is due primarily to
the progress of chemistry. And for the application
of that science to the growing of plants the modern
world is indebted first of all to Sir Humphry Davy
whose treatise antedated by half a century the publication of Lavoisier's more accurate and enlighten-
ing discoveries. Davy gave lectures on "the con-

nection of chemistry with vegetable physiology" as early as 1803,[1] and ten years later published his *Elements of Agricultural Chemistry*, "the foundation," says Lord Ernle, "on which the science of agricultural chemistry has been reared." Among those who built upon Davy's beginnings may be mentioned the Alsatian experimenter, J. D. Boussingault, who made his farm one of the first and best experiment stations; and after him Justus von Liebig who as early as 1840 wrote on plant nutrition in the very spirit, as was later discovered, of Lavoisier's much earlier demonstrations.[2] In 1843 the famous experimental farm at Rothamsted, England, staffed by the scientific experimenters, J. B. Lawes and J. H. Gilbert, proved the efficacy of artificial fertilizers.

These studies aroused universal interest because the world had been waiting for them. Beginnings along similar lines had long since been made in France, Germany, Austria, Switzerland, Russia, and elsewhere so that the minds of agricultural philosophers were on the stretch to welcome the new conclusions and put them to the test of practice.

Liebig et al in America. In America the interest in improved farming, as we have seen, was stressed by the multiplication of agricultural magazines, state and local societies, county and state fairs, and the feeble beginnings of a national agency for pro-

---

[1] Baron Ernle, *English Farming Past and Present*, 216–217.
[2] H. W. Wiley, Relation of Chemistry to Agriculture, *Yearbook*, 1899, 220.

moting agriculture and rural life. It was certain that the publication of Liebig's "Chemistry in its Application to Agriculture and Physiology" would stimulate new experimentation, but the agencies for conducting the experiments would have to be created. Americans in general heartily agreed with Liebig, that: "Perfect agriculture is the true foundation of all trade and industry." The scientific-minded among them recognized how dependent upon chemistry was our exact knowledge of soils and manures in relation to growing plants. America, at the middle of the nineteenth century, had no Rothamstead to serve as an experiment station for agricultural research. But her people possessed an abiding faith in the institutions of higher learning, represented by Harvard and Yale, and there was also a ferment of activity and propaganda on the subject of popular education. Each of those colleges maintained a scientific department, and had already given some attention to agriculture. Yale, however, was the first American institution to respond adequately to the demand for a sound course in agricultural chemistry. This it did by creating a chair in that subject, in 1847, for John Pitkin Norton, a disciple of James F. W. Johnston at Edinborough, who had studied in the famous laboratory of the Agricultural Chemical Association, and also that of Johannes Mulder at Utrecht.

Leadership of Yale—Norton. Professor Norton was an enthusiast as well as a scientist. His lectures at Yale attracted able young men, among them

Orange Judd, greatest of America's agricultural journalists in that day, and Samuel William Johnson, who became his own successor. Norton's lectures to farmers in many parts of the East, notably in New York state, represented agricultural extension in its best estate. His book, *Elements of Scientific Agriculture,* had a wide influence especially through its general employment by editors of the agricultural journals. Though his life was short, Norton's service was great and lasting.

Agricultural improvement, however, seemed too exigent an interest to wait upon the slow process of an educational influence broadening down from the colleges. Improvers were impatient people, then as now. The current agitation about the development of common schools and high schools inevitably suggested the widest possible dissemination of agricultural science as a branch of popular education. Scarcity of well prepared teachers, however, the practical requirement of preliminary training, and the necessity of providing laboratory equipment, ultimately restrained the public enthusiasm within more reasonable bounds.

Manual labor schools. Nevertheless, in the manual labor schools, of which numerous examples were to be found in the period 1820 to 1850, some effort was made toward combining scientific instruction with the farm practice of the student boys.[3] One

[3] See Theodore D. Weld, First Annual Report of the Society for Promoting Manual Labor in Literary Institutions, New York, 1833. The society dates from 1831.

of those schools, the Gardiner Lyceum at Gardiner, Maine, may well be regarded as perhaps the earliest form of the agricultural school or college in this country. It was opened in 1823, and at least two of its principals, John H. Lathrop and Ezekiel Holmes, were scholars versed in science and with a deep interest in agricultural improvement. The school was partially supported by legislative appropriations on the understanding that it would impart to the future agriculturist, "a knowledge of those principles of science upon which his future success depends and let him see them reduced to practice"; and would perform "a series of agricultural experiments adapted to the soil of Maine." [4] Lathrop later was chosen president of the University of Wisconsin. Dr. Holmes in 1833 became editor of the *Maine Farmer,* whose influence was widely felt in northern New England. Holmes saw the end of the Gardiner experiment, due to financial distress. He is reported to have conducted a special class in agriculture, and he also had charge of the farm connected with the school on which were kept "superior breeds of animals, improved machinery, and valuable fruits and grains."

Other examples of the development of agricultural schools out of industrial schools were the Agricultural Seminary at Derby, Connecticut, which lasted only one year; the Cream Hill Agricultural School at West Cornwall, Connecticut, maintained from 1845 to 1869; and institutionally much more im-

[4] A. C. True, *History of Agricultural Education,* 36.

portant, the Rensselaer Polytechnic Institute at Troy, New York, founded (1824) to instruct "in the application of science to the common purposes of life." While embracing agriculture in its plans, this institution trended away from that field into engineering, geology, and general chemistry.[5]

Agricultural colleges. The Morrill act. The manner in which the spirit of agricultural science embodied itself for educational purposes was for some years extremely diverse. In order, however, to shorten our account of the rise of agricultural colleges, and to avoid complicating that story overmuch, it will be best to sketch the origin of the Morrill law, the basis upon which these institutions have been developed. The federal grant under this law, it has been well said, "marks the beginning of one of the most comprehensive, far-reaching, and grandiose, schemes for the endowment of higher education ever adopted by any civilized nation." [6]

The putative father of the Morrill law, Hon. Justin S. Morrill of Vermont, in the course of a legislative campaign extending over a number of years, made the ideas underlying the system so thoroughly his own that he forgot the agency of others in bringing them to his attention. Fortunately, the history of the movement has been fully elucidated with the result that, among numerous contributors, one name stands out as pre-eminent—

[5] True, *supra*, 41–43.
[6] Edmund J. James, *The Origin of the Land Grant Act of 1862.* (Urbana, Ill. Univ. Press, 1910. The Univ. Studies, V. IV, No. 1), p. 13.

that of Jonathan Baldwin Turner of Jacksonville, Illinois.[7]

It is possibly significant that Turner was a Yale College man for, at Yale, as heretofore stated, John Pitkin Norton established the earliest collegiate school of agricultural science. However, Turner, in his own right, was an educational thinker who had gradually, in the course of twenty years, worked out a theoretical system of industrial education supported by an idealogy which apparently radiates from Rousseau but emerges directly from an intensely democratic nineteenth century mind.

Jonathan B. Turner. Turner divided society into the professional group, a small class, and the industrial, a very large class, assuming that at the very lowest the latter would be to the former as ninety-five to five, while ordinarily it would be more nearly in the proportion of ninety-nine to one. It is the right of this second class, he argued, to have the same opportunity for cultural development that society has supplied for the first. The professional group has not only institutions, professors, appliances, but "a vast, and voluminous literature that would well nigh sink a whole navy of ships."[8] "But where," he asks, "are the universities, the apparatus, the professors, and the literature specifically adapted to any one of the industrial classes. Echo answers, where? In other words, society has become, long since, wise enough

[7] Edmund J. James, *supra.*

[8] Jonathan B. Turner, *A Plan for an Industrial University,* 1854, 18, 19. Also printed in James, *supra.*

to know that its *teachers* need to be educated; but it has not yet become wise enough to know that its *workers* need education just as much. In these remarks I have not forgotten that our common schools are equally adapted and applied to all classes; but reading, writing, &c are properly no more education than gathering seed is agriculture or cutting ship-timber navigation. They are mere rudiments, as they are called, or means, the mere instrument of an after education, and if not so used they are, and can be, of little more use to the possessor than an ax in the garret or a ship rotting upon the stocks." [9]

The industrial classes, he contended, do not want to embark in a canoe hauled up alongside of the educational ship provided for the professional class. They want a ship of their own, under a sympathetic captain and crew. Given proper training in the science and art of their future pursuits, and equipped with a literature to subserve the needs of occupational students, the industrial classes will be able to attain to the plane of culture that has long been the monopoly of the professional classes. For an education, to the highest degree attainable by the quality of the individual mind, can be secured in connection with the practical pursuits of life, given the essential keys in the way of basic principles. In fact, Turner was convinced that the professional class itself gained cultural distinction *after,* not *in,* college and through contact with practical life

[9] *Supra,* p. 19.

problems considered in the light of the principles learned and the literatures which illustrated and developed them. "What we want from schools," he said, "is to teach men . . . to derive their mental and moral strength from their own pursuits, whatever they are. . . . We wish to teach them to read books only that they may the better read and understand the great volume of nature ever open before them." [10]

His educational philosophy. These quotations show the philosophy, sound or unsound, upon which the promoters of agricultural colleges proceeded. Carried to its logical conclusion, the plan would abolish the so-called common man, giving him scientific education and the ability to gain the culture appropriate to it. Initially, however, it provided an institutional basis merely for the beginning of a system of universal industrial education. Turner believed there should be a central institution at Washington, with an affiliated institution in each of the states. The first he thought had been provided for in the recent bequest of the Englishman, James Smithson, who endowed the Smithsonian Institution. The great series of state institutions would have to be created and he called upon Congress to provide the means for that purpose. Since Smithson's generous endowment was used for other purposes, we must regard the development of the federal department of agriculture as supplying the

[10] From Turner's *Industrial Education* pamphlet of 1853 printed as Appendix C with Edmund J. James's article, *supra*, p. 59.

national co-ordinating center for the proposed system.

At this point the idea of land grants for educational objects, already more than a century old in American practice, reasserts itself. Land grants for schools were made in the English colonies as early at least as the first years of the eighteenth century.[11] The New England idea of school reservations in new townships was adopted as the national policy with the ordinances of 1785 and 1787 and so became generalized. State common school funds were created from the congressional grant of the sixteenth section in each township or, in the younger states, the sixteenth and thirty-sixth sections; and university funds were created from the grant of seventy-two sections, or two townships, to each new state. Congress had control of many millions of acres of land which could be used for all sorts of promotional purposes, and gradually so many demands arose—for canal construction, for railroads, etc.—that some feared the vast federal endowment of land would be squandered, or absorbed in new state developments, with no advantage whatever to the older states and possibly to their detriment.

The political argument. Here, therefore, was an opening for the educational statesman. Requests had already been made for land grants to individual states in aid of agricultural colleges, for example in

[11] J. Schafer, *Origin of the System of Land Grants in Aid of Education,* Univ. of Wis. History Series, Vol. 1, No. 1, Madison, Wis., 1902.

Michigan. But Turner and his coadjutors in Illinois asked for grants to all the states on a proportional basis. Since the older states were equally, with the newer, in need of the means for agricultural and mechanical education, a truly national interest could be aroused by this move, and that is exactly what happened. The leading agricultural journals hailed the Illinois idea; the metropolitan press espoused it; and politicians here and there were not slow to take it up. The Illinois Industrial League, of which Turner was the active head, wisely sought out an eastern man to present the plan in Congress and happily their choice fell upon Justin S. Morrill. From 1856 the campaign in Congress was continuous. Finally, July 2, 1862, Abraham Lincoln, also of Illinois, signed the Morrill act which thereby became law.

When the legislature of Illinois in February, 1853, responding to the demands of the state Industrial League, petitioned for "a law of Congress donating to each state in the Union an amount of public lands not less in value than $500,000, for the liberal endowment of a system of Industrial Universities, one in each state in the Union, to co-operate with each other and with the Smithsonian Institution at Washington, *for the more liberal and practical education of our industrial classes and their teachers,*" [12] it had, in that language, established the norm adhered to throughout the campaign. The act which embodies the answer to that

[12] Edmund J. James, as cited, p. 96. Italics mine.

petition provides a grant of 30,000 acres of land for each senator and representative to which a state is entitled, the lands to be sold in order to establish a permanent irreducible fund, the income of which only should be used by each state claiming the benefit of the act, for "the endowment, support, and maintenance of at least one college where the leading object shall be, without excluding other scientific and classical studies, and including military tactics, to teach such branches of learning as are related to agriculture and the mechanic arts, in such manner as the legislature of the states may respectively prescribe, in order to promote the *liberal and practical education of the industrial classes* in the several pursuits and professions of life." [13] No part of the fund could be used for building, but ten percent might be employed for purchasing land for experimental farms. The states were required to act on the question of acceptance within five years.

Embodying the colleges. In the sequel the state university was designated as the land-grant institution in twenty-two states; twenty states each established a separate land-grant college in addition to a state university; Alaska, Hawaii, and Puerto Rico, territories, maintain land-grant colleges; six states do not provide state universities and of these Connecticut, Massachusetts, Pennsylvania, and Rhode Island maintain land-grant colleges; and Massachusetts, New Jersey, and New York have designated departments of privately controlled in-

[13] Italics mine.

stitutions as land-grant colleges. Massachusetts divides the fund between a college for agriculture at Amherst and one for engineering at Cambridge. The total number of such institutions is now sixty-nine, of which fifty-two are attended almost exclusively by white students and seventeen exclusively by negroes.[14]

So terse a history of the creation of a great system of educational institutions gives a deceptive impression that all went smoothly and with a kind of inevitability. Not so. Effort, struggle, and contention marked every step of the progress both in Congress before the law was enacted and in the states before it could be accepted and put in operation. The Morrill bill was opposed by southern members on the ground that it was unconstitutional, and when passed by a narrow margin in both houses it was vetoed by President Buchanan on that and other grounds.[15] In the midst of the turmoil of the Civil war, when the southern members had withdrawn from the national Congress and that body as well as the executive was in the control of the new Republican party, the land-grant legislation was enacted. And, significantly, it was only one of several far-reaching acts affecting American agricultural history, for in the same year, 1862, was

[14] Of the aggregate number in attendance in 1930–31—180,515 men and 128,877 women—"slightly more than one third" were enrolled in agriculture and mechanic arts courses. These 69 institutions had, in that year, an aggregate income from all sources of $165,000,000.

[15] The veto was recorded February 26, 1859.

passed the Homestead law and also the law creating the national department of agriculture.[16]

The loyal states, to which its benefits were limited, at the time were so preoccupied by the war and so hard-pressed to supply funds for carrying it on, that little could then be done about building the new colleges. Not until the war was over did practical results begin to flow from the Morrill law. The case of Wisconsin may serve to illustrate the procedure in the separate states. The moot question there as elsewhere was whether the grant should be given to an existing institution of higher learning, or be used to develop a wholly new and distinct college. The state agricultural society was instinctively favorable to the second plan and it was only with difficulty that its members could be induced to accept a union of the agricultural college with the state university, which of course would have the advantage of saving money.

Land-grant college problem in Wisconsin. The contest turned on the argument that the grant could be used to compel a reorganization of the so-called university itself, which had been essentially a classical college up to that time, making it over into a true university by stressing general science as well as agricultural science, engineering, and the mechanic arts. Since the secretary of the agricultural society headed the movement, this plan was finally approved, with some doubts and mental reservations,

---

[16] A. C. True, *History of Agricultural Education,* 95–106.

by the farmers, and the legislature accepted it in 1866.[17]

But the mere formal creation of an agricultural and mechanical institution as part of a reorganized state university did not end the debate as to the best means of promoting agricultural education. For it soon became apparent that the college would educate very few farmers, if any. At Madison the interests of classical studies as a preparation for the so-called "learned professions" continued to dominate as before the reorganization, though a subordinate interest in science and in engineering developed alongside. So utterly was agriculture submerged as to be virtually eliminated as a separate study. The farmers fretted and fumed. They looked to Michigan and saw there a flourishing college of agriculture distinct from the university, to Iowa and saw a similarly successful school of agriculture. They were about ready to insist on a new law, taking the land grant away from the University and creating an agricultural and mechanical college at a distance from Madison when the inauguration by Professor William Arnon Henry, in 1886, of the agricultural short course saved the day for the University.

Making the college a success. The success of the short course and the later dairy course, which took

[17] John Wesley Hoyt, Secretary of the Wisconsin State Agricultural Society and editor of *The Wisconsin Farmer,* was the dynamic agent in bringing this plan forward and in putting it through: *Cf.* J. Schafer, *A History of Agriculture in Wisconsin,* 159 ff.

farmer boys of common school preparation and gave them several winter months' training in elementary agricultural subjects, or in scientific dairying, revealed what was the actual demand among farmers at that time in Wisconsin. Only an occasional student could be persuaded to spend four years in the study of the principles of a subject the practical mastery of which he had already gained through apprenticeship, particularly when it was the almost universal opinion that "anybody can farm" and the contempt for "book farming" was still widely prevalent. Also, the depressed state of agriculture in the seventies and eighties operated to keep students away from the colleges.

Perhaps the popular attitude cannot be better summarized than in an anecdote of "Uncle" Jere Rusk, who was a splendid representative of the best type of the "common people." After his return to Wisconsin from Washington where he served in Harrison's cabinet as the first Secretary of Agriculture, a reporter is said to have remarked to him: "I am told you are now engaged in the pursuit of agriculture?" "Yes," said Uncle Jere, "and that's just it. I used to 'farm' some and made money at it; now I'm engaged in the pursuit of agriculture and can't make ends meet." "High farming" was not the first secretary's forte, nor was it as yet much in vogue among the people.

What the college taught. The simple fact is that the "science of agriculture," as then understood, constituted a body of doctrine which, if spread over four years of college grade work, made an exceedingly thin course. To be sure, it was flanked with botany, zoology, chemistry, mathematics, English, mental and moral philosophy, astronomy, bookkeeping, physical geography, landscape gardening, civil engineering, physiology, French, etc. In other words, four years work was provided, but only a fraction of this pertained strictly to agriculture. It is obvious that this difficulty would militate against the university-attached colleges, which felt bound to maintain something like the prevailing matriculation requirements, much more severely than against the separate agricultural schools whose managements were freer to fix entrance conditions to suit their social environment. Many of the latter, indeed, for a goodly period of years, were on practically a high school plane.

But, whether of high school or of college grade, the work of the land-grant schools was mainly instructing, not research, save in exceptional cases. These institutions measurably failed in that most important function for which they were created. The difficulty was primarily the qualifications and spirit of the professors, but also the want of enthusiasm on the part of administrations and, of course—a convenient excuse—the excessive teaching load. So, gradually, it became apparent that, if agricultural research was to be effectively promoted, it must be institutionalized; it must be specially endowed, staffed and administered, like the Rothamstead station in England, the German and other

European stations whose work was attracting the notice of American agricultural leaders.

Demand for experiment. At this point, again, the standard universities, Harvard and Yale, set the mark by establishing laboratories for research in agricultural science. The Bussey Institution at Harvard and the Sheffield Scientific School at Yale published bulletins describing results of such researches, and the department of agriculture at Washington, in its annual reports, gave accounts of the work of its chemist, its entomologist, and its botanist—a very small staff, indeed, compared with the present, but destined to enjoy a startlingly rapid expansion.

As Yale college gave the country its first thoroughgoing course in agricultural chemistry in the work of John P. Norton, so it also may be said to have developed the first thoroughgoing agricultural experiment station. At all events, though W. O. Atwater's station was opened at Middletown, Connecticut in 1875, it was removed two years later to New Haven where work along similar lines had already begun in the laboratory of Professor Samuel William Johnson, author of the well known studies on *How Crops Grow* and *How Crops Feed*.

The idea of experiment stations was in the air. It had received much attention at the Washington meeting of land-grant colleges in 1872 where a committee reported in favor of the establishment of such stations and the movement was officially launched. Almost contemporaneously with the

founding of the station at Yale, E. W. Hilgard
opened one at the University of California. North
Carolina followed; then Cornell University, and
thirteen other land-grant colleges created experiment stations.

It was an interest promoted by the agricultural
press which published the results of experiments
for the benefit of their more intelligent readers; by
the agricultural societies, the state and national
grange, the colleges, and scientific men everywhere.
Moreover, experimentation appealed to legislators
as a likely means of securing economic advancement. Reports on experiments in making sugar
from sorghum, on silos and ensilage, on the pre-
vention of oat-smut, on feeding pigs, beef cattle and
dairy cows, and scores of other practical problems
all had a calculable money value to the states.

The Hatch act for experiment stations. Under
these circumstances it was natural that Congress
should be asked to endow the stations as it had
previously endowed the colleges, and by the Hatch
act of 1887 [18] that was done, though several subse-
quent laws have vastly strengthened the original
federal grant both directly and through the requirement of conditional grants from the states.

Some of the most productive scientists of the
country were sponsors of the experiment stations.
Samuel William Johnson, successor to John P. Norton at Yale, was a leader in promoting these institutions. Johnson had been a student under Norton and afterwards spent several years in Germany

[18] Approved by President Cleveland, March 2, 1887.

studying under Erdmann at Leipzig and under Liebig at Munich. Two of his numerous publications, *How Crops Grow* and *How Crops Feed,* were for many years the basis of agricultural-chemical instruction in the colleges. But he was not content merely to investigate and write. He trained other investigators, of whom W. O. Atwater is perhaps the most notable example, he lectured to farmers, and in the winter of 1860 conducted at New Haven what is believed to have been the first Farmer's Institute—a method of making scientific farmers, in a few weeks, out of otherwise well educated and progressive cultivators of the soil. His influence in founding the first regular state experiment station, in Connecticut, was only one evidence of his agricultural statesmanship, for he had a large agency in creating and managing the national system of colleges and stations.

Federal supervision of. Atwater, as is well known, gained international recognition for his fruitful work in calorimetry, but in the humbler fields of food chemistry, as for example the study of maize or Indian corn, he performed a great service to farmers. His conclusion just fifty years ago that leguminous plants have the power and function to fix nitrogen drawn from the atmosphere helped to provide the long-needed scientific basis for the widespread faith in clover as a soil renovating crop.[19] As chief of the office of experiment stations of the

[19] Although the complete demonstration of the relation of the legumes to nitrogen fixation and bacteria remained for Hellriegel to produce in 1886. See Univ. of Wis. *Studies in Science* 5, p. 9–10.

department of agriculture, Atwater was for some years in a strategic relation to those institutions enabling him to promote the scientific research to which his life was dedicated. Following him another thorough scholar, scientist and educator, Alfred Charles True, was in charge of that office till our own day, though the office latterly has been called States Relations Service. Like Atwater, he has exerted a great and beneficial influence upon the experiment stations and, through them, upon the entire system of agricultural colleges.

Later appropriations to these colleges under the Morrill act of 1890, the Nelson act, the Adams act, the Smith–Hughes act, and others have expanded the facilities of both the colleges and the experiment stations. They have caused to be developed a complete system of extension teaching that ties to the colleges and stations the farmers of every county, and also provides agricultural instruction to younger pupils through certain classes of high schools. The federal connection with the state schools and stations, and the measure of government control thus exerted over expenditures and consequently over policies, while occasionally resented locally, has on the whole proved beneficial. It has prevented, in a few cases, a threatened misuse of funds, it has served to correlate research projects, and it has supplied through the government's directors, Atwater, True, and their successors wise, consistent advice and encouragement.

Promotion of research. Research, which a dis-

tinguished Briton has called "The fairyland of
science" has led through the agricultural experiment stations into strange new worlds. While often
starting from points of vantage created for them
by Old World investigators, American scientists
have not lacked originality as witness the work of
Johnson and Atwater, chemists, E. W. Hilgard,
geologist and soil expert, H. L. Russell, bacteriolo-
gist, L. R. Jones, plant pathologist, and scores of
others who might be named. In order to illustrate,
from a concrete, definitely co-ordinated project, it
is only necessary to indicate American contributions to the subject of nutrition.

One does not get far in the study of that phase
of agricultural history before coming upon that
unique character, Dr. Stephen Moulton Babcock,
dubbed by one eulogist "The laughing saint of
science," and by another "Finder of the Hidden
Hunger." [20] "Babcock of Wisconsin," says De Kruif,
"was first of all modern men to find this hunger
that doesn't gnaw at men and beasts but only
strikes them down with strange ills, maybe kills
them."

Stephen Moulton Babcock. Babcock acquired, as
a graduate student in the most authoritative laboratories of Germany, and brought back to New
York state, the world's accepted canons of food
chemistry. Then he was set the problem of finding
out how much of each food element certain cows

[20] President Glenn Frank; Paul De Kruif, *Hunger Fighters*,
267.

were digesting and came suddenly upon a chemical picture which at first confounded him and then provoked him to uproarious mirth. The cows were not digesting anything, so far as his double set of figures for intake and outgo proved. In other words, retort and test tube were no measure of the nutritive virtues of feeds, and so the arrogant German savants, as he would have said, were "all wet."

But this he would have to prove by a printable *reductio ad absurdum*, for surely these were great and honorable men, and his own hitherto revered teachers. Babcock was equal to the occasion, however. He attended the American Chemical Association and there suggested that an excellent ration for a cow, considered solely from the chemical point of view, would be a given quantity of bituminous coal! That settled the negative point and provided a new argument for considering well the common methods men employed on the basis of long tradition, before condemning them as unscientific.

Testing feed for cows. Most important, however, was the question which instantly followed: What is, in reality, good feed for cows? On what one of the plants to which we are accustomed can cows best nourish themselves, whatever chemistry tells us about their food contents? Translated to the Wisconsin station in 1888, Babcock was reluctantly given two cows to feed, one with oats, the other with corn. The oat-feeder promptly died under the experiment; the other was more promptly withdrawn, compelling him to wait many years before the authorities would consent to place others at his disposal.

Finally, in 1907, at a time when all the world acclaimed Babcock for his wizardry in inventing the milk test and his unequalled generosity in freely giving it to mankind, he could no longer be denied. Moreover, feeding experiments were a much more normal station activity in the early nineteen hundreds than they had been a quarter century earlier. Accordingly, the Wisconsin College of Agriculture segregated sixteen thrifty grade shorthorn heifers, turned them over to Babcock and his aides, Edwin B. Hart and George C. Humphrey, and the great test began.

The classic feeding experiment. Without going into the revealing series of bovine tragedies attendant upon feeding one group of four wheat, another group oats, another corn, and a fourth (as a control) all three of these plants, we can summarize by reporting the positive conclusions. First: wheat, though fed as a complete chemically balanced ration, and in varied forms as whole grain, whole straw, chaffed straw, etc. is a very bad food for cows. Oats, similarly, in a balanced ration, is better but still defective for some reason. The three together, assumed by farmers to be an ideal combination, is equally imperfect when measured by results instead of by laboratory tests. Only one of the four groups of heifers, the corn fed one, throve steadily, produced living, thrifty calves, gave milk freely, produced another set of thrifty calves and, in short, ran the life cycle in winning style.

Here was a genuine demonstration in nutrition. Indian corn, the yellow variety, is a perfect food for a bovine animal if properly fed as meal, glucose, stover, whole grain. Something was lacking in the wheat diet which made it impossible for the heifers fed upon that plant to bring forth viable calves, despite the moderate thriftiness of the mothers up to the calving crisis. Of the oat feeders' calves three lived but they were not very prosperous, and of those eating the three feeds only one of the four calves lived.

Influence on nutrition history. Vitamins. At last the world knew there was a mysterious something in corn, a mysterious lack of something in each of the other feeds. And now many men in many lands excitedly pushed forward laboratory experiments in the search for elusive nutritional principles. E. V. McCollum of Wisconsin found one of these. Other researchers were making discoveries at about the same time; the philosophy of food, theretofore based on the chemist's calories, now assumed a wholly new aspect in view of the presence or absence of the potent *vitamins* without which rats go blind, Chinese have beri-beri, sailors endure the torments of scurvy, and the childhood of the race is always under the blight of rickets.

Nor are we yet at the end of the researches set in motion by Babcock's discovery of the hidden hunger, of Hart and Humphrey's feeding experiment.

Comes now Harry Steenbock with his elaborate, complicated set of experiments in the feeding of rats which yielded the truly sensational discovery that the ultra-violet rays of the sun generate vitamin D. We now have our breakfast foods irradiated, our milk irradiated, and there has been developed, mainly in recent years, a widespread industry in making sun-lamps to lighten the dark places of the earth. Of course "wonders never cease"; the chain of discovery never has a final link. For our present purpose, however, it is enough to point out that the Steenbock discovery, the McCollum discovery, the striking results in feeding obtained by Hart and Humphrey, all link together and all derive from the doubts and scientific skepticism of Dr. Babcock, the self-liberated disciple of the great German food chemists.

Varied scientific helps to farmers. From what has been said it may be inferred that, if agriculture as carried on in the United States is still often slip-shod and empirical in character, the explanation is to be found in conditions other than the existing means of scientific education. For, as things are now, the individual farmer not only *may* secure help from the varied curricula of the colleges and schools, from county agents, farmer's week conferences, and experiment station or department of agriculture bulletins, and even from the daily and Sunday newspapers, but he can hardly avoid receiving such help. Nevertheless, the question of how rapidly and under what conditions the findings of the scientist have been put in operation calls for consideration.

Attention was drawn in the previous chapter to the elementary science but advanced agricultural practice of John Taylor of Caroline, Virginia, who may represent one of the earliest professional farming types in the United States, comparable to Jethro Tull in England. But a much more scientific farmer of Virginia in the next generation was Edmund Ruffin of Prince George county who actually went to Davy's chemistry for help in solving the problem of soil exhaustion.

Farmer scientists—Ruffin. Ruffin's success in the application of calcareous manures, especially marl, whose virtues as a corrective of acid soils he demonstrated by means of extensive experiments on his own land, and his persistent preaching about it to farmers, gave him a numerous following and a very widespread influence in the improvement of farming in Virginia. "His monument," it has been said, "is the soil of his own state." [21] Ruffin's essay on calcareous manures, appearing first as a short paper, through several editions grew to a book of 493 pages and was described many years later as "the most thorough piece of work on an agricultural subject ever published in the English language." [22] In 1833 he established the *Farmer's Register,* a profoundly influential journal for the farming of Virginia and Maryland.

[21] Craven, *Soil Exhaustion,* etc., p. 135.   Quotation.
[22] Craven, *Soil Exhaustion,* etc., p. 136.

Familiarity with the file of any one of the great farmer's journals, like the *American Agriculturist,* affords some hints about who were applying science in their farm operations. Faithful readers of that magazine during the eighteen sixties and seventies were taught to revere John Johnston, of Geneva, New York, the apostle of tile-draining, top-dressing of meadows, clover, lime and plaster, and of careful, thorough cultivation. It does not appear that Johnston, a Scotch shepherd lad, had much science, and he confessed that his ideas of farming came from his grandfather. His agricultural chemistry was that of the observing cultivator who believes in stable manure and in the demonstrated efficacy of certain well known commercial fertilizers. Probably the student of soil physics had most to learn from Johnston's farming, for he proved, by systematically tile-draining his entire freehold, which grew more valuable year by year, that the thorough under-draining of clay soils greatly improved their texture, in consequence of which their fruitfulness was steadily enhanced.

Joseph Harris. Of different antecedents was Joseph Harris of Moreton Farm, Rochester, New York, who had enjoyed the inestimable privilege of investigating agricultural problems at Rothamstead, under the inspiration of Lawes and Gilbert. Harris, in the sixties and seventies of last century, wrote for the *American Agriculturist* "Walks and Talks on the Farm." He, also, emphasized tile draining and good cultivation, but discussed fertilizers in a scientific yet popular manner which farmers could understand. His books on *The Pig, Talks on Manures,* and *Gardening for Young and Old* were valuable contributions to the literature of scientific agriculture in his day.

George E. Waring. Another contributor to the *American Agriculturist,* author of the Ogden Farm Papers, was George E. Waring, whose title of colonel was acquired in the Civil war. Waring by profession was a sanitary engineer, as his lamented death from yellow fever contracted in Havana which he tried to clean up at the close of the Spanish war, proclaimed to the world. But his avocation was farming, the inspiration for which came from the enthusiastic experimenter James Jay Mapes on whose New Jersey farm Waring served his apprenticeship.[23] At an early stage of his farming experience (1853), Waring wrote *Elements of Agriculture,* a new and better edition of which came out in 1868. It was evidently intended to supersede Norton's book and was in fact a compendium of information about such science as farmers had at their disposal in those days. He divided the treatment into five parts or sections —on The Plant, The Soil, Manures, Mechanical Cultivation, and Analysis.

Ogden Farm, of which Waring became manager in September, 1867, was a run-down, wet, unpromising sixty-acre tract lying four miles from Newport, Rhode Island. He took it because he believed

[23] Waring as a young man was placed in charge of Horace Greeley's New York state farm.

it to be the worst farm in the county, with the determination to make it the best one within a period of ten years. His successive numbers in the *Agriculturist* tell the story of his progress step by step. He teaches effectively because of the frank, intimate manner of meeting his readers. At the close of the experimental period he presents his balance sheet. It shows he had not allowed time enough for the results of his methods to mature, but otherwise he proved that "book-farming" could be made a success.

Waring organized the American Jersey cattle club and edited the herd-book. He traveled much in Europe, studying agriculture in England, Holland, France, Germany, and the Channel Islands. His work was that of a private experimenter having a wealthy sponsor and therefore comparable to what scientific managers were doing on some of the great estates in England and elsewhere. The persistent publicising of his experiments was calculated to inspire practical farmers to follow in his footsteps, so far as conditions permitted.

Near-scientific farmers. Is the definition of scientific or professional farmer flexible enough to include practitioners of agricultural science who are not, in the strict sense, scientists? It seems proper to answer this question in the affirmative. If the professional ranks were to be closed with the long-course graduates of agricultural colleges, they would present but a thin and short file in the procession of American farmers. It is well known, however, that the modicum of science gained in a single winter short-course has led some thousands of young men and women to the enthusiastic pursuit of farming on a thoroughly scientific basis, and the same may be said of many who merely attended a farmer's institute, a farmer's week conference, or who obtained all their help from scientific books and bulletins.

He is a professional farmer who studies to base his operations firmly upon scientific principles, and who succeeds in bringing about thereby a steady improvement of both farm and farmer. Of course farming is an art as well as a science; it is also a business, and a way of life. He who neglects any one of these aspects of his profession cannot be considered thoroughly professional. The pioneer physician might know his *materia medica* by heart. But if he was deficient in practical pharmacology, if he lacked a good "bedside manner," or was socially inept, he was not the best all-round practitioner. But, after all, the scientific aspect is fundamental. Those who would improve the agriculture of any community by teaching bookkeeping to the boys and home-canning to the girls have reason on their side. Yet, even a certified public accountant, or a graduate from a school of domestic economy, would be helpless as a farmer without a knowledge of the principles taught by chemistry, soil physics and bacteriology; by the experimenters in feeding and care of livestock and the growing of the customary farm crops. Science and the scientific attitude of mind are basic, the other qualifications secondary though by no means unimportant.

Case of the ex-preacher farmer. One example of a self-made scientific farmer, published by the department of agriculture, is interesting enough to describe with some detail because it illustrates what might be called a professional type of small-scale farming. It is an example from eastern Pennsylvania in the eighteen eighties. An ex-preacher, with no previous farming experience, bought a fifteen acre run-down farm near a large city. Like Colonel Waring this man determined to be a book farmer. Like him, also, he resolved to use Jersey cows as the "solvent" of his problem of paying for the property. There was yet a third correspondence between this minister and the distinguished sanitary engineer in that both decided to rely upon stable manure, produced on the farm, for fertilizer, and to produce this under the best conditions by soiling the cows, which never left their stalls in the barn. But, whereas Waring at Ogden Farm built a great cellar for manure, the Pennsylvanian kept his manure cart at the barn door, carried to the field daily and spread upon it every pound of both liquids and solids produced in the twenty-four hours.

After a few years, this ex-preacher, who had a regular market for his milk at the modest price of twenty-five cents per gallon, two miles from the farm, was able to keep thirty head of livestock of which fifteen were cows in full flow, and to provide the roughage from the farm itself for all those animals. He bought about $650 worth of concentrates during the year and these he nearly paid for through the sale of young stock for breeding. Obviously, here was a professional farmer.[24]

College "recognition" of good farmers. Cases of a similarly scientific treatment of the problems of large farms, where cows are pastured in summer and fed silage with grain in winter; and where pigs are allowed to "hog down" crops of clover, rye, peas and corn because these are economical methods, could be assembled from nearly every state. The agricultural colleges have a custom, in connection with farmer's week programs, of "recognizing" each year a small number of outstanding farmers selected on the score of their professional character. Probably some hundreds, all told, have been thus honored and certified. But many hundreds, indeed thousands, might be classed with these selected ones if some present day Arthur Young were to perambulate the several states calling attention to the farms that give evidence of being managed by scientific farmers.

Science in dairying. It is probable, however, that aside from those who, like orchardists and market gardeners, are coerced to employ science on account of the high valuations of land, the necessity of intensive cultivation and the prompt, effective meeting of the problems of pests, seasonal variations, and market conditions, the most nearly general class of farmers who approach the scientific standard is

[24] Dept. of Agriculture, Farmer's Bulletin 242.

the organized dairymen. As already indicated, dairying proceeds by communities, and where hundreds or thousands of farmers find their problems similar, suggested solutions will also be similar or identical.

Hence, scientific principles of feeding, breeding, handling the milk, disposing of the manure, raising fodder and grain for feed, will pass by a kind of social osmosis throughout the group and the naturally best farmers, reacting to such stimuli, will make themselves masters both of the ideas and of the learning from which they flow.

All this supports, to a certain extent, the theory of Jonathan B. Turner that given an opportunity, men in the industries and agriculture may attain a high plane of culture through the handling of their occupational problems with the aid of appropriate scientific principles and of an appropriate literature. One could doubtless select a group of New York, Ohio, Wisconsin, or Minnesota dairymen who, in their own field, are as cultured and professionally "knowing" as similar groups of lawyers or doctors are in theirs. On the average, these professional farmers would be the better educated men of their class, using the term in its customary connotation, but many exceptions would be found. Some are entirely self-educated in the science their vocation calls for, just as many lawyers of the pioneer days, including Abraham Lincoln, were self-educated both in the law itself and in the literature that threw about them the aura of general culture. Perhaps the real test of the scientific farmer is his ability independently to apply the principles he has learned by carrying out properly controlled experiments on his own farm, just as the test of professional adequacy in a lawyer is his competency in handling unique cases.

Imitators of scientific farmers. Farming practice tends to become professional, however, not alone through those who are scientific in their own right, but also through others who take their cue from the professional farmers and are wise and careful imitators. We have reached a stage of development in agriculture where scientific principles are no longer pooh poohed as the vagaries of impractical "book farmers," but are almost everywhere respected for what they can help men to achieve in the way of solid advantages. Hence the need of exhortation is no longer so urgent as of yore. Leaders now can lay down demonstrated principles and coolly challenge farmers to disregard them at their peril. With only a single real "professional" in a given community, the farming of the entire neighborhood may yet exhibit many of the acknowledged professional traits.

Herein lies one of the significant present day opportunities of the state colleges and experiment stations. They will be able to make only a certain gradually increasing proportion of the farmers professionals, because only a part of them will be able to master the science upon which professional farming depends. Nevertheless, having the confidence of the farming community, these institutions, staffed with county agents and having other means of appealing to the public, can often put into nearly universal operation principles and policies they deem of importance to the agriculture of the state.

Their importance. When the onset of the severe drought of 1934 occurred, it became clear to the scientific men at one state experiment station that a widespread and tragic shortage of forage was sure to ensue. This calamity they set themselves to avert. Emergency crops could still be planted that would yield a supply of winter feed to take the place of the hay and oats which were already doomed to failure. The work, however, had to be organized and the college made itself the medium for procuring the soy-bean seed, the rape seed, the Sudan grass, etc., which farmers would have to plant forthwith in order to save their dairy herds. The national seed-relief co-operating, in a few weeks the effects of the campaign were already apparent on literally thousands of farms, where emergency fodder crops were growing; and, as a direct consequence, the herds emerged on the pastures the following spring in practically normal condition.

This noteworthy work of safeguarding the livestock interests of a leading dairy state obviously could not have succeeded save for the state-wide organization of agricultural extension through the county agents, and the help of the seed-relief administration. But neither could it have succeeded through the professional farmers alone if the balance had lacked confidence in the wisdom of the advice emanating from the college and station. The professional farmers are a contingent, the near-professional an army.

CHAPTER VI

SOCIAL TRENDS IN RURAL LIFE

An English view of American society. "Witness the United States of America," wrote the gentle Dean of Carlisle about a century ago, and he continued: "Let any thoughtful observer consider the traits of character that distinguish these children of our fathers from Englishmen of the present day, and the probable causes of the difference. We are apt enough, indeed, to ridicule as foibles, or to censure as faults, their national peculiarities—their deviations from our habits. But it would be wiser and worthier of us to trace them to their causes, and to add the result of our inquiry to our stock of legislative experience. We sent them forth, poor and struggling only for the means of subsistence. Is it we that should taunt them with becoming a money-making, trafficking people? We severed the humble from the nobles of our land and formed the embryo of a plebeian nation. Is it we that should find fault with their extravagant abhorrence of rank, or their want of high breeding and gentle blood which we so sparingly bestowed on them? We gave for the new community only some of the ingredients that enter into our own. Can we wonder at the want

181

of resemblance, and of congenial feeling which has been the result?" [1]

Noble blood sparingly supplied. The passage just quoted merits more thoughtful consideration than, from its tone, it is likely to command among most Americans. We should at least recognize that, in his assumptions respecting the elements passing into colonial emigration the distinguished church-man made a guess that has been partly confirmed by the best modern research.[2] The only question about his substantive statement turns on what the descriptive word "humble" connotes. If it is merely a foil for "nobles" and means every class below the aristocracy, we can have no quarrel with him, for it is certain that noble blood was, as he says, but "sparingly" supplied to the colonies. If, however, the word humble is used in its commonly accepted sense of lowly in station and in spirit, we must enter an exception, for all the colonies received numbers of English settlers who were no less stiffnecked and arrogant than the aristocrats at home.

There were among the planters of Virginia, the congregation leaders of New England, the patroons of New Netherlands, the Quakers of Pennsylvania, and the Catholics of Maryland, men of enterprise, wealth, and spirit, who were doubtless as promising

[1] From an Essay on Colonization by Dr. Hinds, quoted in Edward Gibbon Wakefield's *Art of Colonization*, London, 1849, p. 112.
[2] See, for example, T. J. Wertenbaker, *The First Americans,* and J. T. Adams, *Provincial America.*

material for a new world aristocracy as had been for the old world the Saxon merchants who, by thrice faring overseas at their own charge, might become "thaneworthy," or the roistering Norman men-at-arms who helped Duke William subjugate and tyrannize over the successors of the Saxon aristocrats. And those two groups are venerated sources of one of the world's universally acclaimed aristocracies.

How aristocracies are created. To the historically minded, if not to the obsequious genealogist, there is a natural history of aristocracies no less than of peasantries. And, so far as existing nations are concerned, their ladder of ascent has been primarily wealth, principal sources of which have been commerce, in its varied aspects, and land. Military prowess, political and miscellaneous public service have usually been but stepping stones to the attainment of that wealth which is the true pillar of the noble estate. Was not the breadth of their land holdings the basis of the distinction between *greater* and *lesser* barons in mediaeval England, with all that this involves in the history of British institutions?

The truth seems to be that any society which affords scope for individual initiative, will eventually develop an aristocracy if its institutional pattern provides for such a social order. If not, there is at least sure to be an unofficial approximation to it in a limited group of families set off from the generality by one or other of several distinctions, the most

usual and permanent being an affulence of heredi-
tary possessions. Intellectual achievement, or distinguished public service may to some extent serve
as substitutes for wealth.

The American merchant class. America during
the colonial period honored the successful merchant
even as did Saxon England when society by positive
law encouraged him to hope for promotion to an
exalted social rank. Though the colonial merchant
could not be ennobled save by the royal intercession,
he was yet able, in many cases, to amass the wealth
which would have supported noble rank. The great
merchants of the North, indeed, of whom John
Hancock at the time of the Revolution was the
type, affected fine raiment, had splendid equipages,
built handsome houses, amassed rich furniture and
plate, and procured family portraits. They assumed
the leadership in local and colonial affairs, and occupied the highest seats in church and assembly.
Their sons were privileged in the colleges, their
daughters were the reigning belles of their communities.

We speak of America as opportunity and artlessly
translate the phrase only affirmatively, as affording
unusual chances for advancement in economic and
social well-being. In reality, however, opportunity
has been a two-edged sword, involving alternatives
as sharply contradictory as the Puritan's choice of
"God or the devil," the chances of failure being
balanced against the chances of success. The frontier, in that respect, always presented a set of new,

untried conditions, promising extraordinary rewards
to those possessed of answerable gifts. The weak,
the indolent, and those who were too deeply rou-
tinized to permit of new adaptations, were sure to
injure themselves therein.

All the more strenuous, therefore, were the efforts of those exceptional individuals who became
founders of the colonial great fortunes—the ship-
owners, the fur-trade organizers, the merchant
planters, and certain obscure men of no capital but
of dauntless heart and physical prowess who matched
their powers against a resisting but fecund nature
and wrested prosperity from her.

Social basis of the planter aristocracy. It was the
two last named groups, merchant planters and able
workers, that figure prominently in the creation of
the class of big-business farmers. The myth of an
imposing cavalier immigration into the tobacco
colonies has been exploded and it is now known
that the first successful planting society was prevailingly of middle-class origin. Indeed, it has been
shown that some of the prominent Virginia leaders
in the seventeenth century were men who had come
to the colony with little or no capital, in given instances even as indentured servants. It was the
development of the slave-trade, insuring a cheap
and steadily augmenting labor supply, joined to
cheap fresh lands and business ability, that gradually segregated a group of great planters who stood
out from the mass as did the great barons in England. This was the so-called planting aristocracy,

and its origin is seen to differ little from that of the leading northern merchants.

The multiplication of great plantations prior to the Civil war came about, as we have seen, through the expansion of cotton culture. And cotton growing, as a money-making craze, attracted all kinds of persons possessed of means or credit to buy land and slaves. Nevertheless, while the best of the southern aristocracy is thought to have persisted in the old tobacco colonies of Virginia and Maryland, and in portions of the Old South, still the social history of the Southwest by 1860 could present rival groups.[3] It was a Mississippi cotton planter, Jefferson Davis, upon whom the entire Confederacy reposed its hopes during the Civil war and, while conflicting opinions will always be held as to his statecraft and political morality, no one, native or foreigner, who had the privilege of his acquaintance ever suspected that he was not a gentleman of "high breeding."

Spread of the planter social ideals. Ideals propagate themselves most freely on a plastic society, making the ascent from obscurity to a worthy distinction a comparatively simple transition. Social standards, during Colonial times, were English, and

---

[3] As early as 1835 J. H. Ingraham, see *The Southwest by a Yankee,* Vol. II, *passim,* found much to praise in southwestern planting society. *Cf.* Carl Russell Fish, *The Rise of the Common Man, passim.* Also, James D. Davidson, Diary of a Southern Journey, *Jour. of Southern Hist.,* Vol. I, No. 3. "The southerners are too much occupied with cotton and money to think about politics," p. 857 (Nov. 1836). "The southern gentleman is an improvement upon the old Virginian gentleman," 360.

there were also connections between American families and the English squirearchy, occasionally with the lesser nobility. When the anonymous writer of *A Perfect Description of Virginia,* in 1649, called special attention to "worthy Captaine Mathews," a man of middle class origin, he was at pains to point out that: "He married the daughter of Sir Tho. Hinton." The country gentleman in England was the social pattern for the great planters at least until the Revolution. Thereafter the planting aristocracy was self-sustaining, new men looking to the old established houses for their models of social life.

Some astonishing transformations of character and manners resulted from the striving of obscure persons for recognition by the planting society. Andrew Jackson, son of poor Scotch-Irish parents but not for that reason humble in spirit, underwent an epic struggle to tame his impetuous, rebellious nature into social conformity. He might have been a brawling, scuffling, gouging "hill-billy." He became, through the ambition to amount to something socially and politically, not only a successful farmer and planter in the economic sense, but—with occasional lapses from grace—also a planting aristocrat whose deportment was no less courtly than that of the Jeffersons, Lees, and Pinckneys of the older planting regime. His home, his furniture, his hospitality, his turnouts, ranked with the best in the class to which he instinctively aspired and into which his talents forced a way;

and his dueling pistols are to this day a joy to
behold.

Another instance is Henry Clay, orphan son of
an impecunious Baptist preacher gifted with a
mellifluous voice. The "Mill boy of the Slashes,"
became both a leading statesman and a planting
aristocrat in Kentucky as did Jackson in Tennessee.
Clay's dominance of Whig party politics is only
partly explained by his intellectual superiority and
thrilling oratory. To a high but undetermined degree it was due to the princely bearing and the charm
of manners which authenticated his membership
in the highest social class of the ante-bellum South,
for "manner," it has been well said, "is one of the
fine arts."

New planters of the Southwest. "A plantation
well-stocked with hands," says Ingraham, writing
in 1835 about the Southwest, "is the *ne plus ultra*
of every man's ambition who resides at the south." [4]
He observed in the neighborhood of Natchez, Mississippi, that many young men from the East, not
a few of them New Englanders, in coming to the
Southwest immediately cast about for a cotton
plantation. Professional men abandoned the law,
medicine or theology to plant cotton. Farmers from
the North would be farmers no more. Merchants
abandoned the counting house for the sunny fields.
Even mechanics dreamed of the time when fortune
should favor them with land and negro slaves to
raise cotton. "Cotton and negroes are the constant

[4] *The Southwest,* II, 84.

theme—the ever harped-upon, never worn out subject of conversation among all classes. . . . Not till
Mississippi becomes one vast cotton field will this
mania, which has entered into the very marrow,
bone and sinew of a Mississippian's system, pass
away. And not then, till the lands become exhausted
and wholly unfit for further cultivation." [5]

The planters in that comparatively new section of
the cotton belt were already, to a large extent, men
of wealth, which is not remarkable when a man
could buy land and slaves on credit and within three
years pay off all indebtedness and even add ma-
terially to his possessions. Ingraham, who though
a New Englander is not an impartial observer,
found them both intelligent and aristocratic, mani-
festing a refinement and elegance indicative of the
high breeding which, at that very time, the Dean
of Carlisle assumed to be absent from American society even in its best estate. Other visitors to the
Southwest about the same time were less favorably
impressed.[6] We must remember, however, that this
was a parvenu planting society, of so recent creation
that many had not had time to build their hoped-for
mansions, but continued to live in the primitive
log-houses or in flimsy, hastily erected frame structures.

The "best" southern aristocracy. To find the

[5] *Supra,* 86.
[6] *Cf.* Harriet Martineau, *Society in America,* London, 1837,
II, 142 ff. The story told of a New Orleans mistress of slaves by
Fanny Kemble, *Retrospect of Western Travel,* N. Y., 1838, I,
263 ff., shows an exceptional but possible case of ill-treatment of
slaves by brutal owners.

southern aristocracy at its best in that era one must go to Virginia, Maryland, South Carolina or Georgia. There were to be seen the great houses, splendidly appointed, the staff of negro house servants well-trained, polite and efficient, the slave craftsmen—weavers, shoemakers, blacksmiths, carpenters, boat-builders; also hostlers, coachmen, gardeners, nurserymen—in addition to and superior to the gangs of "field-hands." [7] The planter's wife was the manager of the complex household, the master governed the "yard-folks," the overseer the field-gangs. Able managers secured, in what must seem to outsiders a motely crew of dependents, such perfect organization as to command effective service from all except the occasional recalcitrant.

Moreover, whatever the evils of slavery, and they were fundamental, the vast majority of planters commanded their people's affection as well as loyal service. The songs white composers have ascribed to the plantation negroes are often apocryphal in fact and alien in spirit. But when Stephen Foster wrote

> "Down in the corn-field
>   Hear that mournful sound
>   All the darkies am a-weepin',
>   Massa's in the cold, cold ground,"

he captured a genuine surge of negro sentiment. The devotion of the blacks, particularly house-servants

[7] See the description of a Mississippi plantation of 1845 in *Solon Robinson, Pioneer and Agriculturist,* I, 455 ff. Indiana Historical Bureau, Indianapolis, 1936.

and yard hands, to their "wite-folks" in the tragic days of the Civil war would be proof of the absence of any widespread feeling of hostility between master and slave.[8] These facts have a bearing upon the reality of an aristocratic social system in the South, but no relevancy to the question of the permanent economic soundness or the political and ethical justification of slavery.

Leadership of planters. In the first thirty-six years of the constitutional period Virginia, "mother of presidents," gave to the nation its chief executive in eight of the nine quadrennial elections. And each of the four gentlemen whom the people honored with two consecutive terms was a great planter or a planting aristocrat. If in the cases of Jefferson and his satellites, Madison and Monroe, that should appear to involve a contradiction, he being best known as the father of American democracy, it must be remembered that aristocracy conferred no privileges demanding class solidarity for their defense but left every man free to espouse whatever political philosophy he might choose. Aristocracy was a purely social distinction based upon wealth and those graces of character and intellect for the development of which wealth supplied an opportunity but no guaranty of results. Not every wealthy planter was esteemed an aristocrat, any

---

[8] The story *Uncle Lige,* by Jeanette Ritchie Haderman Walworth, as printed in Stedman and Hutchinson's *Library of American Literature,* IX, 463–468, gives a charming picture of the fidelity to their family of the yard-folks during the most trying days of the war.

more than every Junker is accounted a gentleman, for in some instances nature and nurture had neglected to co-operate with economics to produce the proper combination of social qualities.

During the period of the so-called "Virginia dynasty" of presidents, in which American democracy was established, the government of the country in all its branches was dominated by the aristocratic element. "Nobility," says Bagehot, "is the symbol of mind. It has the marks from which the mass of men always used to infer mind, and often still infer it." [9] That may explain, in some measure, the confidence which the people reposed in those who, to them, if not to the world at large, represented the aristocracy of their day.

Truly, as the brilliant British essayist just quoted puts it: "An old lord will get infinite respect." The great planters ruled the southern states at all times and the nation at most times down to the Civil war. This has often excited astonishment in view of their numerical inferiority and the political thralldom in which they, as the reigning slaveholders, held the great, non-slaveholding majority of voters. The anomaly was often pointed out as, for example, in Helper's *Impending Crisis*,[10] but aristocratic control continued until after the war had destroyed the slaveholders and thus permitted the rise to power of different social elements, regimented

[9] Walter Bagehot, *The English Constitution*, Appleton, 1907, p. 158.
[10] H. R. Helper, *The Impending Crisis of the south: and how to meet it*, N. Y., 1857.

by politician leaders.[11] The Tillmans, Bilbos, and Heflins of our own era would have been nearly impossible in the politics of the ante-bellum South. So long as the people had the opportunity to vote for a class of men whom they not only respected but revered, and who stood for democratic principles, the merely clever politicians had no chance.

Other landholding aristocrats. It is not to be inferred, from the above, that American social aristocracy connected with landholding was exclusively confined to the South. The patroon estates along the Hudson, with their wealthy, dignified and respected Dutch families, connected with commercial and professional notables in the city, supplied a controlling element in New York politics for many years. The power of Alexander Hamilton came originally from such a connection. John Jay, who believed "that those who own the country are the most fit persons to participate in the government of it,"[12] was another of the aristocracy's representatives. General Philip Schuyler, one of the great landlords on the Hudson, was Hamilton's father-in-law, and Stephen Van Rensselaer, the greatest land-owner of all America, was his brother-in-law. The Livingston family, who espoused the Jeffersonian political philosophy, were likewise among the landed aristocrats and extremely influential in Republican politics.

[11] Which confirms a pregnant phrase of Lecky's in *Democracy and Liberty*, I, 142.

[12] Dixon Ryan Fox, *Aristocracy in the Politics of New York*. Columbia Univ. Studies in Hist. &c., V. 86, p. 9.

Not all the rural gentry of the North, however, had received their landed endowment during colonial times. The rage for speculation at the Revolution and later brought into existence a number of great estates some of which have persisted to this day. Perhaps the most notable example of these in New York is that of the Wadsworths in the Genesee valley. It was created by James Wadsworth, a Vermont immigrant whose property—practically all in land, listed at $1.00 per acre—was taxed in 1800 at a valuation of $34,500. That, roughly, describes the acre extent of his holdings at the time. The Wadsworth family did not drift west with the wheat-grower tide, but as far-sighted, skillful landlords, controlled the improvement of their properties through a system of leasing similar to those by which English landlords coerced farmers to adopt a regime of improvement.

As great landed proprietors, this family has participated extensively in public affairs, one of the pioneer's sons becoming a general in the Civil war, a grandson having been a prominent United States senator, and still a leading figure in Republican politics. Incidentally, the aristocratic Wadsworth family is connected, by the marriage of the pioneer's daughter, Elsie, to Sir Charles Augustus Murray, with one of the noble houses of Great Britain.[13]

Why not a wheat aristocracy? An inquiry of some interest is why bonanza wheat-growers have not,

[13] See the author's essay, "Lands Across the Sea" in *Wis. Mag. of Hist.*, XIII, 417–429.

like tobacco and cotton planters, established themselves as a rural aristocracy. Some of those in California, the Palouse country, the Red river valley and other portions of the great plains assuredly gained wealth through their operations, yet nothing suggestive of the planting social pre-eminence is observable among them. Individual wheat-growers have, of course, commanded general respect as men, but not as aristocrats.

The reasons are probably to be found partly in the precariousness of the business, its migratory character, dependence upon artificial transportation systems, and upon an impermanent labor supply. In most sections of the United States the big-business wheat-grower knew himself to be a temporary exploiter of a tract of farm land barricaded against expansion by neighboring owners so that the chances of large profits in that location could be his but a few years at best. Under those conditions there was no temptation to erect a mansion on the wheat lands, and surround himself and family with the evidences of wealth and the amenities appropriate to social leadership among which would be a staff of permanent house and yard servants. Considering the short period of his probable stay, it was hardly worth while for the big grower to live differently from his neighbors, the small growers, who meant to retain their farms and adapt their farming to new conditions when wheat should fail them.

Wheat is an excessively bulky product as compared with tobacco or cotton and therefore the

wheat-grower is much more dependent upon transportation facilities than is the tobacco or cotton
grower. With cotton selling at fifteen cents a pound
the charge of one cent for getting it to market was
not excessive. But when a bushel of wheat weighing
sixty pounds and selling at seventy-five cents had
to pay approximately half that amount in transportation charges, the grower found difficulty in figur-
ing any profit whatever. Moreover, for many years
the railroad companies serving the wheat-growers
were utterly capricious in their freight charges, or
rather followed the principle of charging what the
traffic would bear, which left the growers at their
mercy.[14] The novels of Frank Norris comprising
"the epic of the wheat," *The Octopus* and *The Pit,*
are the best literary embodiment of that phase of
American agricultural history.

Machines instead of workers. The bonanza wheat
farmers in the days of horse and mule power were
obliged to employ a limited number of permanent
"hands" to care for the stock. That force, supplemented with groups of seasonal laborers, prepared
the ground, seeded and reaped the grain. The use
of the combine reduced largely the need of seasonal
help in harvest, and the tractor has done away with
the livestock, reducing the force to a smaller group
of machine operators. The gang-plows are now
generally drawn by tractors, also the harrows, drills
and rollers, as well as the combines. Thus a few

[14] See John D. Hicks, in *Surveys of Culture in the Middle West.*
N. Y. and London, 1934, p. 89.

men, boarded on the farm or near it—with autos to run back and forth they need not remain strictly on the farm since no livestock is there demanding their regular care—can do the work with the requisite machine equipment. An overseer or foreman may live in a very unpretentious house on the farm.

Owner's freedom of movement. The owner, however, is much more likely to be living in some city or village remote from the wheat ranch which he can visit, if he chooses, during the two short periods of intensest and most critical activity, seed-time and harvest. There is positively no occasion for him to be on the ground during the balance of the summer and, of course, the winter can be spent where and as he chooses. Thus, the great wheat-growers may perhaps cut a figure as directors of banks or warehouses in the cities, or even as merely opulent residents like the prominent merchants of the town. But they fail wholly to impress society in what it would seem ought to be their natural position as aristocratic rural leaders. The most characteristic wheat-growing regions, indeed, have been condemned as areas devoid of any normal rural society. In them barbarism is nearer the surface than aristocratic refinement.[15]

Despite his widespread cinema reputation for crudeness, the above statement will not apply to the western cattleman. Keeping livestock is a more personal business than growing wheat, owners' re-

[15] See J. Schafer, *A History of the Pacific Northwest,* N. Y. (Macmillan), 1918, 298–299.

sponsibilities infinitely sharper and more continuous. Accordingly, these men have usually lived on the ranches. They were, however, so isolated that no thought of the necessity of exceptionally good living was likely to disturb their complacency; a comfortable house, with a few conveniences and luxuries, making altogether a high class "camping place," being an adequate equipment for a family which rarely expected to remain permanently cut off from the social advantages to be found in cities or in denser settled regions.

Cattle ranches and cattle farms. "Neighbors!" retorted a Wyoming ranchman in 1900 to the suggestion that such social disiderate seemed few and far between: "You don't want neighbors. If your nearest neighbor is forty miles away your cattle and his will graze where they please and there'll never be any trouble. And, if you want to go visiting, you can get on a horse and ride forty miles as easily as five." Thus isolation was positively a desirable condition, which there was no effort to overcome but rather the reverse. Nevertheless, the complete absorption of the grass-lands, by purchase or by the ownership and fencing of water privileges, the coming of the auto which called for the making of roads, and the growing of winter forage by means of irrigation—all of these have tended to transform the cattle ranch into the great cattle farm, to force the ranches closer together and cause the rancher to look upon his business as permanent. The result is better houses, barns, and garages; house servants, and in short the external symbols of gentle living. The big cattle farmers, and big sheep farmers, when not mere corporation managers, are probably destined to form a distinct and leading element in the rural society of several western states. We already hear much about "dude ranches" which are the symbol of a new rather than an old ranching life. They combine with the freedom and heartiness of the old, the conveniences, luxuries—in short the amenities—of modern city living. But that is not what was meant by the slave-holding planter aristocracy.

Farmers as "laborers." One of the most revealing sources for the study of social history is the manuscript census, which describes sketchily every family head and names each member of the family group, giving age and place of birth together with occupation if there was one. The head, who was normally the party interviewed by the census-taker, may be said to have painted his own portrait which, sometimes, turned out to be an unintentional caricature. For example, while there is probably no instance of a land-owner placarding himself as an aristocrat (Americans being proverbially modest) one can turn to the name of a Wisconsin resident who in 1860, despite his ownership of 240 acres of land of which 80 was under cultivation and tilled by his own hand, recorded himself as a "farm laborer."

This, to be sure, was a technical error, but it is not without significance for it shows that independent farmers could unconsciously identify themselves with the laboring class which in all old world societies was accounted not only distinct from but lower in the social scale than the class of land-owners. "Who are the laboring people of the North?" asked Webster in his seventh of March speech, and answered: "They are the whole North. They are the people who till their own farms with their own hands; freeholders, educated men, independent men. . . . If they are not free-holders, they earn wages; these wages accumulate, are turned into capital, into new freeholds, and small capitalists are created."

If the development of a limited social aristocracy, based on wealth and culture but devoid of special privileges, is one important feature of American agricultural history, the creation of a vast society of free land-owning farmers made up of all European and American types but fitting into none of the old world classifications, is a yet more important social outcome of that history. The average ruralite is not a landlord, living off the rents paid him by actual cultivators for the use of portions of his estate. He is not a peasant who feels degraded by the fact of his dependence upon a landlord. Nor, in any strict sense, is he a "farmer" of the modern English type, representing capital, skill, and management, but not the ownership of land, though he often possesses similar personal qualifications for carrying on the business of agricultural production. He has been called a "peasant-proprietor"; but the typical European peasant is not a proprietor and the typical American landed proprietor is not a peasant.

The American farmer is first of all a free citizen of the republic, clothed with every political and legal right pertaining to those we have segregated as a social aristocracy. Like them, too, he obtains his living from land he owns in fee-simple. Also, like them, the amplitude of his income depends very largely upon personal management coupled with the extent of his investment. Here, however, the similarity ends and differences begin. The aristocrat's ideal of a life for himself is to be a man of culture, sustained by a generous income produced by the labor of others under his management or oversight. The farmer's ideal of a life for himself is to be a productive laborer on his own land with a view to obtaining as good a living as such labor, joined with management, will yield.

His hopes, indeed, may compass a situation that will ultimately relieve him of most, or all, of the heavy personal labor perhaps through the employment of "hired hands," possibly through a more complete equipment of labor-saving machinery. But, in the majority of cases, the American farmer expects to wear the working man's garb and to continue personally active in the affairs of his farm until old age or decrepitude shall compel him to desist. Then, as he is apt to put it, he "sits on the verandah" and watches others do the work, or he sells his farm and moves to town. He has been a "worker" all his days; not a "farm laborer" as that

term is properly understood, but yet a laborer on his own farm.

Reason for the "worker-farmer." The conception that an owner of land who was not a peasant might, without loss of respectability till his own acres, originated in the necessities of pioneering, for the Cincinnatuses of old had been forgotten. The colonists had to work in order to live. They could easily obtain the ownership of land, but a labor supply was a different problem. There was in general no working class whose labor could be commandeered and so every man had to "pitch in," as the saying was, and perform his own tasks of tillage. Only in a few localities and at intervals were conditions changed by the importation of numerous indentured servants and afterwards negro slaves, the latter constituting one main support of the planting aristocracy. Until the arrival of negroes to the saturation point, even the planters often tilled their own fields with family labor.[16]

In the subsistence farming stage which nearly all communities passed through, rapidly or slowly, farm labor was prevailingly that of the family itself. Exceptional jobs requiring a larger force were done co-operatively with neighbors on the "exchange of works" basis. A good illustration is the building of the new settler's log-house. This brought together a group of men large enough to accomplish the work in two days at most, falling the trees, shaping the

[16] T. J. Wertenbaker, *Patrician and Plebeian in Virginia,* 151 ff. J. T. Adams, *Provincial Society,* 88.

logs, notching and pinning the joints, framing doors and windows, splitting "shakes" for the roof, whip-sawing plank or hewing puncheons for the floor and loft, and building a chimney with fire-place. It was an event that assembled the entire country-side, but if, as sometimes was the case especially in the Southwest, one of the neighbors happened to be a slave-owning planter, he was sure to bring some of his servants to contribute their labor while he himself, with hands neatly gloved, refrained from touching ax or trowel.

Frontier social dynamics. "Our early history," says Turner, "is the study of European germs developing in an American environment. . . . The wilderness masters the colonist. It finds him a European in dress, industries, tools, modes of travel and thought. It takes him from the railroad car and puts him in the birch canoe. It strips off the garments of civilization and arrays him in the hunting-shirt and the moccasin. . . . Before long he has gone to planting Indian corn and plowing with a sharp stick. . . . In short, at the frontier the environment is at first too strong for the man. He must accept the conditions which it furnishes or perish, and so he fits himself into the Indian clearings and follows the Indian trails. Little by little he transforms the wilderness but the outcome is not the old Europe, not simply the development of Germanic germs. . . . The fact is that here is a new product that is American."

This passage in the well-known essay on *The Sig-*

nificance of the Frontier in American History,
penned in 1893, has become one of the foundation
principles in historical interpretation. One has to
emphasize the point that frontier necessity taught
the importance and the dignity of sheer labor to
all—those who were new to the idea of personal
exertion as well as those to whom labor has always
seemed the primal curse of man. Professor Paxson
suggests that the frontier may have contributed a
kind of "inverted democratization that worked by
leveling the exceptional man down rather than by
lifting the common man up." [17] There is a truth concealed in that remark, but the apprenticeship to
actual physical labor can hardly be said to have
lowered the real dignity of the exceptional man,
while the fact of working side by side with him did
unquestionably help to remove from the mind of
the common man the incubus of the old world
conception that labor was essentially degrading
toil.

The dignity of labor. To that new psychology the
speculative factor in American farm-making contributed a powerful impulse. The professional squatter, whose chosen vocation was that of hunter, set
his rifle against a tree and spent some weeks of
glorious summer industriously clearing, fencing,
planting, and building a cabin, heroically withstand-
ing meantime the temptations of the forest trails
because he anticipated a large profit from his enter-

[17] F. L. Paxson, A Generation of the Frontier Hypotheses,
Pacific Hist. Rev., March, 1933 (II, 34–51).

prise. The improving farmer justified both his
continuous labor and his investments by the expectation that his farm would one day have a value
greater than the expenditures upon it. The exploiter spent his land and his labor in making money
fast. Each type of farming economy, when free
from the influence of slavery, or its substitute indentured servants, emphasized the importance of
personal labor, thereby dignifying it.

The farmers of America have ever gloried in the
thought that they, as a class, cleared the forest and
"made the wilderness to blossom as the rose." They
read with a thrill of self-conscious pride that "Labor
drives the plow, and scatters the seed, and reaps the
grain."

Rewards of labor. Men of every class and condition became farmers in America, and all, with the
exceptions noted above, if they had not known the
virtue of physical labor, learned it in the new land.
But they had their reward forthwith and in ample
measure. "Little children here," wrote a Puritan
leader from New England in 1630, "by setting of
corn can make much more than their own maintenance." "A poor servant here, who is to have no
more than fifty acres can afford to give more timber
and wood for fires than many a nobleman in England can afford to do. Here is good living for those
who love good fires." And at the period of the
Revolution a Pennsylvania farmer wrote of the
rural settler: "Here the rewards of his industry
follow with equal step the progress of his labor. . . .

From involuntary idleness, servile dependence, penury, and useless labor, he has passed to toils of a very different nature, rewarded by ample subsistence."

The democratic spirit. And this laboring, well-fed and well-warmed cultivator of the soil was democratic in spirit. Harriet Martineau pointed out, with pride, that every man in the American towns was an independent citizen, every man in the country a "land-owner." "The bulk of the inhabitants of this vast wilderness," wrote the English farmer, Morris Birkbeck, of settlers in southern Indiana, "may be fairly considered as of the class of the lowest English peasantry, or just emerging from it. But in their manners and morals, but especially in their knowledge and proud independence of mind, they exhibit a contrast so striking that he must indeed be a *petite maitre* traveler, or ill-informed of the character and circumstances of his poor countrymen; or deficient in good and manly sentiment, who would not rejoice to transplant into these boundless regions of freedom the millions whom he has left behind him grovelling in ignorance and want." [18] And James Flint about the same time reports from the same region: "The American farmer, it must be observed, is commonly the proprietor of the land he occupies; and in the *hauteur* of independence is not surpassed by the proudest freeholders of Great Britain." Lecky uses a memorable phrase when he calls the New Englanders of the

[18] *Journey,* 111.

Revolutionary period "hard, stubborn, and indomitably intractable." This describes a vast section of the American ruralites having an English inheritance, and it may seem a bit strange that those whom Kipling might think of as "the lesser breeds" developed under frontier farming conditions a very similar spirit.

When the present-day critic of the Turner hypothesis denies that there is a fundamental difference in spirit between the European proletarian and the American frontiersman, he disregards the balance of testimony of European travelers, many of whom were impressed, like those just quoted, with the presence in the latter of a quality which was described at the Revolution as a "fierce spirit of independence." That spirit had developed in the seaboard colonists, to the distress and discomfiture of the mother country, and when the newly established states found themselves settling down under more conservative traditions, eastern Americans, in turn, were shocked to find the same spirit among the then frontiersmen.

Typical rural frontier leaders. Samuel Bowles and Schuyler Colfax, at the close of the Civil war, discovered Jesse Applegate, living in the secluded Umpqua valley of western Oregon. He was an American type of which Sam Adams of Boston was perhaps the best illustration in 1776. There were keen, logical minds and capacious intellects, resting upon an English social inheritance, as did Applegate, that like him were the immediate product of two generations of far-west pioneering. There were, likewise, men of European birth and nurture, incorporated in every frontier society, who were fully competent to uphold such principles of old world culture as were fitted to survive in the new and simpler environment.

Rural America was not devoid of notables, who were not always duly appreciated. At the close of the Revolutionary war that brilliant and cultured scion of a French-Swiss noble family, Albert Gallatin, fixed his residence on a landed estate in western Pennsylvania. Frederick Hecker, of a noble German house, a powerful advocate and orator, fleeing his homeland as a proscribed revolutionist, settled on a fine farm near Summerville, Illinois, raised splendid livestock and during the electoral campaigns made Republican voters out of erstwhile German Democrats. Thure Kumlien, scientist, graduate of the University of Upsala, opened a farm near Lake Koshkonong in Wisconsin, where he reared a family, studied birds, corresponded with European savants on botanical subjects and received visits from the scientists of the Smithsonian Institute. In the lower Missouri valley near Augusta, was a colony of "Latin farmers," the leader among whom was a theologian and professor from Darmstadt. He lived, said Carl Schurz, not "elegantly, but cleanly—no carpets, but beautifully scoured floors; no upholstered furniture, but tables spread with fresh white covers, with books upon them." [19]

[19] Carl Schurz, letter of July 8, 1867, *Intimate Letters*.

Foreign-born intellectuals and craftsmen. This list could be indefinitely extended. Highly educated and cultivated Europeans were to be found in every community, attracted by the same opportunities for making or sustaining fortunes that were also drawing Americans of every class to those regions. From the standpoint of numbers, however, a much more important meliorating influence was the immigration of well-trained and personable European craftsmen. Some of these, to be sure, went into the towns where they quickly improved the prevailing quality of the service of such skilled workers as blacksmiths, wheelwrights, tailors, carpenters, cabinet makers, millers and locksmiths. But many came to America to acquire land. They might work for a time in the towns but soon they were found on the farms and it should not be surprising that they were among the best, most careful and effective farmers.

The peasant type. Notwithstanding what has just been said about notables and trained craftsmen, the foreign immigration into western states, as into the colonies, was made up for the most part of the poor and lowly. European peasants in the new environment, however, quickly became transformed into independent American farmers. A few years ago a brilliant professor of history in one of the great eastern universities, a man of courtly manners and gallant aristocratic bearing, had been designated for obvious social reasons to sponsor a dinner of women's patriotic organizations. In the

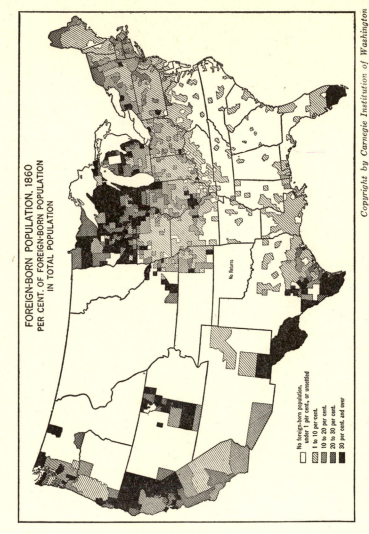

FOREIGN-BORN POPULATION, 1860
PER CENT. OF FOREIGN-BORN POPULATION
IN TOTAL POPULATION

No foreign-born population,
under 1 per cent., or unsettled
1 to 10 per cent.
10 to 20 per cent.
20 to 30 per cent.
30 per cent. and over

No Returns

Reproduced from "The Atlas of Historical Geography of the United States" prepared by C. O.
Paullin and J. K. Wright (1932). Published by the Carnegie Institution of Washington and the
American Geographical Society of New York.

course of conversation, his neighbor on the right, the charming "daughter" of one of the early wars, innocently inquired: "Professor ——, are you a member of the S. A. R.?" (Sons of the American Revolution). "Oh, no," was the unhesitating reply, "I belong to the S. I. F." "Oh," said the lady, and relapsed into a thoughtful silence. Curiosity, however, would not be denied and in a few moments she remarked: "I don't seem to remember what S. I. F. stands for." "Sons of the Irish Famine," answered the professor, which had to suffice though it was obvious that the poor lady was little wiser than before.

The Irish. The immigration into America from both ends of the Emerald Isle was, with exceptions, a peasant movement and it is of course one of the oldest, beginning well down in colonial times. But the mass transfer of young peasants to the new world came in the nineteenth century and affected profoundly the process of western state-making. Being poor and also unskilled as a rule, those immigrants generally began their American life as common laborers, digging the canals, grading the railroads, helping on farms and in the homes. A large proportion of them remained in eastern cities, fitting themselves into the life as best they could, and soon participating actively in municipal politics. But a vast number, in the aggregate, went west and settled on farms, sometimes making up entire rural communities. From those communities have come, in the course of a century, as many able priests and bishops, lawyers, college professors, physicians, and, of course, politicians as any other social stock has produced from similar numbers. And, while there is apparently a considerable vestige of permanently unprosperous Irish through the countryside, the proportion of successful farmers among them is perhaps as high as among the native Americans of English stock. With the impulse afforded by America's free lands and high wages, the native gifts of the Irish racial character have had their chance to flower.

The Germans. German immigrants have also been prevailingly of peasant origin, though with a decidedly larger admixture of trained craftsmen.[20] The Germans also gave to the United States a social element, of very special value, in the considerable group of political refugees known as the forty-eighters among whom were Carl Schurz, Hecker, Sigel, and many others of similar cultural strains. The forty-eighters, as newspaper editors, professional men, musicians, playwrights, and politicians performed yeoman service as leaders of the German masses in the several states, thus aiding them to realize their cultural opportunities. But the German peasants were generally such intelligent, industrious farmers that economic prosperity, on a plane wholly new to them, furnished a powerful impulse upward in the social scale. The German-owned farms of America have probably sup-

[20] That fact was established for certain typical Wisconsin areas by a hand count of census descriptions. See *Winnebago-Horicon Basin* (in press), especially chapter X.

plied more than their numerical proportion of scholars to the present generation.

Cornish and others. And where, today, shall we look for the descendants of those Cornish miners who, driven from their shafts and galleries by economic pressure in the 1830s, came over to dig for lead and zinc and to make farms in Illinois, Iowa, and Wisconsin? One of them, typical of a large number, has just retired from a long and distinguished service as dean of a leading mid-western graduate school. The Welsh, established early as farmers in eastern Pennsylvania, have likewise endowed the Middle West with some of the most scientific cultivators and stock breeders. Their sons grace the professions, and advance the torch of learning.[21] But a similar statement can be made also in regard to Scandinavian, Bohemian, Dutch, Belgian, Polish, and other European immigrant farmers. Some groups, especially the Irish and the Germans, being early on the ground, enjoyed certain advantages over the later comers. But up to a very recent period, the immigrants of whatever origin have found opportunity for rapid social development based upon the cultivation of cheap lands on America's varied frontiers.

Social results of the "mixing bowl." The question naturally arises, what of the net social result of such intermingling of stocks and languages? It cannot be denied that America has had her periods

---

[21] Louis R. Jones, for example, is one of the world's leading plant pathologists.

of trepidation in contemplating the rapid incursion
of non-English elements. These doubts began far
back in colonial times. A classic expression of them
is that of Benjamin Franklin, writing a quarter
century prior to the Revolution.[22] He was frightened
lest Pennsylvania, "founded by the English, become a colony of aliens, who will shortly be so
numerous as to Germanize us, instead of our angli-
fying them, and will never adopt our language or
customs any more than they can acquire our complexion." He would have preferred to exclude all
"blacks and tawnys" and increase "the lovely white
and red. But," he adds almost apologetically, recognizing that his prejudices are involved, "perhaps
I am partial to the complexion of my country, for
such kind of partiality is natural to mankind."

Nordic propaganda. We may conveniently date
the series of Nordic propagandists from Franklin.
He has many successors and doubtless the end is
not yet, for historically almost every succeeding
generation had its anti-foreign movement manifest-
ing itself in alien and sedition acts, in a know-noth-
ing nativist party, an American protective association, or a latter-day Ku-Klux-Klan. Linguistic
non-conformity, which along with the non-English
color scheme was Franklin's chief complaint against
the industrious, wealth-producing German hus-
bandmen of Pennsylvania, has been only one of the

---

[22] Observations Concerning the Increase of Mankind and the
Peopling of Countries, 1751. *Works of Benjamin Franklin,* Bigelow
Edition, 1887. II, 233–234. See also letter to Peter Collinson,
ibid., 291–299 (May 3, 1753).

points of attack against immigrants. In nearly all later agitations the disturbing religious issue was either an avowed or secret dynamic influence. The anti-Catholic inheritance from English puritanism conceals an explosive principle which it has been difficult to control. It erupts in all kinds of unexpected ways.

Massed and dispersed immigrants. The greatest unifier of diverse elements, next to the fact of the foreigners' immersion in American conditions compelling economic and social readjustments, has been the public school conducted in the English language. The establishment of English schools among the Germans was one of Franklin's suggestions for saving Pennsylvania socially. He also thought it important to distribute German immigrants more widely among the English instead of permitting them to mass in distinct communities as they naturally tended to do.[23] Throughout American history the colonization of foreign groups in particular areas has raised a social problem, and such areas are fairly numerous.

No massing of congenial groups was possible where a rush for the lands of a newly opened district took place. And, even when there was no rush but only a normally rapid movement of settlers, the keenness of the competition for the better locations prevented massing. A given section of 640 acres might well be owned, after the land sale, by four or five persons, one of them a Yankee, another an

---

[23] Letter to Peter Collinson.

Irishman, another a German, and a fourth a Scandinavian. In that way the frontier served to mingle the various types together, rendering easier the process of assimilation—for in most places the American element, after all, was most numerous as well as spiritually dominant.

However, in certain situations the land itself selected the settlers. Openlands, for example, were the more attractive to Yankees possessed of some capital or credit which would enable them to break up large tracts promptly in order to raise wheat. Accordingly, the openlands of some of the western states were generally taken by Yankees in the first instance, though later they might be sold as made farms to foreigners. On the other hand, the heavily wooded lands, especially if they lay near means of communication like the Great Lakes or the Mississippi, were quite likely to be taken up by foreigners, notably the Germans. That fact, coupled with a planned colonization such as Birkbeck and Flower conducted in Illinois, resulted in scattering over the West a group of foreign-immigrant colonies. But the original settlements of Germans, Scandinavians, Bohemians, Dutch, Belgians, all tended to expand later by the process of replacing American, English, Canadian, or Irish families who were glad to sell out and go west.

Effects on "Americanization." The public school. Except in the massed centers, foreign agricultural settlers offered but slight resistance to the process of Americanization. And in such centers the schools gradually overcame such resistance as the inertia of habit created. The children learned English in school and spoke it in the home. The parents, knowing the advantage both to the younger members of the household and to themselves, of a command of the language of the country, learned it also, sometimes at the cost of painful effort. But the first generation required tender treatment. For example, the school authorities of Wisconsin, during some years, permitted certificated teachers who were Germans to conduct the public schools of exclusively German districts in the German language, trusting to the teaching of English as a subject of study gradually to win the children to its daily use, and that plan proved reasonably successful.

Persistence of racial purity. Various studies made in Wisconsin tend to show that ruralites of distinctive origins—whatever may be true of those in towns and cities—do not readily amalgamate through intermarriages. The number of inter-racial unions in a given county has been relatively insignificant. The rule is for Irish to marry Irish, Germans Germans, English English, even to the second American generation. The several race elements tend to persist in their purity long enough to permit a gradual approximation to the social type all are striving toward, namely, that of the socially acceptable American citizen. In other words, the human ingredients which go into the mixing-bowl, diverse in origin and still showing appreciable variations, are in character far removed from the postulated

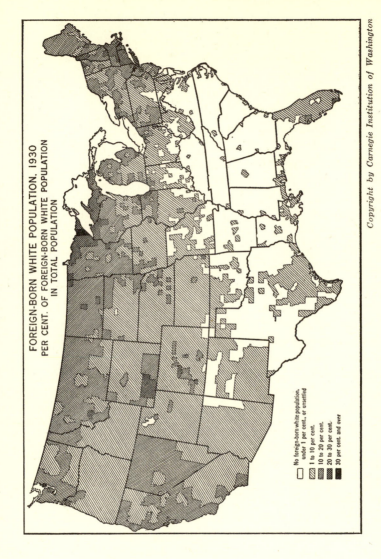

FOREIGN-BORN WHITE POPULATION, 1930
PER CENT. OF FOREIGN-BORN WHITE POPULATION
IN TOTAL POPULATION

No foreign-born white population,
under 1 per cent., or unsettled
1 to 10 per cent.
10 to 20 per cent.
20 to 30 per cent.
30 per cent. and over

Reproduced from "The Atlas of Historical Geography of the United States," prepared by C. O. Paullin and J. K. Wright (1932). Published by the Carnegie Institution of Washington and the American Geographical Society of New York.

"raw materials" of our "melting-pot" theorists. On the one hand, the American is no longer the hard, unimaginative, unsympathetic Yankee, passionately intolerant of foreigners, but a man whose temper has been modified and horizon widened through neighboring with other descriptions of men and women. On the other hand, the European in the mixture has ceased to be a "foreigner." He has become the bearer of many of the standard social qualities of good Americans without having discarded all the valuable traits appropriate to his particular lineage.[24]

The net result is undeniably a diverse citizenship from the standpoints of linguistic origins, racial customs and peculiarities, wealth, and cultural traditions. It is, and will long remain, for the trained observer, a simple matter to analyze a spontaneous gathering, say for political purposes, into its elements, distinguishing old line Americans, second generation Englishmen, Irishmen, Germans, Scandinavians, Bohemians, Poles and Dutchmen in the same assemblage. Yet the observer who would judge solely from the forms of speech used, the ideas presented, and the ideals or objects contended for, might discover in such an assembly no racially determined line of cleavage whatever, though he would be quick to detect religious and economic groupings.

The language handicap. English training. The non-English speaking foreigners originally were at

[24] *Cf.* J. Schafer, *The Wisconsin Lead Region,* 248.

a disadvantage in American society due to the mechanical difficulties with the official language, and one suspects that their children also, for the same reason, have fallen somewhat below the possibilities warranted by native endowment. In other words, a more perfect flowering of talents would probably have occurred if school training for them had been in their native speech instead of an alien language. But the social disadvantages of a polyglot linguistic equipment must have been very great so that, on the whole, America should be well content with the results of her policy of securing unity of language through the public school. She has not, however, made sufficient allowance for the relative difficulties those of non-English inheritance are obliged to overcome in being restricted to the English language. Justice to them demands that their English training shall be carried far enough to enable them to use the language with the ease and the touch of artistry that comes natural to equally acute minds with whom it is native. But time is working its magic. As the second American generation of originally non-English speakers appears on the stage, substantial equality in the use of the language of Shakespeare is seen to have been somehow attained.

Social laggards. Prospects. It would be absurd to deny that, even on the farms of America, not to mention certain socially chaotic large cities, are to be found multitudes of cultural laggards. The peasant spirit here, as elsewhere, manifests something of that sullen resistance to an uplift impulse which is the normal attitude of those who have persisted as a down-trodden class in Europe for a thousand years. Nevertheless, under American rural conditions, so many individuals have already overcome the handicap of that inheritance, so general is the disposition to profit by the educational opportunities open freely to rich and poor, that barring the catastrophic social dislocations incident to war, revolution, or the doom of all farmers which some predict, the attainment of a new and higher cultural plane for all seems assured.

Chapter VII

POLITICAL TRENDS IN RURAL LIFE

A rural democracy. "This nation," says J. F. Jameson, "came to be marked by political institutions of a democratic type because it had, still earlier, come to be characterized in its economic life by democratic arrangements and practices . . . America stood committed to economic democracy, which meant, in a country so occupied with agriculture, to the system of landholding which the classical economists called 'peasant proprietorship,' the system of small holdings where landowner, capitalist or farmer, and laborer are all one, the owner of the land supplying the capital and working the fields with his own labor and that of his family."[1]

The history of the way land passed from the federal and state governments, or from great proprietorships, into the hands of operating farmers, proves that agricultural democracy was a fact in the North and West, and a potent influence elsewhere, before the outbreak of the Revolution. That is why the remaining old world restrictions on freehold tenure, such as quit-rents, entail, primogeni-

[1] *The Am. Rev. Considered as a Social Movement,* Princeton, The Univ. Press, 1926, p. 41–42.

ture, and forest rights, were so promptly abolished after the break with England. The Revolution also cancelled the land-claims of tory proprietors to the extent of millions of acres, to the ultimate enlargement of the already great society of small holders though with a certain temporary encouragement of speculative middlemen.[2]

The shot heard round the world. It is now known historically, not only poetically, that it was the "embattled farmers" and not the merchants, who "fired the shot heard round the world." It was they, supported by laborers and small people of the towns, who supplied the man-power in the movement for independence, while the capitalistic class of merchants stood prevailingly on the opposite side or tried to remain neutral.[3] After the Revolution the farmers for some years were firmly in the saddle, being the popular influence behind the continental congress and the articles of confederation.

It was the demonstrated inefficiency of the articles, coupled with the excesses of Massachusetts farmers in their conflict with the capitalist class, that created an opportunity for the latter to score in the making of a new constitution. The political movement of 1785 and 1786 had for its object to amend the articles of confederation in certain respects, especially to enable the government to raise

[2] D. W. Brogan, "The Rise and Decline of the American Agricultural Interest," *The Economic History Review,* April, 1935.

[3] *Cf.* Arthur M. Schlesinger, *The Colonial Merchants.* Columbia Univ. Studies in History, 78, Chap. XV. Especially pp. 593 ff.

money by uniform duties on imports, to regulate commerce with foreign countries, and between the several states.

Shays' Rebellion. Into the negotiations of state leaders on these high issues broke the clangor of Shays' rebellion in western Massachusetts, an event which struck George Washington at Mt. Vernon with amazement and awe. It was reported to him the malcontents proposed to "annihilate all debts, public and private," have agrarian laws and an unfunded paper currency. The cause of the explosion was the hopeless indebtedness of farmers and their inability, owing to capitalistic opposition, to secure the relief they wanted through the issue of paper money. Besides, they had grievances against courts and lawyers on account of the heavy costs of foreclosure proceedings.

If western Massachusetts had had a more successful agriculture, her farmers need not have despaired of paying their debts, for at the very time they were rebelling under Shays and Shattuck, the farmers of Pennsylvania were prospering. Their wheat, a good crop, wrote Franklin, was bringing eight shillings and sixpence per bushel in hard money.[4] He adds: "Our working people are all employed and get high wages, are well fed and well clad . . . Our wilderness lands are daily buying up by new settlers, and our settlements extend rapidly to the westward. European goods were

[4] Letter to William Hunter, Nov. 24, 1786. Bigelow, *Works of Franklin*, IX, 348.

never so cheaply afforded as since Britain no longer has the monopoly of supplying us. In short, all among us may be happy, who have happy dispositions; such being necessary to happiness even in paradise."

Probably Pennsylvania farmers had been less headlong about going in debt during the period of inflation. In Massachusetts old-time restraint had been largely put aside and "an undue use of articles of foreign growth and manufacture" was the result.[5] In a word, they had forgotten that they were merely subsistence farmers. In addition, the farmers felt that the mercantile class, while contributing to their distress by promoting luxurious living, failed to pay its fair share of the taxes to meet the public debt.[6] An issue was thus raised which pitted country against city once more and that in precisely the manner which was destined to become orthodox in history—the hard-working farmer, ruined by debt, fighting the ogre of capitalism, "the money power."

Political division. The reformers who strove to make a new constitution and to get it adopted had the active support of the mercantile or capitalist class not only in Massachusetts but throughout the country. The Shays rebels, on the contrary, in the Massachusetts ratifying convention were bitterly hostile. The agricultural class away from the sea-board, where it was influenced by the better

[5] G. R. Minot, *Shays' Rebellion,* Worcester, 1788, p. 173.
[6] Mason A. Green, *Springfield, 1636–1886,* 310,

markets created by commerce, either opposed the
new constitution or insisted on various amendments
guaranteeing personal rights and privileges. While
that instrument contained some important compromises, it was felt to be more favorable to merchants than to farmers. The Revolution had
seemed just the reverse, so the score thus far was
even.[7]

Farmer and capitalist each had a powerful
champion in Washington's administration, but the
contest which ensued over governmental policies
between Jefferson and Hamilton left the latter vic-
torious. With the president's favor and a congress
pledged to strong government, Hamilton was able
to create the kind of fiscal arrangements that
pleased the capitalist class and attached them
strongly to the federal government. The acts included funding the national debt, assumption and
funding of the state debts, establishment of the
national bank, a protective tariff on imports, and
excise duties.

For a time Hamilton had almost a clear field,
the members of congress having been chosen in
most cases because they were in favor of a government that could act with vigor; but gradually the
friends of the agricultural classes became alarmed
and set about the task of stirring up the natural
opposition to the commercial and monied beneficiaries of the Hamiltonian system. It was in this

[7] Orin G. Libby, *Distribution of the Vote on the Adoption of
the Constitution,* Madison, Wis., 1894.

way that political parties became formally organized under the constitution.

The two parties. Writing during Washington's second administration, from which he had detached himself, Thomas Jefferson concludes a discourse on the subject of political partyism in these words: "Two parties then do exist within the United States. They embrace respectively the following descriptions of persons. The anti-republicans [or Federalists] consist of 1. The old refugees and tories. 2. British merchants residing among us, and composing the main body of our merchants. 3. American merchants trading on British capital. Another great portion. 4. Speculators and holders in the banks and public funds. 5. Officers of the federal government with some exceptions. 6. Office-hunters, willing to give up principles for places. A numerous and noisy tribe. 7. Nervous persons, whose languid fibers have more analogy with a passive than active state of things.

"The Republican part of our union comprehends 1. The entire body of landholders throughout the United States. 2. The body of laborers, not being landholders, whether in husbanding or in the arts."

Their origin. To the sage of Monticello the origin of this division of the people seemed sun-clear. From being confirmed admirers of the British constitution the Revolution had made the American people, with certain exceptions, republicans. Their first constitution, however, the so-called articles of confederation, adopted when feeling against everything British ran highest, proved too extreme in its republicanism and democracy. Gradually, the major portion of the people saw the need of amending it into a more workable government. The "monocrats," as he called them, the pro-British remnant, refugees and pretending patriots, preferred to keep the articles until the complete breakdown of government should throw the country back into the hands of Britain.

These elements failed, the new republican constitution was adopted (though not without certain twists to the right for which the monocratic minority was responsible) and the new and designedly stronger government went into effect. Now the monocrats saw their chance. Since, naturally, the men elected to the first congress were predominantly favorable to strong government, they hit upon the plan of administering the new system in ways that would make it as nearly like the English as possible in order, ultimately, to have monarchy restored. They therefore funded the national debt so as to make it perpetual, they created a national bank, and, in a word, deliberately fostered a money power and based the administration upon its support.

By the time the third congressional election came around, the masses of the people had come to understand these tendencies, and the result was the return of a large majority of genuine republicans to the House of Representatives. The Senate changing only every six years, it would take longer to rectify its politics, but the operation of time was certain to make that house republican also. Of course, the monocrats had control of the courts, and they were intrenched in the public offices.

This, in brief, is Jefferson's history of American politics during, let us say, twenty years, from 1775 to 1795. It is obviously rationalized to suit his views and propagandist purposes. But it serves to explain his analysis of political parties, and affords a background for considering the farmers' part in realizing the aims he placed before them.[8]

The farmers in politics. Jefferson, like every other successful politician of democratic proclivities, understood the farmer mind. It must have issues presented to it in dramatic form in order to make a sufficiently powerful impression. Once fully engaged, emotional obsession would be sure to carry thought over into action, which is what the politician wants. It was true, as Lecky said of revolutionary New Englanders, that farmers tended to be "hard, stubborn, and indomitably intractable" but, as he also pointed out, they had strong natural intelligence, a fair general education and "many of the qualities of a ruling race." The inertia inherent in the rural psychology once overcome, farmers were as ready to go for radical action as any other social class.

How far Jefferson may have been sincere in his contention that a conspiracy was afoot to restore monarchy, we may never know. It is plain, however, that the idea was perfectly adapted to make the desired appeal to the farmers, who since the

[8] Jefferson's *Writings* (Ford's Ed.) VII, 47–48.

outbreak of the Revolution feared and hated monarchy while in commercial and monied circles such aversion to it as had existed gradually wore away. The farmer holds his fire longer than other classes by reason of his isolation.

Jefferson's program. But, with the threat of monarchy to alarm him into giving close attention to issues, Jefferson could easily prove to the farmer that his interest lay not in a perpetuation of the public debt, but in a determined effort to pay it off, thereby lifting from his shoulders the annual interest charge; not in a protective tariff that would add to the price of manufactured goods he had to buy, but in the freest interchange of his farm productions for the manufactured goods offered by foreign countries in payment; not in a burdensome army and navy, but in "peace, commerce, and friendly intercourse with all nations, entangling alliances with none."

Jefferson's program made a tremendous appeal to farmers of all classes, southern planters and northern small cultivators alike, and although the canvass of 1796 yielded him only a very large minority of the electoral vote, he was so confident in the correctness of his judgment that a vast majority of the farmers were with him in spirit that he went right on with plans of organization. Fortunately for him, the Federalists were unwise enough to pass the alien and sedition acts attacking the principles of free speech and free press, constitutional guarantees to which farmers were firmly attached. All this helped to confirm their suspicion of a monarchical conspiracy and made them more amenable to the Jeffersonian propaganda. The election of 1800 there-

Reproduced from "The Atlas of Historical Geography of the United States" prepared by C. O. Paullin and J. K. Wright (1932). Published by the Carnegie Institution of Washington and the American Geographical Society of New York.

fore was a complete triumph for the Virginia philosopher, an absolute vindication of his judgment in relying upon farmer support.

The "Revolution" of 1800. The farmers of America had enacted what is widely recognized as a political revolution. With Washington and Adams at the helm of state, there had been in fact not the slightest danger of a sudden shift to monarchy. It was well known, however, that Hamilton preferred the English government to any other, that he tried to engraft some of its principles upon the constitution, and that—believing the constitution as adopted to be "a frail and worthless fabric—" he proceeded as secretary of the treasury to administer it into a more coherent political system, particularly through attaching to the central government, in interest, most of the country's wealthy men. In a sense, therefore, Jefferson's analysis, while faulty in detail, held enough truth to give it standing in political discussion.

The whisky insurrection. If the troubles of 1786 in Massachusetts had tended to arouse the farming class politically, those of 1794 in western Pennsylvania produced a much more profound and universal impression of danger upon the rural mind. The new constitution authorized congress to "Lay and collect taxes, duties, imposts and excises . . ." Everybody knew the excise laws would be unpopular in the United States as they had always been both in the mother country and in the colonies. In the congressional discussion the prediction was uttered that such a tax would "convulse the nation." [9] But

[9] An. of Cong., II, 1790; as quoted by C. A. Beard, *Economic Origins of Jeffersonian Democracy*, 249, n. 1.

Hamilton made the excise duty on whisky a feature of his general financial policy and secured its enactment into law.

The tax on whisky and on farm stills bore grievously upon the farmers west of the mountains because they had no opportunity to market grain except in the form of distilled spirits. In response to protests from several state legislatures, and from public gatherings in the West, the duties were lowered and the tax removed from small stills. Yet, since whisky was worth not more than a shilling a gallon, in western Pennsylvania, a tax of seven cents was deemed a monstrous evil which free Americans ought not to endure. Another grievance was that tax-evaders were taken from their homes to Philadelphia for trial.

So fierce was the popular opposition to the whisky tax in four western Pennsylvania counties that Hamilton persuaded Washington to send an army into that region to enforce the law and arrest violators, as well as put down insurrection. Hamilton accompanied that army of 15,000 men on its march to Pittsburg in late autumn, 1794. They marched, wrote Jefferson caustically, "against men at their plows," [10] having found no one in arms to oppose. Though about three hundred persons were arrested, many of them sent to Philadelphia to languish in jail for several months, only two were convicted of serious offenses and those Washington pardoned.

Hamilton was doubtless not wholly mistaken in

[10] Jefferson's *Writings* (Ford Ed.), VII, 42.

believing that the duty on whisky could not be collected through the local courts. On the contrary, he was probably right, for no jury of western men would convict a distiller of a crime when they could not regard his act as criminal. But to give the country such an object lesson in the functioning of strong government as the march of the fifteen thousand implied was, to say the least, risky. The constitution, as he contended, gave the executive the right to employ military power to "enforce law" as well as to "put down insurrection." If that right had been appealed to during the existence of the eighteenth amendment, the government would have required troops in every city and county of the land. Obviously, the army did not stop "moonshining," which goes on to this day in the mountains of Appalachia.

We are not compelled to regard Jefferson's view of the war as correct because Hamilton overshot the mark. He declared Hamilton to be "the servile copyist of Mr. Pitt," making alarms, insurrections, and plots against the constitution for the sinister purpose of "strengthening the government and increasing the public debt." Hamilton undoubtedly exaggerated the need for an army of invasion, Jefferson exaggerated the peaceful and law-abiding character of the western farmers. It is not hard, however, to see which one of the two statesmen would gain the sympathy of those people and all others situated even remotely as they were. This helps to explain the eagerness with which farmers all over the country rushed to the support of Jefferson in the election of 1800. They had been roused from their lethargy and were now prepared to take their place in the political battle lines.

Triumphant republicanism. Jefferson's administration brought republicanism into national affairs with a parade step. The story got around, to the joy of the farmers, that on the day of the inauguration he rode his horse into Washington, hitched him, and walked to the capitol to take the oath of office. The latter part of that legend is true: he walked from his boarding house with several friends, his predecessor, instead of driving with him from the White House as at present, having rumbled off at daybreak in his coach for Boston. The inaugural address, however, emphasized simplicity strongly enough to have justified any Cincinnatus story his friends cared to publish.

"I know, indeed," said Jefferson, "that some honest men fear that a Republican government cannot be strong; that this government is not strong enough . . . I believe this, on the contrary, the strongest government on earth. I believe it the only one where every man, at the call of the law, would fly to the standard of the law, and would meet the invasions of the public order as his own personal concern. Sometimes it is said that man cannot be trusted with the government of himself. Can he then be trusted with the government of others? Or, have we found angels in the form of kings to govern him? Let history answer this question."

His profession of faith included "economy in the public expense, that labor might be lightly burdened; the honest payment of our debts and sacred preservation of the public faith; encouragement of agriculture, and of commerce as its handmaid; the diffusion of information, and arraignment of all abuses at the bar of public reason; freedom of religion; freedom of the press; and freedom of person under the protection of the habeas corpus, and trial by juries impartially selected. These principles," he continued, "form the bright constellation which has gone before us, and guided our steps through an age of revolution and reformation. The wisdom of our sages, and blood of our heroes, have been devoted to their attainment. They should be the creed of our political faith, the text of civic instruction, the touchstone by which to try the services of those we trust; and should we wander from them in moments of error and alarm, let us hasten to retrace our steps, and to regain the road which alone leads to peace, liberty, and safety."

With these sentiments, calculated to encourage his friends and conciliate his enemies, the farmers' first president took command of the government. During his eight years in office Jefferson never forgot that it was the great agricultural majority which he represented directly.[11] He wanted to pay off the

[11] It has been charged, see for example, H. Agar, *Land of the Free*, that he did nothing to undo the work of Hamilton, but at the moment little could be done. He determined to pay the national debt as rapidly as possible and to liquidate the bank on the expiration of its charter. He also reduced the army and navy to save costs.

public debt in order to lighten their taxes, to reduce
the army and navy to the lowest defense terms for
the same purpose; he bought Louisiana because
farmers would some day want that country for agricultural expansion, and it was needed for defense;
and he went to almost any lengths to preserve peace,
knowing that wars bring bankruptcy in their train.[12]

Jacksonian democracy. Jefferson's successors in
the presidency, Madison and Monroe, were like himself representatives of the planting class and both
commanded the support of the farmers, together
with a growing constituency among capitalists, party
federalism having gone on the rocks. But, John
Quincy Adams, despite his formal acceptance of
republican principles, was allied in spirit with
federalism particularly in pressing for public improvements like roads, harbors, lighthouses, and educational foundations, all of them consumers of funds
tending to increase the public expenditure. The
national debt had grown enormously due to the War
of 1812, and it remained for Andrew Jackson, the
uncompromising champion of agriculture and labor,
to pay it off.

Jackson also checkmated capitalism by destroying the second national bank, created during Monroe's administration to help restore order in the
country's finances which the war had disorganized.
He fostered expansion by removing Indian tribes to
the west of the Mississippi, and planned annexations

[12] *Cf.* Charles A. Beard, *Economic Origins of Jeffersonian Democracy*, N. Y., Macmillan, 1915. *Passim.*

of territory in the Southwest and along the Pacific. He checked appropriations for public improvements.

Jackson was a fiery nationalist. In the spring of 1830 the political atmosphere was surcharged with rumors that South Carolina was about to nullify the tariff acts, and it was known that Calhoun, who was vice-president, was the head nullifier. At the annual Jefferson dinner, April 15, Jackson startled the company of leading Democrats when he rose and proposed the toast: "Our federal union, it must be preserved." Calhoun followed, but with less fire and emphasis, proposing: "The Union, next to our liberty most dear! May we all remember that it can only be preserved by respecting the rights of the states and distributing equally the benefit and burden of the Union." Here was the line of cleavage in the Democratic party. Jackson was prepared to hang nullifiers as traitors; the spokesman of South Carolina regarded nullification as a means of preserving the rights of states within the union.

The farmers of America have never forgotten Andrew Jackson's nationalism or his anti-monopoly leadership. It is sometimes facetiously remarked that in secluded mountain valleys they are still voting for him. He embodied the farmer spirit in politics more perfectly than any other president the country has had, and that despite the fact he was a slave-holding planter.

Planters in politics. The attachment of the southern planters to the Jeffersonian party at the outset was logical and in the highest degree significant, for the planters came to be one of the most powerful agrarian interests the world has ever known. The

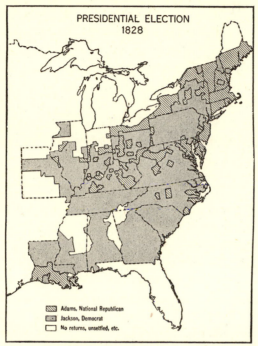

Reproduced from "The Atlas of Historical Geography of the United States" prepared by C. O. Paullin and J. K. Wright (1932). Published by the Carnegie Institution of Washington and the American Geographical Society of New York.

country dominated by them was imperial in extent, and varied in topography,—low, maritime plains, diversified uplands, and broad, fertile river valleys.

"In the factor of climate," says Turner, " 'The South' includes the various zones between the latitude of Philadelphia and the southern extremity of Florida—zones that range from a characteristically northern climate to a semi-tropical one." [13] From Pennsylvania's southern boundary and the Ohio river southward, over a belt averaging some two hundred miles wide, the leading industry was tobacco growing, tempered by the addition of grains and livestock. This belt embraced the homes of the two opposed planter-politicians, Jackson and Clay. A second zone, embracing southern North Carolina, the whole of South Carolina, the coasts and red hills of Georgia, and sweeping westward over southern Tennessee, Alabama, Mississippi, Louisiana, Arkansas, Texas and southern Missouri constituted the world's colossal cotton field. Included areas of rice and sugar lands, important in themselves, were so minute in comparison with those devoted to the dominant fiber plant as to modify only slightly this generalization.

Staple crops and foreign markets. The crops raised on the plantations were world staples. The vast bulk of the cotton had to be marketed abroad, mostly in England. Tobacco had always depended upon that market, and rice was shipped to nearly all the countries of Europe. In a word, the South, as her spokesmen have never permitted the nation to forget, was an exporting section dependent for her prosperity upon the advantageous exchange of

[13] F. J. Turner, *The United States, 1830–1850.* Pp. 144–145. N. Y., Holt, 1935.

her agricultural products for the manufactured goods her people required for a civilized life.

By the year 1824 the South produced 800,000 bales of cotton of which the American spindles demanded only a tithe. Three fourths of the aggregate production was taken by England and from it was made most of the cotton goods she supplied to the world at large. She sent to the United States an amount which required in the making five eighths as much raw cotton as was processed by all the American mills. The balance of her imports was paid for by sending back a great variety of manufactures for southern consumption, among which woolens were an important item. Tobacco, cotton, and rice made up $28,500,000 of a total domestic export of $47,000,000, and cotton alone accounted for $20,400,000 of that huge sum. Since these exports were matched by an equivalent volume of imports, which it was to the interest of the exporting area to bring in as nearly free from duty as possible, it is hardly a matter for speculation what attitude the South would be forced to take on the question of a protective tariff.

Southern "common people." Here it is necessary to point out that the South, in its agriculture, was far from being made up solely of plantations. Her people included the planting class of aristocrats, to be sure, but there was in the region a "common people" as well.[14] The vast majority at all times,

---

[14] Julia A. Flisch, *The Common People of the Old South.* Am. Hist. Assn. Annual Report, 1908, I, 133–142. *Cf.,* however, Robinson, D. M., *From Tillman to Long,* reported on in *Am. Hist. Rev.,* April, 1936, 448–449.

and especially during the period before 1830, was composed of yeomen, small farmers and mountaineers. Geographically, the coastal plain and the tidewater sections of the river valleys, were occupied largely by planters. Intervalley uplands, the extensive piedmont area, and, in fact, the entire old Appalachia, supported a general farming and stockraising population which as yet was comparatively free from the influence of slavery.

Accordingly, at the year 1816, the South was not a unit in its social organization or its economics, and when the protective tariff bill of that year came up for a vote in congress, the tide-water representatives voted against it; but John C. Calhoun, the leader of up-state or piedmont South Carolina, championed the measure. Calhoun also voted for the rechartering of the national bank and supported the bonus bill for promoting internal improvements. In a word, his politics at that time were distinctly and actively nationalistic.

Cotton and planter politics. To understand the change which came over the spirit of Calhoun's politics in the course of a decade, it is only necessary to recall the enormous spread of the cotton and planting industry during the interval between the close of the War of 1812 and the year 1824. As a boy on his father's farm, John Calhoun had labored in the fields alongside of their one negro boy, Sawney. Later the Calhoun family became extensive cotton growers. So did many of their neighbors of the piedmont, while small farmers sold to the larger and drifted west either to start plantations in the limitless southern interior or to become farmers in the non-slave region north of the Ohio. The plantation, in short, extended its influence over the entire South and, while the planters always remained a minority of the population, they succeeded in practically unifying southern sentiment on most public questions.

It is a commentary on the political sagacity, tact, and democratic spirit of the planting aristocracy that, with rare exceptions, men of their class were empowered to represent the entire complex agrarian interest of the South in national politics, and as men devoted to agriculture they were frequently relied upon by the West as political allies.[15]

Southern planter statesmen. That representation was of the highest order of ability. The great planters who commanded the votes of farmers large and small, of craftsmen and shop-keepers, professional men, merchants, and aristocrats like themselves were generally men of distinction. Planters as a rule being well educated, since the nominations for the highest offices were customarily controlled by their own class, only those of pronounced fitness through training or experience were apt to be brought forward.

It was doubtless with a view to public service that so large a proportion of the planters became lawyers, and so many lawyers became planters. At all events,

[15] Compare Solon Justus Buck, *The Agrarian Crusade.* New Haven, 1920, p. 24.

it was the usual thing to select congressmen and senators from the planter class and those thus selected were preponderantly men trained in the law.

The southern representatives and senators were not inferior mentally to the choicest specimens from the commercial centers, while these usually had an acknowledged prestige among northern leaders. Men like Rufus King, Webster, Van Buren, William L. Marcy, William H. Seward, Millard Fillmore, and James Buchanan certainly bulked no larger in the national councils than did James Madison, John Randolph, Henry Clay, William H. Crawford, John C. Calhoun, Robert Y. Hayne, and Jefferson Davis. All of the first list were lawyers and of the second all but two. John Randolph "abandoned law for gaiety," as he said, and Jefferson Davis enterd the field of statesmanship from that of war—or more correctly, from that of cotton, for he had left the army and had been a planter for some years before entering public life.

These are men whose names spring to the mind by reason of their pre-eminence. If one were to take a more inclusive roll from the North and compare it with one of equal length from the South, he would probably find fewer men of ordinary mentality in the second than in the first. To put it differently, the agrarian element in the South, enjoying the leadership of the planting aristocracy, was rather more ably represented than the farmers of the North, who had to rely mainly upon local attorneys or, as frequently happened, small-scale politicians to maintain their interest on the national stage.

Under these circumstances, it was natural that occasions for alliance between the West and the South should occur and the history of political parties, from the days of Jefferson to the Civil war, is punctuated with dramatic illustrations of the way that relationship between the sections affected national politics. Nor is it necessary to close the book at the Civil war, for West and South have frequently acted in concert on agrarian questions since that period.

The unified South. The South, however, after its practical unification under the impulse of cotton planting, which fixed the character of her economics, developed a psychology which was more purely and determinedly agrarian than that of the rapidly changing West, whose affinities came to be increasingly with the industrial Northeast. In other words, the West became the battlefield on which the political South and the political North fought out their differences.

Those differences were fundamental. The North, influenced by finance, and by manufacturing under a protective system, became more and more Hamiltonian in spirit; in fact "out Hamiltoned Hamilton": the South, devoted more and more to staple production depending upon European markets, while professing adherence to Jeffersonian principles, actually pushed these to radical extremes, as in the nullification movement.

The tariff act of 1824 may be taken to mark the point of transition in the South from old-fashioned Jeffersonian democracy to a new view designed to protect the South's peculiar interests which were fundamentally economic but also possessed, in African slavery, a sensitive social factor. The tariff bill was designed to increase duties on cottons, woolens, iron, and some other imports. It held out the promise of direct benefits to wool-growing and hemp-growing farmers, and through the "home-market" argument of Henry Clay, captured the solid support of the West. It naturally commanded the support also of the Middle Atlantic states, and of the manufacturing portion of New England. The shipping interest, however, was still the stronger in that section, so New England's vote was divided, the major part going for free-trade rather than protection. The South, apart from Kentucky, Missouri, and Tennessee in the western section, and Maryland in the east, that is, the "border" states, voted solidly against the tariff bill.[16]

Hayne on the tariff of 1824. In the great debate on that bill no single argument, even that of Webster, who spoke at that time for free-trade or commercial New England, was more searching, thorough, and scholarly than that of Robert Y. Hayne of South Carolina who presents the case of the South more fully than any other speaker. Holding it to be self-evident that "a duty imposed on foreign articles for

[16] Except one vote out of 22 cast by Virginia. See the table in Turner, *Rise of the New West*, 241.

the express purpose of protecting domestic manufacture is a tax on the consumer," Hayne contended that the South, exporting $28,500,000 of the nation's $47,000,000 worth of exports and importing an equivalent amount of foreign goods, was not only paying the major part of the expenses of government, but was contributing millions to enrich the northern manufacturers. To him the modern slogan "the foreigner pays the tax" would have seemed sheer nonsense.

But that was not all, nor the worst of the effects of that bill. "It threatens us [the South]," he said, "with the total loss of our market for cotton, rice, and tobacco. . . . I will borrow the language of a learned writer on this subject and say, 'let gentlemen look to it—they are not threatening us with a system of unjust taxation merely—but with the annihilation of our staple commodities; not with taxation but destruction.' . . . if we do not buy British manufactures she cannot be our customer for the products of our country."

The South Carolina senator added the prophecy, now so amply fulfilled, that the beneficiaries of the protective system would never be satisfied until the government had prohibited the importation of every article capable of being produced at home; that is, until all foreign commerce shall be shut off. He expected to see the time when manufacturers would occupy seats in the senate and they would be sure to demand a monopoly of raw material at their own prices. Hayne lacked the humor to look at home and recognize that, since planters occupied so many congressional seats at the time, they also might be suspected of seeking the interest of their own class.[17]

Hayne's speech was in excellent temper; he made no threats, but warned that the South at the earliest opportunity would move to repeal the tariff act if it should be adopted, as he expected it would be. He did not predict nullification, which came only six years later. It was John Randolph of Virginia who played the fire-eater on this occasion. "If, under a power to regulate trade," he cried, "you prevent exportation; if, with the most approved spring lancets, you draw the last drop of blood from our veins; if, *secundem artem,* you draw the last shilling from our pockets, what are the checks of the constitution to us? A fig for the constitution! When the scorpion's sting is probing to the quick, shall we stop to chop logic?"[18] In another generation the spirit of that protest would dominate the entire South.

Compromise of 1850. The tariff, tinkered once more in 1828, set off such an eruption in the nullification movement that the planting class were as deeply stirred by it as the western farmers had been by the whisky insurrection. A tariff compromise, engineered by Clay and Calhoun, made an unquiet peace. But, by that time the issue of slavery vexed the relations of the two great sections, gradually

---

[17] The speech is in Annals of Congress, 18th Cong., 1st sess., I, 618 ff.
[18] Quoted by Turner, *Rise of the New West,* 241–242.

making the farming anti-slavery West suspicious of the planting South. Both sections wanted expansion, but one sought new areas for slave labor, the other for free farmers. The stormy debates over these issues reached their climax in the so-called "compromise" legislation of 1850 when the South's view was stated most clearly by John C. Calhoun, the erstwhile nationalist and later architect of the nullification doctrine. The aged South Carolinian, hero of a hundred senatorial battles, had risen from his death-bed for the occasion and even so he was too weak to read the speech himself. What he had written, however, with the solemnity of a Hebrew prophet was tremendously impressive, however faulty in both history and logic.[19]

His leading thought was that the constitution had been made by and for a nation half slave and half free. But, he contended, "the equilibrium between the two sections, in the Government as it stood when the Constitution was ratified and the Government put in action, has been destroyed." The address is often referred to as the speech on the *Equilibrium*. Calhoun asserted that in 1790 there had been equality in the number of states that had slaves and that had no slaves, practical equality in population, complete equality in the Senate and nearly complete equality in the House. Much of this is very loose history.

The equilibrium. Contrasting the situation with that of half a century later, he found that non-

[19] See his speech of March 4, 1850.

slaveholding states were already in a majority of one and threatening to bring in California, their population was nearly two and a half millions greater than that of the slave states, their congressional representation in a majority of fifty, and their relative weight in the election of president still greater. In a word, the North was in control in Senate, House, and administration. The South had become definitely and unalterably a minority section, subject to whatever fate the majority should at any time be minded to impose. In effect, the South was politically enslaved. Her old time political importance was destroyed.

"Had this destruction been the operation of time," he said, "without the interference of Government, the South would have had no reason to complain; but such was not the fact. It was caused by the legislation of this Government, which was appointed as the common agent of all, and charged with the protection of the interests and security of all." That hostile legislation, he pointed out, embraced acts excluding the South from a large part of the federal territory, enumerating among such acts the Ordinance of 1787, the Missouri Compromise, and the act creating the Territory of Oregon. The recent acquisitions from Mexico were still in dispute, the North contending that the South should be excluded "from every foot of it." In that case the non-slave section would have arrogated to itself, in the aggregate, three fourths of the common territory of the federal union.

The tariff again. The South's second major grievance was that the government, deriving its revenue mainly from import duties, had steadily drained the life-blood from the South because it had been the exporting section of the union and had most of the duties to pay on imports brought in in exchange for the tobacco, cotton, and rice exported.

A federal tyranny. Concentration of power in the general government, through encroachment on the reserved rights of the states was the third count against the dominant partner in the constitutional system. The central government's claim of the right to decide all questions as to the extent of its own powers by its own instrument the supreme court; the claim of a right "to resort to force to maintain whatever power it claims against all opposition"; —these two claims, if made good, rendered the northern-controlled government, with respect to the South, an unlimited tyranny. "What was once a constitutional federal republic, is now converted in reality," says Calhoun, "into one as absolute as that of the Autocrat of Russia, and as despotic in its tendency as any absolute government that ever existed."

It is not necessary to project ourselves more deeply into the discussion as presented in this great effort of the dying leader, whose every word passed as gospel with the controlling element of the South. Northern leaders had no difficulty in exposing fallacies in his reasoning and presenting Calhoun's own record in rebuttal. But his was the voice of the agrarian South in 1850, and it was stridently aggressive.

The remedy? The conclusion being reached that the national government is a tyranny, Calhoun could expect no safety in future for the minority section, the more so because of the North's ever-growing hostility to its "peculiar institution," African slavery. The union, he held, was in imminent danger. Many bonds, social, religious, commercial had already snapped. The political bond might be the last to break but break it would, unless radical curative measures were applied.

In order to save the union the North must agree to cease agitating the slavery question, and to render up honestly the fugitive slaves. By amending the constitution, the North could restore the equilibrium which the government, by the weight of northern power destroyed, and restore to the South her original equality in the union. "The South asks for justice," he said, "simple justice, and less she ought not to take. She has no compromise to offer but the constitution; and no concession or surrender to make."

Calhoun's discussion of the slavery issue, in the latter part of his address, is of a nature to prove that this had become by 1850, in the minds of the southern leaders, the paramount question. We must remind ourselves that the whole great debate was over the compromise measures designed to settle the problems that emerged after the close of the Mexican war, all of which involved the slavery issue:

The admission of California as a free state; the organization of a New Mexican territory without mention of slavery; compensation to Texas in rectification of her boundary with New Mexico; abolition of the slave-trade in the District of Columbia; and lastly, granting to the South an effective fugitive slave law.

Aftermath of compromise. It is well known how these compromise measures failed in practice, how the slavery expansion issue became complicated by the Nebraska act, the Dred Scott decision, and the springing into power of a new sectional party of northern manufacturers and farmers, allied to prevent a further extension of slavery and favoring the protective-tariff system always regarded as inimical to the South's prosperity. On the other hand, we have the slavery-imperialism of southern leaders like Jefferson Davis,[20] and the various provocative episodes which deepened the hostility of large sections of northern opinion to the southerners even as the North's agitation of the slavery question and her refusal to enforce the fugitive slave act intensified the hostile feelings of the South.[21] The explosion came at last in the form of a calamitous Civil war between an agricultural area devoted to staple productions with slave labor, and a region representing commercial, industrial, and general

[20] William E. Dodd, *Statesmen of the Old South,* Macmillan, 1911. Jefferson Davis.

[21] See a summary of this subject in Webster's seventh of March speech (1850) which was largely a reply to Calhoun who spoke March 4, 1850.

farming interests all united in opposition to slavery. *Causes of the farmers' political crusade.*[22] Fortunate was it for the South, as a country crushed by an exhausting four years' war, followed by more than a decade of "reconstruction," that great planters had been numerically but a small portion of her population. As we have seen, the vast majority at all times had been common people and it was these elements upon whom fell the task of saving the South's agriculture after the war. The great planters were ruined, financially and politically. Many leading families were virtually wiped out. Their pauperized and proscribed remnants either fled, mainly to northern cities, or suffered a painful social reclassification. The reign of carpetbagger and "scalawag" left deep scars on the social body as well as on the political and economic life of the South.

Lands of the great plantations were generally sold for a song, either to northern businessmen and speculators or to the neighboring small farmers. The labor system being revolutionized as a result of slave emancipation, farms had to be tilled by their white owners, by the aid of hired negro labor, or rented either to whites or to negroes. In the gradual settlement of affairs it was found that large holdings could be utilized with most immediate profit under the "share-cropping" system, while

[22] The best, most thorough and illuminating treatment of this whole subject is in John D. Hicks, *The Populist Revolt,* U. of Minn. Press, 1931. An admirable brief summary of the same topic is in the older book, *The Agrarian Crusade,* by S. J. Buck, Yale Univ. Press, 1911.

the small farms, as before the war, were generally operated by owner-managers, often with hired help instead of the former slave help. An influx of northern farmers, attracted by the high price of cotton, mingling with the southerners, did something to dislodge the obsession that a white man could not work in the cotton fields. The influence of new machinery was in the same direction. Southern farming, for all these reasons, began to take on some of the features that characterized northern agriculture.

Share-croppers. Yet, great differences persisted and these were exaggerated by the chaotic post-war conditions. Fundamentally, the South remained a one-crop farming region while the older states of the North were diversifying their agriculture. The sudden shift from slave labor to free labor not only failed to promote improvement through change to a more rational tillage but, on account of the prevalence of the share-cropping plan, the single staple crop, cotton, became a veritable incubus of southern farming. The tenant was always in debt to the merchant and was not permitted to raise other crops which might improve his land. He must buy all supplies including commercial fertilizer at excessive prices from his merchant backer and must sell him his cotton at the lowest price. Cotton alone could pay his debts and cotton he must raise. The share-cropper, in a word, has a tread-mill existence. No longer a bond slave, he is in most respects a serf, though enjoying the right to run away from the land which supplies his meagre living, and, on the other hand, being subject to eviction at the end of any crop year.

The white farmers of the South suffered from the lack of credit facilities only less than the black share-croppers. The prevailing method of financing their operations, till toward the close of the century, was through the merchants who thereby controlled all purchases and charged heavily for services rendered. Briefly, an uneconomic merchandizing and banking system hung like a pall over southern farmers.

Transportation and prices. To this disadvantage was added the heavy cost of transportation, due in part to the inefficient railroad system of that region as compared with the North, and in part to the general railroad policy of the times. As a cap-sheaf for his varied miseries, the southern farmer continued to feel the injustice of the protective tariff which added to the cost of all his imports while his productions—all exports—had to be sold in a free-trade market.

The post-war scarcity prices for cotton lasted only a short time. Then set in a general persistent and fateful decline which, in the period of 1894–1897 became less than six cents. Southern farmers, long before that point was reached, were in despair. They had nothing to look forward to but universal bankruptcy. Taxes were necessarily high if the destruction due to the war was to be repaired, and reconstruction orgies of expenditure made them needlessly heavy. Yet they felt that, at the same time, the financial system of the country, based on gold, was punishing them still farther through the appreciation of that metal.

Farming the dry plains. The sympathy between South and West in pre-war times, which often led to common action in politics, had been seriously disturbed when the two sections parted company over the slavery question. Since the war, however, another West was building up between which and the South similarity of economic and social problems finally created bonds of sympathy that led to practical co-operation in politics. The vast plains west of the Missouri, penetrated by speculative railroads whose profits depended on bringing in settlers at the most rapid rate possible, literally sprang to a new life between 1866 and 1886. The plains and plateaus of Kansas, Nebraska, western Iowa and Missouri, Dakota, Montana, Wyoming, and Colorado received farming settlers by the hundred thousands, all bent on growing wheat and corn and all dependent for every pound of freight, sent or received, upon the railroads. And these railroads charged "what the traffic would bear."

The myriads who went west in the heyday of homesteading because "Uncle Sam is rich enough to give us all a farm" were greedy for the wealth to be extracted so easily from the ready-to-plow openlands. They needed financing and eastern investors eagerly sent bags of money to be exchanged for mortgages on western farms. Pre-emptions had to be paid for, houses built, machinery purchased, stock acquired or improved. But riches were just ahead, so why not borrow the limit and live well while treading the road to opulence! The subsistence farming idea was with these people very much in abeyance.

Unfortunately, the road to riches had many a turning. Grasshoppers ate up the crops. Hot winds blasted them. Chinch bugs killed the wheat in the milk stage. Finally a decade of drought years depopulated whole counties and reduced whole states.

Railroad vs. *farmer*. Those who remained, occupiers of the better lands in the more favorably located districts, struggled against fearful odds to maintain their hold on farms into which had gone the labor and sacrifice of the family. That struggle, all too often unavailing, embittered an entire generation of American farmers scattered over an area larger than Europe. They could raise wheat and corn more cheaply than any other farmers of the whole world. But to what end if freight charges left their corn so worthless that it was more profitable to burn it for fuel than to haul it to market; if wheat which cost fifty cents a bushel to grow had to be sold for forty-five cents.

Here, again, because the surplus wheat had to be exported, the market price was fixed in Liverpool as was the price of cotton. On the other hand, the farmer's cotton goods, woolens, iron, lumber, shoes, even the coffin in which he was to be buried, paid a protective duty to an American manufacturer, or else paid a tribute to some monopoly. That at least is the way the situation impressed the poor farmers of the big, attractive, but cruel open plains. Meantime his mortgage was growing heavier year by year, as the value of gold, in terms of products, appreciated.

Discontent and ruin. The western farmer, like the southern farmer, became desperate and for essentially the same reasons. He felt that "every man's hand"—the merchant's, the money lender's, the elevator manager's, the railroad director's, the manufacturer's, and even the statesman's—was against him. Thus far, his hand had not been against others. His vote, in the main, had continued to swell the Republican majorities to which he had begun to contribute before the war as a friend of human liberty, and during the war because that was the party of the Homestead act, of Lincoln and of his eastern creditors and customers. He had often doubted the virtue of the protective tariff as a remedy for agricultural distress, but his party and financial backers had been for it and these wise men should know best. Certainly he favored building up as much of a home-market as possible, and felt benefited, he knew not exactly why, by every new industry that came to the nearest city. He had been told that the price of wheat was low because too many and too great wheat fields had been opened suddenly, both by extension of cultivation everywhere and the creation of new transport facilities. That might be true. He was only certain that the interest on his loan would devour the profit on his wheat crop and that the mortgage holder would surely foreclose and take his all. When a western congressman computed a profit to the Dakota farmer at forty cents per bushel for wheat, that farmer vented upon the upstart both wrath and ridicule.[23]

Political remedies. No! He would never win solvency by raising forty-cent wheat. In fact, he would never save himself except by drastic measures. Debts must be scaled down; interest rates must be reduced; the means of making reasonable loans must be improved. Briefly, the fundamental question, as in western Massachusetts a century earlier, in western Pennsylvania a few years later, in the cotton South at that very time—the fundamental question was one of *finance*.

That the economics of finance is one of the most complicated of problems the world now agrees. In the last decade of the nineteenth century eastern people, who mistook unreflecting party orthodoxy for financial wisdom, abused those of the West and South as hair-brained cranks because they were not orthodox. The latter were not necessarily right, but they at least exercised their brains on the financial problem. Possibly, like a child that falls into deep water, they instinctively made the very motions which insured their drowning in the unfamiliar element. However, having learned the art of social co-operation through the grange, the farmers' union, the alliance, and other farmers' movements begin-

[23] The farmers called him "forty-cent Johnson."

ning about the close of the war, the stage was set for one of the most widespread "adult education" campaigns in the history of any nation.

Farmers take to study. Farmers, their wives and grown children, traversing the dusty or muddy prairie roads with team and wagon, would meet one afternoon a week at a designated farmhouse and spend several hours in discussion under such leadership as the community might afford. Of course, it was propagandist study, not scientific graduate-school investigation. What these people wanted was to learn to master the arguments on their side! Why should the government issue legal-tender money direct to farmers, at a low interest rate, secured by land, instead of permitting national banks to issue it on their government bonds at a high rate? Why should the government own and operate the railroads, and open to entry the millions of acres of land bestowed as a bonus upon the railroad companies? Why should monopoly be curbed and how would the lowering of the tariff help? Since silver had always been equal to gold as a basic money-metal prior to "the crime of '73," and since there was apparent need of a larger supply of basic money, why should not the free-coinage of silver at the old ratio of sixteen-to-one be resumed?

Had the agricultural depression in the West and South been a temporary or short-lived phenomenon, the agitation would doubtless have evaporated. But ten years is a long time, long enough to ruin a generation, and the generation which came on the stage after the close of the Civil war had no mind to allow itself to sink into virtual serfdom. Since the only way to help themselves was through politics, they combined for political action. The resulting Populist party gave the reigning politicians the third great scare of the century, the first being the triumph of Thomas Jefferson in 1800, the second that of Andrew Jackson in 1828. The revolt of the South in 1860 was a movement more sinister than a political scare.

Populism—its achievements. While they did not actually carry a presidential election, the Populists did win a temporary balance of power in congress and, in a fusion with the silver-Democrats in 1896, they barely missed sending William Jennings Bryan to the White House. Their real triumph, however, lay in compelling the liberalization of the policies of both great parties. The Bryan Democracy became the more effective Wilson Democracy, which gave the country banking reform and other benefits. The Republican party largely deserted to Theodore Roosevelt in 1912, on a platform featuring many Populist ideas, some of which it has retained.

CHAPTER VIII

THE OUTLOOK FOR FARMERS

A quarter century of change. Theodore Roosevelt, in submitting to congress the report of his Country Life Commission, February, 1909, wrote: "Judging by thirty public hearings to which farmers from forty states and territories came, and from 120,000 answers to printed questions sent out by the Department of Agriculture, the Commission finds that the general level of country life is high compared with any previous time or with any other land."

Making due allowance for the imperfections of the evidence on which the statement was based, and the circumstance that it was intended for public consumption, it summarized fairly the considered appraisal of farm conditions by a group of men who ranked high among students of the rural life problem. While both the time allowed them and the funds provided were too limited to permit of a thoroughgoing, scientific survey, it would not have been easy to pick seven men who were better equipped to gain valuable views from the very general inquiry they were able to make.[1]

[1] Liberty Hyde Bailey, of Cornell, was chairman of the Commission. The other members were Kenyon L. Butterfield, Henry Wallace, C. S. Barrett, Gifford Pinchot, Walter Hines Page, and W. A. Beard.

The verdict is couched in relative, not absolute, terms; the commissioners represented ideals of life for the farming community which as yet had been realized by only a small minority of American farmers. Great numbers, they found, had incomes that were quite too small to serve as the basis for a good life, and other multitudes did not know how to live well even with an adequate income. Their second summary, covering shortcomings, is therefore rather more significant than the first. They say: "The farming interest is not, as a whole, receiving the full reward to which it is entitled, nor has country life attained to anywhere near its possibilities of attractiveness and comfort."

Farm prosperity. When this report was written, American farmers were in the enjoyment of that full tide of prosperity which began in 1897 following a quarter century of hard times. Farm prices had been going up either because of settled monetary policy, as some held, because of a new flood of gold from Alaskan and Klondike mines, or for those and other reasons.[2] At all events, farmers were considered so prosperous that the value of farm lands— all land in farms—had risen during the decade 1900 to 1910 from an average of $19.30 per acre to $39.50 or slightly more than 100 percent.[3]

This shows, to be sure, that farm land was be-

[2] New mining processes, like the cayanide process, were perhaps equally important with new sources of gold supply; and still other causes of prosperity have been pointed out.

[3] *Cf.* Statistical Abstract of the United States, 1914, pp. 119, 122.

ginning to have a scarcity value, but there is no scarcity in an article that people do not want, and they wanted farms because farming in that period was profitable. Moreover, it continued to be profitable—very profitable—for another full decade. During the years of the great war, 1914 to 1919, the growing of nearly all food and fiber crops, at war prices, while much more expensive than formerly, made farming more profitable than it had ever been.

As a natural consequence, land prices rose to unheard-of heights. During the summer of 1919 good cornland in Iowa and Illinois was selling freely at $300 per acre and many farms brought $350. Some went to $400 and even $600 per acre. Similar if not equal prices prevailed in other states. Wheat farmers, cotton farmers, dairy farmers, all had their too brief year of jubilee when they knew themselves to have come into their own once more. Thousands sold out, taking part payment down with a mortgage to secure the major part of the purchase money. They expected to live at their ease, depending for income upon the interest and installment payments agreed upon.

The agricultural depression. Then, in the summer of 1920, all prices of farm produce dropped to about one half what they had been. The purchasers of farms at the inflated war prices were crushed. So were their backers, the local banks, among which, beginning in 1921, the country experienced an "uninterrupted sequence of failures" so that, by 1929, 5,515 fewer banks existed than there had been in

1920.[4] Country banks literally fell by the hundreds and along with them fell thousands of farmers.

We think of the great depression as beginning with the securities crash of October, 1929. But the farmers of America had already experienced nine years of ruinously low prices when that calamity broke upon the cities, a period nearly as long and more universally destructive than the drought and grass-hopper era in the far West which ushered in the Populist crusade. Some states and regions were harder hit than others, and in general the fore-sighted "good farmer" who owned his land and kept out of debt was safe, though even he had no chance to make money. On the other hand, those whose farms were mortgaged, a steadily mounting pro-portion, found it increasingly hard to pay both in-terest and taxes, more and more of them going into bankruptcy every year.

Psychological effects. Episodes from our earlier history show what conditions favor an uprising of the rural masses. Shays' rebellion, the Whisky in-surrection, the revolt of the planting South, and the later populism were all movements in which debt and hard times, coupled with real or fancied griev-ances, caused social explosions. Surely it is not sur-prising that this latest distressful period should have given rise to farm holiday associations, which was an attempt to boycott the city users of general farm products; and to strikes for the purpose of getting

[4] *Recent Social Trends,* 2 vols. McGraw-Hill, New York, 1933, p. 262.

better prices for milk. One phase of the farmer protest took the form of nullifying court decrees ordering the sale of farm property to satisfy mortgage foreclosure judgments. In numerous instances neighboring farmers assembled at the premises and, forcibly preventing free bidding, caused the property to be knocked down to one of themselves for a mere song to be then turned back to the original owner. Country people have long memories, or else like occasions suggest like reactions. They may have harked back to the pioneer land-claim days when, in order to eliminate the speculator, claimants united to prevent free bidding at the land offices and secured for each his chosen claim at the minimum government price. The Shays rebels, too, were bent on preventing their fellows from being sold up, but they had had no such experience as the western claim-makers. Their method, a doubly dangerous one, was to prevent the sitting of the courts. Our present-day rural malcontents never went to that extreme, though a group of over-excited farmers in Iowa on one occasion did lay violent hands upon a judge.

The great mass of American farmers condemned such excesses. No class of people is more devoted to law and order, and the disturbances we have described were the acts of what the late Theodore Roosevelt would have called "the lunatic fringe." They show, however, what was the drift of popular sentiment and we may be sure that where one farmer was ready to resort to discreditable methods, a hundred were wrought-up to seek redress of grievances by peaceful means, even if these might be considered radical. The political approach to the solution of their problem, as in the Populist period, was the one the great majority of farmers favored and, as in the earlier case, the question of party was submerged in the deeper question of whether farmers could manage to survive as freemen under American conditions.

Pessimistic views. Nor was it only farmers who, in the bitterness of defeat and the seeming futility of efforts for relief, indulged these gloomy forebodings. One prominent historian concluded a calm and philosophical analysis of the problem with this carefully considered statement: "The time may come when the rigid demands that consume the surplus will leave to the working farmer who makes it as little freedom as he had in feudal France, and as unsafe an existence as the slave possessed upon the estates of ancient Rome. The American farmer has assumed too completely that his scale of life is a necessary and eternal matter . . . And no program based upon the assumption that the American farmer type can be made to last forever can be anything but a misleading disappointment if the facts should establish it that the food producer, by the nature of his job, has always lived on the margin of subsistence and always must." [5]

[5] Frederick L. Paxson, *The Agricultural Surplus: a Problem in History.* Agricultural History VI, No. 2, April, 1932.

Whether food producers in the past, except in the United States, have always lived at the subsistence margin is a question for history; whether they "always must," as the author quoted seems to assume, is a problem mainly outside the domain of history—a problem of economics. It is on all fours with the earlier problem of the subsistence wages of labor which early nineteenth century economists so confidently settled, on the basis of a supposed natural law, only to be proved wrong when labor itself, under the impulsion of democracy, began organizing to secure a larger share of the industrial product.

Cause for pessimism: the share-croppers. Abundant cause for pessimism existed when the above sentiment was uttered, at the close of the year 1931. The country was almost at the nadir of its collapsed and ruined economy, both agricultural and industrial. More than a fourth part of the farmers, by count, the southern share-croppers, had fallen back into the same state of wretchedness and peonage in which Populism had found them and into which a few warming rays of the later prosperity had penetrated. Most of these people, of whom one-third are negroes, the balance whites, were still growing cotton as in the eighties and nineties of last century and they are so bound by contract and by debt to the owners of the lands they till that they must go on helplessly, growing little beside cotton year after year. Their income, recognized by the Country Life Commission as being quite too small to provide a decent living, is believed to be, on the average, hardly $200 per family. And since their landlords commonly maintain commissary stores from which they are obliged to buy all supplies, at exorbitant prices, even that pittance is further reduced in its buying power.

It is manifestly impossible to regard American farm conditions as other than precarious as long as the share-cropping system holds sway over the lives of so large a proportion of the nation's farmers. The remedy proposed, by social-minded southern leaders, is for the national government to acquire the lands from present owners and parcel them out, on the homestead principle, and upon easy terms, to the cultivators.[6]

The real American farmer. But the southern share-cropper is not the normal American farmer. He is one of the bitter fruits of Civil war and reconstruction, engrafted upon the deformed stem of slavery. It was slavery that created the "poor white" class from which the share-croppers are mainly recruited; because it made labor seem degrading to white men, and it was the breakup of slavery that released negroes for the new form of unfree life to which the share-cropper has been condemned. This type of farmer, to a large extent ignorant, vicious and diseased, if not in his utter hopelessness completely apathetic to life, constitutes one of the major social problems of America. All ranks and conditions of people are concerned in its solu-

[6] C. T. Carpenter, *King Cotton's Slaves*, Scribner, Oct. 1935. *Cf. America's Capacity to Consume*, Table, p. 173.

tion. It is no more exclusively a farm problem than the emancipation of women from sweat-shop conditions is purely a labor problem. Nor do the sharecroppers represent the American farming class more fully than slum garment piece-workers represent American labor. The one, like the other, is a phenomenon quite out of harmony with the ideals and the deeper trends of American life.

The real American farmer—the farmer of tradition and of daily observation everywhere in the northern states and over great areas of the South, we cannot too often repeat—is in the truest sense a free man.[7] His essential character remains unchanged by the vicissitudes of "hard times," either those of the late nineteenth century or those of the present generation. The verdict of Theodore Roosevelt's commission, in 1909, that this farmer was in better case than he had been "in any previous time" was not a false judgment, and it encourages the hope that he will weather future depressions without suffering a serious loss of morale.

Conditions of co-operation have changed. But, while this farmer remains as determined a freeman as ever, the conditions under which he lives have become, in the past quarter century, much more favorable to united action among farmers in behalf of their own class. In 1909 it was still felt that the farmer was the "separate man," suffering through

---

[7] In 1930 there were 1,720,961 "full owners" (owning entire farms) in the northern states and 1,190,683 in the southern states. In the North 56 + per cent were owners, in the South 36 — per cent.

the fact that he stood alone while other classes, particularly the industrial, organized to secure their common interests, discriminated against him. The farmer was helpless for the very reason that emphasized his independence, because he was isolated. Co-operation with his fellows could occur, as it did in the nineties, but only at a heavy sacrifice of time, effort, and patience.

When city dwellers sense a grievance that ought to be removed, someone with a voice of authorative sound calls a meeting at Carnegie Hall, or its equivalent, all who are interested attend, speakers discuss, and the assembly passes resolutions, raises funds, appoints committees, in short, does what may be necessary in the circumstances. But farmers, in a like case, have first to overcome the initial difficulty of getting together. The Populists did this by driving with team and wagon, often many miles over dusty or muddy roads, and at best they were able to assemble in a given spot only a few hundred souls. To a great extent final actions had to be taken by thinly attended representations of local groups.

All this has profoundly changed since 1896; indeed a new age of communication has been inaugurated since the Country Life Commission, in the hearings conducted in 1908 and 1909, learned about the farmers' eagerness for good roads, the extension of rural free mail delivery, and the parcel post. Adding these to what they already had in the railway, telegraph, and telephone, and superadding the radio receiving apparatus, we bring the farmers' equipment for communication down to the moment.

Good roads—how secured. One of those hoped-for benefits, good roads, has been realized almost miraculously, and obviously, no single social improvement equals this in its influence upon farm life. Americans whose memories reach back to the nineties of last century will recall how farm homes in most states were beleaguered by mud several months in the year, and that in dry weather, what with sand, dust, ruts, erosions, and hills hardly a single ten mile stretch of country road was at all points suited to the hauling of heavy loads or to moderately fast driving. Local control made anything like uniformity, or the application of scientific knowledge, in building and upkeep of highways impossible. With only local exceptions, America, from this viewpoint, was a land cursed with universal obstacles to communication from which the farmers suffered most.[8]

Academic consideration of road improvement we always had, from the days of Macadam and Telford, and in the eighties writers on civics made that subject a major topic for class discussion.[9] But the dynamics of the subject entered by a different route. There was a league of American wheelmen, or bicyclists whose far-roving members at annual gatherings told of the delights of wheeling in England, France, the Black Forest, and elsewhere in Europe.

[8] Of course, the railway and telegraph systems were relatively perfect, so that communication over great distances was perhaps simpler than in other lands.

[9] See, for example, Jesse Macy, *Our Government*, 1886.

In 1892, at the Chicago World's Fair meeting, these wheelmen organized the National League for Good Roads.[10]

Fortunately, not long thereafter the American world began to ride in motorized vehicles running, as did the bicycles upon pneumatic tires. It is hardly an exaggeration to say that chief credit for the wizardry with which the bad roads of yesterday were exchanged for a system which today yields to the tourist nearly a million miles of hardsurfaced highways must go to the inventors and manufacturers of automobiles, particularly the inexpensive kinds. To be sure, everybody helped—the farmer who had produce to market, the merchant who wanted his trade, the politician who wanted his vote, and the banker interested in finance. Legislatures reformed the road laws radically, state engineers took charge of building, counties initiated patrols for the constant repair and upkeep of roads. Property owners were willing to pay taxes so long as they saw material advantages flowing from the road building activity.

Once a large proportion of the people in any state had become "motor-minded" in this specialized sense, it became a simple matter to raise money for good roads through motor licenses, a tax on gasolene, or by means of loans. In a word, the users of improved highways have generally been willing to pay for building and maintaining them, especially the roads that are of local importance. At the same time,

[10] Frederic G. Young, *Tendencies in Road Legislation,* Univ. of Oregon, 1905.

the federal government has contributed from its treasury hundreds of millions for the trunk lines which now bind all parts of the nation together— roads like U. S. highway 10, which connects Detroit, Michigan, with Seattle, Washington, and U. S. 20, begun at Boston in the "effete East" and terminated for the present at Caspar, Wyoming, the wildest of the "wild West," the place where the Virginian killed Trampas, according to the popular cowboy story of Owen Wister. But the greatest of all is U. S. 40, which joins New York harbor on the Atlantic to the Golden Gate on the Pacific, three thousand miles to the westward. Pouring out billions in the form of concrete for the making of roads, America has achieved in a single generation a transformation such as no other nation has accomplished in a similar period.

Their effect on the farmer. Good roads and universal motoring have made over many features of farm and country life. They have altered space relations fundamentally, bringing farmers closer together, and closer to towns, cities, churches, granges, picnic grounds and parks. They have multiplied many times the average farm family's travel range, thus enriching life in various ways. To be sure, this generally beneficent new agency has seriously injured many local villages, and has eliminated the hamlets as trading points for a limited countryside. It has caused the dismantling of a multitude of the country churches by making the more distant larger towns accessible for trade, worship, and recreation. However, the change from rural to village or city church may perhaps make possible the very advance in the religious influence that reformers hoped would be brought about by strengthening the rural churches. It has caused a notable shift villageward in school matters.

Motor freighting, or trucking, has brought about changes almost as great as motor travel. It has served the farmer well by reducing the cost of marketing fruit and vegetables, swine, milk, and even cattle. But, among new transportation problems, it menaces the railways because country roads being now fit to bear heavy freight traffic, truck lines can successfully compete with railroads for short hauls and medium-length hauls; for some purposes, long hauls. With passenger business cut down by cars and buses, and freight by the trucks, the erstwhile arrogant but highly efficient public carriers are now in a precarious condition. It is a strange commentary on the tricks fate can play with men and institutions to find that the federal government, which in the seventies, eighties, and nineties was being so piteously importuned to come to the aid of the poor farmer against the oppressive railroad, is now being implored to save the poor railroad. The persistent depression is of course a major factor in the railroad's present plight, but the motor car and truck, together with good roads, have inaugurated a wholly new phase in transportation history which time alone can fully elucidate.

If it is difficult to describe, for those of a later

era, the full meaning of the change in the externals of farm life, due to good roads and motorization, the change in its spirit can only be imagined. But the realization that the old isolation has been overcome, and that the farm, once fixed in the monotonous, work-a-day open country, has virtually shifted to town or city suburb; the feeling that the possession and use of a car democratizes the thronging life of the highway; above all, the ability at long last to shop where he likes, and to take vacations at points remote from home, amid new scenes and different people—all these ideas and reflections must have produced a subtle change in the farmer's psychology. If, as some have observed, the farmer today resembles the villager more closely than before and the villager the city man, motor car and good roads should have much of the credit.

No doubt evils as well as benefits have resulted. The general banishment of the horse from the highway by motor vehicles and the tractor's limiting of his use in the field, have deranged the farmer's production schedule and his markets. The unwise financing of motor cars and tractors has contributed to the failure of thousands of farmers. The new car, in far too many instances, has proved a destructive temptation to the young. But, in addition to other advantages, it has made country boys and men mechanical and given country girls and women a new feeling of independence. Above all, good roads and the motor car have reduced, almost to the vanishing point, the farmers' difficulties of united action due to isolation. One does not exaggerate in saying that county meetings today are but little more difficult to reach than school district meetings were thirty years ago; and farmers in most states think nothing of driving to the state capital or, from many parts of the country, to Washington.

Other modernizing influences. Highway development is not the only means by which during the generation the farmer's life has been modernized. His common-school has been "redirected and vitalized" to some extent, particularly through the considerable progress in consolidation of districts, and union of rural schools with village schools. A vastly larger proportion of farmers today have had the equivalent of high school training than was true a quarter century ago, library service has partly caught up with rural needs and, due to the federal appropriations under the Smith-Hughes act, many high schools, in addition to the sixty-nine agricultural colleges, are now providing instruction in agriculture. More important as yet is the instruction of active farmers through the college and experiment station administered by a federally financed extension force in every county of every state. Through these means, the farmer's week gatherings, the farm bureau, or grange, the personal conferences with the county agent and the federal and state farm bulletins, the farmer of today is virtually certain to keep somewhere near the firing line in regard to public affairs affecting his class.

Will the farmer fight? Considering the new background of farm life resulting from the recent social movements here noted, there would hardly seem to be imminent danger of the American farmer permitting himself to be enslaved. When even the down-trodden share-cropper of the South can respond to leadership like that of the truculent but virile, able and clamorous Huey Long, whose now vacant dukedom will doubtless be usurped by another, the case of the upstanding free farmers north and south cannot be quite desperate. One can at least infer from the political movements among them, induced by the agricultural depression, that the old freemen's fighting spirit has suffered no paralysis. While the farmer is a law-abiding citizen, there is a limit to his patience as recent events have shown, and in political battle-array he is no longer negligible. For, partyism rules his conduct less and less, and his self-helpfulness has increased incalculably through the new means of association with his fellows. Let us see how the farmer, thus newly implemented for political conflict, has up to now dealt with the most complicated farm problem this country has had to solve since the time, more than a century ago, when Henry Clay in the days following the Napoleonic wars, advocated his American System.

The surplus. The modern farm problem was precipitated by the deflation of prices after the peace. It was evident, of course, that the expansion of the cultivated area by nearly 50,000,000 acres, that took place under the reign of high prices during the war years, had had much to do with the price drop after the war. But it had been a simpler matter to expand than it proved to be to contract. Growing-pains have their compensation while compression is merely a painful process. Having broken up pasture and meadow land, or cleared forested acres at heavy cost on the assurance that "food will win the war," farmers naturally wanted to continue to use that land for cropping.

This meant great surpluses in crops grown most intensively during the war, cotton, wheat, corn and hogs, and the problem forced upon legislators by farmers was to find some way of dealing with this surplus that might save them from a ruinous price for their entire crop. In plain English, the farmers asked for laws that would give them a profitable price for what they produced on excessively high priced land with high cost labor.

McNary-Haugen bill. The first answer was the McNary-Haugen bill, an extremely complicated piece of legislation designed to maintain, at a level high enough to pay profits on production, the prices of such portions of basic crops like wheat as are sold to supply the home market. This would be done by impounding the surplus of any such crop, selling it abroad at the world price, and taking an "equalization fee" from those profiting from the higher home market price to make up the difference to exporters. The bill was discussed and modified at several sessions, but it was in this form when it passed congress the first time in the session of 1927 and was vetoed by President Coolidge.

In his veto message the President said: "The bill will not succeed in providing a practical method of controlling the agricultural surplus, which lies at the heart of the whole problem. In the matter of controlling output, the farmer is at a disadvantage as compared with the manufacturer. The latter is better able to gauge his market, and in the face of falling prices, can reduce production." He pointed out that the bill not only would have no agency in reducing production but, by raising prices would stimulate further over-production. Other objections, constitutional and practical, were both numerous and searching, but the above quotation indicates that the President was armed with the central economic argument to prove the measure unsound and unworkable.[11]

The Federal Farm Board. A detail of this proposed plan, brought forward politically as of major importance, the Federal Farm Board, whose function was to secure "orderly marketing" and "price stabilization" of farm productions, was later passed into law and signed by President Hoover June 15, 1929. The law was intended, as stated in section 1, "to promote the effective merchandizing of agricultural commodities in inter-state and foreign com-

[11] For a full discussion of the subject in all its phases see James E. Boyle, *Farm Relief,* New York (Doubleday), 1928. An appendix presents a brief discussion of the Export Debenture plan of farm relief proposed as an alternative to the McNary-Haugen bill but lacking in popularity.

merce, so that the industry of agriculture will be placed on a basis of economic equality with other industries . . ." The Board was to accomplish the desired result by minimizing speculation, preventing inefficient and wasteful methods of distribution, encouraging producers to organize effective associations and—significantly: "by aiding in preventing and controlling surpluses in any agricultural commodity, through orderly production and distribution, so as to maintain advantageous domestic markets and prevent such surplus from causing undue and excessive fluctuations or depressions in prices for the commodity." [12]

The Board did promote co-operation in buying and selling, but the only comment on its operations that is needed to prove its failure as respects the control of the surplus would be a schedule of prices of farm productions during the period from 1929 to 1933. Even that is superfluous, for everyone remembers the dark days of the marketing season of 1932 when wheat brought the farmer thirty-five cents per bushel, corn six to ten cents, live hogs three cents per pound, cotton five or six cents per pound. The Board learned, what economists had foretold, that "orderly marketing" is no remedy for a high cost surplus—that the crop itself, not the method of its sale, determines its value. In other words, as long as an actual surplus exists, no merchandizing hocus-pocus can seriously affect prices.

[12] A full discussion of the law is in Stokdyk and West, *The Farm Board*, N. Y., 1930.

The New Deal. The latest attempt to improve the farm situation is the agricultural adjustment act approved May 12, 1933, the formal creation of the Roosevelt New Deal Congress, but the actual proposal of Henry A. Wallace, secretary of agriculture.[13] The theory of the act is that a disparity existed between prices of farm products and prices of industrial products which put the farmer at a disadvantage and limited his buying power. This indirectly affected other classes. It reduced industrial employment, "disrupted commerce, and weakened the nation's credit structure."[14] The disparity occurred, as the sponsor of the measure contends, for a reason which President Coolidge so clearly stated in his message vetoing the first McNary-Haugen bill, because "in the face of a decreased market, agriculture did not bring its production down as rapidly as industry did."[15]

In order to bring production into harmony with the practical demand, the act gave the secretary of agriculture power to lease and take out of production land enough to remove the surplus of given crops, like cotton, wheat and corn. He might and did buy and slaughter pigs and brood sows to reduce the pork crop, and bought dairy products to be consumed by persons on the relief rolls. As in the case of the McNary-Haugen plan, or any of the others, the cost of the adjustment operations,

[13] The paternity of the idea is generally ascribed to W. J. Spillman.
[14] Report of the Secretary of Agriculture, 1933.
[15] *Ibid.*

which is very large, falls upon the ultimate consumer.

Criticism of the triple "A." The policy and working of the act, being flatly contrary to American tradition, have called out much criticism. People read of the killing of young pigs with horror. They condemn a policy which aims to produce scarcity when millions in this country and in other countries are crying for food. More than all, probably, they criticise the method of securing results which is to line up the farmers—"regiment" is the term of reproach used—by contracting with each to limit his crop, to plant this or that on the unused ground or to let it grow up in weeds. It is also argued that, by limiting crops customarily sold abroad in large part, this nation is in effect encouraging similar production in other countries which will thereby supplant us in the world market.

The last named argument applies with special force to cotton, the cultivation of which is reported to be expanding in Brazil, India, Egypt, and elsewhere in a proportion exceeding that of the American crop limitation. Whether a longer experience with such a policy will prove this a fatal defect remains to be seen. We have, however, still to learn whether an act of this general character can be squared with the constitution for the A. A. A. has been declared to be violative of the instrument.[16] Meantime, whatever objections one may feel or express, one thing is in its favor: It seems to have

[16] In an opinion handed down January 6, 1936.

worked as intended. It has actually been a factor in raising prices of the farmer's produce and improving his relative economic position in society.

Defense of production limitation. The larger question of policy, as would be expected, is answered differently by different classes and parties. The farmer, naturally, wants his better prices if they enable him to make a larger net income, even though, like any manufacturer, he dislikes to limit his production. To the complaint of consumers he replies that, for many years, farm prices had been out of harmony with prices of the industrial products the farmer had to buy, at the cost of at least sixty percent of his normal income, and now that he begins to receive a more nearly fair proportion of the national income, the other elements of the population should not begrudge it to him—especially since, in effect, according to the men now in charge of political affairs, it enables him to prime the pump of the nation's prosperity.

The farmer also uses another argument. If the creation of artificial scarcity in farm economy is immoral, so is the creation of artificial scarcity in an industrial economy. The latter we have had with us ever since the inauguration of the federal government in the protective tariff laws. These laws were intended to create an artificial scarcity by cutting off a part of the supply—namely, that part which would naturally come in from other countries—in order to raise prices for the benefit of the American manufacturer. Even Hamilton, father of the protective system, admitted "that measures which serve to abridge the free competition of foreign articles have a tendency to occasion an enhancement of prices." [17] If, therefore, the "general welfare" justified the guaranteeing of prosperity to manufacturers, the general welfare will also justify the attempt to make farmers prosperous. In the one case as in the other, the benefits are widely diffused through the community.

It is also argued that, aside from tariff-created scarcity and partly through its influence, trusts and monopolies have grown up to such an extent that they now control virtually all lines of industrial production, and that the creation of artificial scarcity is the approved method of maintaining profits or checking losses among all such concerns. The manufacturer's method of reducing output, however, is to turn off a part of his workers while the farmer, using mainly family labor, has to support his labor force in bad times as well as good. If, through easy combination, industries may create scarcity, says the farmer, surely the farmer, whose ability to combine is far weaker, should not be denied that privilege.

The home-market once more. For almost the first time in a century, America has experienced a widespread sentiment favoring a self-sufficing national economy. Henry Clay's "American System," proposed in 1824 to solve the problem of marketing America's surplus agricultural products, which went begging after the close of the Napoleonic wars,

[17] Report on Industry and Commerce, *Works,* III, 351. He contends, however, that "the fact does not uniformly correspond with the theory."

seems less bizarre today with the farm population less than half its then proportion and with the doors of foreign trade barely ajar. Far-reaching readjustments would be called for were a strict "home-market" policy to be enforced, and doubtless it would cause much suffering among farm people, at least for a time. The situation would appear to call for international accords, monetary and commercial, and a freer interchange of goods with other nations rather than exclusive reliance upon the home market. That such a policy is comprehended in the New Deal as it affects agriculture may not only be inferred from utterances of Secretary Wallace, the President, and other leaders, but though halting and perhaps not too promising quantitively, such efforts are at least begun in our recent trade agreements with Belgium, Brazil, Canada, and other countries.

The farmer as a favor-hunter. The emergence of the farmer among the groups demanding and receiving government favors, such as we have described, injects a new factor into American politics whose importance cannot be over-estimated. It will certainly result in making the rural element a more coherent and effective body. Organization for a wheat reduction program, a cotton reduction program, or a corn-hog program involves a previously undreamed-of activity for bringing farmers together.[18] School district, township, county, state,

---

[18] "Even though," says Professor B. H. Hibbard, "such coming together is thus far co-operating with the government rather than with one another." See, for example, Corn-Hog Administration in Iowa, by Richard H. Roberts, in Iowa Jour. of Hist. & Politics, Oct. '35.

and national meetings are needed to perfect such programs. Leaders are found on every plane who thereafter function with more confidence and individual farmers become readier to co-operate in large general undertakings. The automobile and good roads render conventions and conferences accessible to ever larger representations of farmers, and the radio practically removes all limits from leadership.

Up to this point the effect is beneficial. The evil is in the dangerous addition to the already vast horde of expectant waiters upon government bounty. If the end result is to be a good one, it will probably be on the principle that fevers must run their course before they can be cured. It is barely possible that largess to farmers, as one of the last classes of society to gain such favors, may call sharp enough attention to questionable trends that have persisted for many years to persuade society to make profound changes all along the line. Indeed, report has it that western farmers are raising a fund to fight the protective tariff in case the agricultural adjustment act shall be declared unconstitutional, though the idea has not been mooted since the supreme court's decision.

The farmer and democracy. If a canvass of world history suggests to some that the farmer is fated to become the servile dependent of other social classes, a study of American history, including its agricultural phases, affords a much more hopeful outlook. Recognizing in farm life the persistence of serious defects, it shows these undergoing a gradual if slow change for the better and glimpses forces in action calculated to produce cumulative good effects.

Such a study, indeed, reveals agriculture as one of the main supports of American democracy because it is an occupation embracing millions of freemen who own property and cultivate land on a somewhat equal basis. The principal differences in the farming body itself are regional, rather than intimately social. The southern share-croppers have no contact with northern dairymen or western fruit, wheat, and cattle growers, and they enter into our discussion as a suppressed population definitely fixed geographically, who constitute a stubborn national problem which, however, is not necessarily insoluble. The situation is not like that in the labor section of society, the other very large democratic group, where there exists a noticeable social stratification based on specialized occupations and skills.

It is true that the successful cattle-rancher despises the sheep-rancher and boasts of being at world's remove from the "hayseed-farmer." There are also grades of material prosperity among northern farmers which are partly regional, and partly local from farm to farm. For example, the farmers of California, in 1930, were receiving incomes nearly six times as large per capita as the farmers of Iowa. This was due, of course, to extraordinary circumstances. Within a given locality, however, while some farmers may be accounted "rich" and others "poor," there are no economic cleavages like those setting off a group of millionaire or multi-millionaire

business-men from ordinary trades people conducting small personal concerns.[19]

Family farm the ideal. Agriculture, in a word,
tends toward the golden mean in material well-
being. A farm represents a "living," which may be
better or worse depending mainly on the character of
the farmer, but neither an actual nor a potential
modern "fortune." In extent, the family-sized farm
is the American ideal and means in effect that
the owner and his son or sons can perform the
actual work of tillage, the female members of the
household smoothing the way by providing home
comforts, assisting about chores, or in field and
meadow as pressure of work may dictate. Hired men
are rather the exception than the rule in this typical
agriculture. So far as they are employed, it is
usually with the instinctive purpose of raising the
labor force to the normal family plane rather than
in the hope of abnormally expanding the business
beyond the family-farm norm.

The process of adding "field to field," so frankly
condemned in holy writ, while common enough, is
still not the rule. It appeared most strikingly in the
wheat belts where a revolutionary change in machinery favored a change from family-size farming
to big-business farming; and in certain districts
drought or grasshoppers induced the emigration of

[19] See H. G. Moulton, *Income and Economic Progress,* Brook-
ings Institution, Washington, 1935. Especially pp. 36–40. And
Capacity to Consume, p. 45 and App. A. table No. 17, p. 173.
"Out of 15 billion dollars of individual savings in 1929, as much
as 13 billions were made by 10 per cent of the population."
Income &c, p. 40.

farmers whose lands were then reincorporated in the big cattle ranches. For the most part, however, farming progress has taken the form of more intensive tillage of moderate-sized holdings rather than of expansion through the acquisition of neighboring properties.

A good argument could be made for a more rapid change in the size of farms to accommodate them to the requirements of economical management, and there is every reason to anticipate numerous shifts of that kind as a result of the persisting depression.[20] Tractor cultivation lends itself better to large holdings than to small. Nevertheless, so deeply implanted are the farm corner-stones, that tractor-associations among neighbors are possibly more likely to be hit upon for solving the economic problem than the obliteration of farm boundaries.

The family farm, outgrowth of land policies and conditions of labor scarcity, has enshrined itself in American sentiment. Like all other institutions, it is subject to change under the impact of social and economic forces. So long, however, as it retains its present hold upon the people of this country, America will possess a very large social class who are not "dollar mad"; a class which, if it shall learn its full opportunities for wholesome, healthful, and delightful living, may in the future as in the past helpfully influence the national ideals. For it must not be

---

[20] See the author's address on the subject: *Some Enduring Factors in Rural Polity.* Agricultural History, VI, No. 4 (Oct. 1932).

forgotten that some 40,000,000 people still depend directly upon the farms of the country.

Faith that the farm will hold its historic place as a laboratory for the production of worthy citizenship is strengthened when we contemplate the measure of achievement in twenty-seven years. Of the good things urged by the Country Life Commission, better schools are manifestly coming, health conditions improving, and cheap electric power for farmers is at hand. Given a new lease of prosperity and the future is assured.

Culture and agriculture. Those thinkers who are able to distinguish between "culture" and "polish" detect, in the signs of the times, a new interest in rural life as the best embodiment of native Americanism. They find that artists are staging a "revolt against the city," [21] that some writers who had succeeded in the great metropolis New York, realizing that the creative spirit would function better elsewhere, are dispersing to their native places in the South and West. They recognize that what is called "civilization" and "society" in the great cities, motivated primarily by wealth, has more affinity to alien Europeanism than to what is historically American. It has been called, not inaptly, colonialism—that is, the apeing of older and more authentic metropolitan life.[22]

[21] *Cf.* Grant Wood, *Revolt against the City*, Clio Press, 1935, who contends that "the American artist need no longer turn to Europe for training and inspiration, and the middle western artist will find his true subject matter near at home."

[22] Herbert Agar, *Land of the Free*. Boston (Houghton) 1935.

As opposed to the great city's mad pursuit of wealth and the things an excess of wealth has made fashionable, the small city, town, village, and the countryside, dominated up to now by a rural psychology, still retain the old primal American virtues: a sense of human values, neighborliness, morality, and religion. The country people are not yet generally blasé, but reflect that buoyant spirit which comports with genuine independence, creative activity, and self-respecting industry. The farmers, from this point of view, are the hope of the nation's future as they have been the chief dynamic force of our country's past.

INDEX

ADAMS, J. T., cited, 182 *n.* 2.
Adams, Sam, leader type, 207.
Agar, H., cited, 236 *n.* 11, 239 *n.* 22.
Agricultural colleges, curricula of, 159–160; number, 155–156; mode of securing, 156–158.
Agricultural department, begun, 122.
Agricultural experiment stations, need for, 161; beginnings, 161–162; Hatch act, 162; foundations, 162; research at, 165–169.
Agricultural seminary (Derby, Conn.), 148.
Alleghenies, crossed, 2.
Alvord and Bidgood, cited, 59 *n.* 17.
American Agriculturist, 171.
American Farmer, cited, 114 *n.* 12, 115 *n.* 14.
Americanization, agencies of, 216–217.
Anderson, R. H., cited, 117 *n.* 18, 139 *n.* 35.
Appalachia, 57–63.
Applegate, Jesse, frontier leader type, 207–208.
Aristocracies, natural history of, 183–186.
Atwater, O. W., experimenter, 161, 163–164.

BABCOCK, S. M., finds "hidden hunger," 165–166; tests for digestion, 166; tests for proper feeds, 167; the classic experiment, 167–168.
Bagehot, W., cited, quoted, 192 and *n.* 9.
Banks, failures of, 265–266.
Beard, C. A., cited, 237 *n.* 12.
Beef cattle, breeds of, 130; feeding and breeding, 130–131.
Belknap, J., 52–53 and *n.* 10.
Benjamin, Judah P., cited, 78 *n.* 10.
Bidwell, P. W., 53 *n.* 11.
Bidwell and Falconer, cited, 109 *n.* 3, 114 *n.* 13.
Birkbeck, M., 25 and *n.* 25; cited, 113 *n.* 10.
"Blast," wheat disease, 47.
Boone, D., on Kentucky, 65.
Boussingault, J. D., experimenter, 145.
Boyle, J. E., cited, 281 *n.* 11.
Bradford, cited, 44 *nn.* 3–5.
Brands, early use of, 95.
Britain, policy of, 2; colonizing motives of, 38.
Brogan, D. W., cited, 223 *n.* 2.
Bruce, P. A., cited, 7 *n.* 6.
Buck, S. J., cited, 61 *n.* 21, 243 *n.* 15, 254 *n.* 22.
Buttles, A., diary cited, 84.

CAIRD, J., cited, 118 *n.* 20, 127 *n.* 27.
Calhoun, J. C., quoted, 238, 244; compromises tariff, 248; on equilibrium, 249–250; on slavery, 252.

THE RED PAVILION

Malaya 1948–Liz Hammond and her mother Blanche are returning to their rubber plantation when Liz's father goes missing and Major Sturgess advises them to return to England immediately. But Blanche and Liz are made of sterner stuff and insist on continuing their journey under the protection of Sturgess and a young Guardsman, Alan Cresswell.

In a jungle—savage, beautiful, part hell, part paradise—Liz is torn between her love for Cresswell and concern for her father, as the country she loves is being destroyed by greed and ambition.

Acknowledgements

This book could not have been written without the constant help of my husband, Alan, who as an eighteen-year-old conscript served with the Scots Guards in Malaya from 1948 to 1951. He passed on to me not only his experiences but also opportunities to know and admire the peoples and country for myself. I also found Noel Barber's book 'The War of the Running Dogs' and F Spencer Chapman's book 'The Jungle is Neutral' especially helpful.

THE RED PAVILION

by
Jean Chapman

Magna Large Print Books
Long Preston, North Yorkshire,
England.

British Library Cataloguing in Publication Data.

Chapman, Jean
  The red pavilion.

A catalogue record for this book is
available from the British Library

ISBN 0-7505-0876-0

First published in Great Britain by Judy Piatkus (Publishers)
Ltd., 1994

Published in Large Print February, 1996 by arrangement
with Piatkus Books Ltd.

Magna Large Print is an imprint of
Library Magna Books Ltd.
Printed and bound in Great Britain by
T.J. Press (Padstow) Ltd., Cornwall, PL28 8RW.

Chapter One

The house stood in the middle of broad acres of lawn, a solid Victorian country property with aged walnut and mulberry trees edging the back gardens, copper beeches and limes, fragrant in the June sunshine, gracing the front.

Elegant without being pretentious. The 'To Lease' advertisement in the 1948 New Year edition of *Country Life* had been quickly answered and the offer taken up. Six months later the personal possessions of the Hammond family had been packed and Pearling House generally de-personalised ready for its tenants.

Elizabeth watched and waited as her mother lingered under the front portico. Finally she switched on the engine of the Riley and revved it. 'Come on,' she breathed through clenched teeth. Her patience had long ago been exhausted by the frustrations of convincing her mother that the expense of the new BOAC flight from England to the Far East was more practical than four weeks on a liner.

'We've not that long,' she called finally. 'I have to take the car to the garage. I want to make sure it's going to be properly stored.'

Blanche's swift glance at her elder daughter, accompanied by nothing more than a flutter of a handkerchief across her face, seemed to symbolise more a wish to wave goodbye than to undertake the journey. Not for the first time Liz wondered whether her mother did not care more for Pearling than for her father and the distant Rinsey estate that had been their home for fifteen years. Liz yearned to join her father, to be back with her friends.

Eight years ago the war had torn her from all she held dear in upcountry Malaya—her amah, her pet monkey, most of all the Guisan family—and now every minute's delay seemed intolerable.

'Goodbye, civilisation,' her mother muttered, climbing into the car at last.

'And hail Shangri-la.'

The sniff of disapproval was followed by the judgement, 'Your sister has the right memories—screaming monkeys and the water always hot in her paddling pool.'

Liz's recollection was that her mother used to wave her umbrella aggressively at the garden leaf monkeys, stirring them into chattering excitement and mischievous retaliation as they shook the branches of the trees, showering suspended raindrops on to the gesticulating woman. Not wishing to give cause for any further anti-Eastern sentiments now Blanche was actually in the car, Liz limited herself to the reply, 'Wendy was only four. I was fourteen.'

'The war got you out of the benighted place just in time.'

Liz opened her mouth to argue merits, but contented herself with, 'I hope to make my life out there, teaching...drawing.' She added the last word quietly, that ambition meant much to her and she did not want it pilloried.

'You didn't need a degree for that!"

' "I ran up against a Prejudice, That quite cut off the view",' Liz quoted. She knew that to have come down from university with a first-class degree rather than a wealthy upper-class husband was failure in her mother's eyes.

'What is that supposed to mean?'

'I thought you considered a good education the supreme advantage?'

The weekend before they had paid a farewell visit to her twelve-year-old sister. Wendy's efforts to keep back the tears had been flattened by her mother's capacity to steamroller through any emotion, anyone else's feelings, for what *she* thought was 'the best for all concerned'. Blanche almost literally tearing her sister from her arms, had managed to combine a pat on Wendy's heaving shoulders with a directional urge towards the hovering mistress as she told her, 'When I know Rinsey is suitable, you can come for holidays.'

'Isn't that why we're leaving Wendy here at boarding school?' Liz asked, keeping her voice a short note below irony.

'Your aim, dear, always seems to be to make me feel guilty about events over which *I* have no control. Ooh!' Her mother's drawn-out exclamation held the exasperation of a woman frustrated in all her efforts.

Spurting the gravel from under the wheels of the Riley as she swept it out of the drive, Liz had a sudden, vivid memory of her mother at Rinsey. She remembered the garden fought for inch by inch by her mother and various garden boys, of her chopping at the liana creepers in fury with a Malayan parang belonging to the cookie—and the Chinese boys laughing behind her back.

She had been a younger, far slenderer woman then, but the passionate exclamation was the same. Liz wondered why she had inherited the passion and not the tall blonde slenderness. She felt she was physically mid-everything—height, brownness of hair, looks...

'At least the Guisans won't be there, something to be thankful for.'

'They may be.' Liz recognised the hurt-for-hurt tactic, but stonily rejected the prospect of Rinsey without her friends. 'They may be. Father may have traced them all by the time we get there.' She pondered the stories of interment and torture by the Japanese but added, 'People are still turning up.'

'The girl and boy probably have five or six children each by now,' Blanche went on as if Liz had not spoken, 'and God knows what *they'll* be like!'

'Why do you say such things?'

'Because the Guisans summed up two things: your father's lack of judgement in employing the man in the first place, and the danger of interbreeding in a hot climate.' Blanche opened her handbag and stood a silver drink flask upright before closing it again. 'I just hope this time your father finds the climate too enervating after England and the navy. He was much too previous in letting the house.'

The bitterness edging the voice and the tight folding of the leather handbag strap left Liz in no doubt that if her mother's will had prevailed she would have stayed at Pearling, continuing to work on the market garden she had created during the war. Funny really, Liz thought. Blanche had fought to wrench a flower garden from the jungle, then worked herself to

9

exhaustion digging up lawns at Pearling to grow food. Now, as Blanche had already surmised, they would be re-grassed.

For the first mile of their journey the lanes twisted towards the village of Pearling, through farmland Liz's paternal great-grandparents had owned and her grandparents had sold to invest in the Far East. She was aware of her family's deep roots in this green and moderate land, but her heart ached for the excesses of the tropics.

She turned a corner and confronted a boy on an overlarge bicycle riding near the middle of the road. He swerved violently to the side, wobbled, caught his pedal on the grass and described a fair dive into the lush verge. Liz slowed automatically, peering back through her rear-view mirror.

'You're not stopping!' Blanche exclaimed.

'I think it's the post-office boy who delivers telegrams,' she said as she saw him stoop to pick up a cap, which he hesitantly raised in their direction.

'Oh! he's fine!' Blanche decided, glancing back. 'I thought we hadn't much time,' she added when Liz did not immediately drive on.

Liz looked in her mirror again and decided he was unhurt and time was short though she resented her mother's dismissive attitude. This time at Rinsey

10

she might not be able to be quite so like the Red Queen in *Alice in Wonderland,* issuing her orders, autocratic to the point of despotism.

The Chinese cookie and office clerks, the happy contented Malay houseboys, the Tamil rubber-tappers would perhaps have different attitudes after having seen their English lords and masters run before the Japanese. Leaving them to the severity of a culture which saw confession as a necessary precursor to guilt and so torture as a weapon of justice. No wonder her father had found his workforce at first scattered and then organised by extremists into rebellious groups demanding higher wages.

A swift intake of breath by her side alerted Liz a second before Blanche shouted: 'Lights! There's traffic lights ahead!'

'I see them, mother,' she said.

'You'd gone off into a dream.'

'I can think and drive at the same time.'

'No,' Liz agreed, for the first time rather dreading the journey herself. It would be a couple of days even after landing at Singapore before they could reach Rinsey, though her mother would undoubtedly be an asset back at her father's side. Motivating unwilling workers

11

had become quite a speciality of hers during the war—and Father, though Liz would admit it to no one but herself, was not good at business, it seemed to embarrass him.

'We'll have a few days at Raffles,' her mother mused. 'Your father said he would meet us in Singapore...no point in rushing upcountry. We'll have some cotton dresses and slacks made.'

What Liz wanted was a complete reunion with her father and the Guisans; Joseph, her first heartthrob, and his sister Lee, her best friend. Contemplating an even longer delay, she frowned. She wanted to travel straight on to greet them all, find them all safe, not to stay poncing about at Raffles for days.

'You're doing it again!'

'Yes.' She admitted the loss of concentration, but, pleased to be distracted from more dour thoughts, turned to her mother with a grin. 'I was about to order you a gin sling in Raffles.'

Blanche tutted but laughed. 'You always have to make life as bearable as you can.'

Liz felt it was the numerous sips from the flask, refilled several times as they flew in the new Constellation via Lisbon, Colombo and out over the Bay of Bengal, that kept her mother going at all.

Once the journey was begun, her mother confirmed her criticisms to the odd ironic remark. A stoical quality surfaced on these occasions. Blanche might raise Cain if her wishes were not carried out, but never continued grumbling once the inevitable had happened. She metaphorically closed her eyes to the situation, and on this protracted flight spent much of the time feigning sleep.

The final leg of their journey from Rangoon to Singapore drove all weariness from Liz's eyes. As the plane came in from the north of the island, she peered down and saw the luxuriant jungle of Malaya bordered by white sandy beaches. The tiny island of Sentosa could be seen off the coast of the larger island of Singapore, and she caught a glimpse of the causeway to the mainland as the plane turned.

The sky was deepening from orange to red as the rapid tropical dusk accompanied their arrival. Blanche, the taller of the two, strained to see over the heads of those waiting but could not see her husband. Any second Liz expected a raised arm and a shout, and held her own greeting ready in her throat, joy and the cry pent up—but as the small crowd cleared she felt choked with childlike disappointment.

Anxiety for her mother took over as she turned to see Blanche slumped on the edge of a bench, head in hands, in the last stages of exhaustion. Leaving her in charge of their bags, Liz walked out into the full heat of the night beyond the reception area. She had forgotten it was quite this hot, to the uninitiated like stepping into a bakehouse with the ovens at full blast. The cicadas were loud in every verge and patch of the coarse-leaved lalang grass.

She looked past the hopefully loitering trishaw boys, trying to push away a growing sense of desolation. After all, so much could delay a person in Malaya. A single train breakdown on the one line that ran the length of the west coast, or a landslip from the rain-soaked, jungle-clad hillsides could hold him up for hours, even days.

She strained to look at every man who loomed taller than the Malays and Chinese, but soon decided that for her mother's sake they would go to Raffles and wait there. It was the obvious solution.

She beckoned a Chinese boy to find them a taxi. He ran swiftly off, then helped to porter their cases, trying to carry them all at once, all smiles and eager for the dollar note she held.

Blanche caught her breath as the heat outside greeted her. 'My God! We're back,' she said to no one in particular.

The teeming life of the city slid by the open car windows, the chattering bustle

14

of some million Chinese, a quarter of a million Malays, half that again of Indians and Pakistanis and tens of thousands of Europeans—all making a living from the island and the peninsula of Malaya.

They travelled across the island from Seletar airport along the river front lined with godowns—the warehouses, piled with goods as if for a gigantic auction sale. The lights of the many bumboats and houseboats were bobbing about like a multitude of fireflies.

The whole populace seemed to be in the streets, bustling around the street hawkers' stalls, eating at the many charcoal barbecues that sprang up each evening. Japanese-made trishaws now outnumbered the local rickshaws, Liz ironically noted as they swung between carts and bicycles piled high with produce. Monkeys trained to pick coconuts rode the back of their masters' bicycles, tethered by thin cords attached to the animals' collars. She pushed to the back of her mind the other things they did to monkeys and other animals in the meat markets. England had coloured her outlook in that respect, but for the rest she wanted to lift up her arms and embrace the whole palm-fringed tropical island.

The car pulled up on the drive between the fan-palm trees and hedges screening the entrance to the Raffles Hotel from the seafront Beach Road. The driver carried their cases in to the reception desk, where an undermanager, immaculate in his tropical suit, stood ready to greet them. Blanche collapsed wearily into a large basket chair and waved Liz on to make the enquiries.

Liz went back to her, shaking her head. 'No news and no reservations made in the name of Hammond.'

'God!' Blanche breathed. The journey and now the heat had drained her face of its last vestige of colour and her usually silky blonde hair hung dark and lank. 'This damn country is bad enough but without Neville it's intolerable.'

'I've managed to get a double room for you and Daddy when he comes and a single for me,' she said as a couple of bellboys came smiling to take their luggage to their rooms. 'I'll come to your room first and we'll telephone Rinsey, see what's happened.'

While Liz hung on for the call to be put through, she wondered at the slight hesitation in the softly spoken Chinese voice when she had requested the upcountry number from the hotel switchboard. Then she heard a swift exchange in Cantonese between the hotel and a telephone exchange farther north. She heard the word 'Rinsey' repeated and the slight hissing intake of breath from an operator.

She listened more intently to the odd words from one operator to the other, the clicks and the whirrs as the call was passed from exchange to exchange upcountry. An odd feeling of suspicion and concern came over her. Voices could hardly be inscrutable but she had the definite feeling that something was being kept from her. Finally a voice burst on to the line, Chinese words but with an accent.

'Kurt? Mr Guisan?' she asked. 'Is that you?'

There was a listening silence, then the same voice asked in English, 'Who is this?'

'It's Elizabeth, Elizabeth Hammond. Is that you, Kurt?'

'There is no Kurt here.' The voice was stony with rejection.

'Then could I speak to Mr Hammond, please? This is his daughter speaking. I'm in Singapore with my mother.'

The silence at the other end seemed to hold a different quality and another thought struck her; was she through to the office instead of the bungalow? 'Am I speaking to the Rinsey estate office?'

The line went dead.

She tried again and again, but now no

17

one answered even when she checked and rechecked that all the links were dialling the right number. Finally an abrupt operator at Bantang Kali advised, 'Try again tomorrow, please?'

By this time Blanche was bathed and in bed lying inert, looking beyond the point of being able to lift her arms from the single sheet on the bed. 'I'll order you that Singapore sling with a side order of iced tonic and some sandwiches,' Liz told her, lifting the receiver to ask for room service.

'Good girl.' Blanche gave a grateful half-smile.

'I don't think there is much more we can do tonight.'

Liz found her single room at the far end of the same corridor. The ceiling fans moving the light curtains gave an illusion of coolness. After she had bathed she felt desperately hungry and tired, but was unable to quell a curious mixture of anxiety and anger. She knew she could neither rest nor eat until she had made some further attempt to understand her father's absence.

More than anything the voice from Rinsey—if it had been Rinsey her call had reached—disturbed her. She dismissed the feeling that it *had* been Kurt on the other end, the tones had been too hard, too unsympathetic—and would she recognise his voice after eight years? Could it have been his son, Josef? Her heart lifted ridiculously at that sudden idea. But why had the call been cut off so abruptly? Had something happened suddenly at the other end? The questions churned endlessly. And why wasn't her father here?

This last thought was like a great shout in her mind. She remembered their arrival and a group of men talking earnestly together in the foyer, men discussing a serious problem, an emergency even, certainly not chatting. If *anyone* knew *anything,* she must find out.

The two men behind the reception desk were the same ones who had denied they had any information when Liz checked in. Could she rephrase the same questions without feeling a fool? She approached somewhat circumspectly, but was purposefully greeted.

'Ah! Miss Hammond, I was just calling your room. There is a gentleman here to see you.' The receptionist indicated a tall man, in his late thirties perhaps, certainly of white origins but whose skin had the permanent colour of one who had been long in the tropics rather than the swift and impermanent tan of a mere visitor.

'Miss Hammond?' he queried. His voice, she decided, was English but as complex as

19

that cut off over the telephone. It was deep, welcoming to a degree, but held a tone of reserve. 'Miss Elizabeth Hammond?'

'Yes, that's right.' She took the proffered hand. 'Have you a message from my father?'

'Is Mrs Blanche Hammond, your mother, with you?'

'She's tired from the journey.' She questioned him by her stillness as he indicated a seat at the far side of the foyer.

'I have no direct information of any kind for you,' he told her, 'but we have mutual friends—the Wildons—who told me you were expected today.'

'I do remember the Wildons,' she agreed. 'But we've tried to telephone to our estate.' She felt suddenly aggressive towards this man with his shuttered expressions. How could she make him see her desperate concern. 'We... I...'

'Yes.'

The single word implied he knew. She decided he could be nothing but some kind of civil servant, some bureaucrat, his words were more official jargon than conversation.

'So what's going on? What's happened at Rinsey? Do you know? And where's my father?' The shout that had been in her head was moderated to a piercing

20

stage whisper—which paralysed all the foyer conversation.

'Look,' he said, rising from the seat and offering his arm to steer her away from the now silently watching group in the far corner. 'Come and dine with me. I can tell you everything I know. It's not simple—'

She withdrew her hand from his arm. 'Don't bloody patronise me,' she hissed at him, and thought with immediate penitence that she sounded like her mother.

'I wouldn't dream of it, Miss Hammond. In any case I really haven't time.'

'Then tell me what you know now!' They had taken a few steps in the direction of the dining room. Liz felt she stayed upright only because she was taut with anger and exhaustion.

'We both need to eat, don't we?' The extreme ends of his lips may have quivered upwards a little, but not so anyone more than an arm's length away would have noticed.

She thought, God, don't let me cry when I sit down. To relax even that much might be a catalyst.

'John Sturgess,' he said when they were seated. 'John Robson Sturgess.'

She stared at him, waiting for the information he had.

'My mother's maiden name,' he added,

21

mistaking her stare. 'A lot of people call me—'

'Now we have the important things out of the way...' She stopped and shook her head. 'No, I'm sorry, Mr Sturgess—but for God's sake put me out of my misery, if you don't want me to start having hysterics. I'm too tired for tact. *What* do you know?'

He lowered his gaze to the table, taking time, she thought to censor what he had to tell, and to avoid her reading anything extra in his eyes. She noted the compression of the lips, the jaw tightening. The silence went on to complete abstraction as he picked up a fork and slowly impaled the bread roll on his side plate. He made it look like murder, like a commando making a deliberate and silent kill.

A sudden nervous laugh escaped her at the disparity between the idea and the action that evoked it. He looked up at her and then at the roll with equal surprise as if he had forgotten one and been quite unaware of the other. Briefly, she wondered if the problems that haunted him were not even greater than her own.

He cleared his throat as if ridding himself of such petty things as emotion. 'The only hard news I have about your father is that he sent you a telegram on 18 June telling you and your mother not to travel, but to stay in England.'

She stared at the fork piercing the bread and remembered the telegram boy they had put in the ditch.

'On the 16th Chinese bandits went to one of the loneliest rubber estates in Perak—not Rinsey, Miss Hammond,' he reassured her, 'and shot the English manager and undermanager.'

'Elphil?' she guessed, remembering visiting that other remote estate with her father, travelling the seemingly endless jungle roads. Neville Hammond had described Elphil with those same words.

'Yes.' He looked at her with slightly more interest. 'You surmise correctly.'

'That's terrible,' she said, but resented the primness of his remark. 'But perhaps just an incident? We knew there had been labour troubles.'

'No!' The denial was harshly emphatic. 'I'm afraid not. There have been other incidents. Most of the planters in the north have seen this trouble coming since the end of the war. The chief Chinese communists held a huge gathering at Sungei Siput about a month ago...'

Liz lost some of what he was saying as she remembered Sungei Siput, one of the chief towns of the state of Perak, as a place for shopping and the occasional cinema trip. Rinsey was in the same foothills as Elphil though some ten long jungle miles further southeast. 'But you said bandits?' she interrupted.

'Bandits was the official line at first, but bandits don't shoot people and leave two thousand dollars in the office safe with the key under their noses and not a damned soul who dare intervene.'

'So what do they want?'

He gave her a strange agonised look which seemed to contain a personal hurt, as if he had been intimately betrayed, and said briefly, as the waiter came towards them, 'To make Malaya a communist republic.'

The implications were left unsaid as the Chinese waiter came to take their order with all the polite attention, lack of servility and inscrutability of his race.

'But how? How they can hope to—' She stopped short, then added her own answer, 'By killing the English? But they couldn't...'

'Not in the towns. It's the classic Mao Tse-tung stuff. Guerrillas attack lonely estates, tin and coal mines...' He pulled the fork from his roll, then used it to chip away at the edges of the bread. 'As well as the English they will attack police, government officials in small towns and terrorise villagers into supplying them

24

with food. They believe if they control the sources of wealth in the countryside the cities will eventually be starved to submission. Make no mistake, they're already well organised...'

For a few seconds they both looked at the exposed white middle of his bread, before he put down his fork and pushed the side plate away.

She waited for him to go on with a growing sense of alarm. She remembered enough to know that the tin mines of eastern Malaya or the opencast coal mines of Batu Arang were no more than holes in the ground, lonely as any rubber plantation and just as jungle-surrounded.

She felt suddenly very curious. Whatever he was saying, however impassive his features, he was emotionally as involved in all this as she was.

'Do you have someone living upcountry?'

'No! I have no one.' The denial was too sharp, too decisive, implied loss rather than the never had. 'I lived in Malaya before the war,' he said, adding with finality, 'but that's all over long ago.'

'So what is your role?' she asked. 'I mean, you're obviously official even if you're not in uniform.'

His spoon stopped between bowl and mouth. She thought for a moment she had committed some social gaffe, but then very briefly he smiled. 'Is it that obvious?'

She kept her face impassive, remembering that her Malayan amah had said there were times when silence brought the most answers.

'I became a major after the war, after I'd stayed behind in the jungle during the Japanese occupation. I...' Pausing, he looked up at her and for the first time she felt it was an ordinary flesh-and-blood man who sat opposite her, for she could see the hurt in his eyes. 'I helped train the Chinese—we knew a lot of them were communists—to harass the Japs. I lived with them in their jungle often not far from Elphil and Rinsey. I'm seconded back because I know where these camps are and how these Chinese terrorists think.'

So this was his *bête noire;* he had helped train men who had turned on his own race. She wondered if her mother would agree to stay at Raffles while she took the train to Ipoh, hoping to find or be contacted by her father. 'So you're travelling up to Perak?' she asked.

'Yes.' He paused and looked at her sharply. 'But I don't advise you to—the police have enough on their hands. Stay here and news will come, I'll see to it.'

'I shall travel up by train tomorrow,' she said simply. 'Rinsey is my home.'

26

Chapter Two

'Oh! Certainly not! We've come this far...' Blanche's reaction to the suggestion that she should remain in Singapore had been as determined as Liz's to John Sturgess the night before. Once Blanche, rested and showered, had been told of events at Elphil, she took over organising their immediate departure.

'They don't want us to go,' Liz felt she should warn. 'Two more Englishwomen to look after is exactly what they *don't* need.'

'And bungling bureaucrats we can do without.' Blanche pushed her toilet bag into her case. 'There were enough people chasing their own tails during the war. *We* know what we want, where we want to go.' She paused, hands pressing down the clothes in her case before she added, 'And who we want to find there when we arrive.'

'And we do *not* need looking after,' Liz affirmed. The two exchanged looks which acknowledged their mutual resolution and their fears.

'So what is this major like?'

27

'A man shut up with his own problems,' she judged sharply, recalling his brusque, uncompromising comment, 'Childhood is soon over,' when she had said how badly she wanted to reach the home where she was brought up. 'He's travelling today, we're sure to meet him before we reach Ipoh. He'll probably have a delegation on the platform to try to stop us going—that was the feeling he left me with last night.'

John Sturgess was in fact standing alone when they reached the platform. He nodded briefly but remained aloof.

Hardly had their luggage been carried to their compartment and the boy tipped when they were startled by a shout.

'Mr Sturgess, sir! Robbo!' A well-built man perhaps a little older than Liz's father advanced on Sturgess with arms outstretched.

'Harfield! George! My God! It's good to see *you!*' The two men slapped each other on the back and gave out cries of greeting and surprise as they performed a kind of spontaneous jig together.

Liz thought what an ill-assorted couple they made. Sturgess was tall and spare, pale with a triangle of shadow under his fine, high cheekbones, his manner off-putting and unsmiling until he greeted the older man. George Harfield looked like a healthy British butcher who might still

28

give a good account of himself on the rugby field as one of the bigger forwards.

'Thought you were in England.'

'Thought *you* were in Australia!' the big man countered, laughing hugely. 'Thrown you out of there, too?'

'Something like that. And I knew *you'd* never stay in Blighty!'

Liz and Blanche exchanged speculative glances and lingered outside their compartment, looking at the two men. Instead of bringing the second man over to introduce him, Sturgess took George Harfield's arm and led him away along the waiting train. It seemed to Liz that she and her mother were being discussed.

'He wouldn't know anything anyway,' Liz concluded, watching them go, 'not if he's just come from England.'

'Don't think much of your Robbo's manners,' Blanche said, fidgeting with their luggage on the overhead racks to ensure it was safely stowed. 'You did dine with him last night, after all. Extraordinarily rude—though he's damned good-looking in a ravaged sort of way, might have a bit of breeding about him.'

Liz laughed at her mother's description.

Blanche sank into her seat. 'I feel a bit like that myself already this morning—ravaged. It's this unrelenting heat. How long does this damned train take? I forget—never

29

mind, don't tell me, let me be blissful in ignorance a bit longer.'

Liz pushed up the wooden shutters that served as windows and hoped that when ignorance turned to knowledge they would be rejoicing, quite mad in fact with the happiness of reunion. She watched the two-toned brown carriages begin to curve away as they moved out of Singapore station on this last stage of their journey.

They crossed the stone causeway from the island of Singapore to the peninsula of Malaya. She smiled to see her mother take out a Delderfield novel to read and, having brought a little of England with her, refuse to be distracted from it.

Liz felt an overwhelming excitement as childhood memories were relived as they stopped at minor stations. She watched locals energetically appeal for the train passengers to raise their shutters and buy from their trays of fruit, tiny highly coloured rice cakes or hand-embroidered slippers, or take tea from the char-wallahs, with their brass charcoal burners and tea kettles hanging from sturdy bamboo canes. She saw a hand come from a window and steal a cake as a tray was carried along on the vendor's head.

This was the Malaya she remembered, the population like the ever burgeoning jungle competing for space, striving for

30

a living in heat like the hottest of greenhouses, growth often outstripping resources. She watched the variety of faces; the Chinese more competitive, their smiles angled to prospective customers; the Malays, she thought, good-natured in the contented way of people whose generous land could grow both basic sustenance and exotica with very little help.

Although the train's speed through the green jungle corridor created a breeze, it was hot and soporific, and she found the effort of trying to see the landscape through the shading wooden slats trying to the eyes. She was drifting into sleep when there was a tap on the door of their compartment.

They were both surprised to see George Harfield standing there with two green coconuts cupped in one huge hand. Blanche lowered her novel and frowned. 'I hope you're not going to offer us those!' she said.

George Harfield laughed, quite unperturbed by her assumption or her manner. 'This, my lady, is so tasty that not only will you want to drink the contents but you'll be scraping out the insides with your manicured fingernails.'

She made a large, dismissive gesture, but laughed at his crudeness, stating, 'You're the man who met Major Sturgess.'

He sat down uninvited and Liz waited for her mother's reaction.

'How does fresh limes, splash of gin and ice sound?' he asked, again offering the smooth green shell of a young coconut, sliced off at the top. Usually the content offered for sale was the coconut milk itself—nice enough but tepid. Liz saw her mother swallow in anticipation and she licked her own lips at the thought of a really cold drink.

'Ice?' Blanche queried. 'Well, then you're irresistible. Do sit down.'

'Thanks!' Harfield grinned quite unabashed as he handed over the drinks.

It was all as he said, complete with straws into the thick-fleshed nut. Quite delicious, and after the first few deep swallows both women savoured and eked out the rest.

'Are you some sort of a magician?' Blanche asked.

He tapped the side of his nose and laughed as she sniffed deprecatingly. 'Local products plus British enterprise,' he answered, adding, 'and I have a proposition to put to you.' The teasing look was gone, his blue eyes suddenly stony. He sat back in the seat and openly studied both women.

'A proposition?' Blanche queried. 'To discourage us from doing what?'

'Of course Major Sturgess has sent you,' Liz surmised.

'Robbo, no,' he denied. 'We've talked, I know who you are, but he's asleep now. Been through a traumatic time and travelled from the far side of Australia before flying back to Singapore.'

She wondered first how anyone could call the inflexible Major Sturgess 'Robbo' and secondly what the 'traumatic time' had involved—but George Harfield was obviously not going to enlighten them.

'He really only knows second-hand what's going on here.' He paused as if to make certain of his ground. 'You are from Rinsey?'

Blanche acknowledged the last remark with a nod before asking, 'Haven't you just returned from England?'

He shook his head. 'I've only been in England for twelve weeks in the last three years. I came back immediately after the war to manage a mine for Pacific Tin. I was a young engineer here prewar, and I understand you lived here too.' He paused. 'I have to tell you this has suddenly become a very different country to the one *you* left. Can you both handle a gun?'

'Of course,' Blanche said brusquely. 'Do we need to?'

Liz felt a weary anger rekindle; these

men really did not know *her* Malaya at all. Twelve had seemed to be the age when planters' children all learned to handle guns. Josef Guisan and she had devised competitions, shooting first at tins on tree stumps, then at pieces of liana posing as deadly snakes thrown unexpectedly from bushes. Finally they practised shooting at bundles of ferns on the ends of bamboos poked out as attacking tigers, the green target accompanied by savage roars—until Liz, startled by a bellow from an unexpected direction, had shot off the toe of one of Josef's sandals.

'It might be the most valuable thing you can do if you insist on going to Rinsey.'

'It is our home,' Liz said firmly. 'We have friends there I grew up with, bosom friends.'

'You make it sound as if the estate is under siege?' Blanche probed for more information.

'Not as far as I know,' George answered but the tone implied it might well be, and he added, 'My payroll delivery has been ambushed twice on the road from Ipoh to the mine. I've been trying to convince the powers that be that we need more guns to protect our property and our employees. The Colonial Office says there are plenty of guns in Malaya. The

34

trouble is,' he finished dourly, 'they're in the wrong hands.'

'We have some at Rinsey,' Liz put in.

'I hope they're still there,' George said. 'I hope everything is fine...'

'But?' Blanche prompted as he let the sentence hang doubtful of conclusion.

'Well, I've met your husband several times, had drinks in Kuala Lumpar and Ipoh with him, know your neighbours, the Wildons—'

'Oh, they're back?' Blanche brightened momentarily at the thought of hospitable, amusing friends re-established on their estate.

George Harfield nodded. 'It was Aubrey Wildon who told Robbo about the outcome of the telegram Neville had sent. *They* had intended to stay at Raffles and meet you but news came their tappers were being intimidated, so they rushed back to their estate.'

'How did they know the telegram had come too late?' Liz wondered.

'The people in your home post office sent word you had already left.'

'That was good of them,' Blanche commented.

'In the circumstances, very,' Liz said dryly.

'And my husband?' Blanche asked.

35

'What did the Wildons know about Neville?'

'They saw him in Ipoh the day he sent the telegram. No one has seen him since. Later they went to Rinsey and found the message saying you were already flying out, but your husband was not there. In fact, they could find no one.'

Liz wondered who had been there when she had telephoned—of all the things they were being told, she still found that distant voice the most chilling. Had there been a stranger, a communist terrorist, standing in their lounge answering their telephone? Had he been holding her father prisoner? Or had it been Kurt or even Josef answering—being held at gunpoint as he spoke? She pushed the mounting panic of speculation aside; she must concentrate on facts.

'And what do you think?' her mother was persisting.

Harfield drew in a deep breath, held it for a couple of seconds, then exhaled in a great gusting sigh. 'I'm worried. You expected him in Singapore, I expected him in KL or Singapore, demanding help from the authorities. It doesn't add up...'

'Because?' Liz prompted.

'Because this lot are into terrorism. They want to create mass panic. They're not into the business of hiding crimes.'

'So people are not just disappearing?'

'Quite the opposite,' Harfield emphasised. 'The atrocities are warnings to all workers not to help the British. We've had strikes and disruption, now we have murder. You two could be playing right into their hands by going to Rinsey without proper protection.'

'If Neville had run into...difficulties,' Blanche said with admirable control, 'you could be right.'

'This brings me to Robbo's proposition—'

A proposition from Major Sturgess! Liz thought it highly unlikely to be anything to which either she or her mother would agree. But whatever George Harfield might have said next was obliterated by the scream of the train's brakes suddenly and fiercely applied. Metal screamed on metal as the train lurched backwards and forwards like a clockwork toy in the hand of a fractious child.

Gripping the edge of her seat, Liz for a fleeting moment felt half annoyed yet half amused as she thought she had expected turbulence in the air, not on the train. Then she was jerked from her seat. They all tried to protect themselves and each other as pieces of luggage fell from the racks. Liz gave one glance towards the window, preparing for greater disaster should the green horizon slant as the train

37

left the tracks, but they came to a standstill upright, the three finding themselves like a little prayer ring in the middle of the floor.

George was up first to push back Blanche's large case, which was teetering precariously above their heads. He was helping the ladies to their feet when the door of the compartment was swept aside and John Sturgess came in.

'George! You're here—good! Keep down, away from the windows. There's something on the line.' He crouched by the window and raised the shutter a fraction, scanning the bordering jungle with rapt concentration.

Towards the front of the motionless train a shrilling escape of excess steam stopped. A child crying fretfully farther along the corridor was stilled so abruptly it sounded as if a hand had been clamped over its mouth. Then an eerie silence and stillness fell over the train and the *beluka,* the jungle fringes. In every compartment the breath-held tension of people listening intently could be felt.

She watched Sturgess, as much intrigued as frightened as she realised that this was probably an ambush, not a rail accident. He had immediately taken charge, motioning George to keep her and her mother well down in the middle of the compartment. The distant manner had vanished and with his jacket off, his short-sleeved shirt revealed a lean and muscled man with the alertness and suppleness of a fighter, a jungle fighter, like a tiger she had once seen—swift, quiet, deadly. There was nothing starchy about him now. He looked, she thought, almost hungry for action.

She started as he went unexpectedly from complete immobility, staring out of the window, to swift, smooth action as he moved back towards the corridor.

'Stay here, I'll go and see what's happening,' Sturgess said. 'Don't want anyone doing anything damned silly.' His glance took in the two women. 'Stay down!' he ordered and motioned his friend to his former post by the window.

'Remember the tricks *we* got up to in the war,' George warned as he left.

Sturgess nodded abruptly. 'Don't panic,' he told Liz in passing.

I wasn't intending to, Uncle Robbo, she thought and wished she dared say it aloud. Women brought up in wartime, who had practised air-raid precautions since they were in their teens, did not panic! Her heart might be thumping a bit but that was it, and her mother looked breathless but quite calm.

They heard the major going quickly away towards the front of the train, then silence, then a shout, and silence again.

'What's he doing?' Liz asked.

George drew in a hissing breath. 'He's out to the left and beyond the train now, weaving, running.'

'Pushing his luck,' Liz conjectured.

'Not his style,' George answered.

Liz lifted a small case from the floor to the seat and felt she could have argued the opposite about his treatment of herself and her mother.

'Nothing happening,' George reported. 'He's dropped in the bushes for another recce.' He half rose as if he wanted to follow.

'We'd be all right,' Blanche assured him.

'No, better do as I'm told,' he said, resuming his post at the window.

'Do you always?' Liz was really curious about their relationship. 'Was he your officer?'

George nodded, not once turning from his observations as he added, as if to himself, 'And he should remember all about booby traps on roads and railway lines—we laid plenty.'

Along the train one or two anxious voices began questioning and it sounded like the same fretful child complaining again. The next moment Harfield reported Sturgess walking back along the tracks.

'No trouble,' he called, reassuring people

who, responding to the flat, even sweep of his hands, pushed up their shutters and leaned out of the carriages. 'Water buffalo on the line. All clear now.'

There were some huffs of exasperation as the calming message was relayed, some puffs of irritation and much relieved, nervous laughter.

'Water buffalo?' Blanche queried when he re-entered the compartment. 'Why didn't the driver just hoot or something, instead of throwing everyone all over the place?' She brushed irritably at the knees of the beige slacks she was wearing.

'I seem to remember he did, but in any case the animal was stuck. It had been tethered to a small tree at the edge of some paddy, pulled to reach better grazing and dragged the sapling along until it became entangled with the track. The driver thought it was a trap. The farmer was hiding in the *beluka*, terrified because his animal had stopped the train.'

Liz reflected she was not the only one giving herself over to imaginings of the worst kind; the whole country was jumpy.

'It shows how unprepared we all are,' George said, slapping the dust from his own trousers. 'I come here with green coconuts—' he picked up the shells from the floor—'but my gun's in my hand luggage.'

41

'Mine's strapped in my case,' Sturgess admitted.

'And ours are at home.' Liz watched Sturgess for reactions as she mentioned their destination.

'Which is why you must be accompanied to Rinsey—if you insist on going,' he said immediately but without looking directly at either woman. 'I have twenty-four hours before I must report to my unit.'

'Thank you.' Blanche accepted.

Liz wondered if they would ever be rid of the man—Harfield at least smiled occasionally.

Whatever objections they might have made about Sturgess driving them on from George Harfield's mine had somehow all been cancelled by the incident. Nothing had really happened, Liz reassured herself, and yet so much had been revealed by everyone's reactions.

George had a jeep at Ipoh station and drove them to his bachelor bungalow on the slopes of Bukit Kinta, the hill after which the mine was named. His home was comfortable with cane easy chairs and low tables, though sparsely decorated. A small fridge stood in the corner of his lounge.

'You do like your cold drinks,' Blanche commented.

'It's a necessity for me these days,' he agreed and dispensed them all cold beers.

His Chinese cook-cum-houseboy came to greet them all and was soon off again to make *hokkien mee,* a quickly prepared meal of rice with fish, prawns and vegetables. There was little time if they were to be anywhere near Rinsey before six o'clock, when night-time would come like a slow theatrical curtain drop.

From the front windows of the elevated bungalow they could see vast opaque green disused pools, as well as the muddy churned tracts of water where two rusty dredgers floated. The vessels were bedecked with an uneven array of bare electric bulbs already lit. The circles of huge buckets scooping up the tin ore and dross washed down from the hillsides by great powerful hoses created a racket which was a constant accompaniment to life there.

By the time they had eaten, George had been off supervising the temporary erection of small-meshed chicken wire stretched taut over an open jeep. It was, he told them, a hand grenade that had been used to ambush his last payroll. 'If one gets lobbed on that, it should bounce off. It's a quick, rough job,' George apologised, 'but better than nothing. I'll refine it later.'

Liz and her mother turned to wave goodbye as Sturgess drove them away.

'I'll be along to see you quite soon,' George called.

'I hope so,' Blanche called, adding, as they were out of earshot, 'It's like leaving another bit of England behind, village cricket and all that.'

Liz noticed how Sturgess's knuckles stood out white as he gripped the steering wheel. She put it down to impatience with these chattering women. She remembered the bread roll—someone should tell him his actions gave away so much more than his words.

'Yes,' she agreed pointedly, 'all the nice homely bits.'

'Salt of the earth,' he said.

Liz found his remark intrusive. 'Do you know the way?' she asked, surprised how imperious the remark sounded.

She thought he said he did, but his answer was lost as her mother remarked that she had not expected to travel back to Rinsey in a chicken coop.

The conversation died as the sky changed with dramatic tropical intensity from blue to silver, silver to gold, bronze to fierce red as the sun dropped away, making the huge fern trees stand out and adding gloss to coconut and fan palms.

That he knew the way became more obvious for though the jeep's headlights were not brilliant, Sturgess drove with what looked like growing confidence, as if he was recollecting the idiosyncrasies of the road as they progressed.

Her throat dry with excitement and anxiety, Liz recognised the last steep rise in the road before they took a sharp left around a huge outcrop of fern-covered rock, where water continually trickled and was ducted under the track. Then, had it been day, they would have glimpsed the bungalow.

'There should be lights,' Blanche said as Sturgess swept the jeep expertly around the bend. 'We should see lights from here.'

'Unless the trees have grown too big,' Liz tried to reassure, but she had noticed, before the last of the light went, the neglect in the plantations, how the secondary jungle had begun to creep back under the trees. Some sections had been cleared but there she had seen that the cups on the trees below the tapping scars had run over uncollected; it was a very bad sign. Tappers were paid for the weight of latex they collected, so no worker would tap his section of trees and then not collect his rubber and his dues.

If her mother noticed she said nothing, until they came in sight of their bungalow and Sturgess slowed to walking pace.

'No lights, no vehicle,' Blanche said as

45

their headlights touched the front of the property.

'No boys, no welcome,' Liz added bleakly as the jeep stopped.

'Stay in the vehicle,' Sturgess ordered, 'while I have a look round, make sure there are no booby traps, nothing wired to explosives or flares.'

Liz found her mother holding her arm as if she well understood her daughter's overwhelming urge to run up those familiar steps. This was homecoming, after all. The headlights made the wide verandah surrounding the whole bungalow look even deeper, the roof reaching out to the farthest edges of the steps out of proportion to the building underneath.

She watched as John Sturgess cautiously crossed the verandah, then, almost beyond the range of the jeep lights, flattened himself against the wall. She glimpsed his bare arm reaching out sideways to push open the door. Then he disappeared inside.

After a minute or two there was still silence. Blanche breathed, 'No one's blown him up yet.'

'I feel a bit of a charlie sitting here.' Liz looked up through the chicken wire to the black velvet sky pierced with huge, bright stars. 'Shall we go in?' It was a decision and she was out of the jeep and up the steps before her mother could answer.

As she moved through the open door into the room, she was aware of the generator thudding in the lean-to at the back of the house. If there was no one here now, it had not been deserted for long. She slid an arm along the wall and felt for the light switch. The next moment she gasped as a hand gripped her arm.

'I could have shot you. Why can't women do as and be where they're expected?'

Angrily she took him up on the odd phrase. 'I *expected* to be able to do as I liked in my own home.' For a moment the grip on her arm tightened as if in contradiction, then it was released as he said, 'I'll close the shutters.'

'Someone has been here nursing the generator,' Blanche commented as the lights were put on and she came into her house. 'It was always temperamental; there was only Neville and the Guisans who could keep it running.'

They separated, going from room to room, switching on lights, flooding every corner, not pausing to exclaim about objects rediscovered or changes made. The front lounge to Liz's eyes looked the same, but in the dining room her mother's treasured bespoke rosewood dining suite had gone; in fact, the room was empty.

'There's fresh meat and beer in the

47

refrigerator,' Liz called from the kitchen. 'Wherever Daddy's gone, it can't be for long.'

'Major Sturgess!' the formal call from her mother, who had gone to the main bedroom, alerted them to something more untoward. 'Come and look at this!'

They hurried to her mother's room, where Blanche stood looking down on a regular arsenal of weapons laid out on her double bed.

'Are these all yours?' the major asked.

She shook her head, but then amended, 'Some.' She pointed to three rifles and two revolvers. 'Neville obviously had his revolver with him, the rest...' She shrugged.

'The rest,' he began, touching them in turn as he spoke, 'Sten gun, spare magazines, 303 Lee Enfield rifles. Dropped in metal canisters to us during the war, stolen and buried in the jungle by the communists—until they needed them.'

For a moment Liz felt a little compassion for him. Standing there head down as he contemplated evidence of the deceit of former Chinese comrades in arms, he looked like a man whom life had completely betrayed. She found herself wondering if he had also been betrayed in Australia. A wife perhaps? A family?

With that sudden, disconcerting switch

from stillness to action, he went to the telephone, snatching up the receiver. Finding it working, he said, 'I think we should tell the local police you're here, that you are unsure where your husband is, and what we've found. I'll also speak to George.'

'Why not speak to George first?' Blanche suggested. 'He could do with the guns. The police will only panic, then confiscate them.'

John Sturgess nodded approval. 'Now I know you've lived here before.'

'Did you doubt it?' Liz asked.

He glanced at her and away so quickly that she wondered if her failure to comply to the letter with his instruction had permanently offended him.

The surplus guns were wrapped and stowed in a wardrobe in the spare bedroom, where her mother decided the detailed inspection of their home would stop. There were differences, dilapidations, but also areas where her father had already made some way towards restoring their home to comfort and elegance. For example, a rather splendid new tiled floor had been laid in the kitchen and dining room.

Blanche had looked but said nothing until the moment she was alone with her daughter. Then it was as if she demanded of Rinsey rather than Liz, 'Where in God's

49

name is Neville? No one here at all—his car gone, his manager gone, his workers gone.'

'We'll find him!' Liz was convinced it was true. 'He'll be back.' Hadn't he always come back from the war, from sea battles, the dangers of which she could only guess at? 'We certainly can't do anything more tonight. Tomorrow's another day,' she heard herself say.

'Very profound.'

'Perhaps you should have a drink.'

'There are times when I believe you think I'm an alcoholic; either that or you're trying to make me one.'

'Perhaps we'll both have one.' Liz wondered how much of her mother's daughter she was.

'I would have time to drive you back to Bukit Kinta first thing tomorrow,' Sturgess said as they returned to join him in the lounge.

Blanche shook her head. 'We're home for good. Will you have a drink? Coffee?'

He refused. Taking one of the rifles, he left them to go and sit on the verandah, where he said he intended to spend the night.

Liz uncharitably thought it was a pity they hadn't got a sheriff's star he could pin on. She still could not reconcile the images Sturgess was making her consider

50

with the laughter she remembered echoing through these same rooms as she and Lee—and Josef, if her mother was not about—played hide and seek. It had been peek-a-boo when they were younger, with Anna, her gentle, smiling Malay amah, leading the game. Barefooted, the lithe young Anna would surprise her charges from all directions, stopping only when they giggled so much she was afraid it might harm them. Liz curled her arms around her waist, remembering the ache of childhood laughter.

She left her mother with a gin in bed and went to her room. It was so much smaller than she remembered. She had grown, and got used to the spacious rooms at Pearling.

She spread one of the clean sheets they had found over the mattress, but before she could rest there was still something she must do—she felt she must really get to grips with Rinsey again. Perhaps she needed to address it as her mother had done. There had to be some communication or perhaps even just some solitary standing and listening, some reaching out of the severed ends of threads towards each other.

There were many impressions of their return she wanted to sketch, as visual record of emotion—the peninsula and islands as they flew in; the bumboats crowding Singapore river; a hand reaching out to steal a cake; an oriental dragon on a shop front—but her home was still an enigma she could not begin to put on to paper.

She left her room quietly, having no wish to be challenged by their watchman.

In the back doorway, she listened to the generator thudding like a heartbeat, always a sign of life in remote bungalows. One day the electric wires would travel even as far as Rinsey, her father had written that and about improvements he was making—'from the ground up' had been his words. She smiled, they knew what he meant now. She clenched her fists, lifted her face to the sky and wished, breathing a message quietly into the soft damp night: 'We're here! Come home soon.'

She listened to all the noises that would cease only with dawn. Near to her ear the high-pitched whine of the mosquitoes, deep in the jungle the whooping communication of orang-utans, the high-pitched scream of lesser monkeys, the booming of great frogs, and so many other noises told of a teeming life that none but the sakais—the aborigines, the real jungle dwellers—could even guess at.

Not too far away a colony of monkeys

was disturbed; their sudden screams of alarm momentarily chilled Liz's spine. Then, in the *beluka* nearer the garden, there was a different noise, the heavy sound of something big coming through the jungle fringe.

She held her breath to listen and the perspiration on her body felt suddenly cold. On the untreated overgrown lalang grass at the edge of what had been garden Liz was aware of a figure, no more than a blacker shape on blackness—but a man, she was sure.

Sturgess's instruction that the back should be kept bolted and shuttered while he watched the front suddenly seemed very sensible. Was this a terrorist coming for the guns?

Without any visible movement she pushed herself farther back into the doorway, melting into the shadows as the figure approached.

Chapter Three

There had been spectres protruding from the curtains at her first boarding school, and howling voices in the cold winter winds, but there had been no bogeymen

53

here at Rinsey—but childhood is soon over.

She thought about screaming for Major Sturgess, but felt guilty about having unlocked the back doors. If only she could slip back inside without being detected! She kept her eyes riveted to the black shape, fearful that once she lost sight of the man she wouldn't be able to relocate him in the jungle night or guess his intentions.

Her heart gave a great leap of anticipation as the thought occurred to her that it might be her father. He would be cautious, of course he would, seeing a strange vehicle in his drive. She breathed quickly and silently through her mouth, gripping the door frame behind herself. She must be sure. The figure paused between the fan-palm trees at the far end of the overgrown garden and she could have sobbed aloud with disappointment, for the man was much too tall and too heavily built.

She watched his bulk pass between the trees one way, then come back again, lingering, irresolute, it seemed. Could it possibly be Kurt Guisan, her father's manager? He had been tall and burly, and there was something familiar... In the moment of speculation, she lost sight of the figure. Then a movement far out to the left made her realise he was moving more purposefully now, going on as if he intended to skirt around the garden, around the whole property perhaps.

Was he making his way round to the front? She slipped back into the dark house, ran swiftly through kitchen and hallway. Her hand was poised to push open the verandah door as she heard Sturgess challenge—and a voice farther out reply.

'Walk in slowly,' Sturgess commanded, adding, with an authority that Liz certainly believed, 'I have you covered and can kill from this range.'

'Is it...Mr Hammond? You're back, sir! It's me, Josef.'

'Josef!' Liz whispered to herself. Of course, grown-up, he had the same burly figure as his father. 'Josef!' she called, bursting from the door. She would have run to him, but Sturgess caught her arm for the second time that night. This time his grip was quite unrelenting as she tried to prise open his fingers.

'Walk in slowly,' he ordered again as behind them the bungalow lights went on and her mother came out carrying her revolver.

'It's Josef, Mother!' Liz called. 'Josef Guisan!'

The man was at the bottom of the verandah steps. Blanche turned back into the hallway and snapped on the verandah lights.

'Let me go!' Liz demanded. 'He's our friend, our manager's son. Mother, tell him!'

Blanche came forward, still holding her revolver slightly raised, looking over the tall, fair young man who advanced another step, arms and hands spread to show he was quite unarmed, smiling a greeting. For a second Blanche appeared to raise her revolver.

'Mother?' The word was low, almost disbelieving, as Liz questioned an action that looked more instinctive than intentional.

'Mrs Hammond, you like to shoot me?'

The revolver was lowered to her side but reluctance was the only word that matched the action as Blanche nodded. 'It is Josef,' she admitted. 'No one else could look that much like his Swiss father, sound so Chinese, and turn up at Rinsey.'

Released, Liz held out her arms as Josef bounded up the steps. 'Now it begins to feel like home,' she said, her head level with the open V of his shirt—even, she thought, her mother's antagonism towards her childhood friend was the same.

He hugged her, stooped to kiss her on the cheek, and exclaimed how she had changed. 'A lady,' he said, bowing with mock solemnity, totally Chinese.

Then he became formal and quite European again as he offered his hand to Blanche, expressing his pleasure that she was home. She shook hands but Sturgess only nodded as he introduced himself and asked, 'You expected Mr Hammond to be here?'

'He is not with you?' Josef frowned. 'I don't understand.'

'You know where he went?'

'Where did he go—and when?'

Sturgess and Blanche questioned together.

'To meet you. To Singapore.'

'When?' Sturgess snapped in the manner of cross-examination.

Josef frowned as if perplexed. 'Several days, two or three—I am not sure.'

'Which day of the week, then? You must remember that,' Blanche said impatiently.

'I'm surprised he remembers anything with both of you snapping questions at him like that,' Liz remonstrated. 'Let's go inside and sit down like civilised people, friends who've just met again after eight years.' She wanted to know about her father, but she wanted to hear Josef's story too. These two were spoiling it all, putting Josef at a distance, Sturgess behaving as if *he* were tuan of Rinsey.

'Where's his jeep? It's not at Ipoh station.'

'Did he drive to Sungei Siput?'

It was only Liz who made any move towards the door as the other two continued their questions.

'No...no...' Josef shook his head, frowning. 'Ah! Yes!' he exclaimed. 'I remember! He said he was going to drive all the way—said it would be easier with the luggage.'

The silence this statement created had its own presence. 'All the way to Singapore?' Sturgess asked.

'It's only like driving to London from—' Liz began, only to be swiftly interrupted as her mother vetoed any such calculations.

'Your father would know I would not undertake such a drive in the heat *and* knowing the state of the roads. I can hardly believe...' Her gaze questioned Josef more directly.

'This is only what I remember, I did not see him leave.'

'Mother! Are you doubting his word?' She knew the answer. Blanche had always doubted Josef's word. Liz had always had to defend him. 'Surely it's the answer! Daddy could have broken down anywhere and not been able to reach us.'

'It is possible,' Sturgess had to admit, for the telephone services were in many places widely spaced.

'And if the local shop had sold out of petrol.' Liz remembered that the supply of petrol was often a stack of cans outside a village store.

'He could have had other reasons

58

for driving, I suppose,' Sturgess added, seemingly lost in thought. The next moment, he demanded of Josef, 'And where have you just come from?'

The younger man appeared stunned by the abrupt delivery of the question and flung an arm vaguely towards the plantation behind him. 'I thought I heard a vehicle, I came to see if Mr Hammond was back. I was,' he added with an incline of the head, 'at home.'

Liz rushed forward and took his arm, determined now to extract him from their questioning. 'Come and have a beer, Josef. Is *your* father at home? And I want to know about Lee and your mother. What has happened to them in all this time? Are they all at your bungalow?'

Her spirits lifted a little at the thought of her friends so close by, just some two hundred yards along a track lined with bananas and bamboo. 'Would your father know more about my father?' There were a million questions to ask. 'When he comes home we must have a party—all of us.' She led him inside, beaming at the idea of all her loved ones together. Turning, she saw his face was solemn, hard.

'The old days can never come back, Miss Hammond.'

Perhaps it was the sudden formality that gave her some inkling of what was to come.

'Liz!' she corrected, waving him to a chair, but his reciprocal smile was brief.

'My father is dead, I think. When he tried to sabotage the Japanese plans for taking over the estate, they took him away. I've never been able to trace even where he was taken.' He tightly interlaced his fingers as he added, 'I think they just shot him out in the plantation and left him for the ants to eat. There were many bodies when the Japanese came.'

Sturgess and Blanche had joined them in the lounge.

'Neville never said any of this in his letters,' Blanche stated. 'You must have told him what you thought.'

Josef smiled ruefully. 'Mr Hammond still thought we would find him.'

'Your mother and Lee?' Liz asked, fearful of his answer.

'My mother and sister, they live far away, and I am pleased because they helped the Japanese—they were traitors.'

'Oh, Josef!' She was devastated to hear such a condemnation. 'Lee was only a child, *you* were only a child, your mother probably collaborated to save you both—and with your father being taken away... You must forgive them, they must come back to Rinsey. We need you all here.'

He shook his head. 'I think not.'

'We must make things as much like they used to be as we can,' she urged.

'I think not,' he repeated and the tone was harder, held a greater note of certainty.

'Then *I* must go to see them.'

Josef shook his head. 'I do not know where they are.'

The stony response sounded like a lie.

'And what did you do,' Sturgess asked, 'through the war?'

'He was only a boy,' Liz remonstrated.

'I helped the Chinese guerrillas who stayed to fight the Japanese.' For a moment the look he gave Sturgess was like an accusation that the officer belonged to the British dogs who ran.

'Did you indeed?'

'Oh, yes.' Josef looked him straight in the eye. 'That is what I did.'

'And is it what you are doing now?'

The innocuous-sounding question had Josef springing to his feet, protesting, 'I work for Mr Hammond. You are calling me a traitor!'

'I am asking if you have contact with any of the Chinese still in the jungle,' Sturgess repeated with a politeness that was curiously threatening. 'If you knew them up to three years ago it's likely you know them still now.'

'No, no. I am no terrorist!'

The denial held fury but Liz was not

altogether surprised. She remembered Josef had a temper when roused, and Sturgess was accusing Josef of associating with murderers.

'Not all communists are violent criminals,' Strugess said evenly. 'I've met many who were idealists, who really wanted equality for all people—weren't ambitious just for themselves.'

'I do not know any of these people,' Josef said, sounding stubborn but chastened.

'No, they are fewer and farther in between,' Sturgess confirmed, 'than the villains.'

'No!' Josef blazed again. 'I mean, I did not know—'

'I think I can do without any of this shouting in my house, thank you.' Blanche's voice was cool, re-establishing the hierarchy.

'Look at me!' Josef moderated his voice but displayed his height, his fairness. 'I was no use in the jungle fighting. I stayed on the plantation—my help was with food and money for the guerrillas.'

'The kind of help they will be needing now,' Sturgess persisted.

'Not from me, tuan, only in the war.'

Liz looked at Josef sharply as he actually called his questioner 'master'.

'I have been too busy,' he went on. 'Mr Hammond will tell you.'

'Did you sleep here?' Blanche asked.

'No, only Mr Hammond.'

'I mean during the war.'

'No, Japanese officer and his wife—'

'Damnation!' Blanche interrupted and she eyed Josef as if she might just have preferred him in her home to the Japs. 'So you've not stayed here since my husband left?'

'Or seen anyone else here?'

Josef shook his head slowly.

'The bungalow was open when we arrived,' Sturgess added.

'Ah! I should have checked, that is bad,' Josef admitted, then smiled. 'Mr Hammond was in a hurry to come to meet his lovely wife and daughter.'

Blanche's facial expression remained pointedly unmoved. Liz smiled as graciously as she could, but realised that the matter of the guns had to be explained. She could imagine no circumstances that would make her father leave guns laid out on a bed, then drive to Singapore. Such behaviour broke every rule he had ever impressed on them all from childhood—herself, Lee and Josef.

The slight obsequiousness in Lee's tone reminded her he had always been a touch too willing to abase himself to her father and mother—but if she or Lee had tried to put him down, that was another matter and his temper would flare.

The ill-timed pleasantry was forgotten as in the middle distance they heard again monkeys screaming protest at being disturbed. Josef too was listening intently and half turned as if he would go to the back of the bungalow. Seconds later there was a high-pitched single screech. In daytime none of them would have taken any account of it at all.

'A day bird's call at night?'

Surprisingly, it was her mother who made the comment. No one answered. Liz had the distinct feeling that her mother and Sturgess were watching Josef closely for any reaction.

'We'll play this for safety,' Sturgess said, picking up his rifle. 'I have a feeling we have visitors on the way who expect to collect some extra equipment.'

Blanche took her revolver from the table.

'I'll fetch my gun,' Liz said.

'Extra equipment?' Josef spread his hands, shrugged his shoulders and asked, 'What can I do? Do you have a spare rifle?'

'Switch the lights out,' Sturgess ordered him, 'and come to the back of the house with me. You two cover the front.'

'If I had a gun...'

'If and when any shooting begins I'll let you have my revolver,' Sturgess told him.

The lights were snapped out and Liz was left to feel her way back to her bedroom. Groping in the drawer of the bedside table, she was surprised how reassuring the weight of the .38 Smith and Wesson was in her hand.

From the kitchen Sturgess shouted, 'Don't go outside, Mrs Hammond. You and your daughter take a window either side of the front door and shoot at anything that moves.'

Liz felt both annoyed to be referred to as an unthinking mere appendage to her mother *and* expected to shoot at anything that moved? Ridiculous! She was about to protest at the order and remind him of his 'military' sortie to deal with the water buffalo as the first shot came from the right of the front door.

'Good God!' Blanche exclaimed, but immediately poked her gun through the side of the rattan blinds and fired back.

'Watch for the flashes, aim at them,' Sturgess had time to shout as another shot came from the back of the house.

Two more shots from the trees were returned with fire from the front and back of the bungalow. Liz found she had undergone a complete change of heart. In the silence that followed she had to discipline herself not to empty her revolver into the night.

Crouched by her window in the hot, sticky darkness, she knew it was no use either rushing out, guns blazing, or trying to identify the night noises that came from the *beluka*. Anyone running or walking without caution might have been easy to hear, but it would be impossible to separate a stealthy human approach from the cracks, drips and unhuman calls the jungle night added resonance and menace to. The twenty yards or so between bungalow and tree fringe seemed a very narrow margin for safety.

'Are they coming or aren't they, for God's sake?' Her mother's whispered exasperation exactly summed up her own feelings.

'Liz!' Josef's voice in the same room made her start so violently she realised just how ajangle her nerves were. She heard her mother swear under her breath.

'Mrs Hammond, Major Sturgess wants to speak to you in the kitchen.'

'What do you think is happening?' Liz asked as she saw Josef's black figure outlined at the other window.

'Are you all right?' he asked and came across to be near her. She could feel his warmth through her thin blouse and his breath on her neck. 'Not too frightened?'

'I'm glad you came when you did—someone we really know.' In turning to whisper to him she leaned briefly against his shoulder.

'I am so pleased you are back.' He paused but she was so near him she could feel him shaking his head as he spoke. 'After all these years, now it has all happened so quickly, it makes me feel...kind of mixed up.'

'I know...'

'He hasn't given me a gun,' he added.

Liz was digesting this information and emotional switch as there was a sudden, violent burst of shooting from inside the bungalow. The shock of the noise made her drop to her knees and she heard Josef say something about a Sten gun, then, as the pumping cracks of automatic fire ceased, her mother was there ordering, 'Stay down!'

There was more movement in the room and the noise was repeated as Sturgess raked the trees and the undergrowth at the front of her home with a similar barrage of fire.

In the tail end of the thudding punishment, obscenely loud indoors, they all heard the involuntary cry of someone hit. It had not sounded far away and she wondered if Sturgess's tactics had stopped them from being rushed. There were other noises out there now, definable noises of men moving in the undergrowth, a groan and then the noises retreated.

'Retrieving their wounded?' Liz wondered.

'Hum!' Sturgess sounded noncommittal. 'It may be all over for this time,' he judged, 'but be cautious. I'll just check the rear.'

'What a good thing he came with us,' Blanche breathed.

'Yes.' Liz felt her agreement was slightly tight-lipped for he made her, and obviously Josef, feel rather like stupid and irresponsible children, not to be trusted.

'Would you go and keep watch from the kitchen, Josef?' Sturgess ordered as he came back. He waited until Josef had moved away, then said, 'We'll only shoot again if they do, but I feel they've withdrawn to reassess the situation.'

'Why should you think that?' Liz felt he should be made to explain as well as to issue orders.

'Two reasons. They were undoubtedly after the guns that were laid out here, so it probably means they want the extra arms or ammunition for another operation. They certainly weren't expecting us to be here, and now they also know we can defend ourselves, they won't want to waste a lot of ammunition just to take a few more weapons. We've also made it awkward for them; they don't like casualties in the jungle. Gunshot wounds are difficult to explain if you need a doctor or surgeon, complicated to nurse if you haven't got the right drugs.'

That was three reasons, she thought, good reasons. 'You're obviously an expert on war,' she told him. It was the only thing she had really heard him talk about.

'I've had plenty of experience in this country.'

She admitted to herself there was only bitterness in the tone of that remark, no joy of the man of war, no hint of the make-up of a mercenary.

'I think we could have a small lamp on now,' he said, going over to the table. The soft upward light made her realise how the immaculate man she had first seen in Raffles had been completely transformed. His light shirt and trousers were much crumpled and the Sten gun had left traces of oil on his shirt. He had the dark shadow of a beard on his face. She remembered sitting by her father in the bathroom there, watching him shave. He had dabbed a blob of shaving soap on her nose and asked if she knew that whiskers grew quicker in a hot climate. She had always thought it a joke, now she wondered if it was true.

Looking back at Josef, she observed how relatively uncreased were his shorts and shirt, how smooth his chin. He looked like a man come back from a meeting, or going out for the evening, dressed to impress.

69

She felt slightly ashamed to realise that they had not thought to offer the man who had given up his last free hours to drive them to Rinsey the opportunity to shave and refresh himself—and he had not asked.

Any good will Sturgess had notched up with her immediately evaporated as he stated, 'Josef can keep watch at the front and I'll take the back this time. Until first light, then I'll drive you two ladies back to Bukit Kinta. I'm sure George won't mind having you as house guests until we...sort out your future plans.'

Liz was amazed at his audacity. 'We've been here before, haven't we?'

Chapter Four

'We could have stayed with Josef!'

'I think not,' her mother denied shortly, obviously not willing to go over the debate she had settled to her own satisfaction the night before.

'Josef could have arranged some security. We could have got some of the tappers to act as guards.'

'What tappers? There's no one working in the plantation this morning—and what

70

do you propose?' Blanche asked stonily as they walked towards the jeep, where Sturgess was loading the guns and ammunition. 'That we throw chicken wire over the whole bungalow?'

Her mother was right about the tappers. The early hours of each working morning had always seemed to Liz a magical time. Tappers moving out between the dark lines of trees, the lights on their hats twinkling, disappearing, reappearing as men and women moved from trunk to trunk making the skilful, shallow cuts into the bark, balancing the cup in its wire hoop.

Once the heat of the day came, the latex ran less freely, so before dawn each worker started work on his or her section of trees. Soon afterwards her father would have been up, and often she was allowed to go with him on his rounds. All the old workforce had known her. Her wish to be a tapper when she grew up had been as keen as any boy's ambition to be the proverbial engine driver. Even now she could remember the exact angle of the tapper's curiously hooked knife and the amount of steady pressure it took to remove a slender portion of bark.

'I could have stayed.' She heard the petulant child lingering in her own voice. 'But you don't trust Josef.'

71

'That is one reason,' she agreed. 'Another is *you* seem prepared to throw yourself into his arms.'

'To balance your prejudices, perhaps.'

'Hu-hu, probably.' Blanche made a tiny assenting noise. 'It seems to be how we work.'

'Right!' Liz agreed nevertheless taking the heavy bag of ammunition clips from her mother.

'The main reason is I want to go to Ipoh and KL and mobilise the police and the military to help locate your father.'

'Of course.' Liz felt a little humbled and suddenly selfish in her wish to remain. 'Another thing,' she said, making amends, 'while we're driving through the villages we could ask when he passed through. Someone might remember.'

Sturgess helped stow the guns and ammunition. 'Unfortunately I won't have time to stop today,' he reminded her.

'I think we should buy a vehicle,' Liz suggested. 'Give us that bit more independence. I'll need my own vehicle soon anyway. Then, when we drive back to Rinsey, we could make enquiries.'

'I should leave such things to the professionals,' Sturgess said, taking the last bag from her hands, 'and it's not a good time to begin driving around on your own.'

'From what you say, "the professionals" already have enough on their hands,' she snapped back and moved quickly past him into the jeep. 'You have nothing good to say, do you?'

'There is nothing good to say about this place at the moment.' He started up and set off at some speed. She glared at his dour reflection in the rear-view mirror, and he glanced up. She lifted her chin in an abrupt challenge, which distracted his attention, and the vehicle lurched in and out of a deep water-filled pothole.

Sturgess swore silently. He must just drive like hell if he was to make KL in time, first leaving Daddy's girl, as he had come to think of her, to George—perhaps he could talk sense into her. Getting them back to Singapore would be the best option. He thought of the two women as the equivalent of all reckless amateurs who climb mountains or lower themselves down potholes, so that good men have to risk their lives bringing them back to safety.

'God! I shall be glad to stop rocketing around.' Blanche braced her feet against the Jeep's floor as once again Sturgess swept around the great outcrop of dripping fern-covered rock from the plantation service road to the wider thoroughfare.

'Makes me wonder if we'll ever catch

up with each other,' Liz complained, 'if no one ever stays in one place.'

'Josef is there. He'll contact us if your father returns.'

'What do you think George Harfield can do to help us make Rinsey secure?' Liz raised her voice, feeling that Sturgess should not be allowed just to sit there and drive. It was mostly because of his total refusal to back her belief in Josef's abilities to defend them that they were on the move again.

'Barbed wire, I should think, lots of it—lights on tall poles all round the property.'

'Like a prison camp?'

'You either have to create a secure zone, or move to one.'

'We're not being frightened out! I was brought up here. I know the people and how they think and work. We are not helpless women!' she retorted.

'I've never thought of women as helpless.' His reply was so even in its flatness of tone, it was as if what he did think was far worse. It took her some moments to absorb the full implications and then it was too late to reply. She reflected, to the tune of a popular song, that it was not what he said but the way that he said it.

They fell into silence then as Sturgess drove back towards Bukit Kinta. The wider

74

road was dry, exposed to the full sun, and they raised a cloud of red dust as they sped along.

Liz wondered if her father had gone to track down his missing tappers and been waylaid—ambushed somewhere. She became more and more concerned as she took note of the junctions where tracks led into nearby kampongs and others followed water pipes into jungle reservoirs—so many byways.

The jungle was a place of sunshine and shadows at the fringes but of wet, dripping dusk in its depths. It lent itself to lengthy games of hide and seek, as well as to sudden attack. The swift cruel strike, the step back into the jungle, as quick to do as tell. She didn't need Sturgess continually spelling it out.

Grim thoughts of what could be so readily secreted in the depths were impinged upon by the sight of neat rows of pineapples growing by the side of the road, the first she had seen since she had been back. The Malay farmer was harvesting one lot of fruit and at the same time slicing off the top of the pineapple and planting this for his next crop.

There was a familiarity about this procedure, even about this section of road. She was suddenly more attentive, holding her breath as they passed a village shop where herbs and spices were the speciality. A cacao tree grew at the far side of the shop and nutmeg trees at the back—she couldn't see any of that, but she remembered!

'Stop!' she shouted. As Sturgess jammed on the brakes, she added, 'I mean, have we time?'

Before either of the others could take her to task for the alarm, she babbled on about this being the kampong her amah came from. 'I've been visiting here with her many times. She used to bring me on the bus. We waited by the rock. You remember, Mother! She might be here, might know something. She would have been to see Daddy since he was back. Sure to have.'

'Have you time?' Blanche consulted Sturgess but Liz was out of the vehicle.

'No! I haven't.'

'Just ten minutes.' The girl was already some paces away from the vehicle.

What should he do? Drag her back? She deserved to be left.

'Anna was always a mine of local information,' Blanche said. 'Never seemed to miss anything. She would certainly know if Neville had been through here.'

'It really will have to be only minutes.' His tone was weary and grudging but Liz was too eager to have the chance to visit

76

her old amah's home to care.

'Ten minutes,' she promised.

'And I'm counting,' he said.

'I'm coming,' Blanche called after her as she hurried towards the centre of the village.

Built on stilts, the bamboo-framed houses thatched with woven *attap,* the plaited leaves of the nipa palm, had many tins and bicycles stored underneath, many hens and ducks scavenging all around and brilliant clay pots of flowers, mostly orchids and herbs. Dogs came to bark, but lethargically, for she was not afraid and no one encouraged them. There were no children, no old people, no wives sweeping and tidying their precincts. The realisation made her stumble mid-stride. This was quite wrong. Stopping to look around, she saw a boy being pulled back from the verandah of a house and a door being discreetly closed.

She stood in the middle of the village, isolated by—what? Suspicion? Fear? Her memories were that should any visitor set foot in a kampong, everyone came to see, children first, then the elderly, all to stare and wonder. One smile and the visitor would be surrounded by young smiling faces and ever hopeful hands.

There were covert movements and the sense of being observed was overwhelming but as she turned around and back it was as if the very houses held their bamboos rigid until her glance passed them by. 'What's the time, Mr Wolf?' she muttered and walked on.

Eight years ago her amah's parental home had been away to the left. She knew she would remember it, for she had always felt vaguely uneasy about the two great flowerpots like sentries either side of the front steps, each one lacquered green and shaped like two great turtles embracing each other in a most difficult-looking manner. They were still there.

She paused at the bottom of the verandah steps, as she had been taught to do, and called in that gentle voice her amah had taught her was polite, 'Anna! Ann Leo! Please, are you there? There are visitors for you.'

There was a soft movement at the top of the steps and an elderly, plump Malay stood in a dark maroon sarong at the half-opened door. The dark eyes recognised, a hand covered her mouth and she stepped back inside, the door swinging closed.

'What is the matter?' Blanche asked as she came up to her daughter.

'Let me go to her,' Liz said. 'She may talk to me.'

'Yes, go on, learn as much as you can.'

With sudden insight, Liz knew that she and her mother were on the edge of devastating events. She hoped it was not their future that had been mirrored in her old amah's startled face.

'Anna, dear?' she called again from the door, but the only sound that came was a soft keening. 'Please. It's Elizabeth Hammond. May I come to you?'

Her old amah sat on a small basket chair, her head bent and her upper body rocking. As Liz came nearer, her head went even lower over her knees, but she stretched out her arms, her hands opened wide, like someone making a dramatic and frantic appeal.

'Anna, dear Anna!' Liz knelt in front of her, tears springing to her eyes. 'Anna, I do love you. I'm so pleased to find you.'

The rocking increased almost to a frenzy and still the woman did not look at her, but Liz could see the tears streaming down her cheeks. Liz could bear it no more. She pulled her old nurse into her arms and they rocked more slowly together.

'Ah! Tidapah! Tidapah!'

Liz was not sure which of them spoke the old comforting word, it was certainly on her lips. *Tidapah*, never mind. Never mind! It had comforted many a grazed knee or bruised ego.

'Anna, what is it? Tell me you're at least pleased to see me.'

'Ah!' Anna's hand came up and stroked her hair, their tears mingling as she kissed the girl's cheeks with all the unstrained smacking wet enthusiasm of old. Liz grinned at her. This she remembered as a proper kiss—unlike the dry and formal pecks her English grandparents had bestowed on her from time to time.

'You are well, Anna?'

'Yes, yes, yes.' She shook her head at her. 'And my naughty Elizabeth Hammond grown up. An English lady!'

'But her heart is Malayan.'

They both laughed then, for Liz, clutching her amah's hand, had made this declaration at the age of five as an English aunt had made the same remark.

In the release of laughter Liz saw the old Anna she knew so well, as full of fun as any child, her only sadness when her charge gave cause for complaint.

'And baby Wendy, she is here?'

'No, stayed at school in England. She sent her love.'

'Better if you all stayed in England.'

The judgement was delivered with such quiet certainty that it was far more convincing than any advice, cajoling or appeal to reason. 'What is it, Anna? What's happened?'

The black eyes had lost any sparkle now and, as her head fell to her chest and her shoulders rounded, she looked an old, old woman.

'Oh, tell me, amah dear?' Liz used her childhood plea for a favour. 'Please.'

'I can tell nothing.'

'Ah! Anna, please! My father...'

'I can tell *nothing*. Miss Liz, you and your mother go back to England. It is safer there.'

'And for my husband—is it safe for him too?' Blanche's voice broke in upon the two earnest women and they both instinctively drew apart. 'Hello, Anna, I'm pleased to see you,' Blanche added.

Anna stood up and half bowed as Blanche took her hands and bent to kiss her on both cheeks. 'It's been a long time. We're both older, Anna.'

Anna accepted the greeting with trembling lips, a slow shaking head and an offer of tea.

Blanche explained the briefness of their visit.

'But we'll come again soon,' Liz added with enthusiasm, 'when Daddy's home and we find Lee and Mrs Guisan. Josef's at Rinsey, did you know—'

A savage crash brought her to her feet, her heart pounding. There was such ferocity in the sound, she was surprised to

81

see it was merely the noise of the bead curtain at the far end of the room being suddenly parted.

A man pushing a young boy before him stepped authoritatively into the room, then stood stock-still. The man was Chinese, the boy Malay, about ten years old.

'I thought,' the man said, 'your visitors would wish to see your grandson.'

Liz noticed how white the knuckles of the man showed as he gripped the boy's shoulders. She glanced at Anna; sheer terror shone from the wide black eyes.

Her mother saw too and moved forward. 'How kind,' she said, as if taking the man's words literally. She held out her hand to the boy, not looking at the man, and talking all the time. 'I remember you being born. Anna's first grandchild. Let me see if I can remember your name.'

The man was so disarmed by her unexpected approach that for a second he looked behind him as if for support, and let Blanche draw the boy away. Released, the boy ran to his grandmother, who covered him protectively with her arms, her hands over his head.

'No, don't tell us,' Liz took up the game, her eyes never leaving the now frowning and uneasy man. 'I know who would remember, Major Sturgess. I could go and get him in a second.'

82

They knew then the man was alone for he stepped back, half bowed and left the room backwards. After a few seconds Liz hurried after him and returned to report, 'He's gone, but who was he?'

Amah shook her head and all eyes turned to the boy, who was now bursting with information.

'They came when we were playing football earlier...'

'They?' Blanche queried.

He shook his head at the very seriousness of what he had to tell. 'Six men. The others all had guns. They sent our teams home to tell their mothers and fathers the communists were here and no one was to come out—but they kept me. I had to learn a message to tell my grandmother.' He stopped and looked at Anna, who nodded once for him to go on. 'I have to say that they will always know where to find me.' His eyes were wide and his lips drawn back. 'That those who work for running dogs will be killed like snakes.' His head dropped right to his chest as he mumbled the last words, 'And those who work for Tuan Hammond will be killed like bad snakes.'

Liz dropped to her knees and took his hands. 'Don't worry. Your grandmother will look after you.'

'He's all I have, mem,' Anna appealed

83

to Blanche. 'I lost my son and his wife to the Japanese. Please leave us alone.'

'Oh! Amah, I'm so sorry...' Liz began.

'Please, go quickly now. They may be watching. Please make no fuss.'

'Do you know anything of my husband?'

'I know nothing, nothing, nothing that will help him, or you—except go away, mem, go back to England.' She leaned forwards over the boy she clutched to her. It was pitiful to see her eagerness to have them gone.

'Anna, don't worry, we're going.' Blanche reached out and touched the woman's hair in a tender and uncharacteristic gesture. 'I'm sorry we meet again in unhappy times.'

Liz stooped to kiss her, silenced now by the many implications of what had been said—and what not. All she asked her mother as they returned to the jeep was, 'Do we tell Sturgess? And if we do, could it make things worse for Anna?'

Blanche looked at her soberly. 'I'm not sure,' she muttered as they approached the jeep which Sturgess had pulled in under the shade of the trees.

'Shall we just say Anna seemed afraid?'

Blanche nodded. Both realised they were already willynilly involved in the conspiracy of silence and terror that was spreading like a contagion over the whole of Malaya.

Sturgess watched the two women coming back. 'Straitened circumstances' was the phrase that always came to his mind when he dealt with people who were unable to open their hearts, minds and mouths to the truth—and these two, he thought, were becoming more straitened by the minute.

He wondered if their old nurse had died. They looked as if they had heard bad news, and as he watched their approach and the way their eyes stayed on him while they talked to each other, he knew they were not going to tell him whatever they had found. Reflecting that he had wasted some seven years of his life and several thousand pounds because his wife had not bothered to tell him things, he slipped in behind the steering wheel and started up the engine.

The women exchanged curious glances at his seeming lack of interest.

'We found our amah,' Liz volunteered. 'She seemed frightened.'

He laughed. 'Really, you surprise me!' He paused to change up the gears and swing out on to the road. 'The bad news came to this place before we stopped here.' He had made a mental note of the name, and of the layout of the main houses. He felt he might well be back here with troops before long.

Chapter Five

'The communists rarely take prisoners, Mrs Hammond.'

Liz felt the police officer had chosen his moment carefully to make the point. They had gone to Ipoh as being the nearest centre of authority and been received with sympathy and understanding.

Smart in the khaki short-sleeved shirt and trousers of the Perak force, Inspector Aba had listened carefully, nodding from time to time, aligning his fingertips in a carefully spaced arch one after the other as if putting their story together point by point.

'Could he have gone somewhere by himself?' the Malay asked most respectfully but for the first time seeming a little diffident as he expanded, 'I mean, even in troubled times we all have our own private lives.'

'Do you mean, has he another woman?' Blanche asked, making Liz feel totally naive for she had been thinking the man was a bit of a fool because surely his wife and daughters *were* her father's private life. She might have felt more affronted by the policeman, had he not been totally embarrassed by her mother's frank response. The dapper Malay rose and paced his first-floor office with erratic speed, uneasy with this outspoken English mem and out of harmony with the ponderous ceiling fans stirring the hot air above their heads.

'I suppose you have to ask,' Blanche began, 'but it would have been very easy for my husband to have kept me at home in England. Hardly a propitious time for anyone to *start* philandering—while his wife and daughter are in the air flying halfway around the world to join him. If nothing else, Neville has more sense than that!'

Liz remembered the telegram, then was annoyed with herself—sow a seed, grow a tree. Of all men, her father was not like that, was he? He might be impetuous, overgenerous at times to the wrong people, but he was devoted to his family, loved her mother.

'I'm sorry, Mrs Hammond.' The inspector stopped pacing, went back to his desk and with an expressive shrug explained the way the world could be. 'What I really should say is, no news is good news. You see, his vehicle has not been found. It is harder to hide a vehicle than a man. As times goes on, of course...'

'Yes.' Blanche acknowledged the worrying reality that three days and nights was a long time for anyone to be out of touch. 'I wondered if you could advise me, should I call on the civil authority downstairs and see if they can do anything more, or should I ask for military assistance?'

'You already have that, Mrs Hammond.' He smiled and nodded indulgently. 'Major Sturgess instigated investigations the moment he reached his command; they in turn called our headquarters.' He paused to lift placating hands as Blanche glanced sharply at him. 'I had to hear your story. I assure you everything that can be done to find your husband is being done. Major Sturgess fought in this particular area during the war; if you had asked for the best man in the world fitted to help you, you could not have chosen a better.'

They left the police station a little stunned by the glowing testimonial Sturgess had received. 'No wonder he laughed when we left Anna's home,' Blanche commented. 'I don't suppose we fooled him for one moment.'

'*You* don't think Daddy's gone off...' She had to hear it said.

'No, I don't,' Blanche said and, after hesitating, added, 'I could perhaps wish he had, he might be safer.'

Liz grasped her mother's hand and

squeezed it hard. 'You don't seriously think he's...' She could not bring herself to say the word; the inspector had avoided it too. They rarely take prisoners, he had said.

'I'm trying not to think anything, and I'm certainly not letting anyone rest until we do know what has happened to him—someone somewhere must know.'

As they turned away from the police station, a small, incongruous convoy of camouflaged British army lorries swept out from the old Colonial style Ipoh railway station. A jeep armed with a Bren gun preceded four lorries, protected at the rear by another jeep with another Bren gun at the ready. The two women were regaled by whistles, greetings and propositions from some young British soldiers.

Waving, they stood still to watch them pass. Several lifted their rifles in salute. 'You English?' one called and when they nodded and waved again they were given a cheer, which in her heart Liz returned with good measure. It felt as if they were seeing them off into battle—'Wish Me Luck As You Wave Me Goodbye'.

Liz noticed one young man sitting right at the back of the last lorry who neither waved nor smiled. He sat quite motionless, the fingers of his right hand curled just sufficiently to keep his rifle steady as it slanted between his legs and across his body. His cheekbones were high, the planes of his cheeks flat, nose well defined—and she itched to put him on paper. She found the pose so poignant, or was it the slight twist of his lips? He made her think of knights of old, of young squires put into the panoply of war, clean, handsome men sent to possible destruction. The intelligent saw the recruitment from the beginning for what it was—and they were the bravest of all. She knew that as soon as she had the chance she would sketch him.

'Not the only one here who doesn't want to be,' Blanche said quietly.

The two stood quite still until the lorries were out of sight. The convoy was a confirmation that this was a war—against terrorists who infested the country like fleas on a hedgehog.

'I keep remembering that other boy's face while that Chinese terrorist had hold of him,' Liz said, wondering where the troops were heading. She hoped nothing the authorities or Sturgess said or did would endanger Anna, her grandson, her village—or the still young man on the back of the lorry.

'Can you think of anything else we can do?' Blanche asked.

Liz went over all they had done since arriving at Bukit Kinta. Seen the police, telephoned Raffles, telephoned Josef. The army were already on the move—somewhere. 'Get back to Rinsey as quickly as possible, I think. If we could find some of the workforce...'

'Your father had already made several reasonable rubber returns,' Blanche confirmed. 'I found a note of them in a book in the bedside table—he always wrote the day's yield down when he was in bed.'

Liz was moved by this detail remembered from their former life, and, as if making a concession about Josef, she added, 'So why aren't they still working? What, or who, scared them off? We should be able to find out much more about that.'

'You're right,' Blanche agreed, 'and seeing those young soldiers has given me another idea. One even Mr Sturgess could not object to.'

'My God! Really?'

'Liz,' her mother reprimanded, 'I wish you wouldn't blaspheme so much.'

Sometimes she thought her mother's reprimands were quite endearing, they were so wonderfully normal—and ludicrous, considering the example she set.

'I thought I might ask Harfield if the army ever billeted any of their men with planters. During the war we had plenty of the armed forces billeted on us at Pearling.'

Liz had uncomfortable recollection of officers' wives being put into spare bedrooms, and of officers coming on leave to stay with them; she had resented having so many strangers in her home.

Blanche paused outside a store with a good display of tinned foods, beer and spirits. 'Shall we take some supplies back?'

'I wonder if there'd be a car for sale in Ipoh?' Liz said. 'We can't keep borrowing vehicles and we shall need more than Daddy's jeep.'

'I wouldn't feel very confident about buying anything like that without a man.'

'If Mr Harfield has time I'd ask him to give it the once-over—if I found something I liked.'

'Yes, I'd trust his judgement,' said Blanche.

'Time is obviously something George Harfield has not much idea of,' Blanche commented later as they waited to eat with him.

Li Kim, his smiling Chinese cook, came to ask if they would eat on their own, adding with a grin, 'I can keep hot for tuan. *He* will not mind.'

'Is he often late?' Blanche asked.

'No, no.' The smile became a laugh.

'He likes his food too much.'

'Oh, we'll wait, Li Kim,' Blanche decided.

'I bring you drink and titbits. Keep you going.'

'We really shouldn't talk in clichés to our houseboys,' Blanche murmured as he left.

Over an hour later they heard George's jeep. He got out, slammed the door savagely and came in glaring around as if wondering what to bang or destroy next. One thing was certain, he had quite forgotten he had two house guests. He stared at the two women for several seconds before seeming to realise who they were.

'What is it?' Liz's words were automatic, hardly a question, for this was a man in shock.

Blanche went to the drinks cabinet and poured a large brandy. He drained it and looked worse, more vulnerable, more agonised.

'Is it my father? Have you found—'

'No!' The denial was immediate, emphatic. 'No, no,' he repeated apologetically. 'It's my headman...it was my headman.'

'Dead?' Blanche queried, taking the glass from his hands and pouring another brandy but adding soda this time.

George stood for a moment, his eyes closed. 'You never get used to it—not that kind of death.'

'I think you should sit down and tell us,' Blanche said.

'It might relieve *my* mind, but it's hardly for ladies' ears.'

'Oh, bugger that!' Blanche admonished. 'Don't you think we're going to hear? You know what this country's like.'

'I'd rather hear the truth than rumour.' Liz remembered a tendency for stories to grow as quickly and as tall as jungle vegetation.

George sat on the edge of a long rattan chair and sipped his second drink. 'You will know,' he said grimly, 'because I shall make sure the *Straits Times* has the full story. Everyone should know the sort of people we're up against.'

Blanche poured a modest brandy each for herself and Liz, wondering if Li Kim had already heard the news, for he had not come in again eager to feed them.

Harfield sighed deeply and shook his head as if still disbelieving what he had to tell. 'Most of my people live in a group of houses, just a little hamlet really, Kampong Kinta we called it. My headman, Rasa, was related to most of the Malays there, and the same families have worked the mine for generations.'

George stopped as he saw Li Kim hovering by the door. He beckoned him in. 'You'd better hear this,' he told him. 'Just

94

before sunset a group of CT's—communist terrorists—went to the kampong and told Rasa he was to collect one dollar a month from each of the men under him. This would be collected after each payday. He told them he could not do it. They tied him to a tree, and assembled his wife, children, his mother—most of the village, in fact.

'The leader said his name was Heng Hou and to remember that because when he asked for help next time everyone must be sure to give it. He stood over Rasa with a raised parang all this time, but he said he was feeling generous today so he wouldn't kill their headman. He'd set him free.'

George drew in a deep breath. 'He raised his parang higher and sliced it down, cutting off Rasa's right arm, then his left. By the look on his face the poor bugger died of horror before he bled to death.'

'Aaaah! Hee!' The sound like a banshee or courting tomcat came from Li Kim. 'Tuan!' he appealed, 'what will we do?'

Liz would like to have joined in the appalling noise as involuntarily she visualised the scene, the man tied to the tree... 'Oh, George!' her mother whispered and lowered herself very carefully into an armchair as the wailing began again.

'Li Kim!' George said sternly. 'Do you

want to go back to your village or stay here?'

The Chinese considered. 'You have guns, tuan? More guns now.' He looked meaningfully at the two women.

'And I'm going to have barbed wire and lights all around this place and all around Kampong Kinta. The bastards have caught me napping three times now, it's cost me two payrolls and now the life of my headman. No more!'

Li Kim cast a glance out towards the teeming jungle night. 'I stay with you, tuan. You want dinner?'

George shook his head. 'Our guests—' but both women were shaking their heads now.

'I give it to the—' Li Kim began.

'Burn it!' Harfield ordered. 'It does not leave this kitchen. I'll make bloody sure not one grain of rice from this mine finds its way into communist bellies.'

Much later in her room, when everyone had been retired for hours, Liz took out a sketchpad and pencil and confronted the atrocity that would not leave her. She worked quickly, barely looking at the sketch when she had finished, then turned the leaf and began to rediscover the young soldier. This she took more slowly, the problem more elusive. It was always easy to recreate horror. Horror pictures used a low mental budget.

There had been a weary tension in the young man's shoulders, a capacity for endurance beyond the normal in the gunholding pose. He would, she thought, looking at the first sketch, make a good figure for a Far Eastern war memorial. The thought made her rise agitatedly, putting the sketch block aside. She wasn't wishing death on the man—it was just something she had seen. She strongly denied apportioning death as the unknown soldier's lot. 'Oh, God!' she exclaimed aloud. 'I must stop this. I need a drink, or coffee or something—mustn't get like my mother.'

She went quietly to the lounge and was startled to see a figure at the window outlined by the lights thrown up from the floating dredgers below.

'Who is it?' the startled figure demanded.

'Only me, Mother.' She went to her. 'Can't you sleep either?'

'They should have built this bungalow on the other side of the hill,' she said, 'away from this bloody continuous noise.'

'I suppose it's like living next to a railway, you hardly notice it after a time.'

'Huh!' Blanche grunted disbelievingly.

'Nevertheless it's true.'

They both started as George Harfield came into his lounge. 'If you pull the shutters to, I can put the light on. No point in making ourselves targets.'

The three seemed irresolute as they were discovered in dishabille. Harfield was wearing only a pair of light cotton shorts, while Liz and her mother had on cotton pyjamas and mules.

'You know what's the matter with us all,' Blanche decided, 'we're hungry. Come on, I'll scramble us all some eggs.'

'Just what the doctor ordered.' George bowed, eclipsing his powerful torso with an even more powerful pair of shoulders. 'I take my hat off to you, ma'am.'

Liz looked at her mother, who widened her eyes dangerously and said, 'Unless too many cooks spoil the broth, let's adjourn to the kitchen.'

George laughed, and Liz wondered if he trotted out the trite phrases just to annoy 'because he knows it teases'. She also wondered at people's capacity for going on with the normal tasks, like having meals, even in the most awful circumstances. It was just as she remembered the war in England, girls at school losing brothers and fathers, everyone rallying round.

She watched her mother as she beat eggs in a bowl and turned chapattis on a flat griddle, competent, controlled. The truth was that they were both so used to not having a man in the house, it could be easy to forget as events continually overtook them that they should be at Rinsey with her father. He had rarely been around for the last eight years.

'I wondered if you thought you were being specially targeted,' Blanche asked as they began to eat.

'It's possible.' Harfield, bending over to his plate, ate ravenously once begun, talking rapidly between mouthfuls. 'During the war I made no secret of the fact that I knew certain red-star merchants in our units were burying the guns and ammunitions air-dropped to us, ready for their own purposes after the Japs had gone. I told them *I'd* bury the first one I caught at it.'

'So...' Liz's ghastly sketch loomed in her mind. 'So aren't you afraid?'

He paused, piled fork suspended. 'No,' he said, 'bloody angry. I was fond of Rasa, he had real pluck. He defied the Japs during the war and now the bloody Red Chinks have got him.' He threw the fork down on his plate. 'It sickens me to the pit of my stomach!'

Blanche pushed his drink towards him, then indicated his half-eaten eggs. 'We need you on top form.'

He sipped the brandy and soda, then, without further comment, finished the meal, wrapping the last scraps of egg in a chapatti. 'I feel like a traitor, being hungry.'

'Soldiering back up the hill of routine,' Blanche said as if to herself, then looked directly at George. 'The trouble is people see routine as ordinary—instead of often the most difficult thing we do in our lives.'

'Keeping the boat steady,' he said, looking at her and nodding his approval of the sentiment. 'The most admirable thing most of us do in our lives.'

'The role of the good wife,' Liz contributed.

'Never sure, dear, whether you're being sarcastic or supportive to the argument.'

'She's young,' George said.

She didn't answer her mother because she really wasn't sure either. The conversation went on, disregarding her.

'I wondered whether any of the military were ever actually billeted at plantations, or went for a few days' rest?' Blanche asked.

'Sort of busman's holiday,' George commented. 'Not a lot in it for the troops at Rinsey right now, I wouldn't have thought, except guard duty and they can do that anywhere.'

'No, I meant when we're living there and properly organised, we could give them a few home comforts, good meals...while their presence—'

'What you need is a couple of resident Gurkhas! They'd put the fear of God into the commies.'

'You don't take it as a practical proposition.'

'I think it is—for you.' He grinned. 'Not sure what the army would get out of it. Some of the men go to safe areas where couples entertain them for a meal and a swim in their pools and I have known them leave a wireless operator at a bungalow, or in a kampong, while they go on a jungle sortie. They're not overmanned, it would all have to relate to a military operation, or recreation for those that have been on long operations.'

'Rinsey hardly falls into the rest-and-relaxation category,' Blanche agreed.

'Self-sufficiency is what we need. This could be a long campaign. My men will be working round the clock as from tomorrow to fortify Bukit Kinta, then we'll go to Rinsey and secure that.'

Liz caught the older man's eye and he read the unspoken question. 'I have to protect my people here first. There is, after all, no one at Rinsey at the moment, no workers—'

'There's Josef, and he may have found some of the tappers by now.'

'Josef.' He paused, sniffed and hummed speculatively under his breath. 'Told Major

101

Sturgess he helped us during the war. Shall have to see.'

'He would only have been a teenager, I don't suppose he could have done much.' Liz pressed excuses for Josef, as was her old habit.

'A teenager's grown up out here and I'll remember him if he ever helped.'

There was a certainty in his voice, a confidence in his own ability, as there was when he went on to say, 'One thing, once we start on your bungalow there'll be no delay. I've requisitioned plenty of barbed wire, electric cable and powerful lamps.'

'I wonder if our old generator will stand the strain,' Blanche said.

'No. Robbo didn't think so, he's sending up a mobile army genny on permanent loan.'

Chapter Six

The work at Rinsey started four long days later, days without news, days when the two women talked to each other less and less as they exhausted every possibility, every speculation of hopeful things that could have prevented Neville Hammond from contacting someone.

Blanche stood in her lounge watching as the work of unloading the four lorries was begun by the drivers and their mates. The Malays worked as hard as usual, the muscles in their brown arms and legs shiny hard balls of willing power, but their smiles were missing. The death of their headman, and the manner of it, would weigh on them all for a long time—but not a single one of George's men had deserted him. He was too positive in his determination to beat the CTs and there was not a man at Bukit Kinta who doubted his ability to do it.

He directed them now. Rolls of barbed wire, fifteen-foot poles, electric cable and powerful lamps were quickly and neatly piled to one side of the clearing. Blanche saw George take the smallest and darkest of the men aside; he seemed to be instructing him to walk the perimeter where the defences should be erected.

She wandered outside, still holding the triptych of photographs which always travelled with her or stood on her dressing table. Arriving at Rinsey once more to find it totally deserted had sapped her energy. When Liz wasn't in evidence, Blanche wondered what she was doing there. Without her man by her side, this uneasy country was unbearable.

George Harfield came over to her. Nodding after the man, he explained,

'Chemor, he's the best tracker I've ever had. I think he must be related to Dyak trackers from Borneo, he can tell whether it's man or beast that's been along a path and how long ago. I've sent him to look around for any particular signs of activity. It might make a difference to how we arrange the lights.'

Blanche knew she should feel more involved in all this, be vitally interested. She was more aware of the leather photograph folder she held and how comforted she felt to have this other Englishman by her side.

'My men,' he was saying as if he had already asked her a question and was now repeating it, 'I would prefer them all to sleep here until the job's done, if you don't mind. They'd sleep on the verandah, just the four of them, and take turns on watch. I must go back to Bukit Kinta each evening, particularly while they're all so jumpy.'

'We should have heard by now if my husband was safe,' she stated, opening the folder and displaying the central photograph of Neville, posed in a formal portrait, flanked by family photographs of herself and the two girls, and the four of them in a sailing dinghy.

He took the folder and, as the two of them looked down at the English scenes and English faces, she added, 'No one can be missing or held up this long. He's either been captured and held for God knows what purpose—or he's dead.'

He gently took hold of her forearm. 'People do disappear. The most extraordinary things do happen.'

'Not that often.' She stared down at his hand and thought it was a long time since a man had made her feel that supported. Then, as if he took the protracted gaze for criticism, he released her. She told herself she was glad, too much kindness sapped her resolve. She had long ago realised she needed to maintain her aggressive veneer to face the world.

'No, but we must hope.' He indicated Liz in the photopgraphs. 'Your eldest daughter is like her father.'

'In many ways,' Blanche agreed. 'Wendy is more like me. I hope so, anyway, we need some practical people in this family.'

'This Josef—Liz seems to have faith in him?'

Blanche took the album and closed it as the clatter of the drivers putting up the tailgates of the lorries diverted them. One of the drivers called something in Malay and George indicated his permission for them to go back to the mine, leaving only the wired-in jeep.

'Josef,' Blanche repeated, her voice starting low and sinking lower. 'An example of how much like her father she is—much too eager to think well of the wrong people. Sometimes I think because Neville is in large part saintlike he expects everyone else to be the same.'

'Life must be a great disappointment to him then.' George took a retractable tape measure from his pocket and tossed it in his hand as if weighing its worth before beginning to use it.

She laughed briefly and admitted, 'Often true.'

'If you have to be on your own...' George gently posed the possibility.

'God forbid,' Blanche breathed and held the leather folder close to her breast, crossing her arms over it. 'I've had my war alone. I only came to Malaya to be with Neville...'

'That's right, m'dear. God forbid. Meantime we take precautions against the troubles we *know* you're likely to have. So what about this Josef? Where is he?'

'We did ask him to contact as many tappers as he could. I presume that's where he is.'

'Hmm! There's a lot here that doesn't add up,' he mumbled, then lifted his head, listening as the sound of more traffic coming towards them was heard.

A few seconds later an army lorry towing a trailer and a cloud of dust came into view. As it pulled alongside them, the air was replete with the smell of hot metal and evaporating petrol.

'The generator! As good as his word,' George said with satisfaction as he went forward to greet the corporal who sprang down from the driving seat. From the passenger's side a taller, younger man climbed down. 'Corporal,' he greeted the driver.

'Morning, sir. Mr Harfield? One genny and one guard stroke radio operator for Rinsey. One on permanent loan—' he nodded towards the generator—'and one sort of temporary.' Blanche raised her eyebrows in surprise as the corporal introduced her to Guardsman Alan Cresswell.

'I've seen you before,' she said. 'On a truck coming out of Ipoh station.'

'That's right.' He shook her proffered hand. 'There were two of you.'

'My daughter, Elizabeth, she's around somewhere.' Blanche thought his gangling height and gaunt features made him look more like someone who needed a few good meals and mothering than like a soldier. 'So you're going to be billeted here for a bit. That'll be good.'

When he smiled down at her she noticed the cleft chin and the dark-brown eyes.

He was the kind of man who would wear well, she thought, probably be far more attractive in his middle years than he was as a young man.

'Seems to me you're going to have an accommodation problem,' George said. 'One minute the place is like the *Marie Celeste*, the next it's bulging at the seams.'

'Major Sturgess said there were some old workers' quarters at the back. With your permission, Mrs Hammond, I'll set up my gear there. I can bivouac alongside my transmitter, I'll have to be on network every few hours. Do you think one of your Malays would take an aerial up a tree for me to see what kind of reception I can get?'

'Let me know where you want to be,' George said.

The young guardsman nodded. 'Once I've called in I can help with the work. I'll not be on standby just yet.'

They watched him begin to unload a prodigious amount of equipment from the back of the lorry. 'A boy in man's boots,' Blanche commented quietly.

'A guardsman's boots.' George nodded to the brilliant shine of the toecaps gleaming through the dust as kitbag was added to transmitter and crates of wet batteries at the far end of the bungalow. 'Spit and polish, drilled across the parade grounds of Caterham Barracks to be a fighting machine in a tropical jungle—and I bet he'd never been farther than Llandudno before he was conscripted.'

'Putting on a good show then.' Blanche remembered how he had sat so immobile in the back of the lorry, catching their eye, serious among his wolf-whistling, gesticulating companions. A rather different young man to the general run.

'Your daughter seems conspicuous by her absence.' George's glance moved along the bungalow windows. 'She's not likely to go off looking for this Josef on her own, is she? They seem to have been very close as children.'

'Quite possible, though I think she's in her room sketching. If my daughter has a problem she usually draws pictures. Don't worry, I'll keep my eye on her.'

'Until we have this perimeter fencing up and a proper secure compound, I wish you would. I want nobody wandering about.'

Liz had waited until she saw the men all engrossed in unloading the fencing and lighting equipment. While her mother was talking to Harfield, she took the opportunity to slip out into the back garden and from there to the path leading to the manager's quarters.

She had been put out to find Josef not

around, had again defended him from any criticism—but she wanted to know what was happening. Where were the workers? What had Josef done since they last saw him? Where was he?

She remembered the track to the manager's bungalow as a broad highway for bicycles and tricycles, but now it was much overgrown, wet and slippery. By the time she approached the other property she was full of doubts. If the path was not used, what should she expect? Nevertheless it was a shock to see the wooden walls apparently locked and latticed in trees. She approached with something of the feeling of one in a fairy tale discovering a long-overgrown realm. The manager's bungalow had been overrun by a legion of saplings, bamboos and seedling ferns to the very walls.

She moved slowly up the steps. The creaking and groaning of the verandah as she crossed it told of long-neglected and probably unsafe timbers. In the window spaces hung the remnants of rattan blinds, dust and leaves lay thick in every niche of the rotting boards and as she pushed the door it dropped sideways and inwards with a terrible clatter. She stood for a moment so startled she was ready to run, but only a parrot screamed and scolded as it stomped about in a nearby clump of bamboo.

Inside there was only debris—the broken staves of a chair, the disconnected telephone, which lay, receiver and rest wide apart, on the floor. She stepped forwards to look at a calendar hanging on the wall above the telephone, but the pages had been rendered illegible and welded together by the humidity. She thought it looked like 1941, but it was a guess. It was all guesses—she felt sick with a sudden, desperate loneliness—for nothing was the same.

She had come to Rinsey to find her father but instead she had lost a friend, her childhood hero and sweetheart. She had lost Josef not just because he was not there, but because she had found out his lie. He had not been living here. And if the Japanese had commandeered the bungalow, where had he lived in the war? If his father had been killed, where had his mother and Lee gone—or had they been taken away?

Walking through the rooms, she remembered how it had been. She recollected the great solid furniture that Mr Guisan had imported, huge wooden beds like decapitated four-posters, chairs with knobs on their arms like cudgels to an unwary child's elbows or knees. They had been specially commissioned and treated to withstand the tropical weather and termites.

111

They could not have just disappeared. Even if Josef had.

She stood in the silent house feeling like one in the immediate aftermath of an awful accident, uselessly wishing time back on itself—so that all could be as before. That was how she wanted Malaya, Rinsey, Josef. Now it seemed no more than the petulant wish of a child. She watched a black bootlace snake in the corner of the room: each was wary of the other and anxious to leave the other alone. The only thing she felt would absolve Josef was if he came with news of her father.

She walked slowly back along the overgrown path, hands clenched tightly by her sides. She remembered the joy of first seeing Josef, remembered being held in his arms, the warmth of his chest against her shoulder during the attack. But how had he managed to arrive so smartly turned out that first evening? What was his game?

Josef had always laughed in a kind of maniacal fit of jubilation when he won at one of their games, even if he had cheated. She and Lee had hated him then, with all the fury of childhood.

She thought of George Harfield's Malayan headman, and of the Chinese stranger holding Anna's grandson—this was life and death, not children's games. Childhood was soon over.

The sight of a man coming along the path towards her made her think belatedly that she should have carried her revolver or that she might be wise to dive for cover. He approached half trotting, as if eager to come up to her, and when she could see him properly he raised a hand in greeting.

'Miss Hammond,' he called with a slight bow of his head, 'Mr Harfield says you go to the house at once.'

'Does he!' She slowed her pace so she could talk to the very dark-skinned native, but turning back she saw he was continuing in the opposite direction.

She was surprised but hurried on. Where the old path divided, she took the one leading to the rear entrance, but as she did so a movement caught her attention. A tall figure was standing in the trees.

'Josef!' She practically hurtled through the trees towards him. He was absorbed in something in the tops of the trees.

'Josef!' Even as she said the name she knew she was wrong, for though the man was as tall, he was not so broad and the clothes were a soldier's jungle green.

He started, turned, dropped a length of wire he was carrying and snatched off his wide-brimmed hat. 'Miss!'

'I thought you were someone else. Sorry! Did I startle you?' She smiled both because

113

she recognised him and because her words and his actions were ludicrous, more like a couple bumping into each other in a peacetime English lane than a tropical track in terrorist country.

'Don't tell my commander I took my hat off to you. I mean,' he said, screwing the hat in his hands and smiling ruefully at his own supposed failure, 'I should really have shot you—well, challenged you.'

It was a relief to laugh. With his wry expression and his military-cropped, sandy hair exposed, he looked much younger than when she had seen him last. 'You're the boy from the lorry.'

'Lorry, yes. Boy—well?' He cocked an eye. 'Just because I didn't shout after you? I was better brought up, but it wasn't that I didn't appreciate...'

She found herself both blushing and laughing under his approving look. 'Why are you here?'

He displayed the wire he was holding. 'I'm looking for a friendly native to shin up one of these trees and fix my aerial to the top. I'm stationed here for the time being.'

'Really? That seems too good to be true.'

'Thanks!' The closed-mouth grin and twinkling brown eyes were so full of good spirits she did not qualify the remark. 'So you'll be the daughter of the house, Miss Hammond?'

'Liz.' She held out her hand, then found herself swallowing hard as his hand enveloped hers. Looking down at her he stood many inches nearer than he needed.

'Alan Cresswell. Until now I thought I was going to hate it here by myself.'

They both turned, still holding hands, as Chemor came back along the path portering a heavy coil of new rope. 'Here's someone who might help you. He's one of George Harfield's men.'

The native glanced at Liz as if questioning the fact that she had not obeyed his employer's summons. 'You come now,' he said.

'Is something wrong at the bungalow?' she asked.

'Something found.' He smiled and with a gesture indicated that someone else was coming. 'All going now to look.'

'What is it?' she demanded as her mother and George Harfield came into sight, alarmed at their sombre expressions and the fact that George was strapping on his gun and holster as he walked.

'Chemor—' he paused to nod to her companion—'has found a vehicle in the jungle. A jeep.'

Consternation and anguish fought to take her breath, and though her lips parted the doubts and fears were too many to be put into words.

'We are going to see,' Blanche said, her face, her lips, absolutely without colour.

Liz turned like an automaton to accompany them.

'Can I help?' Cresswell asked. 'Come with you?'

'I'd rather you stayed here and looked after my men,' George told him. He hitched his revolver in the holster. 'You'd best show us what you've found, Chemor.'

The scout turned and led the way in the direction of the manager's bungalow, but after about thirty yards he turned abruptly to the right through a part of the plantation. He pointed to the ground, parting ferns so they could see the tracks of a vehicle.

Here and there it looked as if dead vegetation had been deliberately pulled over the tracks. For some distance they walked straight into the trees, then turned abruptly left. Looking round, Liz for the first time really understood how confusing these plantings could be. The rubber trees were set some twelve to fifteen feet apart and whichever way you looked they formed lines, radiating away from you like a fiendish maze. You could go only a short distance into the trees before becoming totally disorientated.

116

She did remember that in the direction they were going, to the southeast of Rinsey, were a number of rocky waterfalls cascading from the hills and culminating in a steep, jungle-clad ravine. She glanced at her mother's back as they walked in line—the scout, her mother, herself, George last. Her mother looked like one travelling in a nightmare, dragging her feet wearily free of the encumbering undergrowth, moving only because compelled.

Liz wondered if Blanche remembered the one time they had brought their daughters this way for a picnic. It had come to a premature end as Wendy had ventured too near the edge of the falls. Liz had also found herself the target of parental wrath and anxiety—because she had wanted to stay.

If her father's vehicle had been hidden, it was by someone who knew the area well. She could think of no other place where it would be possible to drive through the trees and find flat rocks and a convenient ravine on the other side.

Once they came to the edge of the rubber trees they were on solid slabs of rock where water gushed down in wide and pleasant falls—until the fourth downward step was reached, where land and water fell steeply away, down into a deep midnight green mass of dense jungle. Against the

117

dark panorama, parrots in hues of brilliant white, red and unnatural green flashed across like players in an airy theatre.

It was noisy standing above the crash of the water and alarming to see where Chemor had found the continuation of the tyre tracks. Losing them at the edge of the plantation and across the hard table of rock, he had found them again at the lip of the ravine.

'I can see nothing down there,' Blanche said, shielding her eyes, then exclaiming, 'Oh, as the wind moves the bushes...'

Liz knelt on the rock. She could just make out the back wheels and undercarriage of a vehicle, which seemed to be almost standing on its nose some hundred feet below.

'Have you been down?' Liz asked Chemor, who shook his head.

'No, need rope to climb back up,' he answered.

'That—whatever it is—could be from the war?' George suggested.

Chemor shook his head, pointing to the narrow stretch of earth and vegetation. 'Tracks through plantation same as here.'

Liz could see where the tyres had dug into the lip, then where the vehicle must have fallen clear and free—down. 'It could have been an accident?' She turned an agonised look up to George. 'My father could be...' She swallowed and turned back, peering down, her ears suddenly singing; she felt very sick. George gripped her shoulders.

'You stay here with your mother.' He began unbuckling his holster to leave his gun with her. 'Chemor and I will go down.'

'There's a way down the other side of the falls,' Blanche said, her voice almost matter-of-fact in its control. 'It's not that far, actually.'

'Would we be able to reach where the vehicle is?'

She nodded at George. 'Neville and I often came here and explored these falls, long before we had the children.'

Blanche and Chemor changed places and she led them across and down the first two shallow slabs of rock to the other side. The route led down a narrow gully which the falls would wash out when in full spate during the monsoons. The noise of the water grew louder as they proceeded and the path was certainly slippery and dangerous for the unwary. Liz adjusted her view of her mother's concern for the tiny Wendy.

The gulley the water had cut fell back so the light came to them through a curtain of water, blue at the top of the slope when they could still see the sky but greener and darker as they descended down the rocky course. Liz could imagine her parents younger, carefree with no children to hamper their explorations, discovering this strange and rather awesome pathway with the wonder of living water before them.

A sharp turn to the right and a level stretch of rock, amazingly quite dry behind the falls, made her realise they were actually at the bottom of the ravine. They had crossed the falls at the top through the water, now at the bottom they walked back to the side they started from, this time underneath the falls.

Chapter Seven

The last hundred yards from the falls were the most hazardous. None of them was dressed for pushing through this mass of growth and Chemor unsheathed his machete.

'Don't catch hold of anything if you can help it,' George advised, and, as the slope grew steeper once more, gripped Blanche's hand and supported her down.

Sliding and slipping, Liz remembered from her childhood that the most beautiful plants and flowers usually had the biggest, sharpest thorns. Under the massed jungle canopy the gloom increased. Perspiration poured from them as they negotiated each step, while Chemor worked with steady rhythmical sweeps of his machete from head height to ground level to clear a way large enough for them to pass through. Roots, ferns, tortuous vines and creepers climbing up to the light, wonderful pale ghostlike sprays of orchids, and butterflies that looked like flowers until they moved, inhabited this dripping, drowned world.

Liz wished she could stop dwelling on the thought that anyone who had gone over the edge in that vehicle would, even if they survived, never have made this climb back up. Then again, they might still be there in the jeep... A gasp of alarm came with the thought and the consequent stumble. She raised an arm to sweep away both tears and the perspiration which was running into and stinging her eyes.

Chemor heard and paused to look at her. Then they both turned to look farther back to George, who, progressing at her mother's pace, was some way behind.

'Your mother a brave lady,' Chemor said. 'This is bad jungle.'

Liz nodded, too breathless to speak.

'You too.'

She shook her head with conviction. She

was terrified of what they might find—a bloated body cooked in a metal jeep for two tropical weeks. Oh, God, stop it! Stop it!

'Go on!' she urged.

They battled on for another half an hour. She felt as if they had travelled to the far side of the peninsula, but calculated they had probably only gone about a hundred yards. She suddenly had a different fear, of not finding the vehicle after all. Once they had descended into the ravine they could no longer see where they were heading. George had taken sightings from the sun and the steep escarpment, but once in the jungle proper they could see neither sun nor rock face.

In another quarter of an hour, George hailed from the back for a halt. It was not until Liz's laboured breathing had eased that the two caught up. George swept his boot and then his hand along a wet but substantial fallen branch where the two women could sit down.

'I think we've come too far,' he told Chemor. 'I feel we've veered too far from the rock face.'

'You stay with the ladies, tuan, I'll go back to see.' Chemor immediately began to retrace their steps along the path he had cut. George too wandered back some paces, then a low birdlike whistle made him go more urgently after his man.

Listening, the two women could hear more jungle being cleared and with tacit agreement both rose and went towards the sound.

Chemor was chopping into the side of their original path. He stopped as the reached the two men. 'You smell something here, tuan?' he asked.

They all sniffed the air. George pushed his head into the new way. 'Perhaps...oil? Or...'

'Rust,' Chemor said. 'I think jeep this way.'

It took ten minutes and the vehicle lay within some five yards of the path he had first cut.

'Be careful, look around.' The anxiety in George's voice matched a sudden concern in Liz's mind as the machete, willingly wielded, swung high and to ground level.

'Let me,' George said, taking the machete. 'Stay well clear, it might move as we cut closer.'

He worked a little more slowly, with more regard to what might be lying around, then reported, 'I don't think it'll move. It's wedged between rocks like something stuck fast in a pair of scissors.'

They watched with terrible fascination as George worked his way near enough to climb on to a wheel and peer into the vehicle. 'I can't see anyone—and I would have thought I could here.' He glanced up to the canopy, which was thinner here, the plants merely reaching across, for the rocks below gave no purchase for roots. He leaned back, pulling at the closed door. It gave and he had to reclose it hastily to keep his balance. He climbed down and reached the handle again, letting the door fall open.

Liz's hand flew to her mouth. Blanche got slowly to her feet as Harfield climbed back on to the wheel and half got inside the vehicle.

'There's no one in here,' he reported.

'Thank God!' Blanche breathed.

Chemor, who was by his side, concluded, 'No one in it when it fell.'

'No...' George was right inside the vehicle now, peering and running his hand over surfaces, looking at the damage. 'I agree with you.'

'So you think it was pushed over?' Liz asked.

'Not pushed—look at this, Chemor.' The two men partly disappeared into the bowels of the nose-dived car, then reappeared with a length of rope. 'The engine was set running and the jeep kept on course for the edge by tying a rope around the seat stays and the bottom of the steering wheel. Whoever sent it over was probably quite unlucky it didn't burst into flames.'

Liz, glancing at her mother, saw the bleakness. 'But do we know it's my father's?'

'I'm afraid we do,' George answered. 'Between the rocks at the other side is part of the front number plate—enough to be sure.'

George and Chemor scoured all around the vehicle, but found nothing else. 'No one has been to or from since it fell,' Chemor was confident.

'So his jeep was deliberately hidden...' Blanche addressed herself to George.

'We must tell the police.'

'And assume that Neville was...'

'Kidnapped—otherwise...'

'Where is his body?' Blanche added the words George was reluctant to say, then asked, 'Will the police fingerprint the jeep?'

'Two weeks in the jungle, already red with rust—the only prints would be inside. Chemor said he will have another look round at the top of the falls. He may learn something more.'

Liz immediately stood, ready to move off; Blanche rose only as George offered his hand to pull her up.

It was hardly with any feeling of success that they climbed back up into the light.

One mystery solved, another deepened. 'The jungle keeps its secrets,' Anna had told Liz when Wendy had been born and, feeling neglected, the elder sister had packed doll, drawing book and crayons to leave home. 'And it will keep *you* if you run away.'

At the top of the escarpment they rested while Chemor looked around the area. Another time Liz would have pulled off her shoes and socks and dangled her feet in the running water, but it was not the time to take comforts.

Chemor beckoned from some fifty yards away where the jungle grew down to the first rocky step of the falls. 'Here, see,' he said, pointing to the ground, 'tiger tracks. He drinks here—' his fingers traced a line from trees over the rocks to where a natural hollow in the rock made a deep pool—'but more.' He moved a few more paces and stooped to show them a tunnel through the undergrowth. 'Way tiger comes, and man goes—once, anyway.' He stood up to show where twigs had been broken above the height of the tiger's back. 'Man pushed through some two, three weeks ago.' Delicately between his finger and thumb he held a twig that had been broken off and displayed where two new young growths sprang from it. He found others the same.

126

'You think whoever sent the jeep over left this way?' George said.

'Someone did, tuan.'

George nodded.

'You want me to follow man's trail, see if he went to jungle or plantation?' Chemor asked, demonstrating the two directions the track could take—straight on or curving back towards Rinsey.

'I don't want you eaten by a tiger or murdered by communists,' George told him.

Chemor shook his head. 'No one here now, and tiger he no bother, he well eaten, big heavy tracks.' He pointed down to a recent spoor and swayed his body, holding his hands some distance from his stomach and grinning. 'He very full.'

George nodded agreement but added, 'Don't go far. I don't want to lose any more men.'

'Quite safe.' Chemor turned and stooped into the tunnel.

George and Blanche turned to make their way back through the plantation. Liz waited until they were some dozen paces away and called after them, 'I'm going with Chemor, I have to see where this man went.'

She heard their protests as she too ducked into the run, like Alice down the rabbit hole, she thought. Indeed, hurrying to catch up Chemor she was reminded of the rabbit runs she had seen through the English hedgerows. This run was just a larger version, she told herself, and provided you could stoop low enough it was a much easier way of travelling then hacking a way through the jungle.

Chemor heard her coming and waited. 'Tuan know you come?' he asked. When she nodded he looked doubtful but moved on. They had not gone far when he stopped. She was both awed and fascinated by the way he crouched quite still, every sense so alert she was reminded of a sea anemone, tentacles drifting, trawling for sensations.

She realised as he slowly looked around that he was motionless because he did not want to destroy any shred of evidence either beneath his feet or by pushing through the undergrowth. Unexpectedly he put out a hand to the wall of the run, gave a low grunt of satisfaction and beckoned Liz off at a tangent through the jungle again.

He used his machete a few times but Liz could see it was merely to give her better passage. In minutes they were in the lesser jungle, the *beluka*. Suddenly her mouth dropped open in surprise. They were at the rear of Rinsey. She could see ahead the old buildings at the back and the young guardsman coming out of one of them.

So whoever had caused her father's jeep to go over the escarpment had come back to Rinsey. She folded her arms over her stomach and rocked with anguish.

Under questioning from Sturgess, Josef had only belatedly remembered his employer had driven down to Singapore, but had been unsure what day he had left. Josef had said he was living at the manager's bungalow. So much pointed to the duplicity of Josef. It was like finding one's brother was a thief or a murderer... She felt the prickly chill of icy perspiration on her forehead.

Alan Cresswell turned and smiled as he saw her. She thought he looked as if he suddenly decided to come to meet them, but was not sure. In the tide of blackness that was rushing over her, she felt her limbs, her life, drift like some hapless thing unanchored from all it knew. Then someone caught and lifted her as she sank into insensibility.

She came to on a long chair in the house. For a moment she thought it was a compassionate, sympathetic stranger looking down at her, then she remembered the soldier.

'Lie still,' he said.

She closed her eyes again, half rebellious.

Was he going to start ordering her about too, like his officer?

'I'll fetch missy drink.' It was Chemor's voice. 'Then go find mother and tuan. They coming long way round,' he said, nodding significantly to Liz as she opened her eyes again.

Alan Cresswell supported the glass as her limbs shook. 'I think it's shock,' she reported as the glass rattled on her teeth.

'I would say that's about right,' he agreed, holding on to the glass and pulling up a stool so he could hand it back if she wanted more. 'The tracker told me you had found your father's jeep.' She looked up at him with such an agonised expression he reached forward and took her hand, held it tight.

'Mysteries about people you love are awful,' he said.

She suddenly realised he was older than she had first thought, probably not an eighteen-year-old conscript at all. She wondered if there was some personal reason he had made that remark, or whether he was just talking to distract her from whatever thoughts had driven her to escape consciousness.

'I heard before I came that your father was missing. I'm not sure how that feels—but maybe something like my father's sudden death.' He stopped, frowned and looked down at their hands, and instinctively she curled her fingers tighter around his as if the role of comforter could be hers too. 'I went to his funeral the day before we sailed from Southampton.'

'I'm so sorry.' Her concern for him now veneered the raw anxiety she had been feeling; innate sympathy and trained good manners prompted the question. 'What happened?'

'I still can't believe it, really. He was only forty-eight. In the air force all through the war, then dies digging the garden. My mother's completely floored.'

The unseemliness of rushing a son from his mother within a day of his father's funeral was outrageous. 'Wouldn't the army give you compassionate leave?'

'I did have extra time, but there was a postmortem and a inquest—and they said as I had an older brother at home they considered my mother was taken care of.' He paused and looked at her a little shamefaced, 'Sorry,' he apologised, 'I shouldn't be...you have enough worries.'

She pushed herself upright, denying the need for apology. 'So your mystery was how he died.'

'More why, really. The sort of question you ask yourself when you're hurt. It doesn't make sense, just gives you a better sense of grievance.' He smiled ruefully.

'But at least you *know.*' She gritted her teeth for a second to stay the tears, lifting her chin as she had been taught. Shoulders back, chin up, don't slouch. She remembered being stood in the school gymnasium, her shoulder blades and the small of her back pressed against the wall, to teach her deportment. 'Are you a regular soldier?' she asked.

'No, just your run-of-the-mill conscript.' He tossed the empty glass in the air and caught it. 'But I wish our drill sergeant at the Guards' depot could hear you ask me. He used to say I was "as upright as the bleeding Tower of Pisa!"'

The imitation made her laugh. Then she heard herself say, 'I think my father's dead. Now I do think he's dead. It's just not knowing where he is, what happened to him.'

He gave her time to take control again. 'He was in the war, I expect.'

'He was in the navy. He was always away, always in danger—but I thought when the war was over...' She looked around as if scanning not just the lounge but the whole terrorised countryside. 'But we've just swopped one battle for another.'

'That was another thing my mother took so hard, my being sent out to a battle area when her husband and first son had fought all through until 1945. She wrote to her

Member of Parliament.'

'Did she have an answer?'

'He came to Southampton to see the troop ship off.'

They both laughed. Looking in each other's eyes they saw the rueful understanding and laughed again but softer, like echoes of people in old age talking of lost loves.

'Hmm.' The sound was that of a man presented with an intriguing emotional problem he wanted to solve, but was totally unsure how to tackle it.

Liz studied him as he now tossed the glass in a series of rapid arcs from hand to hand, thinking of the sketch she had made of him. How strange that *he* should come to Rinsey! She weighed what she now knew, weighing the sadness in his life with her impression, and yet there was still more, some quality that she could not name in words or drawings—not yet, anyway. She felt she might well have echoed his 'Hmm' for she was just as fascinated.

He held the glass suddenly still and caught her studying him. They both smiled again, very carefully.

'I think I can hear your mother coming.' He rose to his feet and, backing away, looked once more a young, tall, awkward soldier in jungle green. Desolate was how *she* felt as he moved away towards the door.

Blanche came in quickly, anxiety making her forgetful of her own exhaustion. She noted the glass in the young man's hand and the complete lack of vagueness in her daughter's face. 'No wonder you felt faint going off after Chemor! What did that achieve?

All the whole expedition achieved was related to the police inspector from Ipoh and his sergeant early the next morning. Liz was surprised when all those who had visited the falls, and Alan Cresswell, were interviewed separately by Inspector Aba. 'As if we're suspects,' she complained.

After her interview she admitted to herself she had told far more about the missing Josef than she would had her mother been present, even going back to her first sighting of him coming through the back garden.

Chemor also spent a long time with the police and afterwards led them off through the plantation. She was helping her mother prepare curry tiffin for everyone when they returned by the back way.

'The inspector's uniform looks a bit worse for wear.' She drew her mother's attention to the window.

They watched as George joined the

police and Chemor. A serious conference seemed to be developing and the guardsman was beckoned over.

Liz wondered about going out to join them, but judged it looked like a closed circle of men making decisions.

'Men only, I think,' Blanche said, as if reaching the same conclusion.

'And it's not about where the perimeter wire is going to be,' Liz was certain. 'They look as if they've got their hands tied to their sides, they're keeping them so still!'

'They know we're watching.'

The serious talk went on for some time, then the inspector seemed to reach some decision and all of them nodded.

'That was unanimous, anyway,' Blanche commented with dark irony.

'I'll go and see what they're discussing.'

'They'd stop. Just watch.'

The inspector stepped back as if leaving his final words for approval. George nodded several times and moved forward, hand outstretched as if ready to help. Instructions now from inspector to sergeant, who saluted his acceptance, then more tentatively to the soldier. He rubbed his chin speculatively, then seemed to make a suggestion that rather spoiled the momentum. The men went back to the circle. The inspector spoke rapidly again;

George put his hand on the young man's shoulder.

Liz saw Alan glance towards the kitchen window where they stood, then he made the dismissive open-handed gesture of one who has tried to help but has been turned down. She would ask him what it was all about. She was deciding to go and tell him about the spare charpoy in the old nursery at the first opportunity, as the inspector nodded himself away from the others and came towards the kitchen door.

'Mrs Hammond.' He bowed himself into the kitchen. 'More men are being detailed to come immediately so we can make a thorough search both around the jeep and around your house.' He paused, then pronounced in more serious and ponderous tones, 'Also farther afield for the son of your former manager.'

'What are you expecting to find?' Blanche asked.

'Well...' The inspector paused to put his finger ends together as if steadying himself against this English mem and her disconcerting directness. 'We cannot afford to overlook anything. Mr Harfield's man found much on his own, so my trained men may find...much more.' He smiled disarmingly.

That afternoon there was a message from Bukit Kinta for George to return immediately—some difficulties with one of the dredgers.

'Shall I try to ring back,' Blanche asked.

'No, I'd better go. It's getting on for time and I've a mechanic whose favourite tool is a big hammer if I'm not there to restrain him.'

It seemed to Liz that hardly had the mine manager left Rinsey than his men digging holes for the fencing and lighting post became severely hampered by the police, whose search was closing around the bungalow. Some of the officers were working slowly over the area just looking, others with stout bamboo poles prodding and poking the ground.

'I wish they'd hurry up,' Liz exclaimed, thinking she had spent most of her day watching men take decisions and do things, while she and her mother wandered around the bungalow from window to window, as if the mental siege they felt under also restricted them physically.

Blanche came to her side, inhaling on yet another cigarette.

'Those poles!' Liz exclaimed. 'Is that really necessary? What *are* they doing?'

'I just know enough about gardening to know a cane goes into the ground much easier where it has been dug.'

She had hardly screwed out her cigarette in the ashtray on the kitchen windowsill, and Liz just begun to put together the possible implications of what her mother had said, when one of the men shouted. Those nearby hurried that way, then the inspector arrived at a run.

The two women watched as the inspector took a pole from his man and gently probed into the earth under the great tree.

In a curious kind of flashback it seemed to Liz she saw her father sitting under the tree, with herself as a child reaching up and begging to look at a sketch he had made of her as she sat at his feet. It was like looking into a picture containing a picture of the original and on the picture another representation of the same scene. She felt a strange conviction that if only her mind had been capacious enough to hold all the images together, it would have been possible to go back in time to the original, to that very time.

So was the image confirmation of the worst possible scenario? Never had she felt so vulnerable, so unprotected.

The kitchen window seemed suddenly like a proscenium arch, with overgrown lawn as theatre apron, the trees a back-drop with policemen and poles. Friendly guardsman entering and coming towards front stage, while lesser players entered stage left, carrying spades.

Chapter Eight

Some of the police had begun digging while others rigged tarpaulins. The very discretion of the screening sheets added to the anxiety. The noise of the spades and the quiet talk of the men went on, it seemed to Liz, endlessly.

Blanche went to the study at the far side of the bungalow where it was quiet. She sat at first looking haphazardly through the desk drawers. Liz stood and watched for a time, leaning in the doorway.

'I'll write to your aunt Ivy,' her mother suddenly decided, pulling out air-mail notepaper. 'I shall write what is happening now and...' She paused, then added quickly, 'add the result of the...police activity. If necessary I'll ask if she'll go and see Wendy, take her home with her for a time.'

'Good idea,' Liz agreed huskily. 'She'll need some spoiling.' Blanche's sister, married but childless, had always been more like a second mother to the girls than an aunt. She left her mother writing with some degree of fevered concentration—while she seemed doomed to spend another day wandering aimlessly about.

A man emerged from the tarpaulins, his mouth and nose shrouded in a tightly knotted scarf. Without the slightest conscious intention she found herself outside and heading for the screens.

Someone called and she began to run.

She peered over: the police were in special overalls; the hole was deep—and the smell appalling. She registered no more as voices were raised in protest and arms waved her away. She turned, gasping, staggering into the path of the young guardsman hurrying to her side. They caught each other, but she snatched free to retch dryly. The smell felt lodged for ever in her throat. 'I had to see if...if there was anything to see. What have they found?'

His height made it possible for him to support her closely, tucking her under his arms as it were, then turning and walking her slowly away. 'They won't tell me, obviously, but something's been buried quite deep there, by someone strong, according to Chemor. Look.' He stopped and turned her round to look back at the scene. 'Chemor pointed out how the leaves on the big tree, there way above the tarpaulins, have died. He says it is because someone has cut the main roots.

I understand he told them to dig there.'

The turn had lessened his supporting hold, and for a moment she wanted to lean back again just for the sheer comfort of a man's strength. Pride made her resist the urge—he'd be thinking she did nothing but faint away. 'I'm all right now,' she said. Then, as she looked from tree to screens, either a breeze or her memory resurrected the smell. 'No, I'm not.'

'No,' he endorsed and held her so firmly that even if she had fainted clean away, she would not have fallen. 'I did suggest you and Mrs Hammond be taken back to Bukit Kinta until this was over and the fencing built. But they didn't think you would go.'

That was a fair assumption, she thought, considering the performance her mother had put up at the Ipoh police station and the persistence they had shown in returning to Rinsey. 'Not so sure today.' She forced herself to smile up at him, she felt that wry quality of it on her lips, but saw understanding in his eyes, intense, total understanding. 'I feel I wouldn't mind running away for an hour or two.'

She felt the span and pressure of his fingers on her waist increase, comforting. 'I don't have to be on network call again until eighteen hundred hours,' he said, then paused as they came to the front of the bungalow, 'but unless we kidnap a police vehicle...'

He felt her body straighten from him and tentatively he released her again. She had walked a few paces when a voice from the site of the digging was raised in a tone of alarm. They both strained to hear. Another man pacified and ordered mildly, then the sound of spades slicing into the ground was heard again.

The incident had caught Liz mid-stride and so she remained until it was over. Then a long shuddering groan escaped her and she grasped her head with both hands as if the thoughts inside might well burst it open.

Alan moved swiftly to hold on to her again as she screwed her fingers into her hair. He was alarmed by the violence of this grief, this biblical rending and tearing, afraid it might be doing her actual harm.

'Please...' As he restrained her, she gestured towards the plantation, beyond the shy, worried glances of the Malays digging out the post holes.

Alan took her gently forwards, both arms shielding and supporting, taking her into the trees, into the privacy of mazing trunks and patches of neglected undergrowth. When he would have stopped, she took the lead and kept walking, following a kind of path which had obviously been walked quite recently.

She walked quicker and quicker, like one trying to escape a nightmare. He went along with her, keeping pace, not attempting to hold her back. He was aware that this was unwise, this was terrorist country; he was supposed to be a soldier, a guardsman. He was aware that his rifle was back by the transmitter—but army training was a veneer quickly bloomed by the present needs of this young lady, this girl, he found so disturbing.

If she had been a fellow student back at college, he admitted to himself that he would have pursued her, wooed her without mercy, never have taken no for an answer. But those had been mad days—free days after the war, when the lights had gone up and the lid had come off all the pent-up joyous emotions of the young. Then came conscription, his father dying and this new campaign.

'It's my father,' she sobbed, as if the word had been plucked from his mind. 'It is my father—that's who they're digging for...who they'll find.' She caught her shoulder on protruding branches and her dress tore but she paid no heed, hurrying on until finally she could go no farther as they came to where waterfalls edged the rubber trees.

The unexpected change of terrain as well

as the sheer beauty of the spot made him momentarily forget his charge until he saw she was running full tilt across to the edge of the rocks and the falls. He leaped after her, his heart pounding, convinced she intended to throw herself over.

'My God!' he panted, his forbearance banished now by fear, as he caught first her arm, then her shoulders, securing her, half holding, half shaking. She was limp under his hands, passive a willing victim. 'No, no,' he told himself, 'this is not right.' He folded her close, one hand cupping and holding her head, gently trying to stay the shaking and the sobbing. All he could offer was a kind of paternal shushing, he could think of no comforting words. Nothing would alter the truth.

As she stood shuddering in his arms with her head pressed to his chest, she could hear and feel the great thudding of his heart. She realised how she must have frightened him, just as Wendy had frightened her parents so long ago in the past. She gave herself up to crying, for Wendy, for her mother, for herself—for the loss of her father.

This was the full time of mourning. She knew beyond any doubt the outcome of the search. Clinging desperately to this young man, she saw her tears make the jungle green of his shirt even darker. She remembered the clean-shirt smell of her father on Sunday mornings when she sat next to him in church. She remembered how white his handkerchiefs looked against his brown hands. She remembered him twirling her and Wendy round and round, one on each arm. She remembered how she and her father had mourned the passing of an old dog who on his last day had dug himself ever deeper into a hole under a japonica bush, waiting to die. He had known—as she knew now.

She thought how strange it was that the young man she had drawn as a figure symbolic of mourning held her now at this time.

He remembered he had held his mother like this when finally she had cried. His brother had been at home, but when she had seen him coming unexpectedly through the door on special leave, only then she had given way—sobbing as this girl was sobbing, realising the depths of loss.

He had to tighten his jaw and grind his teeth to stem his own emotions. He felt she sensed his emotion for she suddenly slackened the grip on his shirt, then spread her hands and pushed them flat on his chest as if trying to reassure herself, break herself of the habit of such clinging.

'I'm sorry,' she said between sobs,

'hanging on your neck...'

'Don't worry about it.' In a less tense situation he might have quipped that he was enjoying it anyway. 'You just hang on as long as you like.'

She lowered her face and leaned the top of her head against him, trying unsuccessfully to bring the crying under control.

He yearned to be able really to comfort her, to find the lotus and make her forget, then perhaps the amaranth and make her remember him for ever. He felt stirrings in his groin that he felt very uncalled for and ashamed of at that particular moment. He held her away a little. 'Ssh!' he breathed. 'You'll make yourself ill. That's enough now.'

'I'm sorry,' she repeated, as if his movement away confirmed she had taken too many liberties, and would have stepped away from him altogether had he not held her.

'No, I'm sorry, I found you too disturbing to hold close any longer.'

She wiped her hands across her cheeks. 'What, looking like this?' Then she endeared herself to him more by offering him her hand. He reached for it and she drew him again to the edge and pointed out where her father's car was. When he spotted it, he told her he had overheard the police inspector saying it would not be practical to raise it and there was nothing more to be learned from it anyway.

'I suppose there's so many Jap tanks lying about from the war, one more wrecked vehicle doesn't matter much,' he added.

'No,' she replied, so resignedly it made him feel heartsick. Holding her hand tight, he looked around with a deep sense of wonder at the jungle-clad hills, the steep ravine, the exotic birds and extravagant butterflies. 'War in paradise,' he said.

'Love, too. Well, years ago,' she said. 'I didn't know until yesterday that my parents used to come to these falls when they first came to live here. My mother showed the police a path down and under the falls—right down...'

'You must show me some time.' He looked eagerly out over the expanse of jungle and waterfalls.

'Why not now?' she said and suddenly it seemed like something she should do—a kind of pilgrimage to a time when her parents were happy together, just the two of them, without children to distract their enjoyment, or war to tear them apart. The tears fell again, just flooding from her eyes, and she began to walk in front of him across the rock table so he could not see. 'I'd be glad of some way to pass more time.'

147

He saw the sudden spring of grief again, but these tears fell more easily, and he wondered if she might have plumbed that awful first depth of mourning for her father—even without the final confirmation. He hoped so.

He allowed himself to be led until they came to the steep rocky flood-water course, then he went first, supporting her down.

She had been surprised how easy it was to remember the way, almost as if she had walked it many times over years instead of just once the day before. In front of her Alan slipped and for a moment, instead of supporting, nearly dragged her over into the final steep descent.

They both laughed with that topsy-turvy reaction to possible disaster people often have—then in the same instant both felt guilty and averted their eyes to the track.

The moment was quickly forgotten for Alan as he realised he could no longer see an obvious way. He was astonished when, taking the front again, she led him under the falls.

Liz noticed other things on this second visit, saw rocks set like a dry shelf where they could sit. She touched his arm and pointed rather than shout in his ear over the echoing roar of the water.

Rather like two people in a fantasy they sat down and stared at the endless sheet of living water before them.

'My father sat here,' she said, quietly, knowing no one could hear, 'and my mother. I feel him here now—I know he's dead, and I feel his...concern for us.' She let the feeling run over in her mind, unhindered by concepts of belief or unbelief, just knowing them as every rock and every bordering fern knew the rush of the waters.

After a time she turned to Alan and saw he had his head leaning back on the rock, looking up to the very apex above them where water leaped from rock at the top of the fall. His lips were moving too as if noise gave freedom to talk aloud to oneself, like ladies under hair dryers, she thought. After a few seconds he sensed her scrutiny and looked down at her.

'What did you say?' she asked close to his ear.

He shook his head but then cupped a hand to her ear. 'I said if lovers had trysting places...and we were lovers...this would be ours.'

He felt her head nod against him and she said into his ear, 'Yes, a very special place.'

A wonderland, he would have said, had it been just a meeting place for lovers and not mourners. He watched her looking all around and felt such a rush of affection he was sure she should have known, was surprised the force did not physically move her—but when she did turn back to him she smiled and nodded as if she had found some deep satisfaction, some calming influence there, while he felt he had come to grips with the very elements: bedrock, fire and water.

After a few more minutes he felt her shivering. He rose and indicated he thought they should go back. She nodded reluctantly.

The heat, the climb and the stifling humidity after the coolness beneath the water made conversation difficult, but even when they reached the top and paused to catch their breath they did not speak, though their silence was that of a couple with too much to say and no easy way to start.

'What are you thinking?' she asked at last as they began to walk into the plantation again.

'That I feel different,' he said hesitantly, 'that I feel maybe we've been down to some underworld, to some emotional depths, and found...' He thought it would have been impertinent to voice what he had really discovered. 'And found it has somehow helped.'

'It has helped.' She took up the words quickly but did not add that she felt they had become curiously linked in some strong, sad, tacit bond. 'I've spent my tears—I feel almost it's been an indulgence. Now it's time to go back to my mother, but I'll be more help now. Thanks for putting up with me.'

'It would be a pleasure to put up with you an awful lot more.'

They stood for a moment under the pretty, sunlit canopy of the delicate leaves of the rubber trees. She looked at him quizzically but saw it was not a skit or a remark to raise spirits, just a statement of fact.

He held out a hand to her and both knew that if she took it now it would mean far more than the clinging in paroxysms of grief, or the helping hand on a steep path—this was quite a different offer.

When she slipped her hand quickly into his, a phrase from some biblical text came to him. 'I am blessed among men,' he told her. She looked so astonished that he grinned and raised her hand to kiss it. 'I did go to Sunday school *and* I was in the village choir.'

'Really?'

His turn now to glance sharply at her, but the look that accompanied the word was of wonder and interest, as if she was trying to picture him back in his surplice processing with the other white-robed boys and men up the church aisle. 'Really,' he said gently.

'Some time you must tell me,' she said as they began to walk back. They heard the noise of a vehicle arriving as they approached the bungalow.

They emerged from the trees as John Sturgess was getting out of his army jeep. He stopped, his legs half out, as if he could not believe his eyes. Then he shouted: 'Soldier!'

Alan said something inaudible, but kept holding her hand until she reached the clear ground. Then he asked briefly, 'You be all right now?' She nodded.

'Soldier!' Sturgess again, his voice full of threat as he came towards them. 'I thought you were taught to jump when an officer spoke.'

'Sir!' Alan came to a halt, saluted and stood to attention.

Sturgess's gaze went to Liz, registering the torn sleeve of her dress and the obvious distress she had been in. 'What the hell's been going on?'

Liz thought what an unimaginative man he was, such stock phrases, such military insularity. 'Your soldier rescued me,' she said, ignoring the soldier's eyes as she continued her story. 'I was so upset I just ran and ran into the jungle, and your guardsman helped me, brought me back.'

She reached over and for a moment put her hand over Alan's clenched fingers, thumb down the nonexistent seam of his jungle green trousers, as he remained standing to attention. The action was incongruous, reminding Alan of a visitor touching the exhibits in a museum—and he was the prohibited waxwork.

Alan had learned impassivity if nothing else while being berated by foul-mouthed sergeants on parade grounds. He was impassive now as he saw his officer look nonplussed. Even a major could hardly question the veracity of the daughter of the house. Could hardly discipline her: 'Keep your fingers *off* my soldiers! Miss!'

'Get back to your post, Cresswell. I'll see you later.'

'Sir!' He executed the high knee turn, one two three, stepping smartly off with the left foot, and marched sharply towards the rear. Out of sight he stopped and listened. The digging had stopped.

'That man behaved...properly?' Sturgess asked.

'That man was a gentleman—a real knight in shining armour, you might say.' She gave him a stock phrase to chew on.

'A knight without his armour, I would have said.' He looked at her more carefully. 'You've hurt your arm.'

She looked first at the wrong arm, which

153

convinced him that the guardsman was probably telling the truth.

'Oh! It's nothing,' she said, surprised by the torn sleeve and the graze.

As they walked together towards the bungalow, her mother came to the front door. Liz knew immediately that she had news—bad news.

'I've identified your father's body,' she said.

Chapter Nine

Liz stood arm in arm with her mother at the head of the grave. The sides had been draped with green cloth and given the dignity of tidy geometric lines. Her father too had been tidied—into one of the long rectangular boxes kept stored by the army at their depot at Batu Caves ready for the crating of their dead. Burials were of necessity swift in the tropics.

The red, white and blue of the Union Jack over the coffin against the artificial green field made her think of England. She clenched her teeth hard as memories threatened public breakdown. They had draped flags from all the upper storeys of Pearling House in 1945 when the war was over and put out even more to blow in the dry winds of that December when finally her father had been demobbed.

She remembered the bigger banners cracking like whips in the bitter piercing winds, remembered her father coming at last, the joy, then the feeling of being partly shut out from him, her mother supremely important. Later, as he shivered in the same winds, helping her take in the flags, he had said to her, 'Let's go back to our Malaya, Liz.' They had danced round the attic room. 'Just like at Raffles,' she had shouted.

'Our Malaya' was a bitter irony now, a bitter country—her heart was sick for this beautiful land. She glanced regretfully at the abundant greenness of the garden, the gloss of the fan palms, the delicate leaves of the rubber trees in the middle distance, the hills beyond—high, green, cool—as near to paradise as Mother Nature could get on this earth.

There would be no more memories of her father to add to her store. There is no easy funeral except one's own—she had heard those words as a child standing at her mother's side in silent respect as a young boy's funeral had passed. He was a classmate who had been bitten by a sea snake. The sentiment had meant little to her until that moment.

Where now were the carefree children who had played and laughed in this garden? Wendy far away, mourning a father she had known for less than half her lifetime; Lee, her gentle friend, banished for war crimes never of her doing; and Josef, whom Liz had loved so loyally, defended so regularly—exactly what was Josef guilty of?

A movement to the rear of the ranked guardsmen caught her eye and she saw Anna there, hands clasped, head bowed. Fear had after all not kept the bent old amah from paying her final respects. Liz stared at her and Anna saw, nodding her head as if confirming her devotion to a tuan who had often larked with her and her charges until tears of laughter ran down her cheeks—or mem had arrived. Liz remembered the hands clamped over the mouth trying to hide and stifle the laughter while the dark eyes sparkled irrepressibly above them, and she cried for Anna.

The tears splintered the symmetry of the small military funeral. The worry for the safety of her amah and her grandson changed her grief momentarily to real concern.

A sharp authoritative command reasserted the formal ceremony and the soldiers stamped up dust as they obeyed. None of this ritual surely was right for the man

Anna had come to mourn.

She and her mother had been swept along by the advice of friends like the Wildons who rang full of concern and sorrow and recommended leaving 'their mutual friend John Sturgess' in charge of all the arrangements. They had arrived from their regularly besieged bungalow as soon as they could.

They were as Liz remembered them, both tall, elegant, beautiful people with an air of deceptive languidity, for they threw themselves into the role of comforters with the same forthrightness as they damned all communists and swore they would never be ousted from their plantation.

John Sturgess and George Harfield had worked together to erase the painful hours along, to think ahead of all the arrangements and formalities. George had seen that everything had been done with the police and the authorities to enable the burial to take place at Rinsey. John Sturgess had secured the services of the military padre, six guardsmen, a trumpeter and extra men to guard the surrounding area.

Liz must have looked overwhelmed and appalled by the idea, for he explained with quiet certainty that it was necessary after an attack on an army burial at Cheras cemetery. Communists had targeted the ceremony from hills surrounding Kuala

Lumpur and the firing party had been forced to take cover in the open grave.

As if her mind must re-establish every painful thought, she now remembered her sketch of Alan Cresswell and how she had imagined his pose right for a memorial. God! No! She shook her head wildly, censoring the thought. Joan Wildon caught and squeezed her elbow, but Liz's concern was to find Alan in the line of guardsmen to reassure herself of his presence.

He stood at the far end, tallest at the extremes, smallest in the middle, in true Guards fashion. Although he was, she had come to realise, no more military and warlike than her father had been. Perhaps only she could acknowledge that his help had been more telling than anyone else's.

He had finally expressed the sentiment that decided where her father's grave should be. Blanche had wondered about the top of the falls, but that was linked in their minds with the hidden jeep. Alan had said to Liz that wherever they decided, the place under the tree would always be of such awful significance that it would be better to allow a proper burial in the same place. 'A kind of exorcism. That's how I would feel, anyway,' he had said to her.

'I do have many good memories of my father under that tree.' He had taken her hand and held it very tight, helping her through the idea like a kindly doctor with a difficult prognosis to make.

'A right act to purge a wrong,' Blanche had replied when Liz had tentatively conveyed the suggestion, instinct making her keep the source of the idea to herself. Since the arrival of John Sturgess it seemed to Liz that her mother had made a subtle relegation of George Harfield and certainly of the young conscript billeted with them.

Under the expert guidance of a tree specialist George had contacted, the big tree had been pruned of its dead leaves and some of its top branches to give it a better shape and a chance of swift re-establishment. Liz had felt an illogical, smouldering resentment as the tree had been tidied; people couldn't be pruned and given a second chance when they had been shot in the back—with the rifle found under the body.

She had been both surprised and resentful when four of their senior tappers had materialised the day before the funeral and offered sympathy and expressions of loyalty to all the Hammond family. 'Where have they been until now? Why weren't they here with—' Joan had caught her arm before she could rush out to join her mother at the front of the bungalow.

'These Malays might be useful to the

159

police—they certainly should be encouraged to stay.'

'If only to tell us why they feel it's safe to come back now,' her husband agreed. 'They obviously know a damn sight more than we do.'

Her mother had lit a fresh cigarette and fired one swift question after she had received their murmured condolences: 'Have you seen Josef Guisan?'

The question had stilled their fidgetings with their round coolie hats, but the only answer had been a minimal shaking of one head, which, when observed, was repeated with growing conviction by the others.

At a signal from the padre these same four Malays stepped forward on either side of the grave, taking the strain of the hessian straps. Liz concentrated on the figures rather than the lowering box and suddenly realised she actually knew one of the men. His face was thinner now so his ears seemed larger and more protruding, but he it had been who had taught her how to hold a tapping knife—and tears were running steadily down his cheeks.

Who had done this to them all? Who had forced them into these acts and roles they did not want to play? She could see Anna's head bent low again now, she could feel her mother trembling by her side. She again watched the falling tears on the

Malay's face and was suddenly very angry as the straining figures took the weight, paying the strap out through their careful fingers inch by inch, lowering her father's body down into the earth. Joan and Aubrey were right, of course, these men must stay long enough to be questioned.

The orders came for the small firing party to bring their rifles to their shoulders and 'Fire!' The six shots rang in unison up and above the trees, echoing mournfully in the surrounding hills. Liz felt her heart impounded by the sorrow and the jungle seemed to listen and take stock, as if some new, sad creature had entered its domain.

Then softly came the trumpet notes to mark the end of all who die untimely deaths. The grouping tiers of notes, the climbing sweetness of life's round told and retold, completed by that long last lingering note that at once questioned eternity and expressed human hope.

As 'The Last Post' ended she felt her mother sway by her side, and immediately she and Joan tightened their hold, a thin line of women firm until the last echo died.

Alan, his gaze slightly off front, saw and willed them strength. The spine-jarring stamp to attention as an order rang out was as automatic as a bird responding

161

to the tropical thermals, but his heart and mind were with the women of the Hammond family. They were becoming more important in his life with every day of his posting at Rinsey. He admired the one and loved the other. He'd heard of love at first sight, had felt immediate longings for various girls, but this he knew was different. In his mind the admission brought scoffing and laughter from his peers, but he mentally fended them off, silenced them.

He knew this was a new emotion because it hurt more, he cared more about her glance than he did about the opportunity of taking half a dozen girls to bed, or the wrath of a dozen Major Sturgesses or his ilk. He wanted to protect her, lift this awful burden of grief from her, cherish her. He saw her in the sparkling novel magic of the jungle waterfalls and yet it was difficult to believe he had not always known her—certainly he knew he had always been waiting for her. From the Midland village where his father had been a small-time builder and undertaker, to the depths of the tropics he felt he had been chosen to come to find her.

He thought of his father and how he had prepared for village funerals, the coffin shaped, planed and sanded in the woodwork shop in the far corner of the builder's yard. The brass furniture was selected from large drawers in the workbench according to size and price and screwed into place, the name plate last. Then his father would lean on the finished box, running his hand along it, nodding, satisfied with the craftmanship and giving a minute to the occupant-to-be. It was like a dedication, Alan thought, looking back. There'd be a summing-up of what his father knew about the deceased, then, after a decent pause, always the same words, 'Ah, well! No use burdening the rest of the day with it. Life goes on.'

Perhaps he would be able to say something of that to Liz—no use burdening the rest of your life with it. Love goes on. Love goes on even when life does not, he thought, and felt a twist of pain as he experienced a keen wish that his father might have made his own coffin before he died. Instead, a stranger's hand had been destined to fashion the wood for Edgar Cresswell's earthly remains.

His eyes hurt with the effort of looking so far sideways at the family party and he allowed his gaze to centre as he decided he did believe in destiny—he certainly believed in love.

He was glad for everyone when the ceremony was over and they could leave the graveside. He admired the way Mrs

Hammond turned with great dignity and invited the four Malays who had lowered the coffin to join them at the bungalow. Blanche Hammond was like her friends Mr and Mrs Wildon, elegant and classy, confident that she knew her place and, he thought ironically, just as surely they thought they knew everyone else's.

There was some delay as, at a word from Liz, the Malays looked around as if to ask someone else to join them, but then turned back to each other with a few hasty words and shaking heads. Then a formal procession moved away. Liz and her mother went first with the Wildons next, their height making George Harfield, who followed, look more square and bulldoggish than ever. Major John Sturgess walked by Harfield's side, of the same ilk as the Wildons but a bitter man, Alan judged, one with a chip on his shoulder and who had certainly taken a personal dislike to him, of that he was sure. Then came the precise police inspector from Ipoh, two of his men and the army chaplain.

Li Kim, the cook from Bukit Kinta, had been put in charge of the meal laid on outside. The guardsmen had been catered for in the shack at the back where Alan had set up his radio. There were generous plates of sandwiches and

Tiger beer. They piled in, pulling off their caps, propping rifles by the walls. He was pleased to be part of the chatting mess-room atmosphere they soon created, boys noisy to conceal emotions, and he knew they were sufficiently removed from the bungalow for their gossip and laughter not to be offensive.

Most of these men were eighteen, three years younger than Alan, and most of them he had sailed across with in the *Empire Signal.* One young man with light-red hair and a pale, freckled face had turned out to be from a neighbouring village and the two had spent much time together on the voyage reminiscing about people and places they both knew. Dan Veasey greeted him now in the melee of youths reaching for bottles of beer to replace some of the fluid they constantly sweated away.

The pair shook hands and slapped each other on the back. Dan was some eight inches shorter and Alan always told him they had added in the width of his toothy grin to make up the height requirement for the Guards regiment. It was wide enough now. 'Ah, it's great to see you! How y'doing, boy?'

'Told him about the present we've brought him?' a dark youth wanted to know. He was cynically nicknamed

165

Babyface because of his acne-scarred cheeks.

'What's this, then?'

'More to the point, have you told him we've all come to stay?'

'Come on,' Alan demanded, 'what's it all about?'

'No, fetch him his present first,' Babyface said.

A lot of ragging ensued, though it didn't interfere with the rapid consumption of sandwiches and beer. Alan had a growing feeling of unease that whatever was coming would bring the idea of his prolonged stay within reach of Elizabeth Hammond rapidly to an end.

He groaned aloud and it was no hardship to make a big show of putting his head in his hands as he was presented with a model-33 radio set—the portable kind, the kind carried through the jungle on operations.

'OK, so when do we go?'

Now the laughter at his expense settled to speculation and apprehension, then to serious consideration about their own temporary quarters. One or two went off to investigate the other nearby workers' huts pending the arrival of another lorry which was following after dark with their kit.

'I think the major's used the funeral as an excuse to get us up here ready to go in. He hopes the CTs will think we're all going straight back to KL—the lorries will, of course, with a couple of men stuck in the back to make 'em think we've scarpered. He's cute, that Major Sturgess.'

Cute, Alan decided, was not exactly the word he would have used.

'Don't take much to be cuter than some of 'em who're supposed to be on our side. Heard about the thousand machine guns and the one ammunition clip?' Dan asked.

This sounded like some stupid music-hall gag, and it took the teller some time to convince the group that it was true, that there was a nearby police section with a thousand guns and no clips to load the ammunition, which made the arms quite useless.

'If you don't believe me, ask that chap Harfield from Bukit Kinta. He's going to try to make some clips in his workshops. I heard them talking.'

'Nothing surprises me about this bloody place,' a morose voice put in. 'Your bloody toes rot off, leeches eat you alive, if malaria doesn't get you prickly heat does.'

'Keep taking the salt tablets, the "Paludrine" and using the blue unction,' another advised.

The soldiers' slang for the gentian violet

167

so liberally painted on, rashes and bacterial infections brought howls of protest.

'Yeah. Being so cheerful as keeps you going, ain't it, Babyface?'

Alan was pleased to volunteer to relieve one of the outer guards left to protect the men filling in and tidying the grave; it gave him time to try to come to terms with the new situation. He walked the long way around the completed perimeter wire at the front of the bungalow and took the place of the man patrolling the side, which gave him a view of the back door as well as sight of people leaving the front and going to their vehicles.

He stood listening to the jungle, aware of anyone who approached that way, but watching the bungalow. He could hear the hum of conversation and see people passing to and fro across the open windows. He could gauge the moment when people were leaving by the pause, then the chorus of voices as some of the guests said goodbye. He saw the four Malays come out, accompanied by the inspector of police and his men. They all drove away in police jeeps.

The Wildons were the next to leave and he heard the woman raise her voice on the front porch to say, 'They usually attack about dusk—must be back at my post, don't want anyone else messing about

168

with *my* machine gun—but we'll be back for tiffin tomorrow.'

Alan raised his eyebrows. In a country where attacks and outrages were almost hourly and where petrol was at a premium, the Wildons could be besieged at night and come forty miles for tiffin the next day! He put a finger to his cap and gave them due acknowledgement.

The bungalow was quieter and soon it would be time for him to be relieved to make his network call. Liz had come twice to his shack at this time. He had felt the very second she had arrived, but had not immediately turned, the first time because he had not believed his intuition and the second because that secret moment of awareness had felt like holding and savouring a wonderful present he still had to unwrap.

He wondered if such a visit could be ever repeated with his mates billeting themselves in the nearby huts. Would he return to Rinsey after the jungle sortie? He had been twice into the deep jungle and each time the relief to be out of the claustrophobic trees with their canopy of leaves and strange plants that rooted and grew in the dense living ceiling had been like the lifting of a death sentence.

His attention was drawn back to the bungalow by the noise of the back door being opened. His heart leaped as a woman's figure appeared, but it was Blanche Hammond. For a moment she stood erect, alone, looking towards the newly closed grave which had been left covered with the green baize weighted by neatly cut slabs of granite which would form the kerb of the final surround.

He thought for a moment that she was going to walk out but suddenly she sat down in the middle of the back steps, just sat, and he started towards her. His mother had done precisely this in the middle of the village—just sat down on the newsagent's step. The niceties of decent behaviour, the concerned and outraged sensibilities of passers-by, the gossips of the community, had not mattered to her any more.

He reached Blanche Hammond as the door opened again and George Harfield came out. The older man knelt immediately by her. 'What's this now?' he asked carefully, then, looking up at Alan, said, 'Get her daughter, will you.'

Alan started through the door but met John Sturgess at the entrance to the hall.

'What's this, Cresswell?'

'Liz, sir, her mother—'

'*Miss Hammond*, sir! Who the hell do you think you are?'

Alan looked the man straight in the eye. 'I know who I am, sir. Miss Hammond is wanted outside. Mr Harfield asked me to fetch her.'

'You on guard, are you?' he growled, glancing at his rifle.

'Sir,' he confirmed.

'Righto. I'd suggest back to your post double quick. I also suggest you keep yourself—' He stopped as if what he had been about to say he himself felt was too extreme, and ended, 'to yourself. I'll tell Miss Hammond.'

Alan left the kitchen and walked back down the steps where George Harfield was trying to persuade Blanche to her feet, talking to her quietly in a slow continuous stream as if bathing her with kind words. 'Come on, my love,' he was saying gently. 'I had you down for at least a front-doorstep sitter, not a back.'

George Harfield had better watch out, he thought, or Major Sturgess would be telling *him* to keep himself...to himself.

But the remark broke the woman's isolation. A noise, half laugh, half sob, escaped Blanche Hammond and then she began to cry with such bitterness Alan felt it must be true that hearts could be broken. He watched as Liz came down the steps and gathered her mother into her arms. Soon she and George were able to persuade her to her feet and they took her back inside.

He felt heartsick for them all, for himself too.

Liz felt completely enervated, though unable to rest, and wandered away from the lounge where George and John were still talking quietly to her mother. She knew her restlessness was partly because she had overheard the exchange between the major and the guardsman and partly because she knew precisely where Alan would be and what he would be doing at that particular moment.

Without further thought she left the bungalow and went quietly along the path to his hut, wondering how many more times she might do this. So far there had been no discussion about going or staying. Her mother had fleetingly mentioned Wendy once but had stopped mid-sentence.

At the hut doorway she paused, watching as Alan sat before the gently humming radio transmitter, headphones over his ears, fingers turning the dials to his frequency. At precisely eighteen hundred hours he made his report. 'Echo Bravo Six. Echo Bravo Six. Routine call.' Then he listened, his voice suddenly rising a pitch as he asked, 'That you, Larry? Any news of the football scores back home?' He listened again, then laughed. 'Next time then, got to keep up with the important things in life.'

He turned as he spoke as if sensing a presence, then blushed, looking as if he wanted to explain to her that the football scores were for his mates. She inclined her head as if to acknowledge the tacit information. He nodded back as he made his final signing-off, moving his head very slowly like someone reassuring a timid child.

He removed his headphones, flipped a switch on the set and came to her, his arms part open, part raised, reminding her of a picture of Christ called 'Suffer Little Children to Come unto Me'. His tallness overshadowing her, his dark uniform touching her, his arms around her, she closed her eyes and leaned to him.

She leaned on him so heavily, for a slight girl such a leaden weight, he almost asked her what was the matter. He rephrased the unspoken words. 'Is there something else?'

Chapter Ten

'Good morning.'
Liz turned from the kitchen dresser where she was pressing oranges for break-fast. She returned the greeting and handed

John Sturgess a glass of the fresh juice. He nodded his thanks.

He was dressed and shaved. It seemed the right time to ask her favour. She sipped her drink and began to make them both coffee and toast.

The night before she had told Alan the story of her old nurse who had come to the funeral and disappeared immediately afterwards. He had mentioned Sturgess's jeep, and she had the distinct feeling that had she asked him outright he would have taken it and driven her to Anna's kampong there and then.

He had been so concerned when she told him how she had first sought out Anna, recognising the turtle pots; how strange her old nurse had been, and the encounter with the terrorist. He had got up and stridden about, then come to take her hand as if he would be off that second to find the old lady. She had in the end felt she must make him promise not to do anything before she herself had asked the major if he would take her back to the kampong, or lend his vehicle.

'Yesterday my old amah came to the funeral—' she began now.

'I wondered if that was who it was,' he said slowly putting his glass down and looking at her. 'The lady from the quiet

174

kampong! She left before the service ended.'

'*I* wondered if you would take me back to her village again to make sure she is...all right.'

'How did she get here?'

'She could have walked.' She felt under cross-examination. 'I didn't actually get to speak to her.'

'Unlike the time we stopped at her kampong.'

'I did speak to her then, of course.' Professional cross-examination, she thought.

'And did something happen there that day?' He leaned forwards over the table and she instinctively leaned back on to the dresser, inching away from his scrutiny. 'This could be vitally important to me—and my men,' he added.

She told him defensively, uneasy as his eyes seemed to be assessing her every move, as if reading from her movements any degree of vacillation from the spoken truth—but she told it all.

'Hmm,' he said when she had finished and reached over for the plate of toast she had made.

'Is that it, then?' she demanded. The revelation of the terrorist's appearance and the terrified boy had been a battle between her amah's trust in her silence and what felt like the common-sense need to speak out now. 'Hmm!'

175

'Sorry, but it's more or less what I expected.'

'So the third degree wasn't necessary.'

He looked at her and laughed. It astonished her how his face changed, the long lean lines vanished, the man shone through the military machine. 'That wasn't even a first degree,' he told her.

'So will you take me to check on my amah?'

He shook his head at her. 'No can do, sorry!'

'But it wouldn't take you long.'

He again shook his head.

'Would you lend us your jeep for a couple of hours?'

'Us?'

'Me.'

'All of us will shortly be gone—until then no one comes in or goes out of here.'

'Gone? But if I...but *I'm* not under your command.'

'You may be endangering my men's lives if you do anything other than stay around Rinsey for the next few days.'

It felt as if he could have told her more without giving away any great secrets. She gave him back look for look, wanting to pierce his strict correctness, to trip up his calculating military mind.

'You know, you remind me of someone,'

176

he said, sounding as if he had made some kind of capitulation.

'Really?' She poured coffee to mask her astonishment as she saw the quality of his scrutiny had completely changed and his tone was bordering on the confidential. She was about to ask who it might be but shied away from letting their relationship become more personal. She picked up her coffee and prepared to go and look in on her mother. 'I think you remind me of somebody, too.'

'Oh! Who?' His turn to sound surprised now.

'Jekyll and Hyde.'

She had not meant it humorously and yet as the door closed behind her she listened for at least a humph of laughter. There was none and it somehow made John Sturgess more difficult to know, impossible to reach with any easy friendship. What was his past? Whom did he remind him of? She was mildly curious.

She went to her mother's room and peeped in. Joan Wildon had left two sleeping tablets, saying, 'I use them when I'm off duty at home.' Blanche had said she would take them if she was still awake after midnight. It seemed she had been, for as Liz watched she slept deeply with no movement.

Going to her own room, she opened

her sketchbook. She had worked late on a picture of the tree; the canopy was detailed, each leaf painstakingly drawn, but she had not been able to fill in the bottom of the picture. She felt there was no base to her life, no bottom to her sketch. She turned to the page before where she had begun a head-and-shoulders sketch of Alan. She thought it a decent likeness but what twisted her heart was that John Sturgess had said they would soon all be gone.

She slowly turned the page back to the tree and, picking up an eraser, slowly and methodically rubbed out the whole drawing. And then she wept.

Alan became certain that they would go into the jungle just before dawn the next day. Their sergeant made an informal kit inspection, paying particular attention to clean socks, insect repellent, and later issued tinned ration packs to each man for three days.

Alan checked and familiarised himself with the model-33 wireless set they had brought in for him, which, though apparently despatched from Canada, had dials labelled in Russian. Profit, even equipment for war, crossed all political divides, it seemed.

He was not sure whether the tension at

Rinsey, which to him seemed to tighten a notch with every passing hour, was not just in his own mind. His dread was that once his jungle operation was put under way, his time at the plantation would come to an end and he would not return. Even the thought had menacing echoes.

He had come to Malaya with a curious feeling of destiny hanging over him. He had almost reached the conviction that he should have been a conscientious objector, but that, he was sure, took more real courage than he had. Conscripted for national service in 1948, he had assumed that he stood a fair chance of seeing very little active service; certainly it had not seemed possible he would be sent halfway around the world to shoot other human beings—not so soon after his and his companions' fathers had come home from fighting the Second World War. The lights had gone on again in a land fit for heroes to live in—the ringing phrases had an empty echo.

Until now he had shot nothing bigger than a hare, and then only because it was needed for the table. But it was free season here on all men with red stars on their forage caps, provided they didn't get you first—and they knew the terrain.

Alan had been entranced by the *beluka*, the jungle edges, where there was room and light to admire the enormous leaves jungle plants produced; one such and a man or woman could be decently covered, fig leaves were poor things by comparison.

The deeper jungle he had found more darkly awe-inspiring, with its dripping constant dusk. It would be a matter of luck whether a shot hit its target with so many trunks to deflect the bullet's flight. He calculated that deflections could probably be the cause of more injuries than direct intentions.

The day dragged through to his final network call. He had seen nothing of Liz all day though he had wandered around making himself as visible as he could. She must have been in the bungalow—with her mother, he supposed, and with Sturgess, who went in and out fairly constantly. If it could have gained him entry, he told himself he would have applied for officer training right away. Instead he sent many yearning thoughts to her—though how was she to know it might be his last day there?

He went back to his shack and lay on his bed as darkness swept down. His mood changed as he decided he was surprised she did not guess something was going on, for even though the work on the wiring and lighting was finished, the perimeter lights were not switched on. Instead, still figures stood guarding either side of the newly erected double gates—fifteen feet of lashed poles and woven barbed wire. Except for a concealed escape for emergencies, this was the only way in and out.

He must find some excuse to go to the bungalow. He cared little for making a fool of himself, or being censured yet again by the major, but there was behaviour suitable for the day after a family funeral, and it was this restraint that had all day kept him from the door. He heard himself sighing heavily in the darkness. He was like a Shakespearian lover, he decided, 'sighing like a furnace'.

He struck a deal with himself; if she did not come while he was making his call, then he would go to the back door and say...what? Another sigh. He glanced at the luminous hands of the army watch. It was time he was at the transmitter. He switched on the shaded light and went to the table, where his hand stopped partway to the dials. A small leather wallet was propped against the set.

His hand shook as he opened it. The leather wallet was a tiny photograph holder and inside was a photograph of Liz. A small oval, it seemed to encapsulate her quiet dignity, yet the direct look from the eyes that followed the viewer showed the spirit.

A slip of paper was tucked into the opposite side. His hasty fingers were clumsy as he unfolded it.

'There is a saying: send a likeness of yourself with a loved one and it speeds their return.'

The excitement of the gift and of the words 'loved one' made his network call late and kept him awake all night. Awake tormented by her nearness and her inaccessibility, with the knowledge that he would leave at dawn. It felt like a separation before they had properly met, a divorce without a marriage.

When the sergeant arrived to say they would shortly be moving out, a torrential downpour was in progress. He carefully cut a piece of oilskin from an old map case and wrapped the leather photograph wallet, putting it into his breast pocket.

With his small pack hanging below the 33 set hitched as high as he could get it on his back, his waterproof poncho over everything, rifle in hand, he was well loaded, like all the others. But he had only to raise his left arm a little to feel the small package in his pocket, to press it close to his heart.

Major Sturgess took the lead with the sergeant, Bert Mackenzie, next, ready to take over should anything happen to his officer; then Babyface; Alan; Dan, who carried a Bren gun; and finally two brothers, Donald and Benjamin Sutherland, who with Sergeant Mackenzie had the distinction (frequently mentioned to conscripts when they were in regular barracks) of being regular soldiers.

Each had to keep his head down low enough to let the rain run off the wide-brimmed jungle hat, but not so low as to be unable to see the man in front. The noise of the rain on the palms and huge jungle leaves made it quite impossible for them to talk to each other even if it had been allowed. It was just sheer slogging work, and soon they were as soaked with perspiration inside their ponchos as everywhere else was saturated by the downpour.

As the light became stronger, they came to the edge of a rubber plantation that had been neglected for some time. The going was hard because the extra sunlight had aided the growth of every kind of bush and scrub around the rows of young trees. Alan wondered if this was part of the Rinsey estate. He felt it must be for they had not travelled far.

Soon they came to a wide track and, as if someone had turned off the tap, the rain stopped, the sigh of relief was palpable if not audible as the major raised his hand for a halt. They took off their ponchos, shook

183

and rolled them and were fastening them to each other's kit when round the corner of the track came a line of khaki-clad men, red stars on their hats and carrying a flag with the hammer and sickle on it, for all the world like Boy Scouts on a camping holiday.

It was debatable who were the most surprised, but by the time the Guards had their rifles to their shoulders the terrorists had dived for cover. They fired after them, the shots whining and ricocheting through the trees.

After the incident the major and the sergeant had a quick huddled conference over map and compass. Alan wildly hoped that meeting the CTs might abort whatever they were about and they might all just go back to Rinsey. Instead the major led them off at a tangent from the path and soon they were cutting into virgin jungle to make their way.

Progress was torturously slow and the continual bang of his small pack at the base of his spine with each movement began to be a repetitive torment. He tried not to think of it, not to wait for it to swing back and hit him just on the nerve centre at his tail end. It made his nerve ends tingle as they anticipated the thud of the pack and their curl and scream as it landed.

He pushed his left arm up under his left breast to feel the photograph wallet and tried to concentrate on plans to be with Liz. The trouble was that private soldiers weren't allowed to plan their movements or their lives, all that and beyond was in the hands of the authorities—he remembered helping to stack the piles of long wooden crates near Batu Caves.

They travelled all that day, cutting with their parangs, jerking their shoulders free as packs and shoulders became caught and entangled by every kind of thorned creeper and branch. At four o'clock they stopped to make camp for the night, each man trying to make a platform of small branches and leaves to lift him a little off the sodden ground. There was no smoking and no campfire, for the smell of smoke filtered for miles, betraying any man's presence. The rations they ate were hard tack biscuits, corned beef and a figgy type of chocolate, washed down with water taken from the jungle streams and shaken up with sterilising tablets in their canteens. It tasted, Alan thought, like the worst kind of chlorinated swimming-baths water. Then, with ponchos used like individual tents, they fell into exhausted sleep where they lay or crouched, dragged to wakefulness only when it was their term for watch.

At dawn they moved off again. For that day and the following night they had no further sighting of any living thing beyond many bright-green snakes, lizards of all sizes and a variety of monkeys, some frankly curious, some disturbed, frightened and aggressive at the intrusion into their domain.

On the morning of the third day Major Sturgess had them cut a small clearing to aid radio transmission and gave Alan a new radio frequency and call sign. It took some repositioning of the set to make contact and when the voice at the other end finally answered Alan was surprised to recognise the mine manager, George Harfield, though rumour had it he and the major had been together in the wartime guerrilla Force 136 in the jungle of Malaya.

Sturgess took over the headphones and microphone and informed their contact, 'Operation Nutcracker in position.'

'Everything to go as planned.'

The little band of men were then called together. 'We're approaching a major settlement which we know the communists are using as a kind of supply depot and post office for a large jungle-based unit. Food, messages, intermediaries, they're all going through this place. Mr George Harfield is with a force coming in from the main road.

At precisely thirteen hundred hours we shall all go in. Our task is to catch the ones who try to slip away. We shall take up positions along the tracks running into the jungle from the back of the kampong, move in as close as we can a few minutes before thirteen hundred hours. Synchronise your watches. It is now eleven thirty-nine.'

Following the briefing, extreme caution and silence was the rule, particularly as they reached and began to follow a water pipeline out from a jungle reservoir to the kampong. As the track alongside the water pipe widened and other paths crossed theirs, they knew they were near their objective.

At a signal from the sergeant and officer, they fanned out sideways, each man understanding the dotting figure gesture of the commander. Taking a track, each prepared to lie in ambush until the time came for them to move forwards at the same minute as George Harfield's unit moved in from the main road.

Slowly and silently the guardsmen disappeared into the jungle by the track sides. Alan reached his track, slid off the wireless and his pack and with infinite care concealed both behind himself, opening the set out so it was ready for immediate transmission, should it be needed. He took note of a giant fern growing behind a moss-encrusted rock, smaller ferns growing from the moss, so if he moved away he should be able to recognise the exact spot without delay.

The art of ambushing was a strange mixture of peace and tension. He lay still so long that lizards, ants and butterflies took him as part of the environment, yet at the same time the tension of listening and—on this operation—watching his wristwatch was a particular torment. For all his antimilitary feeling, he had to acknowledge it was training that made him able to concentrate; at college he would have gone off into a dream about his latest girlfriend, even gone to sleep. He was conditioned now to total vigilance. He merely checked that Liz's photograph was quite safe, looked at his watch again and listened.

At two minutes to one he cautiously began to belly forwards and between his own movements he could faintly hear his mates doing the same.

At a few seconds before thirteen hundred hours he raised his head from his new position and could see the village houses. His lips formed a silent whistle of surprise. On either side of the steps leading up to the verandah of the nearest house were two huge, shiny, green flowerpots, shaped like turtles. He lowered his head so his lips lay on one hand. How many flowerpots like that were there in Malaya?

Cautiously he looked again. He remembered all Liz had told him of her old nurse and the grandson. Sturgess had waited for her during that visit and now had brought the army here.

He could hear an increase in the sound of traffic on the road, then vehicles stopping. It was too late to caution anyone now. His heart began to pound as vehicle doors slammed and men began to shout. He could not make out actual words, but the commands linked with reassurance were clear enough—to him anyway—though if you were Malay or Chinese would you panic?

He eased his rifle forwards so he might either threaten or, God forbid, fire the damned thing. There was some movement on the verandah of the house with the turtles. One man came to the door and listened, a tall, heftily built, blond man.

'Bloody Josef!' Alan mouthed in astonishment. It had to be, from the description Liz had given of her former childhood friend. The man disappeared inside again and was replaced in the doorway by two men, one of Chinese origin, another of mixed race.

From the direction of the main road came more shouts, both orders and hasty warnings shouted on the run. Alan's fingers

189

went to the safety catch on his rifle as he heard more than one person running full pelt along the tracks into the jungle. He waited, nerves at breaking point, praying no one came along his path. Nearby someone challenged, there was a shot, then the Bren gun began its murderous chatter.

A man came charging along his path, but with hands lifted. Alan half raised himself, showing his rifle.

'Don't shoot,' the man said urgently, pushing his hands higher towards the sky.

Alan removed the safety catch from his rifle, slowly stood up and directed the man back along the path at gunpoint.

'Slowly,' he warned him. 'If you dive I shoot.'

The man walked the middle of the path, never veering, never lowering his hands by a millimetre. As he neared the turtle pots Alan saw the major and Dan.

'Good man!' the major said, seeing the prisoner.

'Speak to you, sir,' Alan requested, trying to keep calm. If armed men were still in the house with the turtle pots...

The major nodded to the sergeant to take over the prisoner. Alan walked away a little and placed himself so that he screened Sturgess from possible gunfire from the amah's house.

'I think the Hammonds' old nurse lives there. Miss Hammond mentioned those turtle pots and described Josef Guisan. I'm sure I saw him standing in the doorway before the shooting started. I think he's still inside with two more.'

The major's face hardened but he did not move a muscle. 'Ready to go in with me then, Cresswell.' It was not a question. 'We'll saunter back towards the sergeant, then take the steps at a run. OK, off we go!'

Alan was at the major's side as they walked back towards Sergeant Mackenzie. Perhaps the expression on their faces, or the angle of his rifle as he again drew back the safety catch, made the sergeant ready for action. 'Take the back!' Sturgess shouted at him as he and Alan took the front steps at a run and charged into the house.

Alan immediately remembered Liz's question, 'Did you see my old amah? An oldish Malay woman in a black sarong and a coolie hat?'

The coolie hat lay on one chair and the Malay woman in black lay in the other as if she had just walked back from the funeral. A boy of ten crouched against her, his arms across her body as if protecting her.

Alan made calming gestures with one hand as they circled the room, gently

191

parting the bead curtain to search the far end and look out of the back door. There was a scuffle, a challenge, then shots and more shouting.

'Two of them, sir,' the sergeant shouted.

Back in the main room the old woman now had the boy in her arms. It seemed to Alan that she was restraining him as much as holding him in a caring embrace. Before they could begin to ask questions, the boy made a rolling, exaggerated movement with his eyes—upwards towards the ceiling.

It was not wasted on either of the men, but neither looked up. Both their minds seemed to be working as one, for Alan calculated the spot above them the boy had indicated—and wished they had the Bren gunner with them. Sturgess lifted his revolver as if to put it back in its holster. 'On with the Nutcracker Suite then, Cresswell,' he said.

The shots ran out together. Alan pumped his full magazine up into the bamboo roof. The effect was devastating. There was a cry as of someone being hit, then they thought for a moment they were being fired back at as a series of rapid reports rang out and bullets careered in wild fashion through the house, whining and ricocheting off at all angles. A mirror shattered behind them, glass ornaments burst as if in excited sympathy, the whole structure of the house shook and cracked as above them flames took immediate hold of dry inner wood. It was like being shut inside a gigantic box of prematurely sparked fireworks.

'Christ!' Sturgess exclaimed, grabbing the boy's arm. 'Ammunition in the roof. Let's get out!'

Alan bent low and swept the old Malay up into his arms. The bright heat of flames was spreading all around them with the rapidity of a petrol-soaked bonfire. He saw slithers of bamboo like shards of sharp steel impale themselves into the cushions of the chair he had lifted her from. Crouching low over her, he ran.

As he reached the verandah he glanced back, glimpsing a man, the tall blond man, dropping down from the roof like Lucifer into hell, rifle in hand.

Alan jumped down the steps and fell but tried to keep Liz's old nurse shielded from the man above. He heard Mackenzie and the major bellow challenges. Someone ran across to where they lay; he could feel the vibration of the ground, saw a pair of army jungle boots near him. The man above him challenged.

'All right, Guisan! It's over!'

There was a shot. The man above him swore and dropped to his knees. Several other shots rang out.

Alan raised himself to find George

Harfield bent over him, holding his forearm. Some paces from the house Josef Guisan had dropped his rifle and was clutching his face. He nearly fell, but then he began a half-crouching, swerving run towards the jungle. Shots came from several directions in the village, then more from farther down one of the tracks. Even as Alan rose and helped the nurse farther away from the still exploding house, he was sure the man had escaped.

'Next time, Guisan!' George Harfield said quietly. He still clutched his forearm.

Alan nodded at it. 'I'll put you a pad on it.'

'I don't think it's much.'

'Take care of it, though, better covered straight away,' Alan bound up the deep score over the outside of the mine manager's forearm.

'Glad it wasn't my head,' George commented dryly as the field dressing was wound puttee fashion up his arm.

The major took the nurse to sit on the steps of another house and appeared to be questioning her. When he came back he seemed fairly satisfied, and all in all when notes were compared they felt the operation had been a success.

'We've got six and three dead, two of those I think are on the official wanted pictures with rewards on their heads. That was undoubtedly Guisan, he's obviously been terrorising the old woman into concealing him. She says the ammunition was down inside the bigger bamboos in the roof. She has marks across her face where he struck her for attending Neville Hammond's funeral. If ever there was a bastard... Unfortunately he seems to have got clear,' Sturgess commented as the last of two units collected in the centre of the village.

'But he's injured.' There was a grim note in the broad Glaswegian postscript from the sergeant. 'That'll be no picnic in the jungle—and he may be out of favour with his mates after this little lot.'

'And we're not finished with him yet,' the major said grimly.

Just then the hut, which had looked as if the fire was dying down, exploded with some force. There was little of it left at all now, but with an inclination of his head Alan asked permission of Sergeant Mackenzie to go over to the owner and her grandson.

'Where will we go now?' the boy was asking as he approached.

She did not answer, only shook her head, looking up at the blackened, smouldering ashes that had been her home and all her possessions. Alan noticed that the boy had no shoes and the woman no hat, and the hopeless perplexity of having nothing in the world but what they were wearing was in the dull despair in their eyes.

Alan looked back to where the men were giving reports, comparing notes, binding the prisoners' hands. They were all busy about their duties, or work, or whatever it was they were all doing in this woman's country. This stoical little Malay in a black sarong, what could he do for her?

Then he knew. He reached for the oilskin-wrapped photograph and held it up before her eyes. 'You should go to Rinsey,' he told her. 'You're needed there.'

Chapter Eleven

Alan stood under the 'shower'—a bamboo frame surrounded by a tarpaulin, a bucket tipped by a string—and had difficulty in not breaking into song as the three-day grime and sweat was washed from his body. Three cheers, he thought, for dark-red Lifebuoy soap and the order long ago in England that had sent him on a signaller's course.

He had driven George Harfield, Anna and her grandson back to Rinsey in the mine owner's jeep, while the rest of the units had been taken straight back to base camp near Ipoh. He had no illusions that had there been another signaller the major would not have sent *him* back to the plantation. When the order was given, and Alan was helping the Malayan woman into the jeep, he had been able to sense the major's personal irritation with him. He had half thought he might order him to show what he had put back into his breast pocket.

But now, with the bucket angled to release the last of the water and gently wash the lather from his body, he felt wonderful. He ran his hands over his chest, his shoulders, his thighs, revelling in that rare moment in the close tropical heat when he was wet all over but clean, smelling good.

He tied the towel around his middle and stepped across the path to his hut. Completely enervated, he did not attempt to rub himself dry but lay down on his bed letting the wetness evaporate slowly from his skin.

Rest after labour, peace after aches and pains, he thought. His mind wandered and wondered over legions of soldiers over the ages who had learned not only how to fight and perhaps even die, as he had seen the young communist boys die that day, but also to live, to value every minute granted to them.

With his hands under his head he lay contemplating this bonus of time he had been granted at Liz Hammond's home. He turned his head to see the photograph he had propped open against the wireless. He vowed he would take his opportunities now he knew how she felt. He sensed he would not have long, that there was more action to come very soon, and wondered how she felt about having an affair with a man who might die in battle. The way the major had said they were not finished with the blond escaping man had sounded more like ready conceived plans than vague threats.

There had been nothing vague in the reception Mrs Hammond and Liz had given to Anna and the grandson. They had been hugged and comforted. Liz had given Alan a look of intense gratitude when Anna had told some of his part in the rescue, and as he left to radio in that he was on the network again, she had invited him back in a couple of hours so they could eat the evening meal all together.

He left Liz settling Anna and the boy in a room and Blanche tending George Harfield's wound. He closed his eyes with the sheer happiness of his present state. If only they could have found Liz's father unharmed so that family had no cause for grief! If only it had been just the old nurse's hut that had been lost...

He awoke to a sensation of touch below his ribs; he woke but did not stir. He calculated that his rifle was within arm's reach. He would never make it if this was the gun barrel he had half expected in his belly ever since he had landed in Singapore—but the touch was too warm. Although fully awake, he did not move a muscle. The touch was also too gentle—a finger touch, no more, tracing the line of his bottom ribs as he lay with his hands still under his head just as he had fallen asleep.

Very cautiously he raised his eyelids a fraction, just as Liz, who was sitting on the edge of the bed, turned her eyes again to his face. She pulled her finger away from his chest like a concert pianist releasing the sound cleanly from a note.

'I didn't want you to stop,' he said, finding it difficult to unlock his arms from their crooked position. His instinct was to grab her and hold her tight; his reason said he'd better not. 'You may make free with my body any time,' he said instead. He realised that it was quite dark outside and she had put on the light.

'I wanted to wake you gently. You were so deeply asleep.' Her colour rose, delightfully blushing her cheeks, replacing the pale, drawn look that had been so

199

much part of her appearance since he had known her. It made him wonder what other tactics she had used to try to wake him. 'I didn't want to make you jump,' she added.

'What time is it?' he asked.

'We're about to sit down to eat,' she told him, glancing at the towel around his waist. 'Shall I tell them you're coming?'

'Five minutes.' He sat up so he was very near to her, and when she remained sitting he leaned over and kissed her cheek, gently, tentatively, alert for the least fraction of withdrawal on her part. 'Thank you for the photograph.' The lightness of tone he tried to affect was betrayed by a sudden huskiness as she leaned towards him.

'It worked, didn't it? I mean, you soon came back.'

'I'll keep it always, wherever I go.' The gruffness sounded like an affliction now.

'Don't talk of going.' She stood up quickly as if to escape the idea—or not trusting herself.

'Well, not before dinner, anyway.' The words were flippant to dispel her distress, but the tone confirmed that he would never go willingly.

In clean shirt and shorts he hurried to

the front door, smoothing his hair with his hand as he knocked and entered. George Harfield offered a beer as he saw him standing in the doorway of the dining room. Alan hesitated and Liz asked, 'Iced tea?'

'Please.' He nodded. 'Not sure about beer on a stomach as empty as mine feels.' He smiled an apology towards Blanche as if he had committed some social gaffe.

'There's plenty to eat,' Blanche said, going towards the table. Alan stepped forward and pulled out her chair. 'I was surprised,' she said, 'that Major Sturgess did not come back with you.'

He felt, rightly or wrongly, put in his place. If Major Sturgess had been at this dinner table, Alan wondered, would he have been eating outside? He glanced across at Liz and his heart leaped—no, he thought, she would have made sure of his presence.

'Robbo,' George said, as the rest of them took their places, 'is likely to be a very busy man for the next few days, questioning those prisoners, collating information.'

And planning our next trip up the ulu, Alan thought but did not voice the army slang for the jungle aloud. How useful, he thought, were the restraints of customs and manners! He marvelled at Blanche Hammond and Liz playing hostesses, controlled and dignified when their world was seemingly falling apart.

What a disparate looking pair were their guests. He tall laying claim to a few muscles perhaps but no spare flesh while George, with his arm freshly bandaged, plus a fresh nick on his chin from shaving, looked as if he had just come from the boxing ring or the rugby field—a veterans' game maybe, but still solid.

Alan grinned as George caught him looking. 'You enjoying that?' he asked, nodding to the piled plate of meat Li Kim had roasted, served with rice and a tropical selection of colourful vegetables.

'Everything tastes wonderful after a few days of army rationing, but this is excellent.'

'Prefer beef with two veg and a Yorkshire pudding, though,' George persisted.

'I've never been out of England before, but it seems to me one has to try the local fare,' he answered. 'Their ways are more suited to their climate, I suppose.'

'Of course,' Liz supported.

'When in Rome...' George began.

'We won't trot out the old clichés,' Blanche said, raising her eyebrows at him.

George laughed good-naturedly. 'We can't all be originals.'

Alan looked from one to the other. They were such opposites, yet they appeared to be at ease in each other's company, one might even say there was a kind of understood repartee between them. He felt George Harfield was not a man easily offended or roused to anger, and Blanche Hammond would not be easily diverted or suppressed. Alan found himself glancing uneasily in her direction at the idea of trying.

He turned to Liz and asked after the amah and her grandson.

'Anna won't come and eat with us, but they've eaten and a short time ago they were both asleep—like you,' she added.

He heard forbidden intimacy and indiscretion in the two words. His knife slipped from the unidentified meat, hitting his plate with a crack.

'Alan,' Blanche said as if cued by the sound, 'you'll eat with us while you're here on your own.'

It had the air of an order but one he was pleased to obey.

'Our nurse,' she continued in a conversational tone, giving him time only to nod rather than voice his acceptance, 'tells me that Josef has been hiding at her house since the search for Neville was intensified and has been using it also to make contact with his Red friends.'

'I think you can take the word of the workers that are returning to Rinsey, who think Guisan is gone for good,' George told her.

'But he escaped!' Blanche protested.

'But the men see Rinsey fortified, soldiers around and Josef Guisan as a wanted man. They'll feel as safe here as anywhere these days, *and* they want to earn some money.'

Alan remembered Major Sturgess's ominous threat that he had not finished with Guisan yet.

'Did you see the marks on Anna's face? That woman loved and looked after him when he was a little boy! How could he? I'll hang for that man before I'm through here,' Blanche vowed.

Liz looked sharply across at her mother. Alan thought he read her anxiety; how long would that be, before her mother was 'through here'?

'Will you go back to live in England, Blanche?' George asked as if he too was questioning the exact meaning of the same words.

Blanche lined her knife and fork up very precisely on her plate, then straightened the fork and spoon still on the table. 'There's a lot still to be done here, and I suppose I mustn't assume that Rinsey is mine. Neville could have left it to our children,' she paused and glanced over to Liz. 'There's Wendy in England, and...Liz here. Actually I'm not too sure I care what happens to me now.'

There was a few seconds' awkward pause, a swift searching of faces, but before anyone could come up with a suitable reply, Li Kim came in to clear the plates. The silence continued as George's cook carried in a platter of individual crème caramels and loaded baskets of fruits and nuts.

'The men who have already arrived are eager to get back to work,' George added as a belated postscript to their topic. 'There are trees planted just before the war that have never been tapped—the yield should be enormous.'

'I could organise the tappers *and* do the plantation book-keeping, I've watched it all so often,' Liz offered. 'I honestly do know how it's done.'

'The men also want to form themselves into a kind of security force. I could set up a roster of guards.'

'I'd appreciate that, George; in fact, I appreciate all the work you've done. Lending us Li Kim, but we have to...' She made a brave attempt at a gesture of moving on, though her arms lifted as if weighted with lead and did not match the smile she conjured, too bright, too brittle. 'I know when Liz came here she wanted to make her life at Rinsey—' Blanche looked

205

across at her daughter,—'while I certainly did not, but things have changed.' She paused and gave a short ironic laugh, 'For the worse, of course, but—' she blew a speculative smoke ring before stubbing out her quarter smoked cigarette.

'I think we have to carry on here at Rinsey as Daddy would have wanted to do—for the time being, anyway. We'll decide big issues later.' Liz's tone was controlled but then she jumped up and went round the table to put her arms around her mother.

Blanche gave her daughter a swift hug and a kiss, then rose. 'Excuse me, George, and...' she nodded at Alan. 'Please finish your meal, Liz, all of you,' she added and left the dining room—but striding out, head up. In the silence that followed they heard the master bedroom door firmly close.

The next morning very early Alan wondered if the invitation to eat with the Hammonds included breakfast. He strolled hesitantly around the corner of the bungalow, and stopped as he saw Liz near the grave.

She had on pale lime-green slacks and a matching short-sleeved blouse. The colour suited her, he thought, gave her a Peter Pan look—or perhaps standing over her father's grave like that he should think of her as one of the 'lost boys'.

He watched her from a distance for some time, then drew a little nearer. She still stood so quiet and contemplative that he was not sure she had heard him come. He saw there were fresh scarlet frangipani blossoms on the mound; their fragile blood-redness spilled on the soil expressing an emotional shock like another death.

'You were right about the tree,' she said quietly without looking up. 'He feels right here. He loved this country and the people. Anna, he loved old Anna. Though of course she wasn't old when we were babies...' She paused as if taking breath, then went on again quickly. 'It'll be a good thing, Anna and her grandson being here. It's made my mother busy again. She was busy all through the war; when Daddy was away she created and ran a market garden, did I tell you that? It's right she should be busy again now.'

He watched her, hardly listening. 'What's the matter?' he asked. 'Something's happened.'

She looked at him then and her bottom lip looked fuller, as if she was going to cry. 'Major Sturgess rang last night. He's coming back in just two days' time.'

'Ah!' he breathed out his understandings. He wanted to leap to her side, comfort and hold her, to be close in their mutual disappointment, but felt inhibited by the chance of being seen from the bungalow—yet why should he care now? He compromised by moving to her side and taking her hand into his discreetly while it still hung by her side.

By mutual consent they turned and walked from the garden along the path towards the wireless hut.

'Did he say anything else?' he asked.

'It was George who spoke to him. George is a bit upset because the army won't let him go "on this one". In any case there's some trouble at his mine, the daughter of one of his foremen has gone missing—that's all I know.'

It was enough. A few moments ago Alan had stood with his heart lifting at the mere sight of this girl, now his time with her was curtailed, condemned to a quick end. Two days. It would be so easy for this time, this emotion, this love all to pass away without being marked. He was afraid of the curious inertia an allotted span could inflict; one could watch the feeling go like a tropical sunset, blazing, glorious, unbelievably beautiful, and be left blinking in the dark at dazzles existing only inside one's own eyes.

'What are you thinking?' she asked.

'That we shouldn't waste any time.' He

felt his colour rise at his own words, they sounded apt but plain and crudely put after his thoughts. 'I mean,' he tried to express himself more elegantly, 'we must use every minute to get to know each other properly.'

She gave him a long, curious look, as if she was both looking at him and beyond him. 'And to plan how to keep in touch when you do have to leave,' she said.

They neared his hut and could hear the chopping of bamboos and the chatter of the men.

'They've started rebuilding their quarters,' she stated. 'I didn't realise.'

'Came at first light to tell me,' he confirmed, 'the four tappers who came to the funeral...'

She nodded. 'The police have exonerated them of any involvement with the terrorists. They want to bring their families inside the security fencing as soon as possible.'

'Pity they couldn't wait another two days,' he said ruefully as they reached the doorway of his hut and two of the tappers came by carrying the parangs they used for cutting the thick bamboos.

A third man called to the first two, who turned back and acknowledged his request for a greater quantity of wood, then smiled and nodded to Alan and Liz, friendly, deferential to Liz—and intrusive.

'I think,' he said, 'we are going to have to use our initiative. What time do they all stop work and go to bed?'

'I've a better idea,' she told him. 'You know the place to the east where George has made a concealed exit under the wire?'

He nodded but wondered if she knew quite what she did to him standing so close, looking so cool and determined, a smaller, darker, more compact, infinitely more lovable version of her mother, like a dryad.

'Can you meet me there in an hour?'

He nodded, then, unable to resist her nearness, he took her arm and gently pulled her the last few paces so they were out of sight inside his hut. He pushed the door to with his foot and kissed her quickly. She had not expected the swift kiss and her mouth was slightly open, he felt her teeth under his lip.

'I feel as if I've joined the Secret Seven on *Children's Hour* or something,' he whispered. Something in the ineptitude of the kiss made him feel so very young, gauche, but he delighted in her laugh.

'Alan, I...'

'I love you,' he breathed.

'And I love you.'

A greeting was called nearby and George Harfield answered. A moment later they were standing discreetly apart as George came to the hut door.

'Oh, you've beaten me to it,' he said to Liz, then paused and added, 'I mean, coming to tell this young man his breakfast's ready.' He hooked a hand on Alan's shoulder. 'Look, I have to leave after breakfast, but I've organised a twenty-four-hour guard roster. You've eighteen men back now,' he told Liz. 'They're fair flocking back.' He grinned and winked before slapping the young guardsman on the shoulder. 'You've got a brave chap here,' he said, before turning and leaving them.

'Did he see?' Liz wondered.

'Even if he guessed, I don't think he would say anything to anybody else, not even to his friend Robbo. I think he's too straightforward for that. He'd tell me off to my face if anything.'

An hour later he felt sure a court martial would be his fate if anyone did say anything about this liaison, this planned jaunt beyond the bounds of safety.

He took his rifle; if they were going out beyond the wire he was not risking being caught unarmed. He still felt uneasy about the man he had seen jumping down through the flames of the hut. He'd had the luck of the devil to escape, and Alan had an illogical fear that Josef Guisan

211

might somehow make his way back to Rinsey. He had come before, several times, it seemed.

Alan wondered just what Liz had in mind; the waterfalls were too far for such a tryst. What they needed was somewhere secluded, safe and nearby.

He was quite out of sight of the workers and the huts as he approached the section of the wire which had been underrun by a short, reinforcement tunnel. This emergency escape route in case of out-and-out siege ran out into the undergrowth beyond the cleared area immediately beyond the perimeter wire. It was just like an escape tunnel from a prisoner-of-war camp, the only difference being that these 'prisoners' had voluntarily built their own compound.

'Alan.'

The soft voice behind him made him spin sharply round.

'You've gone by.'

He turned back to the small store hut which contained the bungalow end of the tunnel. 'I was looking for you.'

'I'm here.' She looked solemnly up at him from where she had moved the boxes covering the trap door, raised it and was standing with her feet on the rungs of the home-made ladder leading down into the roughly wood-lined tunnel. 'Come on before I'm missed,' she urged. 'We won't have too long today.'

'Is outside the wire going to be any better than inside?' he asked as he followed, closing the trap behind himself. 'It could be more dangerous.'

'And more exciting,' she said as she switched on the small torch she carried. Bent low ahead of him she made rapid progress while he was somewhat hampered by his height and the rifle.

'Hold on,' he whispered. 'I feel like Alice and this rabbit hole's not big enough.'

'No, I'll be Alice,' she hissed back at him, 'the hair ribbons will suit me better. You can be the White Rabbit.'

'OK,' he said in a mock-resigned tone, 'but you know what rabbits are like.'

He bumped into her as she came to a halt, gasping with sudden laughter and for some reason switching off the torch.

'This is an emergency situation,' she told him. 'We're not supposed to be...giggling.'

'I'm not,' he said truthfully, 'just stating fact, ma'am.'

'Are we saving the batteries? It's not that far, is it?'

He heard her tut. The torch was switched on again and they went another twelve paces.

Seeing solid earth in front of them, he caught her arm. They had reached the end of the escape route. Holding his rifle ready before him, he eased up the trap very carefully. Between the vegetation, sunlight seared into their darkness. He peered all around but could see nothing but soil and ferns. A real rabbit's-eye view, he thought, but it was not the moment for more quips; he did want her to take him seriously.

When he could neither see nor hear anything untoward he pushed the trap right up and found they had emerged in a patch of thick undergrowth some fifteen yards beyond the fortifications. He could just see the high barbed wire stretched between the tall posts, the lights high on the corners and inside the long, low bungalow, quiet but embattled. He leaned down, took Liz's hand and helped her up. Together they closed the exit and re-covered it with soil and ferns.

'Come on, this way,' she said. She led the way out of the undergrowth, careful not to tread down more than was essential to their passage, and quickly led him to where an overgrown but still plain path crossed their way. She turned away from the direction of her home.

He stayed her once to listen, but the busy noise of parrots and other birds in nearby trees suggested that no one had been around for some time.

They soon came in sight of a building

he had not seen before. She ran up the rickety steps to the verandah and turned back to him with the air of an estate agent displaying a prize property.

'Our old manager's home,' she explained. 'No one will look for us here.'

Chapter Twelve

To Alan the place looked as if it had grown up with the vegetation, some parts even seemed supported by the trees that grew pressed right against its walls. The jungle soon claimed back its own spaces, he thought. In the same instant he remembered the terrorists who had melted from the path to *beluka* in seconds. Bounding up to the verandah, he silently indicated she should stand aside and he would go first.

'But...' she protested.

He put his fingers to his lips and went slowly forwards, rifle at the ready.

By the time he had made his way over the creaking timbers and was inside, he was convinced that no one was hiding there nor had anyone been there very recently. He had learned from listening to Chemor that it was the smell that gave men away as much as anything. All this place smelled of was of man's neglect and of nature's busyness.

There was much debris blown in by the monsoon winds and rain. The dust had been piled in some corners and fanned out like raised ribs on old wood in others, and a banana palm intruded its leaves through a window frame.

A movement at another window made him lift his rifle again, but it was no more than a breeze moving the remnants of a blind in a single flap like a derogatory dismissal. It did not endear the place to him. He wondered if he wouldn't have been prejudiced anyway because presumably the Guisan family had lived here.

He had certainly not expected such privacy. This wasn't going to be anything like the stolen moments in a shop doorway or by a field gate, which was all most young people back home managed. If he had known Liz several years, courted her for one or two and been engaged for another, then, he felt, it would have been all right.

He glanced at her covertly, thought of his own homely mother compared with Blanche, and wondered if people of Liz's class were more free in their lovemaking. There had always been stories of the antics of the wealthy leaked by the disgraced

216

maid or sacked man-servant.

Not that he was sure the Hammonds were quite in that class, but he wondered if *he* could handle this situation, this place. At the same time he was aware that he had pushed into his pocket the rubber sheaths the army supplied before jungle patrols as a protection against the ever invasive leeches.

'Of course, it wants cleaning up.' She kicked a few dry fern fronds away to the side of the room.

He saw her disappointment at his negative reaction to this place she had brought him to.

'We're not exactly going to set up house here,' he said gently.

'No, but if we're to meet here just...'

'For a day or two.' He propped his rifle against the wall and went nearer to her.

'It might not be just for a day or two. Just because John Sturgess is coming, doesn't mean you'll go immediately.'

'It means...' he paused, reaching for her to ease the sudden desolation in her face. She came to him quickly, clinging around his waist.

'It means—' he began again.

'Sssh! Don't think about meanings.'

'But...I...' He was quite unable to express either meanings or feelings as she held him so close he felt moulded to her delightful curves. He had a vague feeling that he might be drowning for a million thoughts were trying to crowd in before he was utterly lost.

'People don't do this kind of thing,' he heard himself say. 'It should all take time.' He had a picture of village courtship as he knew it, the self-conscious separate stroll beyond the houses, the first holding of hands, touching of arms, the kiss, the attempt of the hand towards a budding breast. Even students had intellectual discussions as they eyed each other. 'Not so quickly,' he added, throwing the words out like a last lifeline, and was glad none of his peers could overhear such a lame remark.

'Things do happen like this, love at first sight. In wartime and on the films all the time.'

'The films!' He gave a humph of indulgent laughter, then was very serious. 'This is real life.'

'Very real,' she said just as solemnly. 'I know—and neither of us knows how long it will last.'

'I feel as if you're saying my lines.' Every throb of his heart, every pulse pressure, every nerve ending, was urging him to make love to this girl.

'If I'm sure...' she said.

'Why should a man hold back, but...'

'I've never done it before,' she said quickly, 'not gone the whole hog—but I know what to expect.'

He slid a hand up under her breast and saw her lips part as if in shock. He pulled her to him as he felt her nipple respond tight and hard under his gentle fingers.

He looked at her face, her eyes closed slowly in a kind of gentle acquiescence. He wanted to say something frivolous, like 'This might be the last stop this side of heaven', but it was already too late.

In what afterwards seemed like a frantic rush he pulled off his shirt and laid it on the floor, sweeping the branches, everything, aside like some kind of sex maniac. He nearly ejaculated into the sheath as he put it on, and was amazed that she looked at him with such adoration afterwards.

'I love you,' he whispered, seeking reassurance.

'And I love you,' she replied, her voice so full of an emotion that went beyond the soon accomplished act, that he leaned down to kiss her neck, hiding his face, and fought the mundane words he understood were said at these times, 'It'll be better next time.'

After they had lain a time together, it was.

'We must go back,' he said at length but

219

made no move as they lay close, her head cradled near his shoulder.

She sighed deeply. ' "What needest with thy tribe's black tents, Who hast the red pavilion of my heart?" '

'The red pavilion,' he breathed.

'I remember it because,' she paused to swallow, 'I was hiding behind the lilacs at Pearling and overheard my father quote it to my mother. Later I looked it up. Francis Thompson 1859-1907.'

She sat up suddenly. 'I must have been an awful pest, always around when they wanted to be alone! You don't realise when you're a child.'

He rose and pulled her to her feet, held her tenderly as grief at the loss of her father threatened to engulf her again.

'It says a lot about my mother really, because she did follow her heart rather than stay with her people in England.'

He wanted to ask if she were like her mother, would she follow her heart? Instead he said gently, 'Come on pest, I'd better take you back before we're missed.'

'I shall think of this as the love tunnel now,' he told her as holding hands they made their way back to the main bungalow.

She paused to laugh and again put out the torch.

'My Lord!' he exclaimed and his voice thrown back to him by the walls he thought sounded just like his father's. 'No wonder rabbits breed like they do,' he murmured as he found himself close behind her stooped form with his free hand on her buttock.

'Promise,' she whispered, 'that you will always make me laugh. In the worst, worst ever circumstances we ever find ourselves in.'

'You promise to be there and I'll always be able to raise a cheerful word.'

'Promise to write to me when you're away.'

'I promise.'

'And always to come back.'

'Always. And I never break a promise made in a dark tunnel.'

She put on the torch and slowly raised it so she could see his face.

'Or in torchlight.'

'What about tomorrow morning at the same time—and I'll wait for you at the love end?' He was silent blinking as she raised the light higher. 'Alan?' she prompted.

'Yes.' Her final words had quite taken all rational speech from him. 'Yes,' he repeated, while somewhere in his brain there was a question he never asked about why they shouldn't meet at the beginning of the tunnel.

She was already making plans as they parted. Convention still had a role to play as she went back towards the bungalow first.

She turned to look at Alan once more. He was leaning in the hut doorway watching her go. She stopped, stood quite still looking back at him and it was as if a great, almost biblical sense of contentment came over her. He was the subject of her eye, the object of all her love. In response to her regard he straightened in the doorway, tall, filling the space. She would make a sketch of him standing so, in jungle-green issue holding his rifle—but in the doorway of an empty room, the light coming from a window framed with banana leaves.

There was no need for any hand lift or nod of the head, the feeling was between them, a sense of completeness, of knowing that they had each found their perfect partner. She walked on out of his sight, but already she was planning their return.

In her bedroom were loose cushions she could take from her chairs and a rug from the bedside; those would probably take two trips through the tunnel.

She was surprised at her own deviousness when, in order to move the soft furnishings on their way towards the other bungalow, she took them first to the front porch and established herself with a kind of office:

plantation books on the table, the rug and a large string bag folded under the cushions.

There *was* much paperwork to be done, new rubber yield and payroll books to be drawn up. During the late morning and early afternoon she worked there fairly solidly, and if anyone later saw her carrying away the cushions, no one ever said anything.

She took them in two self-conscious journeys to the hut at the top of the tunnel, trying to ignore the thought of what she might say she was doing if discovered. Then, feeling distinctly more like the villainous Red Queen than either Alice or the White Rabbit, she lowered them all down into the tunnel and pulled them after herself in the string bag.

She managed to be back on the right side of the wire only just before night fell. Later, at dinner, she could hardly contain her wish for Alan to see all that she had achieved. But even had she been tempted to tell him in a whispered aside there was not the opportunity, for her mother was particularly restless.

They all missed the stabilising influence of George Harfield. Blanche had taken a large gin before the meal and another after. Then, instead of, as Liz had hoped, taking her third drink to bed, she asked to see the account books her daughter had been working on all day.

'If we're going to run this bloody place, better get it right from the start.' She cleared a businesslike space in front of herself at the dining table. 'Right!' she said, looking up at her daughter. 'Let's get started.'

'I'll leave you two to work,' Alan said, rising.

'Goodnight to you both. Thank you for the meal, Mrs Hammond.'

There was no answer; Blanche concentrated on making the tablecloth perfectly wrinkle-free for the books. Liz went with him to the back door and they were exchanging a brief hand squeeze as Blanche followed. He wondered if she saw or suspected anything, but it seemed she felt she had dismissed him too brusquely.

'Goodnight to you,' she said. 'See you for breakfast, same time.'

'Same time,' Liz repeated with a remarkable degree of innocence.

Liz was at the dilapidated bungalow well before time, complete with vase and orchid sprays and some of the flame-red frangipani blossoms.

She arranged them and put the vase near the mat and cushions she had placed in the

224

middle of the old lounge which she had first swept clean with a bunch of banana leaves.

She stood back and imagined Alan there, the two of them together, and moved the flowers a little farther away. Like any other housekeeper, she did not want her efforts spoiled!

She smiled, imagining his arrival. He would look astonished and say, 'But where did all this come from? How did you possibly manage?'

'I did a few trips yesterday,' she'd say casually, ignoring the sheer hard labour it had been pulling the four cushions and the mat through the tunnel.

He would take her into his arms... She tried to find words for how safe she felt in his arms—unassailable, invulnerable, impregnable, a charmed life... She laughed silently at her own game, wrapping her arms around herself. Then, thinking she heard a sound, she held her breath listening, waiting for his next footfall—but she was wrong. There was no one.

She gave herself a consolatory squeeze. He would soon be there, and he loved her, he cheered her. When the awful time came and he did have to leave, he had promised he would write; and when the army released him from his national service, they would plan a future together. She had never felt so sure about the rightness of anything in all her life.

She listened again. The appointed time had come; she bit her bottom lip with eager anticipation. She had a last look around the room as every enthusiastic hostess does before the keenly awaited guest arrives.

She noticed now that since the day before several leaves had blown into the far corner. Everything must be as near perfection as she could achieve. Just as she was about to dispose of them through the window, a spectacularly large white butterfly flirted in the air just outside, then fluttered in with all the hesitation of the uninvited. It had brilliant red quarters on its upper wings, the red outlined and with interstices of black making the sections look like old-fashioned red feather fans.

She stood perfectly still as it found the flowers and settled. How she wished Alan would come just at that moment! She listened, tense with excitement, then slowly she stretched out an arm and dropped the leaves out of the window. Still the butterfly found nectar in the blossoms and gently so as not to disturb it, she walked around the room to the door.

'Look,' she would say, 'everyone can arrange flowers, but not everyone can arrange to have a butterfly.'

She glanced at her watch; he was late, a little late, fifteen minutes past nine. She wondered if her mother was up yet, whether she had been missed and how her mother might see this liaison. Like the squire's daughter meeting the proverbial gardener behind the pigsty, probably. An old-fashioned view, now the war had, she thought, largely levelled out the class structure—a levelling for the worse and downwards as far as Blanche was concerned. Liz could not, she reflected wryly, have imagined such as George Harfield among her mother's invited company before the war. The war had changed values, made people, even young people, aware of their brief lives.

After a few more minutes she fetched the bundle of banana leaves which she had stowed in the old kitchen and brushed the front step so she could sit down to wait. The revolver she had carried in her slacks pocket she placed on the step beside her and listened. She knew by the behaviour of the birds and the monkeys that there was no one about. She watched a chameleon, green as the leaves it stood among, as it waited for the insects to come within reach of its swift, long tongue.

What could possibly be making him late? Had someone like the major come to see him? Tomorrow perhaps—but not today! This was only their first full day of life as lovers.

She picked up the revolver and went back to the lounge. The butterfly rose as she entered, circled the flowers but then settled again. She went back to the step.

He was three-quarters of an hour after the time they had arranged. How long should she wait before going back? She remembered him being called to the phone just before they sat down for breakfast, but this was not unusual. It had happened several times, routine instructions regarding his radio watch, usually. When he came back to the table that morning he had merely smiled and said, 'More red tape.'

She listened to the lesser sounds of the jungle—the birds, the insects. She peered around as she had not had time to do since she was a child here. It was like renewing acquaintanceship with old friends. She could make out the brilliant blue fluorescence of dung beetles under the leaf mould, the angular green praying mantis and along the old path to Rinsey an awesome column of soldier ants. Anna had taught her a healthy respect for these red, nearly inch-long carnivores. They marched in

228

a meticulous line down the trunk of a tree, across the path and up a tree trunk on the other side, like guardsmen under orders—she wondered if their leader's name was Sturgess.

Where are you, Alan? What is keeping you? She wondered if Anna had woken yet. If her amah had been anything like her old self Liz would certainly not have been able to slip away like this. But Anna, like her mother, had been sleeping in, while her grandson at George's suggestion had been taken by one of the tappers, who had a son the same age, to join the school run by Kampong Kinta.

She finally allowed herself another look at her watch. It was an hour and twenty minutes after their appointed time. She rose and went back into the lounge.

The butterfly was fluttering along the walls looking for a way out. It panicked as she entered banging itself with audible thumps at its prison. She watched for a moment or two, then went over and, as it settled momentarily within her reach, gently cupped her two hands around it.

She could feel it struggling in the dark of her palms. She held it for a second or two longer, knowing it was like her heart, dark with fear of the unknown. Then she took it to the window and opened her hands. For a moment it rested before taking to the air, rising up into the clear sky.

'Gone,' she breathed.

Liz went first to Alan's hut. She felt her heart burst in anguish as she stood in the doorway. It was as if no one had ever been there. All the bedding was gone, the wireless was gone and even as she stood there some of the tappers came, carrying pieces of furniture.

'We have best hut now,' one of them told her with a broad smile.

'But the soldier?' she asked.

'Gone, miss.' The grin was wider. 'Have our home back now.'

Her heartache was such that she wanted to lash out and on the tip of her tongue was the sentiment that they could have their bloody country back too.

Fighting hard to discipline tears of disappointment and anger, she approached the kitchen door, determined to find out exactly when Alan had been sent for, where he had been ordered to go and by whom—though the last was not too much of a problem.

The sound of John Sturgess's voice as she approached the back door infuriated her and banished immediately any tears. How dared he still be here if he'd sent Alan away? She was about to burst into the kitchen and confront this Jekyll-and-Hyde character when she heard her mother's raised voice.

'Rape! For God's sake!'

Liz stood transfixed, hand raised in the act of opening the door. Inside, her mother had also paused as if to try to understand what she herself had exclaimed, then repeated with terrifying anger, 'Rape!'

Liz stepped away from the door. Is this what they believed? Was Alan in prison? Had he been arrested? Was that where he had gone? 'No!' she exclaimed and went quickly in, ready to defend and absolve her lover.

Her mother and John Sturgess both turned to look at her, but their eyes had that look of being focused elsewhere. She felt she just caught Alan's defence in her teeth, as she realised there was no accusation for him, or for her. This was some quite other problem.

As if to reinforce her impression Blanche turned sharply away, walked across to the sink and *threw* the glass she held with some force into the washing-up bowl. Liz heard it crack. John Sturgess winced and held his teeth askew, obviously not quite sure what to say next for the best.

'Rape? Did I hear the word?' Liz asked.

'Yes.' Sturgess frowned and looked at his feet. 'I'm sorry about that—'

'George Harfield has been arrested in Ipoh for rape!'

Blanche burst out. 'Did you ever hear anything so bloody senseless in all your life?'

Chapter Thirteen

The extraordinary news so overwhelmed them all that Liz knew her own misunderstanding had passed unnoticed. She took hold of a chairback to steady herself as John Sturgess revealed the reason for his swift reappearance in full jungle-green kit and laced jungle boots.

'The trouble is time. I have to make a quick visit to my headquarters, then we need a final briefing before our next operation, which must begin promptly or we'll lose all the advantages of the raid on your amah's village. We have more information then we dared hope for. I just *cannot* take time to go and see George, but neither can I just leave things—we go back too far together.'

'How can we help?' Blanche asked.

'All I know is the charge and that he was taken to Ipoh police station. I...'

In the pause Liz thought he looked like

a man doing his duty against the odds. An honourable pose? She wondered.

'I know it's an awful presumption, particularly at this moment,' he went on, 'definitely not a good time.'

'Shouldn't think there's ever a good time to be charged with rape,' Blanche retorted; then, looking at Liz, she nodded and confirmed, 'Don't worry, we'll go. We'll sort it out!'

'Find out all you can. I didn't know who else I could ask...'

'We'll be glad to do something for George,' Liz replied. With unplanned swiftness and dishonesty she added, 'Could you do something for me in return? I have a book belonging to the guardsman who was here. Could I ask you to return it for me?'

'Cresswell!' There was something between censure and surprise in the exclamation. 'I do have to leave straight away.'

She nearly commented that he often seemed to have to rush off—when duty called—and take his men whether they were willing or not. 'I'll fetch it from my room at once,' she said, turning away so he should not see her satisfaction. At least she had extracted the tacit information that the major was going to be seeing Alan again, so presumably they were going on the same operation.

Liz went to her room, her mind racing over what she could send to him and what it might mean if she did. Picking up a slim book titled *New Zealand Poets*, she found a clean flyleaf and swiftly in bold outlines she sketched the figure of an anonymous guardsman in jungle gear with rifle, standing in a far from anonymous empty room. As an afterthought she added, 'Waiting to hear' as a kind of caption. She dared do no more and take no more time. She slipped the book into an envelope and took it back to the kitchen where the major was preparing to leave.

She held it out. 'Of course, if Mr Cresswell was coming back here, I need not trouble you.'

He reached for the book. 'There will be no call for any of my men to be at Rinsey now you have your own guards organised.'

'Thanks to George,' Blanche said.

'But I shall come again as soon as I'm able,' he added.

Liz returned his coldly questioning stare without, she hoped, giving away her true feelings, but something flickered in his eyes like a camera lens as if he had registered an impression for future use.

He left as Anna came into the kitchen.

'I do washing now, mem,' she said. When Blanche protested, she said, 'No,

234

I want do, be busy, please, mem. You fetch towels and you,' she said to Liz, 'your dirties, please.'

'I'm going to telephone for a car to take us to Ipoh first,' Blanche said.

Anna watched Blanche go, then beckoned Liz back, whispering, 'Your young man, he touch pocket with your photo in and nod to me to tell you what happened.' She paused to throw up her hands like a magician producing a rabbit. 'He had no time to do anything. The major come and—' she paused to stand with her hands on her hips and, curving down her lip, went on in tones of extreme bossiness, 'said pack *now*, would answer no questions and did not leave for one second. All pack and gone in ten minutes. I think that major—' she made a significant downward thrust of her thumb—'but I think young man you give your photo to...' She gave thumbs up and nodded sagely.

Liz embraced Anna. 'Did he say anything at all?'

'No time. Major no answer questions, no speak, only orders: Do this! Do that! Now!'

'Thanks, Anna.' In the background she could hear her mother negotiating very loudly for a car. 'You won't tell...'

Anna shook her head. They had shared too many secrets for there to be any need to spell out what should not be told to whom.

'What we're getting, basically, is a taxi,' Blanche said, coming back, 'as far as Ipoh, anyway, then we can talk to the man at the garage ourselves and buy something.'

Liz nodded and the two exchanged looks which acknowledge the fact that they really had no man to advise them now.

'Anna.' Her mother's tone softened. 'Will you be all right on your own here?'

Anna gave a rough, short laugh. 'Mem, I'm safer here than I've been since the end of the war, with that Josef coming and going to see them communists—using my house! I'm *glad* it burned down!'

'Oh, Anna!' Liz was quietly appalled that anyone should be driven to wish their home destroyed. 'But your home is here now, isn't it, Mother?'

'We will always see you're provided for,' Blanche agreed, then asked, 'Would you tell us more about all those years while we wait for this car?'

'That boy Josef was always greedy for more and more,' Anna began as they sat at the table. 'The Guisans move here when you all left.'

'Into the bungalow?' Blanche demanded, and Anna nodded confirmation.

'Not the Japanese?'

'Them too, later.' Anna went on, 'I went

236

home to my village. Then there was much killing by the Japanese—my family, Mr Guisan... Long time, years, before I see Josef again. Mrs Guisan and Lee came once to see me after her husband shot slashing trees so Japanese cannot have rubber. I have never seen since.' The old lady paused and the incomprehension on her face was echoed in both her listeners' minds.

'Josef said his mother was a traitor in the war—'

'Josef traitor now,' Anna commented matter-of-factly before going on with her story. 'At first it was all buddies using my home to leave messages for Chinese fighting in the jungle against the Japanese. Then I thought we were all helping Mr Hammond win the war.' She paused to sip the sweet lemon tea Liz had made for her. 'But I knew he really wicked when Mr Hammond come back. Josef he so, *so* angry.' She shook her fists in the air to emphasise the point.

'Why should he be angry, for God's sake?' Blanche asked.

'Josef thought he was the new tuan until Mr Hammond came back.' Anna nodded with deep conviction. 'Soon then the communists with the red stars on their hats came to village and demanded money to pay their soldiers. I told I must store things in my roof—and hide terrorists—or they would kill grandchild and cut out tongue, make me "dum-dum amah". They laughed about that; one caught and twisted tongue out, pretended slice off.' Anna's voice fell as she admitted, 'I very afraid.'

Liz remembered her visit and how the old lady had refused to speak. 'Anna, I'm so sorry, we didn't know...how awful!'

'The bastards!' Blanche breathed.

'They gave me papers to bring out, but...' She stopped and shrugged her shoulders. 'I never...I let them burn in house, all but one in pocket.'

'Papers?' Blanche queried.

Anna fumbled in the pocket of her sarong and brought out a folded leaflet.

Blanche took it, spread it out on the table and read:

The Min Yuen, the masses' movement of the Malayan Communist Party, call for all members to prepare for more effective violence. The people cannot tolerate British imperialist suppression any longer and are pledged to use action to smash their reactionary legal restrictions.

We drove the Japanese out when the British ran away. Now it is time for us to drive out the imperialists.

DEATH TO THE RUNNING DOGS!

'Where do these papers come from?' Liz asked. 'Where are they printed?'

'Josef brings them out of the jungle,' Anna answered, 'is all I know.'

'We should ask Joan about the best guns to get,' Blanche said thoughtfully, 'and where's best for us to set them up.'

'I should learn to shoot,' Anna said.

The laugh that rose in Liz's throat at the thought was silenced as her mother answered, 'Yes.'

In the back of the Sikh-driven hire car Liz asked whether her mother thought Anna would be able to settle again at Rinsey.

'She gives every sign of knowing her role will be different.' Blanche's tone was brisk, unsentimental, as if she was already preparing herself to deal with the authorities in Ipoh.

'We mustn't ever, ever let her down again,' Liz urged. 'She's been through too much.'

'Again! I didn't think we ever had.'

'No, perhaps not...'

'Definitely not.' Blanche settled the matter and went on to what was before them. 'You know it'll be that same precise little Inspector Aba. Well, we can deal with him!'

'No problem,' Liz agreed and put her fingertips together in the fastidious manner of the Ipoh police commander before asking, 'Do you think the police will be involved in this latest thing Major Sturgess is planning?'

'No idea, though with this being an "emergency" and not a declared war they are the ultimate authority, so quite probably. Why?'

'I wondered how busy the inspector might be.' Be still my heart and my conscience, she ordered. The silent yearning to know where Alan was and what the new mission involved quite blotted out what her mother was saying, though it sounded like a mighty tirade.

When they arrived at the police station and walked inside, the man behind the desk rose and backed up a step as Blanche demanded, 'Is the inspector in?'

'Inspector Aba busy, can I help you?' the man asked hesitantly, obviously recognising them from their last visit. He appeared somewhat flustered as at that moment they all heard the sound of footsteps coming down the stairs.

The inspector came in, holding out a handful of blown-up photographs. He looked, Liz thought, as if he wished he had the courage to spin on his heel when her mother waylaid him in no uncertain manner.

'Ah, Inspector Aba, just in time! We may

be just the people you need to save you a lot of trouble. We can take Mr Harfield home with us.'

'Mrs Hammond.' His features spelled resignation as he bowed in the direction of Liz and her mother. With a little shrug, as if he had absolutely no alternative, he said, 'Perhaps you should come into my office.' He ushered them towards the stairs, then went back to speak rapidly to the man behind the desk. The withering tone of his voice was so different it sounded like quite another man.

'This ludicrous charge against Mr Harfield,' Blanche began as the inspector closed the door of his upstairs office.

Inspector Aba held up a hand. 'Madam,' he began, 'Mrs Hammond, I do not have to speak to you, but out of respect for your grief I do so. Mr Harfield is, however, held under damning evidence so damning I could not possibly release him.'

Liz could see her mother was shocked but she did not give up. She was insisting that bail be arranged when Liz noticed the photographs that lay on top of the inspector's pad of blotting paper. They were blown-up photographs of a Chinese girl's face. One eye was swollen, one lip split and bleeding, and there seemed to be marks on the girl's neck. She could see one photograph underneath was of the upper legs; these bore marks as if clawed by an animal. She swallowed and looked away so quickly that Inspector Aba turning his glance to her momentarily, did not realise she had seen.

Was this the girl George Harfield was supposed to have raped? Someone had viciously attacked her, that was for sure.

'I cannot believe you are actually going to keep him locked up,' Blanche went on. 'He has a mine to run! His people rely on him. Surely he can prove he was not there?'

'Mem! He was there.' The Inspector seemed to become aware again of the photographs under his hands, for the fingers were suddenly spread and still over the glossy prints. For a moment Liz thought he was going to display them, but instead he picked them up, levelled the stack with a quick tap on the desk and slid them into a drawer. 'We had a call and he was found in the room with this distressed girl.'

'Then we'd like to see him,' Blanche demanded, taking hold of her handbag and preparing to rise. 'And arrange for him to consult a lawyer?'

'His solicitor has been. All the business has been done, all statements taken and Mr Harfield was transferred to Pudu Gaol, Kuala Lumpur, early today.'

Blanche rose, all formal courtesies forgotten now. 'All damned quick, isn't it? All a bit cut and dried, isn't it? Does the British High Commissioner know?'

'He is being informed.'

'Is being? George Harfield fought in the jungles against the Japs for you lot, is this how you reward him?'

'I know Mr Harfield before the war,' the inspector said with some quiet dignity, though Liz noticed his fingertips shook a little as he meticulously put them together. 'I was there, Mrs Hammond, when the arrest was made—the girl who accuses him is the daughter of one of his foremen. At Pudu Gaol they have facilities for visiting; you must apply there in a few days' time. Until then...' The fingertips pressed together until the ends were noticeably paler. 'Regulations must be kept and rules obeyed.'

'Of course!' Blanche rose quickly. 'That is what we want, for the law to take its course—and set an innocent man free!'

Outside, she exhaled an exasperated breath. 'Now what?'

'If we've got to drive to KL in a few days, let's go and see the local car dealer. I feel in the mood for haggling,' Liz suggested.

'Good idea!' Blanche agreed.

'This girl being the daughter of the

foreman?' Liz posed the question as they walked away.

'I know.' Blanche's tone was dour. 'This I do not understand. George certainly went off one day because some girl belonging to one of his workers was missing, if you remember.'

'It must be this same girl. There were photographs on the desk of a Chinese girl who had been dreadfully beaten. Did you see?'

Blanche shook her head. 'I'd feel happier if I could talk to John Sturgess again. I'm not at all sure it's going to be that easy to get into Pudu Gaol.'

'Oh, we'll do that all right,' Liz answered, a little surprised her mother should doubt that. She was also more than certain she would feel happier if she could talk to Alan again.

They bought an old black Ford. The garageman looked a little ragged around his emotional edges after having dealt with these two belligerent Englishwomen.

'I give a good deal,' he shouted defensively as they drove away. 'A bloody good deal!'

Three days later they had learned nothing of either Alan or the major, but finally had permission to see George in Pudu Gaol the following week.

Their personal situation seemed to mirror the frustration of the whole English business community in Malaya, caught in an inexplicable muddle, without information. Fear ruled as more and more reports of murders and atrocities reached police stations up and down the country. Planters and miners at a series of meetings displayed an unprecedented fury as their properties and loyal workers bore the brunt of the communist attacks. Their demands for weapons, protection, action, a guard on every bungalow, were dismissed as 'alarmist' by the High Commissioner, Mr Edward Gent.

Their faraway Attlee-led government seemed to many to be more concerned with improving relations with Red China than with the protection of Britain's own citizens and armed forces. Self-help consequently became the order of the day. The isolated day-to-day lives English miners and planters lived had always needed vigorous resourcefulness, to which a new frustrated aggression was now being added.

The first payment for the newly begun tapping operations at Rinsey came as a boon and relief to the workers. Blanche and Liz put their profit into buying the machine gun Joan Wildon recommended—from a source they did not ask questions about.

With the new freedom of the car, Liz made it her business to take one of their tappers as shotgun rider and visit Bukit Kinta so she and her mother could make a direct report to George. Rasa's son and Chemor were largely running the mine while they waited for a new manager to be appointed. It had never occurred to Liz until that moment that George would lose his job and his home if this trumped-up charge should ever be proved against him, unthinkable as that idea was.

Production of ore at the mine had dropped and the whole place had an air of waiting for the next disaster to strike. The morale and confidence of the workers was totally sapped without George or Rasa to guide them.

Perhaps the one positive thing they could tell George was that the scheme to drop payrolls from the air rather than risk having them ambushed and provide more funds for the terrorists was under way. Bukit Kinta was on the flying list for drops. The only casualty in their area had been the tin roof above Joan Wildon's gun position. A wage bag containing $25,000 went hurtling down on Joan's prize machine gun. Joan had rung Rinsey in a fine old temper. 'I have to compensate well to the left now to hit anything, it's a bugger!'

As Liz drove to KL she felt it was rather like going to visit someone in hospital, one tried to have a store of cheerful stories to tell the patient about the outside world. But as they drew near Pudu Gaol her heart sank; the whole edifice was so forbidding, so cheerless. The twin colonial-style spires either side of the main entrance gate seemed only to emphasise the plainness of the barracklike blocks with small barred openings visible behind. '1895' was the date emblazoned above the entrance. Liz felt it should more appropriately bear the message 'Abandon Hope All Ye Who Enter Here!'

The two Englishwomen were regarded with some curiosity by the many Chinese and Malays who were also waiting for visiting time to begin. But soon the starers began to realise that, like them, the Hammonds carried bundles of food and whatever other comforts they could take into the prison. There were a few under-breath comments and one or two laughs as Liz and Blanche joined the waiting ranks.

The appointed time came and to the minute the visitors were admitted. Inside it seemed curiously calm after the bustle of the streets and the tense, nervous movements and burst of conversation there had been in the queue while they waited to see their loved ones.

Liz and Blanche found themselves siphoned off to the left with several other women. They came to three small separate areas where their menfolk sat. Liz's heart lurched as she saw George; he looked, she thought, like an old dog, lost, kept captive where he hated to be, but still belligerent.

When he saw them approach his lips parted and his cheeks suffused with some colour. He rose to greet them with an expansive show of manners, exactly as if they were entering his sitting room. It was this more than anything else that touched her heart.

'My dear man,' Blanche said gently, and it seemed more comment than greeting.

'You're both a sight for sore eyes,' he said, reaching out to take their hands. There were no spare chairs and George insisted Blanche should sit down while he and Liz perched on the table.

It seemed to their Western eyes a very casual approach to prison visiting until they remembered the armed guards and the huge gates. The level of chatter rose in the background until they might just as easily have been in one of the market places, with the singsong pitch of Chinese voices dominating.

Blanche was suddenly very busy with

the bag she had brought and covertly, not knowing what was allowed, produced a glass, whisky and a soda syphon. She mixed the drink and handed it to George, who swore gently like a blessing, then sipped as if it were nectar.

'Fair exchange,' Blanche said. 'You remember on the train when we first met?'

'That seems a lifetime and a half ago,' he replied, lifted the glass and drank their health.

'There's two bottles and a syphon in here.' With her toe she touched one of the bags she had brought, then asked, 'Can you tell us what happened? Inspector Aba told us so very little, the civil authorities told us less than that, and with John Sturgess away there was no one who would listen to us. Have you seen a solicitor? Why haven't they allowed you bail?'

'The charge is too serious. If I had done it I wouldn't expect to see the outside world for a long, long time.'

'We needn't waste time discussing that,' Blanche said. 'Just tell us what on earth it's all about.'

'What it is about is a communist plot, trap. I've been a thorn in their sides for a long time, and this last raid on your amah's village was the final straw.

We not only captured two of their high-ranking men, we found information which we think will lead us to a big jungle camp, one capable of housing five hundred or more terrorists, one *we* used in the war.'

Liz glanced round to make sure they could not be overheard before asking, 'Is this the sortie the major and Alan will have gone on now?'

She felt sure he remembered seeing Alan and herself together in the hut, remembered putting his hand on Alan's shoulder, as he gave the briefest of nods. It precipitated her into a torment of anxiety. A camp of terrorists that large! How many guardsmen would have gone in? Sorties as far as she could gather were small units of five or six men, with large operations spoken of when five or six such units went into an area at the same time. A camp that could hide five hundred was something quite different. She felt a terrible premonition that she might never see Alan again.

'I wish I were with them!' She jumped as George put his hand over hers as it lay on the table between them and repeated what he had said. 'I wish I could be with them.'

'But this trap?' Blanche insisted. 'George, our time will be short, I expect. We can't

250

do anything about Sturgess in the jungle, but we might be able to help you if you tell us all about it.'

'Right!' George was reminded of his own desperate situation. 'I had a message I thought was from the police to say that my worker's daughter had been found in the hands of a brothelkeeper who was holding her by force to use her for prostitution. I was to go to Room 21 at this particular boarding house to help the police identify the girl during a raid they were planning to make.

'I went to this kind of rooming house; there was no one about. I went up to the first floor and found the room. I listened at the door and could hear a girl crying. I knocked and went in. It was dark and the girl was whimpering like a whipped puppy. I called her name and she answered from the bed.

'I went over and sat down on the bed, put my hand out and touched her shoulder.' He paused and swallowed at the recollection. 'Then all hell broke loose. The light went on in the room, there was the noise of boots pounding up the stairs and from under the sheet this thing...this girl emerged. Her nose was pouring with blood, her eye and mouth were split and bleeding, her blouse had been ripped from her shoulders, her trousers torn away. She

251

shouted, "Rape! Help me! Rape!"

'Rape,' he repeated quietly, shaking his head, 'but what I shall never forget is her eyes. *They* didn't shout rape, they were like the slogans on some of their posters, they glittered and shouted, "Revenge! Death to the running dogs!" '

He finished the whisky. 'Then the police were in the room, the girl curled into a sobbing ball on the bed—and the rest, as they say, is history.'

'But who attacked her?' Liz asked, remembering the photographs.

'It has to have been one of her own,' George said solemnly. 'There is no way such a trap could have been sprung so neatly otherwise.'

'You mean she let someone do that to her?'

'She'd volunteer,' George said and his eyes were hard with certainty.

'One of your workers' daughters,' Blanche commented.

'I obviously have communist sympathisers in Kampong Kinta—fanatical activists would be a better description, remembering little Li Min's eyes.'

Liz remembered her visit to Bukit Kinta, and the creeping aura of fear she had felt at the mine. 'But I thought many of your workpeople were related?'

'Bad apples in every barrel,' he said.

252

Chapter Fourteen

Having looked through a sketchbook Elizabeth Hammond had left in the lounge at Rinsey, John Sturgess was sure the picture drawn inside the book of poetry was her work.

What he doubted was that the book really belonged to Guardsman Alan Cresswell. He searched through the pages but there was nothing written anywhere to indicate ownership, nor, he thought cynically, was the way some of the pages were stuck together indicative that the book contained favourite works of either one.

The only thing he was sure of was that the drawing portrayed just a plain run-of-the-mill guardsman, there were no insignias of rank on his jungle-green kit and he held a rifle. Where the man was supposed to be standing was quite unknown to him and seemed quite meaningless.

He felt no guilt at taking the book from the envelope and scrutinising it—he had censored many men's letters in his time, and this seemed no different to him. Cresswell was under his command; his life, so to speak, was his to order.

Sturgess closed the book slowly, calculating that he could draw immediate lines of Cresswell's life with more ease than he could seemingly order his own. The course he had really wanted his own life to take was, he bitterly admitted, beyond his own powers. Elizabeth Hammond could, on the other hand, be an excellent secondary objective, a compensation. He slipped the book of poems into his locker drawer.

Liz was so like his wife, his lost wife, in looks. She had some of the same qualities too, he mused, some he'd have to be careful of. They both had a certain meekness of appearance, like the proverbial mouse, yet both had proved to have remarkably sharp little teeth. Elizabeth could more than hold her own in private conversation—but marriage brought a man authority. He was sure that had the war not come along he would still have had Audrey by his side and sons of his own by now.

He lit a cigarette and walked out. It was marginally cooler at night and the huge moon reflected in the water in the deep monsoon ditch made a natural guiding line for his stroll—towards his only half-acknowledged objective.

He turned to look at the camp, rows of rectangular tents, most with their sides rolled up to take advantage of any breeze. He could see his sergeant writing to his family as usual, a man who would be totally destroyed, he imagined, if his wife ever played fast and loose. Most of the men were lying on their beds, the legs of which all stood in round cigarette tins filled with insect repellent.

He walked on, cupping his cigarette so its glowing end should not be seen, until he could see Cresswell. He was reading. He watched the young man sprawled on the bed, one knee crooked, book tilted to catch the best light from the Tilley lamp tied to a tent pole.

Sturgess felt envy and could no longer ask himself what a girl might see in such a man, he knew. He even felt a stir of a forbidden attraction. Stripped almost bare, the guardsman's body had the lithe attraction of a girl's. Sturgess was forty years old and knew it could be argued that he was too old for Elizabeth Hammond.

He straightened his shoulders; he had never failed as a soldier, an officer... He did not intend to let one of his own men beat him in this competition.

Tactics, that's what I need, he thought, having been trained to figure out the way to win. He convinced himself that this girl was a better catch than his lost wife, the daughter of an impoverished Hampshire village schoolmaster, had been. For one thing, he could not see Blanche Hammond staying on their Malaysian rubber estate without her husband.

He felt better when he planned things, it alleviated the ache. Stooping to extinguish his cigarette under his heel, he moved nearer to watch Cresswell as he put down his book, yawned and stretched.

'Have the sides down now, shall we?' Cresswell's voice came sleepily, almost seductively into the night, irritating Sturgess. He turned and walked away. Then he turned again and silently appraised Cresswell of his situation. I have the ordering of you, he thought, visualising the man as if he stood before his desk for reprimand on company orders. Even after this major sortie, even should you survive everything I put you to, I'll make sure you never go near the Hammonds' plantation again.

'Goodnight, sir.' The soldier standing smoking outside a neighbouring tent made him start.

'Goodnight,' he responded sharply, then, realising it was one of his own picked group and they would all be together the following day and for some considerable time, living, sleeping, risking their lives together in the jungle, he added, 'Time for your beauty sleep, Babyface.' He needed the rest of his team on his side.

'Right, sir.'

He thought of making it an order when the man did not move immediately, but remembered that the last words his wife had said to him had been, 'You were always good at orders, John, but my life is no longer yours to order.'

Before that she had gone on a lot about the way he had ordered every second of her existence and that the Japanese might have overrun Singapore and captured the whole of the island and peninsula, but they had set her *free!* Preposterously sharp little teeth.

He gritted his own at the memory and moved restlessly on through the tents. Somewhere he could hear the slap of cards and some quiet, good-humoured banter as men had a final game before sleep. He envied their easy companionship. This he had never had, from lonely childhood to bullied schoolboy to strait-laced cadet.

When they were first married, Audrey had said he was at his best when in a position of power, in control—alone. He had taken it as a compliment.

Once begun on this trail, his mind slid easily back to 1942, to the agonies he had undergone when his young wife had been torn from his side. The six intervening years seemed sometimes no more than days, so vividly did he recall the noise, heat and panic all around them.

He had queued with her on the quayside, pushing her ever nearer the gangplank of the ship with other wives, women and girls who had lingered on working in essential jobs or caring for children, their menfolk all desperate to get them away from Singapore.

There had not at the end been a real moment of parting for she had been swept away from him by the tide of anxious embarkees as yet again Japanese warplanes bombed and strafed the harbour. For a second he had seen the top of her brown hair, a raised arm, finally just a hand, as if she was drowning in the sea of people pushing relentlessly towards the ship.

The moment had only recently been refocused and magnified under the clear lens of hindsight. Since his journey to the Blue Mountains of Australia, the memory was more harrowing with each recall. Before there had been so much hope, now it was a repeated bereavement.

The truth had taken so long to learn. Immediately after the fall of Singapore he and many remaining men who had trained for just such an eventuality had retreated into the jungles of the peninsula. All through the war they had struck at the Japanese in any way they could. He had eventually learned that the ship she had embarked on had been sunk, and had agonised over the lifted arm as if it had been some omen of a drowning.

That was the first time he had thought he had lost her for good.

Then he'd heard survivors had boarded another vessel bound for England. But though there had been coded messages sent from the secret jungle radios asking for news, there had been no reports of anyone landing in England by the name of Audrey Rosalind Sturgess.

He had had to wait until the war was over and he could travel back to England to learn that some of the people on that first stricken ship had been transferred to one going to Australia.

Walking back to his own tent, he let down the sides, opened his locker and looked at the book inside. Then he closed it and locked it away again. It was time he had his chance, time for a counterattack on life.

He saw again the bungalow on the banks of a river, the mountains blue with the aura of gumtrees in the distance. He was irretrievably bitter. He had spent the war years pining and mourning for her, then two years looking for her, as well as hundreds of pounds—and the worst thing of all had been finding her.

'Hope you all behaving yourself in 'ere.'

Alan lifted his head to see Babyface's cratered face grinning in at the tent flap.

'Clear off and go to bed!' Alan told him.

'That's what the major just told me to do,' he said with a jerk of his head in the direction of the night as he went to sit on Dan's bed.

'What's he snooping about at?' Ben Sutherland asked, but Babyface was watching Alan as he drew himself up to a sitting position.

'Watching you.' He nodded in Alan's direction. 'Watching you like a bloody hawk.'

Alan scowled but did not speak.

'So what's so special about you?' Babyface obviously thought there was a possible source of entertainment here. 'You did know we'd got enough signallers without you being fetched back from that plantation? What you done to him? Why does he want you in the ulu with 'im?'

The other five men in the tent all looked for his answer. Explaining was something Alan had been pressed to do ever since he found himself reunited with the men who had been at Rinsey. For it seemed what Babyface said was true; a signaller from Headquarters Company had found himself sent on unexpected furlough to Penang Island. There was no way, though,

Alan was going to try to explain his real suspicions about his cavalier removal from Rinsey.

'Perhaps he couldn't get on with the other chap,' Dan tried valiantly to be on Alan's side. 'After all, an officer has to work pretty closely with his signaller in the jungle.'

Alan still did not respond and Dan went on, 'I'm bloody scared of going back into the ulu, I don't mind telling you.'

'Everybody is,' Alan answered, thinking that the heat made Dan's freckles look almost black against his cameolike complexion.

'It's not the ulu that's worrying our Al, it's leaving the girlie behind at that plantation. Ideas above his station, that's what he's got!'

'That's not true!' Dan sprang to his aid with the devastating remark. 'If anyone fancies that Miss Hammond it's the major. I saw him looking at her when he thought nobody knew.'

'Sounds as if you'd better watch your back, Cresswell!'

'Aye! Strange things can happen on jungle patrols.'

'Aye.' Dan again sought to be on Alan's side. 'And it wouldn't be the first officer who'd been shot by his own men.'

'Thanks, Dan,' Alan said mildly, 'that's a great help.'

'Well, you know what I mean.' Dan protested his good intentions. 'You know as well as I do that officers can't afford to throw their weight about so much when they're having to muck in with you and we've all got live ammunition and that...'

Alan raised his eyebrows, remembering his admiration for Sturgess in action at the village, but there were murmurs of agreement from several throats.

'I've known a time-serving drill sergeant I wouldn't have minded walking behind with a loaded rifle,' Sinclair, the elder of the Sutherland brothers, muttered.

'Hey!' Dan asked in an excited whisper, 'and have any of you lot seen the amount of top brass we've had in this camp the last three days?'

'The Smiths reckon it's something big this time,' Babyface said with a resigned sigh, quoting the other two members of their group, no relation, but always together.

'I'm sure it's different,' Alan agreed. This was one thing he was quite prepared to talk about. 'For one thing there's a lot more men going in.'

'Yeah! And there's a lot more dropping zone tape and maps around. We're going after something specific.'

'Or someone?' Alan wondered. 'Heng Hou perhaps.'

'Christ!' Babyface blasphemed vehemently. 'Don't want anything to do with that bastard. You heard what he did to that Seaforth sergeant!'

They had but it didn't stop him refreshing their memories.

'Threw him down a pit lined with sharpened bamboos all pointing downwards from the sides.' Babyface stood up so he could better display the arrangement of the trap. 'He was impaled in the bottom and if he tried to get out he spiked himself worse. Every time he moved he—'

'Very heartening!' Sergeant Mackenzie had come and stood unobserved in the doorway. 'If that's the last bedtime story, I'd say get your bleeding heads down before it's time to get up again. Otherwise I'll tell you a story that'll really make your toes curl. Now stop your yapping and get to your own tent, Babyface.'

'Well, we won't be able to talk much once we get into the jungle, will we, Sarge?' Dan, everyone's champion, commented. 'It'll be all hush and hand signals.'

'Very true, Veasey.' The sergeant made a few meaningful jerks of his thumb towards Dan's bed.

As he made the gestures, 'Lights Out' was sounded by the trumpeter and all over the camp the Tilley lights were extinguished. As Dan slid into the bed nearest the door, the sergeant pulled down the mosquito netting for him.

Alan thought it a kind act to close his eyes upon, and soon the camp was threaded by the assorted snores of men who were too exhausted to be worried, while others lay staring into the darkness and into their own particular thoughts and fears.

Alan lay thinking of Liz and Rinsey, then of tomorrow's mission. It all suddenly felt so different for him. If he believed what was said, he had really not been needed. He need not be going. The thought needled, made him nervous and resentful. He hoped the camp cook would be prompt in posting his letters—to Liz and to his mother. There seemed so much that was not quite right, so much plotting, lots of rumours being spread.

By the light of the moon he could see his pack and wireless all ready for the morning. An early breakfast, porridge, perhaps even fried bread dipped in egg and bacon, then into the jungle.

Rumour again had it that they were to be gone some time because of the amounts of stores and ammunition that had been shared among the loads to be carried. Then someone said the patrol was being delayed because George Harfield had been arrested in Ipoh for raping a Chinese girl and the major had been to see about it.

Alan had found this rumour so outrageous that he had hopes that some of the others were false too.

Nearly two weeks into the jungle operation Alan felt he had never been out. The few days in between had been mere illusion and the time at the derelict bungalow sheer fantasy.

Sight bleared with the sweat he had no free hand or energy to wipe away, he moved after smeared green figures in a green and brown world booby-trapped with rocks, ground creepers and those damned vicious thorns.

Worst of all, he knew he was becoming bitter, for it seemed to him that whatever he did Major Sturgess was never going to approve. He had done his best to make radio contact when asked, risked his neck getting his aerial up trees, did his share of other work, but while the odd approving pat on the shoulder or nod of confidence could go to the other eight in the unit, he was never given more than a swift hissed order or a peremptory gesture of command. He had not realised how important these small acknowledgements were until they were denied him.

Perhaps, he reasoned, it was the surest evidence he had of Liz's love, this change in the other man's attitude to him, this split in Sturgess's character. The soldier he admired and had worked so well with in the old nurse's exploding home was a giant compared with this man who plainly could hardly bear to look at him.

He pressed his arm to the oilskin-wrapped photograph; the action stuck the package to his chest.

So Sturgess was jealous. Babyface had probably not been far wrong when he had warned him to watch his back. It seemed at once over the top and yet petty to think in such terms, but if it was petty of him to think it, it was even more petty of an officer to indulge in such discriminations.

Dan had noticed for he had given a decisive V-sign to the officer after he turned his back on the two of them. Alan thought it was pretty unprofessional of Sturgess to allow his men to see any sign of prejudice to any soldier.

On the thirteenth night they were told that there would be an airdrop the next day, so as soon as the dropping zone was cleared and ready they could rest up for an hour or two.

The following morning all ten began clearing a circle of jungle flat enough to allow the broad fluorescent orange strips to be laid in the prearranged Z-shape. Then they retreated into the surrounding jungle and waited, rested and listened.

By the time the Dakota was heard it was near midday. Waiting until the unmistakeable drone of its engine came nearer, Alan radioed to ascertain that it was their dropping aircraft.

There was a crackly affirmation with the added information that they had located the marker and would circle once and drop on the second run.

Alan acknowledged. Then all waited expectantly for the supplies to be parachuted down, aware that the activity could also give away their presence to the enemy.

The Dakota circled once, then came in tighter and as the aircraft came down within a few hundred feet of the clearing they could see the men in harness standing in the open doorway. The plane tipped to one side to make it easier for the men to push the large wooden crates out with their feet. Almost immediately the aircraft was up and riding out of their sight over the jungle, the noises retreating into the distance as they watched four parachutes open and the crates tumbling rapidly down, towards the dropping zone, they hoped.

They watched carefully. 'Bugger!' Major Sturgess exclaimed as one went completely out of sight, well short. Two others landed spot on and the third hooked itself in a perimeter tree, hanging for a few moments until branches creaked, groaned and cracked under the weight, seeming to the watchers to lower the crate down from one layer to the next and to the ground.

'Full marks,' Sergeant Mackenzie approved.

'Three out of four,' Alan said.

'Reckon we could have a fire tonight then, sir? Plenty of dry wood.' Dan tapped the first crate with his toe. 'Make a hot meal.'

'The drop's bad enough, we don't want to alert the whole of Perak to our presence,' Sturgess said shortly, then added, 'Sorry, chaps, nothing hot until this one's finished—it's too important.'

'Sergeant, you, Veasey and the Sutherlands open these three, distribute the loads between the packs, while I take one man and find that stray crate.' As he took his compass from his pocket, he signalled to Alan to go with him, while Entap, their Dyak tracker, and the Smiths were detailed to keep lookout.

Danny caught Alan's eye as he left, grinned but put his hands behind his back as if shielding it. Alan nodded grimly. His recent speculations had taken any humour from the situation.

The two of them had not gone far, making sure they marked their way back on various trees, when they could hear a different sound.

'Can you swim, Cresswell?'

'No, sir,' he lied.

'Let's hope the crate's not in the water then.'

Alan thought, judging by the sound, that if it was it would have been washed away. Then he caught sight of a drape of parachute over a tree to their right. The major obviously had not seen it, so Alan bounded forward and touched the officer's arm. Sturgess drew away as if burned. Alan stood still for a moment, looking the man straight in the eye, then pointed out the chute.

Without a word the major turned in that direction. Alan, following, seethed. It had to be Liz, the older man was sweet on Liz and resented a mere guardsman being preferred to a high-ranking officer.

Sturgess came suddenly to a halt and turned to see the contempt on his inferior's face.

Before him Alan saw a rushing, raging torrent and in front of it his officer, whose face was suffused with fury.

'What is it with you, Cresswell?' he hissed. 'What makes you think you're so bloody superior?'

'No, sir. I don't, sir,' he answered, gritting his teeth against what he wanted to say, that he certainly had the advantage in the matter of Elizabeth Hammond for their love was mutual, consummated, a meeting of two made in heaven for each other.

Faced with the fury of the other man, the man who had for the moment forgotten his role as superior example-setting officer, he remembered an old soldier saying that the only weapon a private had against victimisation by a higher rank was silence and the capacity to keep taking the abuse.

'You worthless conscripts, you're more bloody trouble than you're worth! What'd you say if I told you I've had complaints from the Hammond family about you?'

'I'd say produce your evidence,' Alan said carefully, the educated mind refusing to be quelled though his voice shook as he added, 'and if you couldn't I'd say you were a bloody liar.'

'Why do you think I took you away from Rinsey?'

Alan toyed with a choice of words ranging from 'jealousy' to 'spite'. He was not a man who naturally resorted to violence but it occurred to him that it would have been remarkably simple to tip the snarling major into the raging waters of the jungle river just behind him. In and gone he'd be. He doubted there was even a monkey to witness such a dark act in the green damp gloom of leaf and moss, huge overhanging ferns above their heads and the slippery bank—and he could see where the huge crate was being twirled in the muddy brown water like a matchstick in a plughole.

'It was a question of standing cock having no conscience, wasn't it, Cresswell? The girl was there and so were you—and such as you never miss a sniff, do you?'

This, Alan judged, was definitely the time for silence. He was so appalled at his officer's crudeness that all wish to retaliate vanished. He wanted to laugh now, not kill, astonished and dismayed by the man's brand of vicious fishwife spite.

He heard a movement behind him and swung round, rifle at the ready, as Sergeant Mackenzie and Dan came along the track they had made.

Sturgess swore. 'Thought I told you to supervise the unpacking of the other crates!'

'All under control, sir,' the sergeant answered, his glance going from his officer to Cresswell. 'Brought a rope up in case you need one.' He paused to look over the Major's shoulder. 'And looks like we do.'

Alan nodded gratefully at Dan, wondering if he had after all shared some real

271

anxiety with the sergeant which had made Mackenzie come after them.

'Don't like the look of that,' the sergeant added as the crate, hit by an extra surge of water, bounced about in the river like a canoe shooting the rapids.

'Right! Let's get at it!' the major announced. Gesturing to Danny, who was carrying the rope slung around his shoulders, he added, 'think it's your turn for the dip, Cresswell. Get the rope round yourself.'

Alan wondered if this was why he had lied about being able to swim—to test the major.

'We could really do with another rope,' the sergeant said, 'one for Cresswell to keep round himself, the other to tie on the crate.'

'Come on, man! It'll be dark before we've finished. He'll manage.'

The sergeant took up the rope and helped secure it around the guardsman.

Alan thought briefly of alligators and leeches as he waded into the water, but by the time he had gone three steps he felt the water was far too rough for alligators to survive. In another two steps it whipped his legs from under him and he was going downstream at some rate until the rope the others held braced around a tree stopped him.

He soon realised that the only way he was ever going to reach the far bank and the crate was to allow himself to be taken by the current to a bend. Below where they were, he could see the far bank looped towards him, though the water hit and streamed past it at great force.

Trying to signal, he held up the rope with one hand, going completely under as he did so. He tried again to indicate he wanted some slack. The rope suddenly gave, and he hurtled downriver, choking as he spun uncontrollably in the water. In a flash of vision as he surfaced he saw the bank rushing towards him and managed to get his feet forward in the water just before he hit the bank. He thanked God there were no rocks, then he saw there were—either side of where he had landed.

Laboriously he climbed clear of the water, stood gasping, trembling, taking a moment to recover and wave back to the other side. He could see that Danny and the sergeant still held their end of the rope, while the major stood in a critical attitude, hands on hips. His voice came faintly over the crash of the water, 'Get on with it, man! Get hold of it!'

Alan turned away and swore under the roar of the water, 'You frigging bastard! I'll get your crate back, but not the way you want me to and be bashed to death by it.'

As he undid the rope he could hear Sturgess shouting again, but he ignored him. He'd make his own plans.

Without looking across again, he made his way, slipping and hanging from nearby *lliang* creepers, towards the tree ensnaring the crate's parachute. With infinite care he lowered himself down by the branches towards the great box bouncing about on the swirling waters.

He was out of sight of the men from the other bank, and he was scared. 'Father,' he heard himself saying, 'make me an ark of gopher wood.' He was unsure whether he addressed his God or his late father, until he recollected the ease with which Edgar Cresswell approached a new task, a new piece of timber, then he slipped. He was down, able to touch, or more accurately fend off, the crate as it first swirled out into the stream, then was slammed back towards the bank.

If it trapped him he could be knocked senseless or have an arm or leg shattered in an instant. '...Careful! No room for errors,' he heard his father advise as he took the full force of the crate on one boot sole.

'Right, you bastard,' he told it, 'next time in you're mine...Oh, Christ!' he cried as next time it drove towards him at head height. He crouched and put his hands over his head, but the current pulled it back before it hit. It was like being in the path of a killing pendulum.

His heart thumping, he waited for the next swing, calculating that what he had to do was reach the top of the crate, where its straining harness allowed for a rope to be passed through.

The next time he was surprised by the swinging power and force of the box as it came towards him. The time after that, he managed to push his hand through the harness but was not quick enough to loop the rope through. Instead he felt his hand caught. He pulled back and thought his whole arm might be jerked from its socket; he felt the rough wood of the crate grate at his hand, the sharp angular edges tearing his skin, but then he was free.

He realised that he would quickly become exhausted battling with these forces. Grimly he set himself to succeed the next time.

'Right! Come on, you—you thing on the side of the bloody high and mighty officers! Come on!'

He waited, but aggression wasn't his best motivator, and as it swung in again and again he muttered, 'This time for Liz.'

It came closer this swing, nearly pushing him off balance. Using the extra seconds, he got his arm through the harness, grasping the rope from the other side and pulling it through. For a frantic moment or two he slithered and was drawn down the bank as he held on, then his foot found a root which stopped him sufficiently to secure a knot on the harness.

He climbed the bank until he could see the men opposite. Dan lifted his fist in salute. He motioned to them that he would sever the parachute above the harness, then they should pull the crate across. 'Take up the slack,' he bellowed.

He hauled himself up the tree to cut the parachute cords, leaving them as long as he could. Once free of the bonds holding it to the tree, the crate fell and, no longer being pulled by two forces, floated with less agitation. When the other three began to pull it across, Alan took a tight grip on the trailing cords and was towed back safely after it.

Dan thumped him on his back as he reached the shore. Then all three seemed automatically to glance at their officer, waiting for his comment. The major walked to the far side of the now safely beached crate and released the parachute harness from it.

Sergeant Mackenzie cleared his throat rather like a parent reminding a child of its manners, but, as Sturgess busied himself with rolling and tidying the cords, he took on the leader's role—as he was trained to do if anything untoward happened to his immediate commander.

'Well done, Cresswell! Reckon if there'd been someone shooting at you as well, that would have been worth a medal.'

Alan gave a humph of laughter as the comment relaxed the tension of the situation, and, as Dan promised to strip him when they got back to the others and 'go over him for leeches', he quipped, 'What more could a man ask?'

Chapter Fifteen

If vigilance had been the order of the day before the airdrop, afterwards the tension of the exercise was screwed several notches tighter.

Before they moved off on the fifteenth day, the major beckoned them round for a briefing.

'I worked this area for most of the war with the help of old Entap here, "the best pucking scout in Perak!" ' He paused after the imitation of the Dyak's response to any remark made to him, and Entap self-consciously put his blowpipe to his mouth and made the spitting noise that preceded the expulsion of the poisoned darts.

'And unless,' the major went on, 'our calculations are seriously out we're within a day's march of the camp we think the commies use as area headquarters. All kinds of activities point this way—a major link in their jungle postal system, raids to extort and terrorise, printing of leaflets, training, indoctrination, we believe it all goes on at this base.

'Anyway, Entap and I are the reason this unit's come in from the longest cross-jungle route—not, Veasey, because I had a personal down on anyone. I thought we'd get that clear now.'

Alan glanced down at Dan, who shuffled a jungle boot in the undergrowth and scowled like a guilty schoolboy.

'The other units on this op won't have started so soon or have travelled so far, but we serve to complete the encirclement. If the CTs make for the deepest jungle we'll probably be heavily involved in picking them off. I hope we will anyway, though we're running a little behind time.

'We had a decent result at the kampong; this next could be the best result of the whole campaign so far.'

They murmured their support and even Alan was impressed in spite of his alienation as Sturgess went on.

'Entap has found elephant tracks just off to the left. I propose to use these provided they don't veer off our course too much. It'll give us the chance to move more quickly and to keep a better lookout for their tripwires.'

It was the practice of both sides to guard their positions with elaborate systems of alarms or booby traps—a tin set to rattle against a pole, a bundle of tins in a tree, a flare or an antipersonnel mine.

They moved cautiously though much quicker all that day, following the paths the elephants had trampled, marvelling at the branches torn from trees and saplings uprooted as the animals had grazed their way through the jungle.

Sturgess read his compass and consulted Entap at regular intervals, and early in the same afternoon the Dyak came back to the line of soldiers with the speed and silence that astonished Alan and gestured them all down.

He was pulling his tube of poison darts from his belt as he went forwards alone. They listened intently, rifles at the ready. Alan thought he heard a noise like a tree keeling over, as they often did on the soft jungle floor, except that the next moment Entap reappeared grinning, holding something down by his side.

Sturgess, who was nearest, swore softly.

'Pucking guard,' Entap reported, lifting his left hand to reveal he carried the guard's head.

Behind him Alan heard Danny bring back his breakfast. Several men swore and blasphemed under their breath; Alan swallowed hard several times. He had heard that this was something these Dyaks did instead of carrying the whole man back for identification purposes. In camp he had seen them sitting around their tent, continually honing their parangs to razor-edged sharpness.

'You know?' Entap asked, holding his trophy higher for Sturgess to examine. 'You take picture!'

'Yes,' the major said patiently, 'then you can get rid of it. I said I would use my camera so you do not need to do this.'

A look of hurt and stubbornness came over the tribesman's face and after the photograph had been taken Alan suspected he took the scalp before finally disposing of the head at the major's insistence—at gunpoint.

'We don't want anything extra to carry,' he told the tracker. 'Now on we go. But good work, good work!' He patted Entap on the back and his grin came back immediately.

About an hour after this Sturgess halted the line and called them in again. 'We've made good time so we'll bivouac early, keep a low profile in case they miss their man—we don't want to trigger anything too soon.

There was a heightening of morale, for now their officer was working as a fully committed soldier. Alan too admitted his superiority as an officer in action. Every soldier had heard of officers and sergeants who deliberately made their presence known in the jungle—to make sure they never did encounter any terrorists. He watched Sturgess as he went from man to man with a word for each one; in action he was of a different calibre.

'Have a listen in,' Sturgess asked as he reached Alan, 'just make sure there's nothing we should know about.'

The signaller had barely swung his radio and pack from his shoulder when from some distance came a single reverberating echo. It was hardly more than the sound of an eardrum popping as an aircraft climbed, but they all froze, listening intently. The single shot was followed by the unmistakeable stutter of an automatic weapon.

'Chrrrist! Someone's blown it!' Sturgess spat out the words.

'Not all that walking for nothing!' Dan stood and shook his head.

Alan dived for his radio, put on

headphones and throat microphone, switched on and listened to the operation frequency. Silence. Then he switched to their headquarters at Ipoh. His hand was just reaching for the knob to retune back to the operation call station when the smooth, upper-class and unmistakeable voice of the commander in chief came on the air.

'Sunray here! Attention! Sunray here! All units Operation Tight squeeze! Go in now! I repeat. Go in now! All units...'

Alan looked up at the major, slipped the headphones off and handed them to him. Sturgess listened, nodded, handed them back. 'Acknowledge,' he said turning back to the men. 'We're going in now!' he told them. 'I estimate we're about a quarter of a mile from the camp—a bloody long way in jungle, but if these tracks go our way a bit farther and the CTs want a quick way out, we may pick some of 'em up.'

He gestured to Alan to let him have the throat microphone as well and, pressing it to his larynx, reported in no more than a whisper.

'Unit One to Sunray. We're on a natural escape route so won't go in hell for leather, we may pick up more if we let 'em funnel in rather than scatter them around the jungle.' He listened out, then passed the instruments back to Alan.

'The other thing is it'll be dark in about

an hour,' he told the group. 'We'll move off right away, then lie in ambush along these tracks for the night. Signaller, see what else you can pick up as we go.'

Alan reassembled his kit, loaded up, locked his radio on to the operation frequency and, wearing his headphones and throat microphone over from the set on his back, followed the major and the sergeant. They had barely gone two hundred yards when they were again given urgent signals from Entap to disperse.

Alan slid the headphones aside a little so he could hear what was happening around him. It was not difficult. Whoever was coming, he thought, was not Dyak or Iban and sounded in a blind panic. The jungle trapped the sounds, sending them rolling along the track like the echoes in a tunnel. Soon, he thought he could actually hear laboured breathing, the regular suck and pump of air, then he realised it was his own heart thumping.

He swallowed hard, took deep breaths and tried to remember his training, the drills men said came automatically when action began. He had two conflicting thoughts; one was that he had still never actually shot a man, never seriously hurt a fellow human being—and would he be able to?—the other was the drill of bayonet practice, the instant response to the command to charge in and the 'in, twist, pull' of the bayonet. He wondered if a real body felt anything like those heavy, awkward dummies they had screamed at in training.

Listening, his state of apprehension bordered on terror as the noise of those who approached sounded to him more like trains than terrorists. They passed within yards of where he lay. What was that bloody major playing at? Alan could have wept with the frustration of seconds hanging like sentences. He was sure he heard a stifled sob, a swift, involuntary gasp from Dan. Alan held his breath as if to compensate, then realised that the bandits were making so much noise they would never have heard.

He also dimly realised that the major was waiting until he was sure all the communists were in their sights. Alan reached the pitch were he really did not care what he fired at as long as he shot his gun off.

Then the challenge rang out. 'Halt or we fire!'

The communists dived and the soldiers fired. The shots exploded, whined and ricocheted along the line.

'Follow me!' Sergeant Mackenzie was on his feet, crouching low, running to an ellipse of untrampled undergrowth in the middle of the tracks, an island of cover. As he moved more shots rang out, then answering fire from both sides as in the jungle gloom men saw where bullets were coming from. There was more firing and the swift cry of a man mortally injured.

Alan felt a shiver go over his spine as he was up and running. His sergeant seemed slightly behind but gestured he should take one side of the patch of central cover while he went the other. They emerged firing. Alan saw a hat with a red star in the undergrowth ahead of him and fired as fast as he could as he ran towards it.

When he got there it was just a hat caught in a bush. He grabbed at it and looked around for its owner. Mackenzie called to him, 'I'm coming on your right, Cresswell.'

'We got him then.' The sergeant nodded at the hat. Alan turned to deny it, when he saw the young Chinese terrorist at Mackenzie's feet, three shots splayed across his chest like a dotted line. 'Make up for Veasey!'

A burst of automatic fire from farther back was followed by high Chinese voices, gabbling, appealing, the major's command, and 'All right! Stand still! Stand still!'

'Come on!' Mackenzie went ahead to where the major and one of the Sutherlands had two prisoners at gunpoint.

They indicated their surrender with hands as high as they could reach above their heads.

'Disarm them,' Sturgess ordered.

Alan went forward, pulling hand grenades from back pockets, knives from belts. He gasped as he pulled a hefty parang out of the belt and across the chest of the second terrorist, and drew back as if stung. 'This one's a woman, sir.'

'Is it!' The major sounded unimpressed. 'Lucky you. Right! We want some good long bamboos and Mackenzie will show you how to tie these across their shoulders, hands at each end. They won't run very far or very fast in the trees then, should they try to escape.'

Alan had moved towards Entap, who was already cutting at a clump of stout bamboos, when he turned back to the sergeant. 'Make up for Veasey?' he questioned.

Everyone's eyes was on Mackenzie as he looked directly at his officer and reported, 'I'm afraid Veasey bought it, sir.'

'That who screamed?'

The Sergeant nodded.

'But I heard that...' Alan began as if in the fact he had found out their lie, 'He can't be!' Alan turned and went quickly back to where he and Danny had been lying almost side by side. He had run forwards, he thought, with Danny following.

Alan did not see him come but the sergeant reached the spot midway between the jungle and that central island of cover at the same moment. He knelt by the body as Alan stretched a hand down to Dan.

'Sorry, lad, afraid he's gone!'

Such a rage overtook Alan, he wanted just to shoot off his gun at everything—friend, foe, jungle, sky, everything was his enemy now.

'Take a hold of yourself, lad,' Mackenzie said, gripping his arm.

'Don't bloody lad me,' he said between clenched teeth, repeating the words again very slowly, 'Don't bloody lad me.' Then he asked, 'Are you sure?' and dropped to his knees by his sergeant, though even as he asked he remembered the cry. He remembered *knowing* the man was dead. He stretched out a hand towards Dan's shoulder as he lay on his side, facing away from them.

'He's dead, soldier.'

'Not sure...'

The Sergeant tried to catch his hand before it reached his friend's shoulder. 'He's dead, Cresswell—half his bloody head is shot away.'

Their two hands lay together on Danny Veasey and the pressure rolled him on to his back. Only his light-red hair was recognisable. Bile exploded from Alan's mouth. He dropped his rifle and bent double until the retching stopped. Danny had been sick when Entap had produced the head. They needed Danny, he was a kind of weathercock, he knew how they were all feeling, he championed them all!

As he raised himself up, he saw the two prisoners coming towards where he knelt, their hands roped to long bamboos as if in crucifixion. He groped for his rifle.

'We all feel like that at these times.' The sergeant was there first and, picking up Alan's rifle as well as his own, managed to stand between him and the prisoners as he helped him to his feet. 'All right?' he asked before passing the gun back to him.

'Came from your part of the world, I understand,' John Sturgess said as he came to them. 'You'll miss him, we'll all miss him.'

'What do we...?' Alan sounded panic-stricken as he thought the major was walking on, for he remembered what he had said about the head and not wanting anything extra to carry.

Sturgess came back almost immediately with Danny's pack and began to unstrap his waterproof poncho cape.

'We take him with us,' Alan asserted.

'Of course.' As if seeing in Alan's

concern all the questions of what happened to a body in the heat, he explained 'There's a road much nearer the far side of this camp we're heading for. Don't worry, we'll get him out. Do you want to...' he held out the cape questioningly, then added, 'wrap him tight?'

The sergeant took the cape and Alan nodded. They laid it on the ground; Alan closed his eyes as the sergeant took his shoulders and poor half head while he lifted the feet and placed him on his cape.

'Wrap him tight,' his brain was saying, 'for he sleeps well tonight. Wrap him in swaddling clothes and lay him in the tropics thousands of miles away.'

When the body was neatly swathed, Mackenzie produced two lengths of cord. 'Twist and tie the ends,' he ordered and, when Alan looked up questioning the added indignity, he added, 'We don't want anything in there with him.'

The time of darkness was nearly upon them and there had to be much swift organisation. The major photographed the dead terrorists. The prisoners were gagged and their lashed feet tied to the trunks of trees. Alan watched critically, determined nothing should be left to chance. He saw how, with her hands lashed to her pole, the girl's black shirt was pulled tight over her breasts.

Danny had talked a lot about his mother. Alan's heart gave a sickening thud as he realised he must write to her, tell her how her son had died—well, some of how he died—and how in half an hour or less, all their lives had changed. Dan's mother wouldn't know for days; he hoped she would have a nice time until she was told. He wondered what day it was, perhaps the weekend?

He went back to his radio duties, reporting to headquarters. He was informed that other units had been under similar fire in areas surrounding parts of the camp. Things were quietening down now it was dark, but they were to proceed into the camp at first light, 'taking the normal precautions'.

The major had decided that now they had prisoners they should withdraw a few yards into the jungle and Danny's body would lie in his place in the line.

They rigged a string between the ten of them so they could signal if need be without giving away their position. The two Sutherlands had extra strings to the arms of the prisoners, with Ben taking first watch. No one, prisoner or soldier, could move more than a arm's length without waking the others.

Alan lay keeping vigil by his friend's body. He stared wide-eyed into the night

290

and his mind went back to the villages he and Dan had known: a litany of Sheepy Magnas and Sheepy Parvas, of Littlethorpes and Great-thorpes; of being on the opposite sides at an inter-village cricket match; of the sleeping mounds in the village churchyard, generations of the same family laid to rest in the same place. But where would this son of England be buried? 'Some corner of a foreign field...'

His mind slipped out of control into total despair. Liz loved this country, this jungle he felt bearing down on him, doom-laden. In the heat and tormented noises of the night where creatures preyed on each other he felt he would never see her again. Then his body fell into exhausted sleep while his mind played the nightmare on. He started awake, overwhelmed by terror, as he found the string on his wrist pulled violently by the sergeant. 'You're shouting, Cresswell!'

Well before dawn he was awoken again by something moving nearby. He lay rigid with listening until he was sure what he heard was the foraging and grunting of wild pigs. Around him he could begin to make out what looked like a ghastly painting of a ghostly cathedral: the pale and dappled greens, blacks and reddish silver bark of the tree trunks rising high and true as pillars to the vaulted canopy of leaves a hundred or a hundred and fifty feet above. Still and straight, the trees seemed at once to witness and to judge man's presence. The verdict, he felt, was not favourable, and the sentence was carried out by cutting off light for ever to the floor below where man murdered his fellows.

He wondered if it had been his shots that had killed the communist with the face like a startled schoolboy. He knew the sergeant was wrong: it didn't make up for Dan. The khaki peaked cap with the red star had belonged to some mother's son...Babyface had kept it as a souvenir. Alan hadn't wanted it—all the deaths in the world could not remake a single life.

Beside him Sergeant Mackenzie stirred, awakened by the increasing activity of the pigs. He immediately roused the line and breakfast was handed out from the airdrop rations of hard square biscuits and thick chunks of corned beef. The prisoners were given nothing and no one suggested they should be.

The soldiers were all pale and haggard; any continuous spell in the sweltering, enervating gloom of real jungle made them look like men who had been incarcerated underground.

The major proposed fixing Danny's body under a thick bamboo pole, so two of them could carry the burden between them. A litter which four would have had to porter would have forced them to take twice as long to travel in double file, for the elephant tracks now moved away from the human settlement.

When, after several false starts, Alan realised that to do what the major suggested meant they must tie Danny's hands and feet together, pass the pole through them and carry his friend as if he were some kind of hunting trophy, he said, 'I'll carry him.' His tone brooked no denial of his intention and, as the major made no immediate objection, Ben Sutherland added, 'I'll carry the radio.'

'And I'll take your pack,' his brother added.

The major looked at the determined men. 'Right, let's get on,' he conceded.

The prisoners were forced to walk like crabs to get through the path cut by their captors. Occasionally the major ordered a stop so they could listen; the distant, spasmodic firing that had begun again at first light seemed to ebb and flow like a tide.

'I'll take him for a bit now.'

'It's OK, Sarge, I can manage.'

'The major wants to listen in on the radio for a bit.'

Alan was dropping under the weight, yet

reluctant to give up his friend, though his body had lain on his shoulder more like the weight of sandbags than flesh and blood.

'Gawd!' The sergeant took the weight as gently as he could. 'Good job his grin was the biggest thing about him.'

'Right!' Alan agreed, choked, nearer to tears than at any time since it had happened. He went quickly to open up the radio pack, pull out a small portable aerial and listen in as they walked on. The reception was poor and he could obtain nothing but a crackle, certainly with voices mixed in, but completely unintelligible.

The major halted them while Entap went ahead to scout. He came back quickly, reporting that the first huts they would come to were all empty.

'Sergeant, you bring up the rear with Cresswell, find a place to secure Veasey, then join me. Babyface, you take charge of those prisoners and guard them with your life. They may be the most important things to come out of this botch-up.'

They all went slowly forwards, relieved at least to be able to lay Danny's body down under the raised floor of the first hut they came to. Emerging cautiously, they could see the extent of the camp. They viewed what amounted to a parade ground complete with flagpole and raised dais, surrounded by substantial-looking huts, the main one with verandah and easy chairs.

'Really roughing it,' Mackenzie muttered.

'We built a lot of this during the war, even made furniture,' Sturgess recalled. 'I was here with Harfield...'

'A bit too quiet for my liking,' Sinclair muttered as they still stood in a little group peering round the corner.

Alan desperately missed Danny. He would have been voicing all his own and everyone else's impressions and feelings aloud, making those who shushed him feel braver as he confirmed their own worst secret fears.

'We'd better have a look, see what we've got,' Sturgess said, detailing Mackenzie, Alan and the two Sutherlands to take one side of the square and the other four to follow him.

They did not need cautioning how to proceed; this part at least of their training had been covered. In a series of diving runs, crouching pauses and door-kicking entrances, they searched the huts one after the other.

'Chrrrist!' the sergeant exclaimed as they found themselves in a wash house with latrines with bamboo seats. 'They've got running water! This is better than *our* camp!'

'I wonder what else we'll find,' Alan muttered grimly. 'Can't imagine them giving this lot up easily.'

The next hut was the one with the verandah, grandiose enough to be nominated a bungalow. The sergeant and Alan took the steps at a bound and kicked in the front door, waiting either side lest a burst of fire should greet their arrival. Then, cautiously, they went in.

'Strike a light!' Mackenzie muttered, standing blinking as if he could not believe what he saw. 'It's like bloody Hansel and Gretel!'

Alan looked at the huge furniture, the enormous bed in the centre of the room packed tight with settee and easy chairs of the same type, hefty and beknobbed. *His* surprise was because he knew where it had come from. This was the furniture Liz had described as having been made for their plantation manager, shipped in specially. So Josef the half-breed Chinese-Norwegian must have had something to do with its transportation from the deserted bungalow to here. 'The bastard!' he mouthed. The only satisfaction it gave him was to know that there was some road fairly near, for this heavy stuff could not even in pieces have been portered far through jungle.

As they threaded their way through the furniture, the sergeant exclaiming at the weight of the chairs, they heard movement.

In an instant both were still, rifles at the ready.

They heard the movements coming nearer, then whispers. Question, swift answer. Holding his breath, Alan thought the voices sounded like women. Chinese women. They waited—cat and mouse—expecting whoever it was to try to make a break either front or back. Ben was covering the back of the hut; they could see the front through the window.

There were sounds of at least two people coming along the passage towards the open lounge door. Alan bit his lip and sighted his rifle at the open doorway at chest height. He held his breath and stood, rifle steady, waiting to fire at the first sighting.

A girl's voice called in excellent English with just the touch of Chinese inflection, 'Please do not shoot, we wish to surrender.'

Alan saw the end of his rifle sight waver a little. He controlled it, stood firm. He remembered the stories of tricks played by communists, fatal deceptions.

'We have our hands up,' the girl added as she edged into the room, pushing it wider with her foot for an older, smaller Chinese woman to follow her in.

There was something different about this girl, Alan thought, as she led the way into the room. She moved with a freedom more associated with a Western woman, a longer, striding step, though the older woman had the sliding walk which always seemed to mark a more deferential Eastern approach.

'Pleeze,' the older woman said with no other request attached than that the girl had made.

'My mother is Mrs Guisan,' the girl said.

'Who is Mrs Guisan when she's at home?' the sergeant asked.

'The wife of the old manager at Rinsey,' Alan supplied.

'Huh! I may have bells on the other. We'd better put 'em with the other prisoners.'

'Just a minute, Sarge. I may be able to prove what they say.'

The sergeant looked very sceptical and as the women went to lower their arms he made a meaningful upward jerk with his rifle barrel. 'Go on, then.'

'Where did this furniture come from?' Alan asked.

'It is mine!' the older woman said with some dignity.

'It was stolen by... It was stolen and brought here.'

'By?' he persisted.

'By my son,' she admitted, 'my son Josef.'

'He's a traitor!' the younger woman stated vehemently.

Her mother said something low and condemnatory in Chinese and the girl's answer in the same language clearly indicated she did not care and it was the truth.

He reached for the pocket of his shirt, managed to undo the button in the sweat-soaked material with one hand and drew out the photograph. 'Keep them covered, Sarge.' He laid down his gun and unwrapped the small photograph. 'Who is that?' he asked.

'That Elizabeth,' the girl said, regarding him as if he was part magician, part God. 'How you have her photograph?'

'She gave it to me.'

'She here in Malaya? Not at Rinsey?'

'Yes, she's here and at Rinsey.' Alan warmed to the girl as her face showed astonishment and delight, and thought for a moment she was going to throw her arms about his neck. She regarded him with the air of one diving into a new relationship with a stranger, the slightly roguish expression of one who was viewing the boyfriend of her girl friend for the first time.

'The Hammonds are back at Rinsey?' the older Chinese woman asked and went on with rising disbelief and enthusiasm,

'Mr Hammond, Mrs Hammond, Miss Elizabeth, Miss Wendy.' Then her face suddenly clouded. 'But no, no, or Josef would have told us—if he had known.'

'He would have known,' her daughter said stonily.

Alan glanced at his sergeant as Ben called from outside, 'Any trouble?'

'We'd better take them back to where the prisoners are,' the sergeant decided before going to the door and shouting back, 'Just two women, check there's no one else in the back.'

Just two women, Alan thought, who had a lot of heartache to come as they learned the extent of Josef Guisan's infamy. He felt a greater sympathy for the mother, who seemed determined to defend her son at all costs. Suddenly remembering the girl's name, he opened his mouth to say it, when there was the sound of running footsteps and shouts at the far end of the camp.

'They've found—' Alan began, but the sound of extended and excessive shooting was heard, coming nearer. There were shouts, orders and counter-orders. He looked at his sergeant.

Mackenzie gestured to the women. 'Get down!'

The young one hesitated. 'Lee,' Alan shouted, 'get down!'

The two disappeared beneath the solid

300

bed and Alan thought they wouldn't find a better place than that this side of Ipoh.

'Come on, don't think they'll go anywhere.'

'Stay under the bed,' Alan instructed as his sergeant left the room. 'Liz would never forgive me if anything happened to you two now we've found you.'

He followed his sergeant out to see at least two different units of English soldiers come pouring from the jungle, retreating, it seemed, dropping back to the huts, a hail of fire following them.

Sturgess came weaving and running low across to their side. 'The police have got them pinned down on the road, and Unit Seven have their escape route plugged—they've got to come back this way!'

Alan pulled a low bamboo chair on to its side on the verandah. The sergeant crouched in the doorway, while Sturgess spread the news to the others in his unit. The last Alan saw of him was as he zigzagged his way back to the far side of the camp.

The firing increased in fury and they could hear the shattering explosions of hand grenades, still at the far side of the camp, then the stuttering of automatic fire came nearer. He heard the sergeant mutter, 'Wish I had a couple of Bren gunners.'

Danny, he remembered, had been a Bren gunner. He was missing this lot. Lucky bastard! Alan thought as several bandits came running to the camp. One's arm was raised and a grenade went off at the side of the compound; another had some kind of automatic and as Alan took aim the man sprayed the whole bungalow front with fire.

Alan felt a strange hot feeling across his head. He felt peeved more than anything. His hand still hurt from securing the crate, and this as well seemed too much. He clenched the sore hand into a white-knuckled fist. Then he relaxed, fingers outstretched, as he saw Danny smiling and surrounded by a great light coming towards him. He smiled back and tried to get up and go to meet him.

Chapter Sixteen

'We shouldn't leave Anna alone at Rinsey —not overnight, anyway,' Liz said, standing at the front window of the Wildons' bungalow.

'No.' Blanche's tone was of reluctant agreement. 'I wish now I'd gone with Aubrey to KL.'

'You'd have been a hindrance, darling, believe me. Half the information Aubrey'll get will be from the gossip in men's clubs and the best part of all that'll pass in the bog!'

Liz thought only Joan could get away with a remark like that to her mother—well, Joan and possibly George Harfield. She wondered if this was why her mother was friends with these two disparate people; they dared tell her the truth.

'And if we're going to motor back in daylight, we'll have to leave soon,' Liz added.

'He might also pick up some news of this big op that the major's been on,' Joan added. It sounded an innocuous enough remark, but Liz glanced at her sharply and, finding her adopted aunt's gaze on her, felt her colour rise.

'He's obviously all right, though,' Joan went on, reassuringly smiling, 'it's in the newspaper.' She riffled through the pages on the desk near the window. 'Here you are...' She read snatches of the text, ' "Largest operation of the emergency so far...hundred troops raided area headquarters jungle camp...captured two terrorists, one man and one woman, who have been taken to Ipoh for interrogation. Four other terrorists dead...two identified on the wanted list." ' She paused and looked up. 'We lost one man killed, one man missing—so I presume you would say two men dead. Major Sturgess, it says, is working with the police at Ipoh, so he's obviously safely returned.' She stopped and smiled at Liz. 'That's some comfort.'

'He has his uses, I suppose...'

'Come on, Liz, more than that, surely?' Joan urged.

'Well, at least he's on our side!' Blanche interjected.

'It didn't feel like that when we first met him in Singapore,' Liz reminded her.

Blanche stood up and stretched. 'That seems like several lifetimes ago,' she said, adding thoughtfully, 'and in a way it is. Neville's, plus these soldiers that have just lost their lives.'

'What's the matter, Liz? You suddenly look terrible.'

Joan went to catch the girl's arm.

'I...' She sat down in the nearest chair. 'I just hope it's no one we know.'

'How could it be?' Blanche asked, suddenly alerted by the sound of a vehicle sounding a horn for the front gates to be opened by the guards. 'Unless,' she added, on her feet and making for the door, 'it was that boy who was stationed with us. Alan somebody. I never caught the name of any of the others.'

'Cresswell,' Liz added quietly to her

mother's back as she went out to meet Aubrey.

Joan stood looking at her, then stooped and caught her hands. 'Oh, my dear! I thought it was the major who had caught your eye. He seemed to think so—you've certainly caught his!' She glanced after Blanche. 'Your mother doesn't know,' she surmised, searching the girl's face. 'N-o-o.' The negative included both the knowledge that Blanche would definitely not approve and that she saw the same implacable determination in Liz.

'An approaching impasse, I think.' She patted Liz's hands and whispered, 'Don't look so awful, darling, we'll find out about your Alan Cresswell.' She stood up to greet her husband as he and Blanche came back into the room.

'Aubrey, darling! All right?' Joan kissed her husband on the cheek.

He nodded and, looking searchingly both at his wife and all around the room, asked, 'And here?'

'Perfectly fine, darling. No enemy activity and all the tappers are in, everything secure. We're just hanging on what you have to tell us.'

He tossed his hat on to the table and helped himself to a stiff gin and tonic.

'Did you see the high commissioner?' Blanche asked.

He shook his head. 'No, he's away, next in command, but it was apparently arranged to take George to KL because he'll have a better chance of his case coming up much quicker and there will be less chance of any local prejudice against him.'

'Local prejudice! What the hell do they mean?'

'Blanche, you have to understand this girl is of a family who have worked for the Bukit Kinta mine for years, generations! That a girl like this should accuse him is very emotive. If it had been a stranger...'

'I don't see it makes any difference. If the little tart is a prostitute, anyone could have beaten her up.'

'The trouble is, my dear, that there is absolutely no evidence that she is or ever was a prostitute. There is no record of George receiving a message begging him to go to that house of ill repute in Ipoh. It's just George's word against all the evidence, which I have to tell you is pretty damning.'

'The evidence is a put-up job, isn't it? George Harfield has been a thorn in the side—' she paused momentarily and tutted at her own cliché—of the communists ever since the war. He told them he'd bury them up to their necks if he found any of them caching away English arms supplies then and he's been the target for all kinds of attacks. Look at his headman, Rasa, look what they did to him!'

'M'dear, this is what makes it so much worse for him. His barrister says the prosecution are likely to bring these things up and use them as evidence to say how damned unlikely it would be for a girl born and brought up at Kampong Kinta to be a communist sympathiser.'

'I don't see that counts. All youngsters kick against the parental traces however they're brought up!' Blanche argued.

'Not sure that's politically true,' Joan said, shaking her head. 'Generations of our village folk back home used to vote Conservative whether it was a lord or a cabbage who stood in their constituency.'

'This is more about ideals, isn't it? About fairer shares for all,' Liz said quietly.

'For God's sake!' Blanche exploded. 'What it's about is a man being set up by some fanatic who's prepared to let herself be beaten up to trap an enemy to her cause.'

'Her cause is ideal,' Liz emphasised. 'People have to have ideals to be prepared to suffer.'

'Probably sees herself as a martyr,' Joan confirmed.

'But we all agree the evidence is contrived.' Blanche was pacing the floor

307

now, throwing her arms wide to appeal to her audience.

'But,' Aubrey said with infinite patience, 'it is difficult to deny that evidence when it was the police who were in fact the ones who found George at the girl's side, actually with his hand on her shoulder.'

'He was sent for urgently—the girl had been missing.'

'Yes, yes, we know this because it is what Harfield says—but it all seems to work against the man. It seems the girl was in the same room all the time she was "missing" and a white man was seen going in and out—and there are witnesses prepared to say it was Harfield they saw.'

'Paid witness!' Blanche asserted.

'Possibly,' he began and as Blanche glared at him, amended, 'Most probably, even most certainly—but I saw the photographs of the girl's injuries.' He shook his head. 'I can't see any jury doubting the attack or the rape.'

'Well, George Harfield didn't do it! I'd stake my life on that.'

'What makes it worse is that in her statement the girl says she always thought of Mr Harfield as a second father or a favourite uncle. She trusted him.' He rose and sighed deeply, taking Blanche's glass from the table and his own for a refill. 'I saw George, you know. He says she's a damned convincing actress.'

'The girl!' Blanche suddenly shouted. 'The girl! What is her bloody name anyway?'

'Li Min,' Aubrey told her quietly.

'Li,' Blanche repeated, 'that's appropriate anyway.'

'I'm afraid I agree with Harfield's advocate; unless we can find some evidence that definitely links the girl with the communists, the man's defence is very thin.'

'We will then,' Blanche said as if to herself. 'We will then.'

'I wondered if you heard anything more about Major Sturgess's last jungle operation?' Liz asked. Her voice sounded high, thin, quite unnatural. 'There's so little in the paper.'

'He's safe, saw him briefly. Called at Ipoh on the way, why I'm late really. He's helping interrogate prisoners, and...er, he does have a funeral, unfortunately. One of his own unit, I understand.'

Liz felt as if someone had swept her whole world away. 'Do you know who it was?' she asked, voice no more than a whisper.

'Sorry, I never asked. Did you think you might know...?'

'Liz wondered if it might be any of the men who were stationed at Rinsey, that

309

was all.' Joan came to her rescue.

'Possibly,' Aubrey said. 'Quite possibly.'

'Could we find out?' Joan asked and, as Aubrey opened his mouth again, caught Liz's eye and added sharply, 'Don't say "possibly", darling, I don't think our nerves could stand it. Just tell me if you could find out?'

'I suppose...' he said languidly.

'We'd better make tracks,' Blanche said, 'come one, Liz. I'll see what I can find out at Bukit Kinta and be in touch. Thanks for everything.'

'I'll tell your man you're ready.' Aubrey went to find the crack-shot Malay tapper they had brought with them as guard.

'Remember, don't stop for anyone or anything,' Joan reiterated the emergency code of safety, 'and, darling—' she caught Liz's hand—'I'll make him get through to KL as soon as you've gone, and the second I find out anything I'll let you know.'

Aubrey went to the barbed-wire gates and helped his guard open them, waving their guests on their way. Joan stood on the verandah waiting. Aubrey came and slipped his arm around her waist.

'Two unhappy people,' she commented.

'Umm. Neville, bad show, coming out and never seeing him again.'

'Don't think I meant Neville, really, darling. Young Liz has a crush on

310

that young guardsman, the signaller you remember they had billeted on them at the time Neville's body was found. Could be a problem if her mother has to know.'

'Not sure it will,' Aubrey said thoughtfully. 'He's either the one killed or the one missing. I particularly remember Sturgess mentioning his signaller, seemed to be preying on his mind a bit.'

'Oh, dear!'

'I tell you something else, Blanche is going to have a shock about that Harfield chap. He's going to prison for a long time.'

'You don't think he's guilty!'

He shook his head but said, 'All the evidence points that way—and no other. If they've set him up they've made a damned good job of it.'

Liz drove the Ford at speed as the twilight was swiftly replaced by darkness.

'We should have left earlier,' her mother stated.

Liz might have retaliated if she could have found room in her mind for anything else but Alan. One missing, one dead. What had Joan said, 'so I presume you would say two dead'? Two dead out of ten that had stayed so briefly at Rinsey, two dead in one unit out of the whole operation. That couldn't be fair.

'Liz! For God's sake, take your time. There's no point in us killing ourselves!'

'You worry too much, Mother.'

'You're frightening our guard to death.' She turned round to the Malay who, while gripping his rifle, was endeavouring to stay still long enough on the back seat to keep a lookout for possible roadblocks or people trying to flag them down. 'He's pale yellow around the gills now. And it's not going to get any darker now it is dark.'

'You begin to sound like George Harfield and his clichés!'

'He's certainly on my mind,' Blanche admitted, gripping the overhead panic handle as they hurtled around another corner. 'Liz! Keep a sense of proportion or we'll all either be travel-sick or dead!'

Liz had to make a real effort to drive more slowly, consciously making her foot lift from the accelerator a little—and then feeling they were creeping along. Speed seemed the only thing that made any impact on her sensibilities, a kind of consolation for not being able to take any action that might help. Until she knew...what could she choose to do?

She supposed she could make assumptions, use logic. She could work from what she knew. She knew she loved Alan totally. She knew that to be without him would be to know the rest of her life was over, useless.

It seemed unbelievable to her that he could possibly have been killed and she had not known, had not had some premonition. She remembered darkly that Alan himself had said he felt doom-laden from the moment he had left England, then he had met her and obviously the feeling had been all nonsense. She blinked, bit her lip as tears welled.

The lights of the car picked up something or someone at the jungle edge. Was it a figure of a man? Tall, hefty, wearing a peaked cap, carrying a rifle. He was gone in the same second, so she was not sure.

The next moment she was jamming on the car brakes as she was confronted by a torrent of water over a huge rock. She looked up at the curtain of falling water as they hurtled towards it, and remembered being under the waterfall with Alan.

'For God's sake!' Blanche cried, while in the back their guard gave out a whimpering cry of relief as the car stopped a hand's span from the outjutting rock indicating the turn for Rinsey.

'All I can say is I'm glad we're nearly home. You totally oversteered there. We're no use to anybody dead.'

Not sure I'm much use to Alan alive, she thought.

'Did you see anyone on the corner?' she asked. 'I thought...'

'No!' Her mother's stony response seemed to indicate she thought her daughter was just looking for an excuse.

'No, missy,' a shaky voice came from the back of the car.

Some instinct, some premonition stopped her from saying more. Perhaps it had after all been some trick of the light on wet leaves, the shapes of trees or ferns?

She restarted the car with shaking hands and went at a cautious twenty miles an hour the rest of the way to Rinsey's barbed-wire gates.

She was relieved to find all quiet, the gates properly manned, even pulled a face at her mother as the guard literally fell out of the back of the car with comic haste—while inside the telephone was ringing.

Anna greeted her in the hall on the way to answer the telephone.

'I'll get it,' she said, asking, as John had done when he arrived home, 'Everything all right here? Your little one safely tucked in?'

Anna nodded and went to the door to greet Blanche. Liz picked up the telephone.

'Liz?' Joan Wildon's voice asked. 'I promised to ring as soon as I knew.

314

I've just spoken to John Sturgess on the telephone.' She paused as if apologising for doing it all so quickly, then asked, 'Is your mother there?'

'Yes,' and Liz with the same unmoving tone her mother had used only minutes before, and clamped the handset harder to her ear.

'I'm afraid, darling, the two guardsmen lost were among those who stayed with you.' Joan went on, 'The man killed was a Daniel Veasey and the one missing...is your Alan Cresswell.'

There was a pause as Liz stood rigid, knowing but not accepting.

'Liz! Darling! Are you all right?'

She made some kind of murmur of confirmation.

'Let me speak to your mother.'

Without a word Liz passed the telephone to her mother.

Blanche, who had followed her daughter in and watched as she took the call, took the receiver quickly and asked, 'Who is this? Joan?'

Liz walked away into the kitchen. She heard Anna and her mother exchange a few words, then she supposed her mother was listening intently to all Joan had to say. She guessed that because Joan would be concerned for her she might tell her mother everything.

There was something she had to do and quickly.

She went to her bedroom and took the torch she had used to go through the escape tunnel from her bedside table. Hurrying to the kitchen, she took a box of matches from the kitchen drawer, then left the bungalow by the back door before anyone should try to stop her.

She could do nothing for Alan but grieve, but she could stop Josef, the traitor, the murderer, the man she was convinced she had seen momentarily in the jungle opposite the rock, from finding any sanctuary near Rinsey.

She started the fire in the room where they made love. It began with the symbol of their passion for she fed the first match strike with the dried red frangipani blossoms and the stalks of the orchid sprays. They made a brave, quick show. Anxious that they should not go out, she ran to fetch the twigs and dried leaves that still lay in other rooms, then she carefully applied the raffia mat so she did not exclude the air from the flames. When that was well established, pyre-shaped and blazing, she added the cushions.

'Only the butterfly escapes,' she said as the room blazed around her. She felt the heat of the flames easier to bear than the new sorrows life had brought. The opposite wall suddenly caught fire in a sheet, lapping hungrily, roaring out of the windows and up, up into the butterfly sky. She lifted her face and listened; she could hear the timbers of the roof crackling over her head. It felt like a cleansing. Now Josef would never sully this place with his presence.

She wondered if her mother and Anna could see the flames from the main bungalow yet. In this thought outside her own grief came the guilty knowledge that what she was doing would only heighten the sorrow for them. Any further deprivation would be another victory for Josef. He had always been greedy for more, gathering childhood triumphs around himself with the speed of these swift flames that scoured the room for new conquests, reaching out for her so she must snatch her dress to her legs.

But no more, Josef. No! Her amah's home had been destroyed, her father murdered, her love destroyed—now surely was the time of retribution. She fled the place, the heat swirling after her, flames shooting as far as the verandah as if in a last bid to take her.

She turned back, awed by the blaze—hotter than the tropical night, bright as the tropical sun and, like the jungle, dangerous to those who misused it.

317

Once convinced her place was back with her mother and Anna, she ran as if the flames pursued her even into the tunnel. She left the far end of the tunnel gasping in the closeness as if the heat of the flames still took her air.

She was almost back at the bungalow when she saw her mother on the back porch. Blanche saw her at the same moment and came out to meet her, staggering as if her legs were stiff with long standing, long watching. She held out her arms wide and there were no questions. Just a silent coming-together of the two women, embracing as if they would never release each other again.

Now the tears came, for both—and they finally could stand no longer and sat, arms around each other, on the back-porch steps, watching the pulsating reds and oranges in the sky.

Liz was numb with loss. Blanche was dumb with the shock of all Joan had told her, of how little she really knew about her daughter. Then tears began again as she remembered Harfield had said he had not thought of her as a back-doorstep frequenter. Neville, Liz's Alan...and George.

'If Alan is dead there is no one here for me any more,' Liz said very quietly.

It was the kind of thing daughters

318

say and mothers have to bear. Blanche reminded herself that these unthinking rejections were easier provided the mothers still had things of their own to do in life. She told herself she had a lot of very immediate things to do—she had a burning ambition to see justice done. Justice in and out of courts.

She remembered her grandfather, not too far from Pearling, shooting a rogue dog which had led several murderous attacks on his flocks of sheep. One spring afternoon she had stood with him watching the lambs playing together, crossing a little bridge over a stream in the follow-my-leader games they loved, when the dogs came in, teeth bared, romping, excited for the kill.

'Get behind me, Blanche,' he had ordered as he raised his gun. She remembered how the great rogue dog screamed and reared up into a sky across which was written a scrawl of blood. The pack of village dogs had howled and whimpered as if they had been hit. Her grandfather had shot again over their heads, then had turned to find his granddaughter looking up at him.

'They won't come and kill any more lambs, will they, Grandfather?'

'No, luvy, rough justice—but it had to be done, you understand that?'

She remembered nodding solemnly and

walking home hand in hand with her grandfather.

Josef was as a rogue dog, she had known that since she had found him stealing as a little boy. Neither her family nor the one she had married into, nor their children, shirked their perceived duty, she thought as she watched the Guisans' bungalow in the distance blazing still like a second sunset.

Chapter Seventeen

From the unburned section of the jungle camp's main bungalow, Lee watched her brother approach. She glanced at her mother, who lay on the long chair they had salvaged from the unscorched end of the verandah.

He kicked at a few pieces of charred wood as he drew nearer but greeted neither her nor his mother.

'So where were you when the soldiers attacked?' Lee demanded, resentful of the ease with which her brother always stayed out of harm's way, turning up when the worst was over. He would never ask how they had survived in the intervening weeks, or where the food she was cooking came from, or how long their mother had lain sick with fever.

He sneered but did not speak.

She must, she reminded herself, be discreet. She stared fixedly down at the food she was preparing, trying to control her tongue. There were some questions it was much better he did *not* ask.

'Got wind of the raid, did you?' she demanded as his silence continued. 'Went off to bury some more arms to keep in favour with *your friends?*' She was quite unable to stop herself goading him, voicing her guesses to pierce his selfish vanity.

He had been helping himself to a pan of cold rice; she saw his fingers pause loaded with the grains.

She laughed. *'That's* what you're doing!' she exclaimed. 'I knew you couldn't still be finding arms from the war. There had to be an end.'

'You bloody hellcat!' Josef foolishly approached his sister as she began shredding vegetables to make a soup with the rice for her mother.

She raised the knife, her firm intention of using it in her eyes.

'No, no, no! You not fight!' The old woman's voice rose in protest, making her cough so it racked her small frame. Lee went to give her a drink of water.

'And why—' the old lady raised a finger at her son—'you not tell us the Hammonds back at Rinsey?' Tears fell from her eyes and ran down her cheeks, their copiousness seeming too great for her frailty. 'You leave us here...'

'Stop crying, Mother,' Lee said firmly. 'Don't waste tears on your...son.' She spat the word as if it were distasteful, then turned to him as if he were a child, not a towering, dishevelled, bitter man. 'Bad apple!' she cried, picking up the knife again and waving it. 'Bad apple! Mrs Hammond, she knew. Always she knew.'

'Why you not tell us? We could have gone home.' The workworn Chinese lay back despairing, tears still welling from beneath her closed eyelids. She had become sick after hiding in the jungle from their communist masters. By the time they had dared to return, the British had fired the camp and left.

Lee threw the knife to the table and knelt by her mother, gathering her into her arms, terrified her mother had given too much of her energy and too much information with her questions.

'Who *said* the Hammonds were back?' he asked stonily.

'You think the communists are your friends,' Lee scoffed, 'but when you're not here they gossip and laugh about you. They say now the Hammonds are back you are "out on your ear, boy".'

The half-concocted, half-exaggerated story had a greater effect than she had expected. Josef snatched up the knife and stood holding it over them both.

'You don't need knife to kill Mother.' Although her black eyes were bright with fever, the frail woman's voice was full of dignity and reprimand as she told him, 'Your mother died long time ago when you brought us here.'

Lee gasped at her mother's words but when Josef laughed disparagingly she felt a sudden release of all restraint. A sense almost of freedom, even in that place, came over her; with everyone gone and only her mother and brother to hear she could say whatever she wanted.

'When you deceived us, Mother means!' she told him. 'Sure we ran away from the Japanese, that was right, they killed Father—but after war we should have gone back to our home at Rinsey. But you tricked us, you brought us to the communists and made us their slaves. But now you're on your own, aren't you, nobody wants you! Failure here!' She stabbed a finger towards the middle of the burned-out camp. 'Traitor there!' She tossed her head up over the dense jungle to the wider world.

'Get the meal!' He gestured with the knife to the pan of rice. 'I'm hungry.'

She noticed he had on a different wristwatch with a silver-metal bracelet. She wondered if he had stolen it or bought it at a shop? She had not been into a shop since she and Elizabeth had been taken shopping by Mrs Hammond. Her heart leaped at the idea of going back to a world where there were shops and cinemas and people not interested in politics and power. She just wanted to live an ordinary life, have a boyfriend, have fun.

Josef had brought them to this camp and kept them penniless. It was fear—fear for her mother, fear of the terrorist leader—that had prevented her from trying to escape, and fear, she thought, kept many of the young men they recruited there under his domination.

Early in their confinement she had tried to follow one of the men who, she realised, formed a link in a sophisticated postal system, a series of jungle runners who, each keeping to their own section, passed messages across vast and complex territory. She had hidden on the first part of the jungle track she had seen one man use, hoping gradually to build up enough knowledge to take her mother and find a way out of the jungle to a roadway. Once on a road she had been sure she would find someone who would help them.

The smooth-faced Heng Hou had caught her, stepping out of the jungle into her path. His face had been impassive as he came towards her and she felt stricken to stone by his implacable evil. When he took a second step towards her it had felt like a death sentence, and when his eyes moved over her, from face to breasts to sarong and feet, she had felt naked before him and had thought he would rape her and then kill her.

'If you try to run away again,' he had said gently, 'I first cut your mother's toes off, then her feet and so—'

She had screamed aloud as he suddenly raised and sliced down his hand like sweeping knife.

'And so...and so...and so!' The hand sliced and sliced again. 'In small bits, very slow.' He had smiled, and the smile had widened into a grimace, showing his teeth and the whites of his eyes so he looked like an old threatening Chinese god. Lee had turned and fled back to the camp.

After Heng Hou anyone else was a lesser evil, she had thought. But now, facing Josef, she wondered if his evil was not even greater, for he was working against even his own mother and sister.

She stood up, her lips in a twisted sneer of defiance, and walked around the table towards him until the point of the knife touched her chest. 'Run out of buried arms to bribe the communists with and run out of credit with the Hammonds? Back at Rinsey, all of them—that's my guess.' She looked up at him defiantly.

He laughed at her now, and caught her chin in one great grip while teasing the knife tip across her stretched throat. 'Now we're fishing, aren't we, little sister, because you don't *know* anything! Do you?'

'We don't know the truth, that's for sure! We only know what you told us.' In spite of the punishing grip on her jaw, her fury drove her on. She threw out a hand, gesturing towards the burned-out huts that had been classrooms as well as offices and dormitories. 'And what these fanatics tried to indoctrinate everyone with. They need classes in common sense, not dazzling with the mystic powers of communism. They need their eyes opened to see you and Heng Hou are just thieves, gangsters, murderers, making trouble and war for your own ends—gain, money.' She lifted both her hands in front of his face and drew the fingers of one hand across the palm of the other in a gesture of greed.

He clamped her jaw tighter, closing her mouth completely. 'You here to do as you told, not talk, not make trouble!'

'Josef!' Their mother had pulled herself up and was standing weak and trembling by the table. 'You leave your sister alone. She good girl—'

'Oh! I know, not like me!' He sounded and acted like a petulant boy as he released Lee but hurled the knife so it quivered upright deep in the surface of the tabletop.

'I didn't say,' his mother denied, looking down at the knife just a handspan in front of her.

'No, you never say, you good Chinese mother!' Lee defended her, but, poking herself in the chest, shouted at him, 'I say! *I* say! I say you liar, cheat!' She sought for more words. 'Rotten bastard!'

He laughed now. 'All Chinese when you angry! You know the only thing that's kept you alive these times is that you've amused the men with your bad language and your outbursts.'

'You know something?' She poked her chin forward at him. 'I know that! I work at it! But that over now...'

There was something in her voice, some knowledge she was keeping to herself, hinted at in that touch of self-satisfaction laced in the half-finished sentence.

'What you up to? What do you know? Have you seen someone from outside?'

'That's your problem, isn't it! *You* don't know!'

'I know if you could have found your way out of the jungle after the raid, you'd have gone. When the camp was empty there was no one to stop you, was there?' He explained their behaviour aloud, made the statement, but watched Lee with narrowed, piggy eyes, ever suspicious.

She stared back straight into his eyes, mocking but revealing nothing of the decision to remain in the camp so Heng Hou would not send his men out searching the area.

'So,' he went on, 'this camp is over, but soon we have another—soon I take you there. Heng Hou, he likes your cooking, your cleaning...' His lips began to curl in amusement as he listed their chores, 'your washing, your sewing, your nursing...and—this time perhaps I'll say yes—your fucking.'

'No!' The scream startled both of them. 'No! Never!' Their mother stood and used the last of her energy on the protest, banging the table with her fists. 'I kill!' Crying at the threat she had made, she repeated in an anguished whisper, 'I kill.' Then she crumpled to the floor.

Lee was by her side once more, feeling her forehead, cradling the small, limp form. Sure her mother was unconscious, she hissed at her brother, 'Soon she too will be dead if I don't get her proper medicine and to hospital. I think she has pneumonia.'

She tried a new ploy, wheedling for more information. 'Why can't you take us back to the Hammonds now? Mr Hammond would make you new manager at Rinsey—all would be as before. Mother could spend her last years in some comfort—we would live in our old bungalow. These murdering bandits—' she paused to throw a scornful glance around the camp—'they hate you, they despise you, have just used you, and you've made us serve them, you've kept us prisoners here.'

'I don't want as before!' He stooped and spat the words into her face. 'They—' he too indicated the departed communists—'Heng Hou himself promised me Rinsey, for mine! I don't want to go back as before.' He pranced away, tugging his forelock. 'Yes, Mr Hammond, No, Mr Hammond—and his wife!' He spat into the pan of soup his sister had been preparing. 'I hate! I kill her, too.'

'Too?' Lee repeated the word in disbelief.

'Too, meaning also?' she asked, thinking he might be like his mother in one way—he too said unguarded things.

'Everyone kills these days,' he bluffed.

'Hammonds, though—if you've killed any of the Hammond family! I ask you?' She paused, desperately trying to remember

what the soldier had been saying before
the attack came, then added, 'Even your
mother would not forgive that.'

'Rinsey is finished anyway, burned up,'
he added sullenly, 'like this camp.'

She knew he was lying. Knew what the
soldier had said before he was shot had not
meant Rinsey was finished. Anguished she
tried to remember exactly what the English
soldier with Elizabeth's photograph *had*
said? That the Hammonds were back. He
had spoken of Liz. Yes. 'Liz would never
forgive me if anything happened to you
two'—and Mrs Hammond? Lee groaned
aloud as she could not remember—and
what if he had looted the photograph?
There was no way of knowing.

'Yes!' He took the groan for despair at
his words. 'Make the most of your next
two days of freedom. Then I'll come and
collect you both, take you to the camp.
It's deeper in jungle, far, far away from
here—no one will ever find that or either
of you again!'

Lee picked up the bowl of stock he had
spat into and threw it in his direction.
He sidestepped but the splash caught his
sleeve.

'Filthy cat! You'll pay. I'll see to that!'
He began to walk away, taking a direction
in which she had seen the messengers go.
'Don't you try to follow me!' He turned

330

back and aimed his rifle.

She watched him go. Don't worry, brother, she thought, I don't need to.

Hardly had the noise of his progress away through the jungle ceased when a movement at the far side of the former parade ground caught her eye. A small black man wearing only the briefest of loincloths stood there, a small bundle of leaves in one hand, in the other a blowpipe so long and thin it looked twice his height. His physique was that of a slender athlete, though she knew from seeing him at close quarters that his face was lined and the touches of grey in his black frizz showed he was well over middle age.

Lee raised her hand slowly in greeting. The Sakais were timid people at best, though kindly. So quickly had this Sakai come to their help, Lee realised these jungle dwellers must have known of the camp and of the movements of the communists, though they had kept well hidden for at no time had there been any talk of any Sakais living close by. Yet once the men had gone this man had come with aid for the two distressed women.

She put her hands together Chinese-fashion and bowed respectfully. She warmed to anyone who could outwit Heng Hou. He grinned and mimicked her movement, coming forward offering the leaves.

Inside was a grey powder. He took a small flat stick and divided the powder in half; he pointed to her mother, then to where the sun would set and one half of the powder, then to where the sun would rise and to the other half.

'Night and morning,' Lee said in Malay. She felt he understood what she said, but he never spoke.

The Sakai tribesmen gently took the leaf back and mixed the one half in a cup of water, nodded and smiled, looked at her mother and nodded and smiled again.

I do hope you're right, she thought, then, pointing to herself and her mother and back to the Sakai, indicated that they might all go the way he had come.

He looked at her mother, pursed his lips in the same manner as prescribers of medicine the world over, then nodded but shrugged at the same time.

'And?' She made the sign that had come to mean the soldier to them both: a stroke across the top of her head which indicated the deep passage of the bullet over the top of the man's head.

Now the purse of the lips was more positive and the eyes looked into hers with concern. He frowned, then gave a low whistle like a bird call, and from the jungle came a tiny, beautifully proportioned young woman wearing just a waist sarong.

He spoke to her rapidly. The girl nodded, then came forward and in perfect but slow Malay said, 'My father says the man is very ill. They have taken him to Pa Kasut in the hills where cooler, better for patient. But he thinks needs own kind to talk to him, bring him back...'

She struggled now for the right word.

'...to consciousness,' Lee supplied, then, as the girl looked puzzled, added, 'from coma, from deep sleep?' The girl nodded gravely while her father spoke again to her.

'Father says if want to see should come quick or may be too late.'

Lee realised the meaning of the young girl's presence. It seemed the effort and peril of dragging the soldier out of the sight of the retreating terrorists might well have been in vain. They had not saved his life, merely prolonged it.

'Pa Kasut, all Sakais, done all can,' the girl added earnestly.

'I know and I thank you, my mother and I both thank you,' Lee assured them both. 'Without your help the man would certainly have been shot dead and we would have starved.' She smiled and accepted the length of thick tapioca root, staple diet for the Sakais, the girl now held out to her.

This was the first time Lee had been able to communicate with the Sakais directly and she was anxious not to let the girl go until she had dealt with this new problem.

'The man,' she said, 'is a soldier and carries in his pocket a picture of my friend Elizabeth Hammond. She lives at the plantation Rinsey, north of Bukit Kinta—'

'Along the Sungei Woh,' the girl said.

'This I do not know. Would you or your Sakais take us there so then we could bring the girl Elizabeth to the man? She could talk to him—before it is too late.'

The girl turned to her father and they talked together for a long time.

Lee saw her mother move and went to reassure her, but when she saw that Josef was gone and only the tribespeople were there she rested back content.

'He has brought a powder for you to take—' she began.

'Give it to me.' Ch'ing reached for the cup. 'I must be strong soon. We must go before communists come back.' She reached for the cup and drank it down.

'The girl speaks good Malay I can understand,' Lee told her.

Ch'ing called her thanks.

'They say the soldier is very ill, unconscious.' She sat on the end of the long chair and spoke quietly. 'I think if he is Miss Liz's boyfriend we should try to take her to see him—very quickly, they think. I've asked if they would guide us to Rinsey.'

The old lady's mouth opened and a look of such eagerness came to her face that the girl spoke to her father and pointed to Ch'ing.

He shook his head and the girl turned back. 'My father said too far for old lady and too dangerous, Sungei Woh in great flood from hill storms.'

'But you must go,' Ch'ing insisted. 'You go! Go!'

'We take mother to our village first,' the girl said. 'Father says no time to waste.'

Chapter Eighteen

The tea chests were already half full of George Harfield's possessions when Liz paused and said reflectively, 'You know, as soon as things could be arranged I'd like to go back to England. I could find a flat and a job and keep house for Wendy at holiday times. I just feel a kind of aching despair here.'

Blanche reflected that 'aching despair' exactly summed up how she too felt, and how she had felt ever since Neville's murder and George Harfield being committed to prison. Two things occupied her mind; bringing Josef to justice and procuring George Harfield's release. She had no doubt of the former's guilt or the latter's innocence.

She found herself calculating how old she would be on George's release if he had to serve his full sentence. Even making allowances for an early parole, she would be well into her middle fifties. She supposed just making the calculation proved how furious she still was at the efficiency of the trap and showed how much she cared about their complete failure to find any witness or anything that could have helped George at his trial.

'Will you go back...?' Liz began.

Blanche rose from her knees where she had been folding George's underwear and putting it neatly into a leather suitcase. She went to look out of the window at the mining complex laid out below. The muddy green waters, the dredgers with the noisy buckets, the jungle down to the water's edge, sliced into here and there to make room for the wooden workplaces and office—and Kampong Kinta. All safe behind the virtual stockade George had ordered built and supervised, but she had come to be certain that there were as many communist sympathisers within the barriers as without.

Some thirty feet below in the roadway she could see the new and unfortunately spotty young manager the company had sent out. He had already been to see the Hammonds and officiously instructed them that the furniture in George's house went with the job. Watching him pointing and gesticulating to the men on the dredgers, she decided they would take the American refrigerator from the lounge—she was sure *that* did not belong to the company.

'After all, you didn't want to leave Pearling,' Liz added.

'Perhaps going back is not what I'm about.' Blanche spoke slowly, almost as if discovering the truth of the words as they came to her lips.

After a moment she turned to look at her daughter, remembering how George too had lost weight. In the dock he had looked as if years, not weeks, had passed. He had appeared dignified, pale, tense—and angry. Anger under control had been more awesome at that moment than the passion that screams and rails against fate, but it was also, she knew, the kind of anger that ate into a man like a canker. She turned back to the window; somewhere within her view at that moment there must be some shred of evidence that would prove his innocence.

She thought it a pity they did not still

have the rack. She could quite easily have stretched that girl until she told the truth. What made it all worse was that Li Min was back in the village, her family drawing wages from the company—George's former company.

Blanche had seen the bitch and talked—crossed swords—with her several times, each time remembering what George had described as the look of triumph in the girl's eyes. Blanche had seen that same gloating look and after several infuriating useless confrontations had said to her, 'Your eyes tell the truth.'

The girl had sniggered. 'Eyes do not talk,' she replied in a low, malicious tone.

Blanche had stepped closer to the girl and said, 'Just look into mine.'

The girl had raised her eyes, a supercilious expression of scorn on her face. A second later her mouth had dropped open and she had taken a step away from the Englishwoman. The moment had been satisfying, but had achieved nothing, Blanche reminded herself.

Then, as if conjured by her thoughts, she saw the girl walking towards the new young manager, Ira Cook, who swept off his hat as he saw her approaching. My God! You've got a lot to learn, she thought and, looking at the girl, promised, I'll get you. If it takes all the time I have left, I'll get you.

The girl was laughing like a coquette. She had reason to feel pleased; a smart cookie, making up to the new young manager. Having seen the last imprisoned, this one should be a pushover! Avoiding clichés did not seem so important these days, Blanche admitted to herself.

When Blanche and Liz had arrived for George's possessions the acned new recruit had made them feel like pariahs. He had spoken of how much George had cost the company and 'now there is the matter of compensation for the girl and her family'. Liz had caught her mother's arm as she seemed about to hurl herself at the young man's throat. 'I think you should go about your business,' her daughter had advised the nervous bureaucrat.

She watched as the Chinese girl went off waving cheerily back to the raw young American, who then glanced nervously up the hill. Probably wondering what we're taking and if he dares come and see. She felt certain that Bukit Kinta would not be attacked again; the girl's presence plus the ease with which the new manager could be duped probably ensured that.

'It feels as if it is what I am about.' Liz seemed to lay the words on top of the clothes she was smoothing, layering them gently. As her mother looked at her questioningly after the long silence, she added, 'Going back—being defeated.'

'Not defeated,' Blanche said firmly. 'We're never that until—'

'We're dead,' Liz supplied and sighed. 'That's what I mean: defeated, finished, extinguished...'

'Liz!' her mother said sharply to stop the run of negatives, then softened her voice to add, 'I wish you would stay on.' She paused, 'sick at heart' were the words that came to mind when she studied her daughter. It tore her heart to see her daughter so stricken, so enervated. She tried to lighten the mood. 'And it was you who wanted to come back!'

'All my loves have gone now,' Liz said.

Blanche wanted to say, 'But not all those who love you', but she knew exactly what her daughter meant. Her relationship with her father had been special for many reasons, probably because when he returned on leave he came as a cross between a hero and Father Christmas. During the war they had all lived from leave to leave rather than observing the normal calendar festivities. This new beginning in Malaya was supposed to have been permanent, a final settling.

And to this young man, Blanche could not forget him sitting, his rifle propped between his knees, on the back of the lorry coming from Ipoh station. Seeing him there had been like a kind of recognition. She remembered how Neville had haunted her after she had seen him for the first time at a friend's house playing tennis, in white with a red striped scarf for a belt. She should have recognised the omens too; tropical whites on a hot summer's day, the arty scarf, the sunny unbusinesslike nature.

'I need you, you know.' Blanche closed her full suitcase, ending her dreams, with a businesslike click of the locks.

'You?' Liz looked at her with surprise.

She nodded. 'I really do. I'd feel very alone...' She did not elaborate. It occurred to her that she ought to present a plan, as she had done in school holidays: today we'll go to the park, tomorrow you can help hoe the onions—it was expected of mothers.

'Your aunt Ivy has written to say she feels Wendy should be allowed to come out. She says Wendy should have the opportunity to come to Rinsey, to put flowers on her father's grave, to mourn at the place. Ivy says the girl is...all right though not quite herself. She thinks Wendy should be with us for a time at least.'

She paused but when Liz made no reply she went on. 'I have decided that in spite

341

of any danger she should come out for the Christmas holdiays. She should see her father's grave, Liz, don't you think?'

Liz had picked up a handful of pens and pencils from George's desk and tapped them into an orderly bundle. The mine's books had been rather ostentatiously whisked away when they entered the bungalow. She reflected that she had kept the rubber accounts ever since work had restarted at Rinsey—but that could easily be taken over by one of the foremen.

She patted the points of the pencils into line. She had sketched nothing, nor wanted to, since Alan had been reported missing, presumed killed. Drawing had been part of her life for as long as she could remember. Her first memory of her father was sitting on his knee and being helped to draw a monkey hanging from their tree. There was no more sketching, no pleasure in her life any more. She was just amazed that they went on doing things like getting up, going to bed, dealing with the business, eating. 'You're asking me to stay until after Christmas,' she stated.

'And you don't want to?'

Liz imagined that distance might ease her grief, that she might leave behind this tortured creature she had become.

'You have Anna and her grandson,' she said.

The remark cut but Blanche was still stifling the mind's cry of hurt, balancing it against her daughter's surprise that she should need her, or anyone. Doggedly she went on with the plan she was devising as they talked.

'Ivy won't, of course, leave your uncle Raymond on his own particularly not at Christmas, so Wendy would have to travel alone. If you stayed until after her holiday you could go back together.' She paused, wondering what she had to say to reach her daughter. 'I do believe she has to come, to grieve here, perhaps to hit some kind of bottom—like us—before we can begin to go upwards again.'

'I never shall,' Liz stated.

'Oh, Liz! Believe me.' Her mother clenched both fists and pounded them silently on the closed case. 'Believe me, you will! We both will in time.'

'Thanks for not saying "you're young".'

'Well, you may have stopped me just before I reached it.' Blanche held out a hand and Liz suddenly came to her and took it, helping her mother to her feet, their grip tight with mutual need and tacit love.

'Let's leave Spotty down there to his fate,' Blanche said, reaffirming her support in an extra squeeze. 'Come and help me load up. We're taking George's fridge, by the way. We'll put that on the back seat first, and we'll use it when we get it back home.'

In the end Ira Cook helped them load the fridge. He came protesting up to the bungalow, until Blanche had told him in her most regal manner that it was *her* refrigerator which the previous manager had borrowed. She added that she hoped he did not expect her to leave it for *his* benefit.

'Mother, you are a liar,' Liz said as the car cleared the driveway of Bukit Kinta.

'Right,' Blanche admitted uncompromisingly. 'I've tried doing things the legal way, but now I'll use any way I can—just like these terrorists and their molls.'

When everything was unloaded at Rinsey, Liz watched as her mother took a glass of tea Anna had waiting for them and went outside. Most days now she spent some time on the long stone seat she had had placed alongside her husband's grave. Stirring the ample amount of sugar she liked in her tea, Blanche seemed to sit as one might by the side of a patient's bed in hospital, leaning forwards exchanging pleasantries and news.

'Go sit by her, Miss Liz,' Anna said, coming to stand next to her at the window. 'She shouldn't be out there by herself.'

'No!' she heard herself say sharply. 'No,

344

I can't, Anna, I can't be a comfort to her when I almost envy her. She's had her life, her marriage, her children. She's even got the grave of *her* loved one to sit by, she can talk to him.'

'Miss Liz!' Anna was shocked. 'You young! You know nothing or you would not say such things. Your mother suffering. She need you.'

'She's so used to coping alone. I don't mean to sound hard, it's just a fact, isn't it!'

'Alone is not when expecting someone come back,' Anna said, slapping her hands together sharply as she used to do to catch her charge's complete attention.

'I know,' she answered, with the ring of such loss in her voice that her amah caught her in her arms.

'Now all three know,' she said. Liz held her tight. Their great sorrows seemed as close as the ghosts of their lost ones around them.

'Perhaps I will go out.'

Liz was looking out and Anna nodding at the correctness of the thought, but just then the sound of a shot came from the front of the bungalow.

'Oooh!' Anna wailed. 'And children not home from school.'

'The jeep's not left to fetch them yet so don't worry.'

Anna held the door open for Blanche as she ran in, leaving her tea on the seat. 'Must stick more rigidly to this gun rule,' Blanche said, snatching up the rifles from the corner of the kitchen and handing one to each. 'Let down the shutters on the windows, Anna. I'll bar the door.'

'I'll do the front,' Liz said. But as she reached the door and the sandbagged windows and looked out across the wide shadowed verandah, she could see their guards standing in the middle of the drive arguing.

'What is it?' she called.

'This man thought he saw someone prowling around.'

'I sure. Twice, three times I see man going from tree to tree.' He made graphic pictures with his hand, half-circles moving rapidly along. 'He coming closer without coming in the open. So I shoot.'

'And missed?' Liz asked.

He shrugged apologetically. 'I think he big man.'

Chemor, who had opted to stay at Rinsey after his boss's arrest, came from outside the gates. 'We're looking all around, miss. There was someone, been here some time by the look of the tracks, but he gone now.'

'Good,' Liz said, 'and thanks, Chemor, all of you. We must all stay alert.' But as she went back to the bungalow she thought that, as for herself, she did not much care what happened to her.

She reported to her mother and Anna, then went to her room. She could settle to nothing, wandering aimlessly around. When she turned to the sketches she made of Alan, she felt the most exquisite sadness. There were also sketches of her father and Wendy. Oh, God! How could I be so selfish? Even when you're old it must be a terrible pain, Liz thought. She left her bedroom and went to try to make amends.

From the kitchen window she could see her mother and Anna sitting close together on the seat by the grave. It looked almost as if they were engaged in a three-way conversation, so closely did they concentrate on the mound at their feet.

Older women were right to comfort each other, but she wondered if they did not forget what it was like to feel deprived of all that made life worth the trouble. They had a grave to grieve over; she wanted flesh-and-blood arms around her. She needed life, not death—unless death brought reunion.

She must get away, out, leave the house or she'd suffocate. She had to go, walk out, just be free of this compound with its grief and panicking guards—outside was her country, too. She picked up her rifle and left by the front door, then made off to the side and the tunnel. Even as she went she knew it was foolish with possible prowlers about.

At the far end of the tunnel she carefully re-covered the trapdoor, then moved away from the path that led to the burned-out bungalow and towards the cleared section of the plantation, where now the tappers were daily cutting and collecting phenomenal yields. Beyond sight or earshot of their own guards, she knew where she wanted to be: in a beautiful place she had shared with Alan.

As she drew near to the falls she also remembered tracking her father's car to the edge and beyond. On the second visit she recalled running to the edge and how she had alarmed Alan—how he had caught her and held her close.

He had tried to still her weeping, afraid the depth and ferocity of her sobbing would make her ill. She had touched the depth of mourning for her father that day, but now there were no tears. Her grief seemed sterile, without a physical centre. She felt a sudden great pang of pain for all the women who had lost their men in the war, men with no known grave. For the first time she began to know what that meant. It was like having a terrible pain you could not locate; there was no focus, only the pain.

Reaching the flat platform of rocks above the falls, she recalled how awed he had been by the beauty of the place. 'War in paradise,' he had said, and she had said, 'Love, too.'

The falls were much swollen by the recent heavy downpours. She guessed the path they had walked on the far side would be under the swirling rush of white water. The flat tables of rock they had walked across so easily were covered by a swift-moving deep slide of water. She longed to go to the cavern under the falls and sit on the shelf of rock, drowned in the sound and the memories.

She knelt down by the edge, watching, feeling stupefied by the ear-filling crash of the waters and pulled forwards by the sight of the speeding torrents. After a while it seemed easier to think of just slipping over into the water, into oblivion, than to walk all the way back to Rinsey, to explain where she had been, to go on living.

It would not be painless, there were rocks she would strike and she guessed that even in extremis her body would still make frantic and futile efforts to breathe—but it should not last long. She felt it a sin, was vaguely afraid of divine retribution—felt exasperated by some stubborn streak of life force that still held her to the rock refused to accept being thrown down, extinguished before its time.

'Some part of my mother in me, deep down,' she mouthed, sitting back on her calves. 'A lot of Daddy, the outside bits, the arty bits, but perhaps the core is Mother.' She sighed and sat down with her legs outstretched, put her arms straight behind her and leaned back, head turned up to the sky.

She tried to review what she was certain of. It would certainly grieve her mother—and poor Anna—if she killed herself. No, she supposed, like Hamlet, she had to go on, haunted by almost the same ghosts—the murdered father, the lost lover. She rose, quickly aware she must move away from these falls; like Hamlet, she should put the temptation behind her.

As she turned and her eyes adjusted from the glare of the sun, her eyes scanned the fringes of the jungle and the plantation in front of her—and a movement caught her eye. Someone or something? Someone, she decided and instinctively her hand sought her abandoned rifle. She raised it towards the rubber trees.

Then she caught a second move-ment—two people at least. Her heart began to thud and she recognised the irony or hypocrisy of her self-indulgence—one minute seeking a way to end her life, the next panicking to save it.

She sighted the rifle rapidly and instinctively, finger curled ready to press the trigger, as a figure stepped out from the trees directly in front of her. Liz saw it was a girl and did not fire, but nor did she lower her sight.

The girl stood very still, then called, 'Elizabeth! Is it Elizabeth? Elizabeth, it's me, Lee.' The girl began to move towards her, slowly at first, then running.

'Lee?' Liz repeated, then recognised her beyond doubt. 'Lee!' She threw down the rifle and ran towards the girl, struggling like someone in dream or nightmare on ground that seemed less than solid and legs that hardly obeyed.

They threw themselves into each other's arms crying, disbelieving, each examining the other, stroking, hugging, unable to speak, unable to let go each of the other for long, long minutes.

'Lee! Where have you been all this time? I don't understand.' Liz held her at arm's length and saw how gaunt and pale she looked, how torn were her clothes.

'You, Liz, you...' Lee looked but could not find words for how gaunt, pale and sad her friend looked. 'You...' Tears drowned

351

the words. 'You have to come...' She swallowed, trying to stem the tears. 'You have to...' She turned and called, once, twice. In the trees Elizabeth saw the native.

'You've been in the jungle travelling with the Sakais,' Liz guessed, seeing all the evidence in Lee's appearance.

'The soldier with your photograph—'

'Alan!' She felt as if every hair on her head rose at the words, her skin was ice cold. 'Alan! You've seen him. But how...I...is he?' She could not go on. 'Lee, tell me.'

'It's not good news, Elizabeth,' she said, tears streaming from her eyes as if the fault was hers. 'I'm so sorry. He is very ill—'

'He's not dead? You mean he's not dead!'

'The Sakais have been nursing him since the raid on our camp. But he is in a coma, Liz, I don't think there's much hope.'

'I must go to him,' she said, almost laughing with relief, with hope. No one could deny her that if he was alive! 'Lee...' She shook her head at seeing the girl she thought of as a sister restored to her. 'Your camp? I don't understand! I can't believe all this—but I must go to him.'

'This is why we have come.'

Chapter Nineteen

The emotion of the next hours was epitomised for Liz by Anna. The amah soon had an arm around each girl, alternatively beaming as if her face would split and almost bursting into tears. Liz and Lee took turns talking or burying their faces in her shoulder, stooping and snuggling like overgrown fledglings trying to return under her wings.

Blanche in the meantime came first to touch one and then the other as if reassuring herself of Lee's presence and the safety of both girls. In between she paced up and down, raging about the infamy of Josef condemning his mother and sister to a life of drudgery and abasement, pausing as she remembered taking the squirming youngster to his father for punishment, dragging him protesting all the way from one bungalow to the other.

The ever indulgent Kurt Guisan had to her fury laughed when she described his son as a thieving magpie. And Mrs Guisan had been too weak to control him. Poor Ch'ing. 'So your mother is...?' she asked again.

'The Sakais have taken her to their village, while the soldier is farther away in a cooler hill camp.'

'I always knew that boy was a total waster, but even *I* didn't think...' Blanche's mind returned continually to Josef while at the same time trying to grasp this amazing reunion and think of the best way to deal with all its implications.

There was one thing she was quite certain about. Liz had come to life again with the news of Alan Cresswell's survival. The boy must be given all the help he needed as soon as possible. From what Lee said, this was the presence of someone who loved him, someone to try to talk him back to life. There had been such cases, she seemed to remember, people tended in modern hospitals and continually talked to by their loved ones had survived... But Alan Cresswell's predicament seemed to her chillingly like Neville's disappearance; the circumstances and the time involved were against a happy outcome. This boy's injuries had been suffered some weeks ago, he had languished in the jungle among aborigines and been carried from one place to another. Then there was the journey back—with a Sakai, which guaranteed it would be through remote primary jungle. God alone knew how long that would take! She dreaded to think what extra heartache

354

Liz might have coming to her.

'You're sure Sardin will wait until morning?' Liz asked anxiously. 'And that there's nothing more we can give him?'

Lee and Liz had gone back to take him cooked rice and meat to the gates when he would not come nearer. He had carried the meat away into the trees. Later the bowl, empty except for a spray of tree orchids, had been brought in from the main gates—though shamefacedly even Chemor had to admit no one had seen it returned.

'I have great respect for all Sakais,' Lee said. 'Sardin said he would wait by the big rock. He will do that.'

'I wish we could go now,' Liz murmured.

Lee shook her head. 'He will not travel at night.'

'So first light then.'

Blanche was alarmed at the thought of the two girls going off God knew where in the company of one aborigine. This needed organising—tactfully. 'Lee, you can sleep in the old nursery, I'll make up the bed, but first I must ring John Sturgess. He has to be told there's chance of recovering one of his men.'

Liz felt her heart plummet. He had opposed everything she had wanted to do since she arrived back in Malaya. 'We

355

don't need him, do we? We don't want him to come. He's so officious.'

'But he's also efficient—and what about a doctor? He could send an army doctor with you.'

'We don't want him arriving like a troop of cavalry and frightening our man off. Then no one will find Alan.' She looked anxiously at Lee.

Lee shook her head. 'The Sakais are clever in the jungle. They live all time by CT camp, Heng Hou, no one know until they come to help us. I think Sardin will see army but army not see Sardin until he is ready.'

'And to take a doctor, is that a good idea? Is it worth waiting around while they fill in forms in triplicate or whatever they have to do?'

'Can doctors bring people out of comas?' Lee shrugged.

'But I do feel I have to tell Major Sturgess,' Blanche intervened gently. 'You do understand that?'

Liz, back turned, shoulders tense, made no show of assent but neither did she protest as Blanche went to make the call in the study.

'Don't look so worried, Miss Liz.' Anna hugged her two girls. 'You not in army...'

'No, that's right, he can't order us about!' It was the truth but it felt like

356

bravado. The trouble was, Alan was in the army.

Anna wanted to put Lee to bed but there was too much to tell and too many questions to be asked. In the end they compromised, making her comfortable on pillows on a day-bed in the lounge. Then they all sat round talking, filling in some of the gaps of eight traumatic years, while Anna bathed and iodised some of the many jungle sores and scratches on Lee's arms and legs, her grandson holding the bowl for her.

There was so much to tell, so many questions to be asked, they rather forgot the presence of young Datuk. Liz noticed that his hands shook a little as Lee talked of the sadistic Heng Hou. He kept his eyes lowered though he was obviously listening with all the big-eared stillness of the young, who know they will be banished once their presence is noticed.

Realising that the boy had some first-hand experience of communist methods, Liz wondered if he would be able to sleep that night after hearing some of the details of life inside the communists' camp. She felt Anna had rather overlooked him since his return from school with their foreman's children. He had been given milk and biscuits and then more or less ignored. She caught her mother's gaze and gave the briefest of nods in the boy's direction.

'Don't you have homework to do, Datuk?' Blanche asked. 'You could use the desk in the study.'

'Aaah!' Anna exclaimed. 'You still here!' Datuk was despatched with some alacrity to Anna's room. 'You have table there!' he was told when he tried to take up Blanche's offer of the desk.

'John Sturgess said he would be here shortly. That was hours ago,' Blanche commented after Datuk had been despatched. Then she motioned towards the day-bed. Lee had fallen asleep.

'Leave her there, I think,' Blanche whispered. 'Let's adjourn to the kitchen.'

'I thought I'd get some of Daddy's old puttees. I can bind them round my trousers. And I might borrow some of his socks, they're thicker than any I've got.'

Blanche and Anna exchanged glances as Liz went off to look for them. Blanche reflected that she had worn some of Neville's puttees when they had gone on jungle safaris during their early days in Malaya.

'She loves this boy,' Anna said.

'I'm convinced she does.' Blanche paused, then asked, 'So we totally believe Lee?'

Anna looked at her mem of so many years and knew exactly the comparison she was making between Lee and her brother.

358

'Yes,' she said, 'we right believe.'

A short time later they heard a vehicle come racing into their gate. 'The major,' Blanche said as Liz reappeared from her room.

'The galloping major,' Liz echoed without enthusiasm.

Blanche went to meet him and bring him straight to the kitchen so as not to wake Lee.

Regarding him with total objectivity, Liz felt he was like something out of a *War Pictorial Encyclopedia,* all khaki and belts and guns and emblems of rank. Through the front door she glimpsed the army jeep with driver and rear Bren gunner, who remained in the vehicle. She thought this was a good sign: he wasn't staying.

Although invited to sit down, he stood to listen, which he did in silence until the facts were all told and speculation began to enter the two accounts.

'So this girl is actually Josef's sister who's been living at the camp? She can tell us a lot. I'd like to take her back to Ipoh.'

Liz turned as if she had not heard right.

'For questioning. I haven't the power of arrest.'

'You haven't—' Liz for a moment felt she might just be physically sick. 'You haven't the power of arrest! What are you talking about? You haven't the power of anything in this house! Lee will help you when we've come back.'

'Come back?'

Liz watched incredulously as *now* he sat down, as if he considered the difficult part over. He placed his cap upside down on the table; somehow the gesture seemed to requisition the whole place and make it his office. 'Come back,' he asked again, tone steely, 'from where?'

'Lee has come to take me to Alan.' She repeated the information with emphasis. 'He's sick in a Sakai kampong, and the jungle people think it might help bring him out of a coma if someone of his own goes to him, talks to him.'

'Yes, yes, I know all this. Your mother told me first on the telephone. I have arranged for a special unit with a doctor to come here tomorrow, then we'll leave the next day.'

'I'm leaving tomorrow with Lee.'

Sturgess shook his head. 'Neither of you young ladies is going anywhere. We've had an ambush today on the main Taiping-Selama road north of Ipoh. We nearly lost a high-ranking civil servant; his wife and daughter were killed. The whole state is on high alert and there is a dawn-to-dusk curfew. Inspector Aba is convinced the communists we ousted from their camp are regrouping and are hellbent on revenge.'

'High alert for a civil servant you *nearly* lost and bad luck about his wife and daughter.' The sarcasm fairly dripped from her tone. 'But nothing, *nothing* done for weeks for the soldier you *did* lose! And left behind!'

'Liz, please.' Her mother's intervention was so mild it was a mere formality.

Sturgess looked fixedly across at the girl. Was she accusing him of neglect? He refused to try to explain to a non-combatant woman the heat of action or the search for his man afterwards. He noted she had called him Alan.

'He is, of course, under my command,' he said. The lack of weight on any particular word made it the message of an absolute authoritarian.

She was appalled. 'Even though you have no idea where he is? What condition he's in? You still feel he's under your orders!'

'When we have a witness such as your manager's daughter who has lived with the communists and has travelled with a friendly Sakai, *I* count that as knowing where he is.'

'But I don't count it as doing your best for him. You will be holding things up—collecting a unit tomorrow, travelling the day after...'

'When we do go we'll go quicker than two women.' His voice came lower, with more weight, his lips barely parting now as he answered.

'Two women *and* a Sakai.'

'No.' He shook his head most positively. 'I can if necessary get Inspector Aba to put Lee under protective custody.'

Blanche glanced at her daughter and hoped she had sense enough to back down at this point, or they would have all kinds of extra official complications to deal with.

'Lee is exhausted and I would much prefer her left in peace here with me,' she intervened as her daughter seemed about to loose herself verbally at the major's throat. 'Surely you would trust me to look after her and she could be interviewed here? In fact, I don't mind making a formal request to the civil authorities to allow this. I know Inspector Aba well.'

Sturgess blinked rapidly as if refocusing on the double attack on his authority.

'After all, she and her mother have been kept prisoner. They were not in a jungle camp willingly. You have no evidence to refute that!' Blanche challenged.

'No, that is true,' he admitted stiffly.

'So why mention custody?' Liz asked.

'Protective custody was what I said, and what I meant.'

Liz felt he almost added 'young woman,' for he turned abruptly to her mother and spoke as if only to her, the senior generation.

'What we do have,' he went on, 'is evidence that her brother has promised this girl to Heng Hou in return for his life. We know that "girlfriends" were kidnapped and taken in blindfold to this camp. The officers had their pick, but Josef was careful always to keep his sister clear of all this, though Heng Hou was always interested in her. The man used his sister as a kind of insurance against bad times. Those times have come and he has to pay up. Josef Guisan is hunting his sister to save his own skin.'

'One of the guards thought they saw a big man outside the compound today,' Liz intervened, 'but it was before Lee arrived.'

'It would be Josef.' Lee had come unobserved and stood listening in the doorway. 'He said he would give me to Heng Hou.'

She shuddered and staggered. Sturgess was by her side and supporting her to a chair. 'He is terrible man,' she looked up to tell him. 'Heng Hou and Josef have much food, many girls at their camp, but I hear other men say in other places communists starving. Young men with good intentions to make everyone equal, Heng Hou not interested in them.'

Sturgess patted her clumsily on the shoulder. 'We know this m'dear. What I need from you is immediate information about people you have seen in this camp, what you know about their organisation. This is so important—'

'I give now,' she said immediately, 'before I think about Heng Hou too much.'

Liz wanted to be with her but Sturgess insisted it would be better if he questioned her alone.

'Then you work in Father's study with the door open,' Liz heard herself say.

Blanche turned away for a second to keep a straight face at so serious a time, for the major huffed and puffed for a few seconds like the proverbial Colonel Blimp, quite unable to believe his ears.

'Lee would only have to call if she needed anyone or anything,' Blanche reminded her daughter. She pulled Liz's hand through her arm and stood shoulder to shoulder with her, facing the momentarily speechless officer.

Lee too came forward to reassure. 'I'm quite rested, don't worry.'

'I'll show you the way.' Blanche passed

her daughter's hand into that of her amah.

Liz stood trembling as the three left the kitchen. Turning to Anna, she was shocked to see her hand over her mouth, her eyes creased above. 'You're laughing!' Liz accused.

Anna shook her head in denial but kept her hand in place until she saw the anguish in her girl's eyes. The laughter at the major's discomfort vanished. 'What you do? What you thinking?' she asked suspiciously.

'I'm thinking women are just helpless,' Liz said darkly.

Anna wagged a finger at her and said crossly, 'I know you not thinking that!'

Blanche came back shortly. 'He wants Lee to go to Ipoh tomorrow. The police have rounded up quite a few men who've materialised in the kampongs who they suspect are not locals, but the villagers are too frightened to identify them. He feels Lee may have seen some of them at the camp.'

Liz did not answer immediately. Her fears were quite different. She dreaded that the waiting Sakai might be frightened away; she fretted at the thought of delay. She remembered what Lee had said about Alan's condition. Images of him kept coming back to her—as he had been and as he might be now. That was most heart-rending of all and she tried to repress it with many journeys in and out of the hall, past the study door, where the voices went on and on.

'Lee will be exhausted again,' she complained as she reached the kitchen once more.

'As you will be,' her mother said dryly. 'Sit down.' Her words were unheard as Liz again paced from kitchen to hall to bedroom.

At last they emerged. Lee looked pale, mentally bruised, Liz thought. As soon as she could she took her friend away to her bedroom, leaving Sturgess to explain that he was going to Bukit Kinta from Rinsey to interview more people there. She heard the rise in pitch of her mother's voice as she related their experiences with the girl and the new manager.

She closed her bedroom door. 'Lee?' The one word held all the questions about what they were to do and whether Lee felt strong enough to take any more.

The girl looked up, smiled ruefully and held her hands out in front of her, palms down. They shook uncontrollably. 'That is talking about Heng Hou...' she said.

'And Josef is out there, too,' Liz said, feeling she must remind her of all the hazards before she should decide.

'I know.'

'But Major Sturgess will be at Bukit Kinta.'

'And I see you! What you do.' Lee nodded knowingly. 'Brandy and medicines in father's old rucksack. And we have Sardin waiting for us.'

'Oh, Lee!' Liz knelt. 'My best frister!'

They both gasped and embraced each other as the name they had invented as children for how they felt about each other, half friend, half sister, leaped from memory.

'I'll defend you with my life,' Liz promised solemnly.

'I've got a revolver for each of us and a rifle as well.'

They stared into each other's eyes. 'Whatever the outcome, Lee. I'll never forget this, never.'

'And what are you two plotting?' Blanche asked, standing in the doorway. As neither replied, she shook her head, added, 'Come on, dinner! Let's get a proper meal inside this child.'

Blanche was strangely quiet, they thought, through dinner and she pushed them all off to bed early, going to her own room soon after darkness had fallen. The fact that Liz made no comment, no enquiry, added to the little she had overheard, confirmed Blanche's anxieties.

She spent a wakeful night and before

dawn heard the two girls depart. She went to the kitchen door and listened as they made their way to the escape tunnel. In her mind she followed them to their meeting place with the Sakai at the rock. After that it was all guesswork, and heart-tearing anxiety.

Had she done the right thing, letting them go? Sturgess would be furious, but she was fast coming to the conclusion that in this campaign rules were for fools. Her brain said no, but her heart said yes, Liz had to go; she had seen it in the girl's eyes.

Chapter Twenty

'So where is the girl?' Heng Hou's voice was low and threatening, his temper shortened by exposure to a rainstorm which had all the blinding ferocity of the beginning of the annual monsoon. The daily ration of hill thunder and lightning had been increasing and Heng Hou, used to his creature comforts, was on edge.

Josef stood with his hands half raised in a pacifying gesture as Heng Hou's bodyguards kept him covered. 'I thought she'd make for Rinsey, but the journey was bad from the camp. She would never have made it, Heng Hou, the river was already too swollen and there was her mother—she would not have left her mother.' At the back of his mind he momentarily remembered she was *his* mother, too—but this was serious trouble he was in.

He had seen that malcontented look on the communist leader's face many times before he maimed or injured someone Malay, English, Chinese, Tamil—anyone who crossed him or even merely glanced his way at the wrong moment.

'She must have gone to the Hammonds' friends, the Wildons, they have the Kose estate. Yes! I should have thought of that before, it would be an easier journey,' he gabbled on, desperate not to leave pause for any decision until he had presented a new course of action. 'They may have been able to follow one of our routes out to the road near their estate. The main communication tracks...'

Heng Hou narrowed his eyes, not listening any more, playing with the idea of just shooting the man there and then. He was in no mood for more amusing but time-consuming ways of despatching a man. On the other hand he was not quite sure whether he had wrung every last advantage out of this

Eurasian. Certainly he had proved much in the way of arms and ammunition—until the planter Hammond had returned. Then they had lost a consignment from Rinsey *and* their store in the Malayan house Josef had sworn was safe. He growled gently to himself, musing whether to let the man live or die.

'If they are at the Wildons' bungalow, I know it well and they have many arms there, machine guns. This I do know.'

Heng Hou grunted, speculated. He needed guns; then he might kill this man.

Josef's heart gave a thump of hope. 'The girl and guns...' He repeated the prizes slowly.

'Your sister?' the terrorist queried. It amused him to see what this man would sacrifice for his skin.

Josef nodded energetically. 'I know the layout of the plantation and the bungalow almost as well as I know Rinsey.'

Heng Hou grunted again and nodded his agreement to this last offer.

Josef turned to lead the way, lifting his head for a moment to allow the rain to flood over his face. Reprieved! Time brought opportunity.

The moment Aubrey set off for his morning rounds at Kose was always a moment of anxiety, and each morning Joan held him in her arms with a gentle, sad passion, so unlike their embraces at any other time, so unlike a husband going off to routine daily work.

In that final quiet embrace was the fear each had for the other: fear that Aubrey might be attacked on his inspection of the plantation and his tappers; fear that the bungalow might be attacked while he was away. They had made a rule never to agonise about risks; they parted with a smile and the mutually spoken slogan, 'Chin up!'

Joan as always watched him go off in the car they called 'the warrior' since armour-plating it with sheets cut from the Japanese tank still stuck in their riverbed.

Before setting about the morning's chores she decided to ring Blanche to see how the Hammonds were, Liz in particular. That they should both have lost their chaps seemed particularly galling. Liz, of course, would find someone else. She might come round to that major yet? Joan had serious doubts whether either Blanche or her daughter would stay at Rinsey in the long term. She listened as the telephone rang out, then her friend answered.

She knew immediately something had happened by Blanche's voice. 'Don't think I should talk on the telephone. Can you

371

and Aubrey come over later? I've done something...' She paused, seeking the right description. 'Something pretty indiscreet.'

'Didn't know you knew the meaning of the word, darling.' She waited for Blanche to laugh, but the empty quality of the silence on the other end of the line made her add quickly, 'The second he's back from his rounds, darling.'

Blanche hesitated. 'I suppose there's no particular hurry...now. I'll make us all lunch.'

Joan left the phone thoughtful. No hurry now, about what? To be there for lunch would be a rush. Aubrey wouldn't get his lunchtime gin sling. And she remembered she had not, after all, enquired about Liz.

She wandered to the front door again as if she had some chance of catching Aubrey before he left, though she knew that by now he would be heading for the far reaches of the plantation, then gradually working his way back to the bungalow.

The area around the Kose bungalow fell away and was planted with small new rubber trees. Aubrey said the troubles should be well over before the trees grew much taller. The recently cleared ground certainly made the bungalow easier to defend.

Silly to worry or speculate, no useful purpose in it, she told herself. Chin up and get busy. She decided to make one of those Dundee cakes Blanche and Liz were so fond of. If she started straight away it should be cool enough to pack by the time Aubrey came back, but she still stood thinking what a curious note Blanche's voice had held, depression underlaid with a kind of excitement. 'Most intriguing, darling.'

'Intriguing,' she repeated, gazing out over the verdant, burgeoning land around her home. 'It *is* beautiful,' she said as if she must confirm aloud a fact she had always known. She had spent half her lifetime in this country, and loved it as her own. Now she knew many planters felt abandoned. News from England said their plight was hardly reported in the newspapers; the Berlin airlift and the fear that America and Russia might be sliding towards war dominated the news.

She grimaced ruefully at the triple barbed-wire fences, the spotlights, each with their own unsightly batteries so that all could not be put out at once, the machine guns. Aubrey had left nothing to chance.

'Baking, that's the thing,' she told herself, 'then strip down and clean old Bertha.' She glanced at her gun. It began to feel like the one reliable friend she had when Aubrey was away. Her houseboy was loyal enough but not bright and often when she wanted to indulge in a little cooking and thinking she employed him in the garden. She had set him to construct long lines of low attap thatched 'cloches' to protect her sun-shy English lettuces.

A most satisfactory cake had been turned out, almonds baked beautifully even on the top, but it was still hot when she heard Aubrey's car coming back. She always heard the car well before the prearranged signal on the horn—long, short, long, short—which announced his safe return and was the prerequisite to the gates being opened.

She frowned as she thought the car had come on through the gates without the hooter having sounded, or had she really been so engrossed in the beautiful evenness of her almonds that she had failed to register the daily signal? The car came right up to the front of the bungalow, so she must have done.

She slipped off her apron, pulled her dress in order, fluffed up her hair, put on a smile and went to meet her darling Aubrey.

Her pace slowed as she reached the front door. The car stood just beyond the shadow of the verandah, the rainstorm so lately stopped that the sun was striking brilliant prisms of colour, blue, red, orange, yellow, on the car's armour. She could see no one inside and glanced round, looking back to where the guards where closing the gates. Two of them seemed to be having words, arguing. Had Aubrey gone back to see what was wrong?

Then one of the men seemed to make a decision and lifted an arm to her. Even from a distance she thought he looked alarmed. Something was wrong. Where the hell was Aubrey? And there was something about their car...something hanging from under the door.

Her heart bounded to her throat as she recognised the strip of material hanging from the passenger-side door. She had bought that blue and beige striped shirt in Airey & Wheeler's, Piccadilly.

She turned away and was heading for Bertha as, with a sudden explosion of action and firing, all the doors of the car were thrown open. The impact of the bullets lifted and span her round. As she fell she saw Aubrey's head and shoulders sagging from the passenger seat.

Five or six men spilled out of the car, two treading over Aubrey's body. One made for Bertha and cut down the Kose guards as they scattered in curious slow motion with legs turned to lead as they realised their mistake.

'Damn!' The word formed on Joan's lips but was never spoken.

As Heng Hou and his men raided the bungalow, Josef shot his way out of the gates. He was well aware that if he was going to escape with his life he needed to do it before Heng Hou realised he had been duped. He privately thought that his mother and sister had wandered into the jungle and got lost and would probably have perished by this time. If they had found a road, though, they would undoubtedly be taken back to Rinsey; it was all his mother ever seemed to crave.

Heng Hou saw his men wrench the machine gun from its stand. Bursting into the house, he grabbed a pile of hand grenades which were arranged like fruit on a glass stand near the door. He swept the bowl to the floor, then kicked it furiously when it did not break. The cut glass rang with a clear, true note as it rebounded from the wall and rolled back toward Heng. He stepped back and shot it to smithereens.

He went through the house like an angry demon, as if furious with everything that dwelt inside, every piece of furniture, every ornament carefully chosen and placed. If he did not want it he broke it.

'The girl! The girl!' he screamed when they had turned over every room. 'Bring Josef to me!' He turned on his henchmen who stepped back a pace, pockets bulging with trinkets. Heng Hou repeated the demand and stamped his foot. 'Search outside.'

The two in the room fell over each other in their haste to be outside. Heng sneered, then picked up the cake from the cooling tray and broke it in half, pushing it into his mouth, spitting the browner almonds to the floor.

He was plundering the kitchen cupboards when the bravest of his men came back. The square-built Chinese did not report the escape of the garden boy, just that there was no sign of Josef.

'You want us go search outside?'

Heng Hou considered that it was dangerous to linger too long in an area they had attacked; anyway, he knew where Josef would go sooner or later. All the man could ever think of was the plantation where his father had been manager. 'No,' he added, 'we'll just go wait for him near Rinsey.'

The square Chinese face split into a grin of appreciation.

When they were ready to leave, they fired the bungalow. They dragged the Englishman clear of the car and threw him by his dead wife. 'Long dogs!' Heng Hou growled, then laughed at the sight of these two, tall in life, long in death. His henchmen laughed too, more outrageously than their leader, and one lifted Aubrey's arm and placed it around Joan, because they were all terrified of falling foul of Heng Hou.

The next second their leader's face fell into its usual lines of discontent and he gestured them back into the car before the smoke from the bungalow grew large and aroused suspicion. He poked the driver, indicating the direction towards Rinsey.

Heng Hou pondered with all the hungry sagacity of the greedy predator. Josef had nowhere to go but back to his old home. No home for him in the jungle, no home for him in the towns. Heng Hou had already made sure Josef was a marked man, for he had not trusted him for a long time.

He growled under his breath again. The fact that the man had slipped away from a raid he was personally in charge of was another reason for the unrelenting hunt he would initiate.

'Mem and Tuan Wildon not come yet,' Anna commented as she added a bowl of floating fragrant frangipani blossoms to the long-prepared dining table.

'I'm hoping they'll arrive before any of the army. Think I may need some moral support.' Blanche paused, watching as Anna went on making tiny adjustments to the mats and cutlery. 'What do I say, Anna?'

'You say,' Anna said with great emphasis, 'little as possible.'

'In case it incriminates me,' Blanche agreed.

'In case gets you in trouble.' Anna nodded vehemently. 'You no see go, no know where gone. Just gone!'

'I'm sure you're right. I just wish Joan would come first so I could unburden my soul by telling the truth first.'

'You like baby need comforter.' Anna pretended to suck her thumb. 'You eat, feel better. Friends not mind.'

'No, I'll wait. I'm just so worried about the girls.' Next moment she swore as they heard vehicles approaching and then Chemor's loud, harsh challenge.

'Even the British army doesn't get by George's man,' she commented.

She went to the front door to meet Sturgess. She saw there was a team of men plus a Dyak tracker. Sturgess came towards her with a slightly smaller man, who managed to look dapper even in army jungle issue. 'Dr James Wright, Mrs Blanche Hammond.' As the two shook hands, Sturgess announced, 'We're going to make a start today, get straight off. The girls will know where their Sakai is, I suppose.'

There was a pause as he registered the expression on Blanche's face. The last time either she or Anna had seen the girls was about nine o'clock the night before, she told him, and neither of them had actually seen the Sakai at all.

'You mean you've let your daughter go off into the jungle? Why, I...I can hardly believe such—'

'Such what?' Blanche prompted, her natural assertiveness at last coming to her aid, overwhelming the guilt.

He was going to say 'such carelessness' and that was really what he felt, such casual disregard for Elizabeth's safety. He substituted 'foolhardiness'.

'Liz is enamoured of this young man. One tends to go halfway round the world for that kind of foolhardiness.'

'She *thinks* she is...' Sturgess could not bring himself to say the word. 'Whereas *I* know it has to be just calf-love, moonstruck calf-love.'

'*You* know! How would you know?' Blanche was at once astonished and furious. 'I presume you will allow that I know more about *my* daughter than a comparative stranger.'

'We all know more about Elizabeth than strangers do,' he agreed.

'Do *we* indeed! *I* had assumed I knew more about my daughter than *you* did.'

She was furious to have got herself into such a stupid argument and astonished to see that he did not realise she meant *he* was the stranger. 'Unless there is something I am not aware of?'

He frowned. 'Well, no...not at all.'

'I can assure you my daughter is for better or worse in love with this young guardsman, and I have no doubt she is at this moment fighting her way through whatever jungle hazards lie between her and him. I am not saying I wouldn't be happier if you, the doctor here and all your men were with her. I am saying I understand the feelings that made her take off secretly, without waiting for you.'

The doctor nodded agreement. 'You have daughters?' she asked.

'And sons,' he replied, his eyes twinkling.

'Behave like dogs when a bitch is on heat sometimes, I guess,' she said, watching to see how much the remark chosen to shock Sturgess succeeded. It obviously staggered his sensibilities, whereas the doctor gave a great hoot of laughter at the unexpected comment, but did not risk an answer.

'They are at least half a day's travel ahead of you,' she stated pointedly, 'though I see you have a tracker.'

'The girl's gone too, I suppose, Lee Guisan?'

'Your witness is with my daughter. That

is my consolation, that and the knowledge the Sakais have of the jungle in all its moods.' She paused as thunder again echoed around the nearby hills. 'Lee and Liz are closer than most sisters.'

'They haven't seen or had contact with each other for years,' Sturgess commented.

'The deep bond was immediately renewed, I assure you,' Blanche replied coldly to the sardonic remark.

Sturgess did not speak again but marched outside.

'Makes me feel he's never without a mental cane to slap in the palm of his hand,' the doctor commented ruefully, watching him go. 'But he's a good officer, perhaps because of that.'

Blanche pushed a long and mild gin sling into the doctor's hand, then stood by his side to observe Sturgess instructing his Dyak tracker. 'Someone's drilled all the humanity out of him.' She shook her head sadly. He looked as if he was drilling a troop of men at the Guards Depot at Caterham Barracks. The Dyak obviously felt much the same for he gave a fair imitation of a good Guards' salute, longest way up, shortest way down. Although they had issued the tribesman with army shorts and shirt, his blowpipe and quiver made the ritual ludicrous.

'The modern army,' the doctor quipped,

added 'Cheers!' as he downed his drink and promised to keep a good lookout for both the girl and the young man.

The major came back some minutes later and it seemed to Blanche there was some kind of petulant satisfaction in his voice as he said, 'It will all take longer now, of course.'

The doctor was beginning to show less and less liking for his officer's company. 'Shall I go and tell the men to stand by?'

Sturgess nodded brusquely. 'Right!'

Left alone, they avoided each other's eyes in an uneasy silence. 'Can I offer you a quick drink? Or tea, or whatever?' Blanche asked formally.

He shook his head.

'To say the least, I sense your disapproval, but you know one can't order affections—least of all one's daughter's.'

'But you could curtail her actions.'

Good God! she thought. Won't the man let it drop? She turned so she faced him squarely and saw disappointment on his face. My God. He wants Liz. He wants to—what did he say?—curtail her actions!

'Well, yes,' she began her answer in very measured tones, 'all parents can do that, I suppose.' There was something in this man that made her again want to shock him off his godlike male pedestal and she went on, 'And many husbands, too, try

383

it on, I suspect. But love is a bit of a vagrant. It doesn't take kindly to rules and boundaries.'

'As a child I was told that rules and discipline were all that stopped children growing into rampant weeds, the bad growing over and smothering the good.'

'And where did love come in?' Blanche asked so softly she was not sure he would hear, for now she began to feel sorry for this man. She could imagine the lovelessness of his upbringing. Probably started with a nanny. Nannies if they were good were very, very good, but if they were bad they truly were horrid. Then public school, Sandhurst probably, the army.

Sturgess felt like being honest and admitting love had not come often into his life—but owning up to being less than in total control of all areas was something he was trained not to do. A wife would complete the world's picture of what a man should be; the career, the home, the wife and family. That was the role he saw for Liz.

'Love doesn't win wars,' he said, 'and this one's not over—and as far as we know there may no longer be another contender.'

'I don't think,' Blanche said slowly, thinking that she was at last seeing him as clearly as Liz did, 'that will make much difference to your chances.'

'That is your opinion. I hope in the near future to have the pleasure of making you change it.'

She took a moment to remember that this man was going out to try to find and bring back Liz. She hoped he did not think it entitled him to lay some kind of claim on her. She had to frame her words very carefully, she decided.

Her pause gave John Sturgess the chance to smile and bow and for them both to register the sound of yet another vehicle coming to the gates.

'No one else is due,' Sturgess commented.

'I'm expecting someone,' Blanche said, following as he walked out and adding under her breath, 'and it is my house.'

But it was a police jeep that had arrived.

Inspector Aba shook hands with John Sturgess and bowed to Blanche. 'I have bad news,' he began, 'I think we should go inside and sit down.'

'My daughter Liz?'

'No, no.'

'Lee Guisan?'

'No.'

'Who then, or what then?'

As they reached the verandah chairs, Inspector Aba signalled for Anna to come forward as if she were a waitress in a restaurant. 'A drink for mem,' he said,

385

and turned back to Blanche. 'I have just come from the Kose estate...' he began.

'Joan?' An awful fear swept over Blanche, her friend so late. 'Joan?' she repeated.

'I am sorry, Mrs Hammond. Both Mr and Mrs Wildon have been killed, shot dead, very quick, and the bungalow fired.'

'Christ!' she murmured like a paternoster, waving away the drink the inspector took from Anna and pressed upon her.

'Mrs Hammond, Blanche...' John Sturgess came forward. 'I'm so—'

'Go and save my daughter,' Blanche interrupted.

Chapter Twenty-One

The strange world was sometimes light but mostly dark, with unintelligible sounds, sometimes like language, sometimes like the wind or the waterfall. Alan strained to keep the sound of water, it seemed to mean much more than anything else, and yet the effort made him weary.

Light or sound, never both together, came in flashes as if his brain had loose connections which occasionally sparked across a void.

Then he was vaguely aware of slipping

away from the rim of consciousness, sliding away with a vague feeling of unease as if it was something he should not do, a kind of self-indulgence.

Pa Kasut boiled roots in great hollowed bamboo stalks and told his women they must keep the soldier's lips and mouth moist with the solution all the time. Then he looked above the high peaks and saw the signs of a great wind bringing the greatest rains. He sent his son Bras to look for Sardin and the soldier's woman to bring them quickly to the hill camp.

At first light on the third day Sardin drew the girls' attention to the man coming beaming towards his fellow, teeth shining momentarily white even through the sheeting monsoon. Standing exhausted, soaked, heart labouring, Liz realised that the storm worried this man about as much as rush-hour traffic bothered a Londoner. The two Sakais shouted to each other above the din of the rain, just as two Cockneys might shout across Oxford Street at sale time.

She watched the new man come nearer and just wanted the whole experience over. If Alan was dead, she too wanted to be dead—and that moment felt like a reasonable time to want to go, while she felt so absolutely awful in mind and body. Poor Lee, now making the journey for the second time, was slumped to the ground. Every time they stopped, Lee, fast reaching breaking point, her legs buckling under her, just fell on the spot. Liz knew her friend laboured on only for her sake, and she only for Alan, for the hope that he was still alive.

Then, as her pounding heart managed to push more blood over her brain, she realised that the arrival of another Sakai who had obviously come to meet them might mean they were near the end of their journey.

'Sardin,' she gasped, 'ask him if the soldier is still alive.'

The man, whose name she learned was Bras, understood her. The smile vanished but the answer was that he was alive but sleeping deeply the way he had been the whole time Bras had helped carry him up to their hill camp. He pointed almost vertically up into the air. Lee groaned.

'How long will it take us?' she asked.

'Seven hours,' Sardin answered, but then, glancing at Lee, he corrected himself. 'Two days.'

'No!' Liz was overcome by a terrible fear that she would reach the hill camp *just* too late, that just for the want of one last supreme effort Alan would slip away without her having the chance to talk to him. 'No,' she repeated, 'I'll go on with Bras and you stay with Lee and come in two, three days, take time for Lee to rest.'

The two Sakais talked rapidly together in their own tongue that she could not follow, but after a moment, they nodded.

'Lee, darling, do you mind if I leave you with Sardin? Would you understand?'

Lee smiled ruefully. 'Wish I had boy-friend,' she gasped, 'make me like god, walk for ever.'

'You want come now?' Bras asked.

'Yes.' She took Lee in a gentle embrace, kissing both her cheeks and pushing her hand up under the soaked, jet-black hair, easing it from her friend's neck. 'You will come on to hill camp? Sardin thinks your mother may be there by now.'

'I shall see you there,' Lee confirmed and waved her on her way.

They had not been travelling long before Liz was consumed with wonder that Bras could travel with such ease yet cover so much ground. She felt like a small child trailing behind an officious nurse in an endless hospital corridor, the pace seeming ever to increase.

The green corridor grew rockier as they climbed for a time, following minor watercourses re-created by the recent storms. Then they travelled against the natural lie of the land, walking up and down the hills, ignoring the valleys.

Bras appeared to sense her unspoken comment for he turned and grinned. 'Quickest way,' he said, then added, as if it made his credentials as a guide indisputable, 'I go cinema Ipoh one time.'

With no breath for conversation, she widened her eyes at him and nodded, genuinely impressed. She wondered what Bras had seen and what he would have made of a film like *Tarzan* and the Western version of a jungle.

She had the greatest admiration for the steady pace he could keep up, whatever the terrain. It was a great relief when they reached and followed the banks of a river which had the look of swirling whisked chocolate. The walking was easier and she tried not to look as the water roared past her right shoulder, tearing great chunks of soil from the banks and spinning them into the dizzying swirl of its waters.

As time went on, her exhaustion made her stumble more and more often. When she faltered or slipped down to hands and knees, she forced herself up, drove herself on, saying 'Alan' with every footstep, 'Alan, Alan.' In the back of her mind the words 'beyond endurance' were wanting to take over. She drowned them out with the repeated mantra, 'Alan, Alan, Alan,' more quietly sobbed than spoken.

Once for a few blessed strides they crossed quite a broad beaten track, but before relief could take over Bras plunged across and into the jungle on the other side. But it was easier than before because they were travelling alongside a large water pipe—the need to pipe water anywhere seemed ludicrous at that moment when it gushed and gurgled in every crevice.

Now she felt she fairly flew along, with the padding footsteps of an athlete. It was suddenly quite intoxicating and she didn't hurt any more. She recognised the state as 'second wind'. Bras, seeing her keeping up, increased his pace. She felt as if everything around her was dropping away. This, she thought, was no second wind, this was more like being a kite, soaring over the ground. She had no feeling of her feet on the ground though she was going forwards. She felt drugged, her heart seemed to be beating gently, her head seemed wonderfully clear. After a time she giggled.

The Sakai turned curiously to look at her, and immediately eased his pace. Slowing down made the pain and heat return into her feet and ankles; exhaustion flooded back while her heart pumped deafeningly. Now she moved in a different trance, a pain-ridden state where only the thought of seeing Alan at the end of the journey kept her going. Soon, she was beyond thought, she was all pain, hot aching agony which began in the burning soles of her feet and seared up her legs in waves. On, on, on, she pushed herself forwards.

Suddenly she found herself struggling against some obstruction. She raised her arms as if fending off foe, before words and gentle restraint made her pause. It was a woman, whose voice she struggled to recognise. Liz saw an elderly Chinese standing before her. She felt total despair that this frail woman should be able to stop her and bar her way. 'Excuse me,' she gasped as if to negotiate this new barrier she must be polite, move round.

'Miss Lizabeth? It is Miss Elizabeth! Where is my Lee?'

Shock of recognition sent goose pimples over her overheated body and her knees failed spectacularly. The woman knelt quickly before her, then, as her breathing eased, Liz leaned forward into the woman's arms. 'Oh! Mrs Guisan! It's you!' Liz sobbed with exhaustion, Ch'ing because the girl was a woman and had not recognised her.

'Lee's coming. I just came quicker.' She paused. With heart-stopping anxiety she asked, 'Alan? The soldier?'

'Rest a moment,' Ch'ing said, looking at the young woman's torn clothes and scratched arms and legs telling of the headlong race to arrive in time.

'No!' She struggled to her feet again, swaying. A little group of fascinated Sakai women and children watched and parted as Ch'ing led her the rest of the way to a large hut built just below the brow of the hill. The hut sides were hinged to the roof and propped up on poles to allow every cooling breeze to blow through.

She could see the bed as she approached, the still figure on it. The thin, thin, figure with a Sakai grandmother dipping her finger into a bowl and moistening his lips. Her heart leaped as in the caring she saw he survived, he was not dead...but as she drew nearer her traitor mind added 'yet'.

She ached with the sadness of hardly recognising the young man who seemed to have been replaced by a bearded emaciated man many years older. Sparsely fleshed, even gaunt before, now the angles of jaw were hidden by a sandy growth of beard much lighter than his hair but the cheek bone was acute—and across the top of his head was a smoothly healed scar. For some stupid illogical reason she remembered the shot-off crepe sole of Josef's sandal, how her bullet had torn a clean semi-circular

393

swathe through the white rubber.

She wanted to run her hand soothingly over the wound, take him up into her arms and forcibly bring him back to life. Instead she went down on her knees gently, like one preparing to pray, and took his hand, cradling it between hers, kissing the inert fingers.

'Alan, I'm here now. It's Liz. You'll be all right now. Of course you will.' She cradled the hand by her cheek and anxiously sought the movement between the hollowed ribcage as he breathed—it was so slight.

She woke with a start, finding her head on the bed over her arm, her legs collapsed under her. 'Alan! We're still fine.' She straightened, reassuring him, recollecting herself. 'Just waiting for you to open your eyes to see me. It's Liz, Alan.' She glanced to the far side of the bed, where the old Sakai woman nodded approval as she continued to smear Alan's lips from the bowl. Ch'ing too was there by her side.

'Come and eat,' Ch'ing said, hand on her shoulder. 'You need strength too.'

'I can't leave him.'

'Then I bring you food here.'

She did eat ravenously, once begun, of a meal of roasted semolina root, like the most delicious floury potatoes, with game, rice, fresh-cut pineapple. Then Pa Kasut had a bed brought in so she might rest alongside Alan when she wanted to.

'I want to thank you so much for all you have done,' she told the old man. She put her hands together in the Chinese fashion and bowed her thanks to him.

He rocked a little on his heels, looking quite embarrassed and overwhelmed. Walking round to the far side of the bed, he re-established his composure by ordering the old woman to go and refill her bowl with the liquid he had brewed.

Liz thanked her when she returned and asked if she might take over the duty of moistening Alan's lips. The Sakai woman showed her how to introduce tiny drops into his mouth. Once Liz introduced too much and he swallowed with a gigantic and unnatural effort, then coughed. She thought she might have killed him. She was much more cautious after this.

The liquid was clear and bright like spring water. It was curiously heart-wringing to be physically near him yet knowing he was unaware. Gently she traced his smooth lips between the unfamiliar beard and moustache and felt the action more like one indulged in by lovers in English meadows full of long-stemmed buttercups. She fantasised that he only feigned sleep and might suddenly snap at her fingers. 'You promised always to

395

make me laugh. I mean to keep you to your word.'

Experimentally she tasted the liquid herself and was reminded of a kind of gripe water used in the nursery; it tasted partly sweet, partly alcoholic. She put the finger from her own lips to his in a kind of reverent kiss.

She watched and talked to him, sensitive for the least response. Once she thought his eyes moved beneath his eyelids as if he was dreaming.

'Where are you, Alan? Come back to me! Alan, it's Liz. I waited for you at the bungalow, waited a long time...' She told him about the mat and the cushions, about the flowers and the butterfly.

Ch'ing came to sit with her and they talked, including him in the conversation, trying to pull at his mind, tug his memory.

'His father died unexpectedly—like mine,' Liz said. 'It created a bond between us to talk about this.'

'Your father dead?'

'Oh, Ch'ing, you didn't know?'

She told the story as simply as she could. Ch'ing's eyes never left her face and when all was told, she uttered two words which were fair trial and honest verdict, 'My Josef.'

She rose soon afterwards and when Liz would have gone with her she shook her head and motioned towards Alan. 'I all right,' she said, 'back soon.'

Liz watched her go. She walked out and towards the hut the Sakais had allotted for the women visitors, an old, bent solitary woman in the moonlight, her shoulders eloquent of this new burden of knowledge. A son who had murdered a man who had done him nothing but good, a man who, Liz knew, had regarded himself more as an uncle than as the employer of the man's father.

Beyond the hut Ch'ing entered, Liz could hear the Sakais calling to each other. She was surprised how loudly some of the men talked to each other. When they were on the edges of others' habitation they appeared shy, but here in their own home they were obviously joking and chattering with spirit and humour.

Alone with Alan she put her hands on his shoulders, leaning gently down to kiss his lips. 'They say a kiss without a moustache is like a meal without salt,' she whispered to him, then kissed his forehead and eyes. Just the way her father had once roused her from sleep to leave early for a holiday. Kindly but firmly his tones had reached into her sleeping mind; now her voice must reach into Alan's. It was like an intercession as she talked on and on, pleading for the darkness to let his mind go, let him back into life.

'The jungle is never still, Alan, always there is growth, and after the rains the young shoots grow inches overnight. Life and light, Alan. Look! Over between the trees I can see lights, tiny dancing sparks. Fireflies. I used to think they were fairies, Tinkerbell and her friends, I used to tell Lee. You remember Lee? She and her mother were at the camp, they saved you and brought you to the Sakais. Lee will be here soon. You could wake up and say thank you.'

She put her head down on the bed, cradling his hand under her breasts, talking still.

'The fireflies have gone now, perhaps they know it's going to rain again. Alan, I think my jungle is like the living green threads on a gigantic loom through which man weaves his threads of good or evil. The jungle accepts all alike, hides the good and the bad. We have to be on the side of the angels, Alan, us and the Sakais, Lee and her mother, *my* mother. That reminds me of how I used to say my prayers. The Lord's Prayer, then a list: "God Bless Mother, Father, Wendy, Anna, Lee and Mr and Mrs Guisan...Josef..." '

Lightning flickered and crackled all around the camp, then almost immediately the rain sheeted down, making the thunder almost inaudible. She glanced up at the woven leaf roof; not a spot of water penetrated it.

No use to try to talk now. She moistened his lips again, then lay on the bed by his side. She remembered tracing his ribcage with her fingers to wake him for dinner at Rinsey—it felt like several light years ago. She wanted to put her arm across his chest but was afraid even the slightest pressure might hamper his breathing, so light, so insubstantial. She held his hand in the darkness of the storm as a blind woman might and cried tears on to it for its thinness.

In the privacy of the darkness and the noise she sobbed aloud, calling his name. She felt she could have raised her head and howled louder than the savage downpour for very loneliness.

Then in the darkness and the storm Ch'ing came struggling back. She lit a small lamp in one corner and, taking up the bowl, began the duty of keeping the patient's lips moist, motioning to Liz to sleep.

There was something in the woman's intention to act as night nurse that made Liz feel Ch'ing wanted to do so as some kind of act of reparation. When Liz reached across and squeezed her hand, Ch'ing gave her one agonised look, then dropped her hand for shame of her son. She went on plying this other young man with the medicine of the Sakais, as if service to this new man in the Hammonds' lives might make some recompense.

By midday the following day Lee reached the camp. She came and sighed over the still motionless young boyfriend and in her eyes Liz saw she thought that if he did not soon recover he would never do so.

Her mother drew her away quite soon and in the privacy of the women's hut Liz could hear the quiet keening as Ch'ing grieved for a man still alive, but lost to her.

Chapter Twenty-Two

Blanche walked from the taxi towards the gaol gates. The small crowd were used now to seeing this Englishwoman among their number, but today, in black, with wide-brimmed black hat and veiled face, she created both awe and unease.

Mostly Chinese, with a healthy respect for their dead, they recognised extreme mourning and grief and fell quiet. One eventually offered a small folding seat.

'Thank you, but no,' Blanche said

quietly. She wished they would go on with their chatter and at least pretend some kind of normality. She knew her presence weighed heavily on them every time they came, but today, straight from Joan and Aubrey's funeral, it was as if she had cast some ghastly spell on them.

The Wildons had many friends. News of their double murder had spread around the East, bringing appalled and grieving friends and acquaintances from as far away as Java. Blanche had felt completely disoriented as she recognised faces and voices from prewar parties, bridge afternoons, tennis-club tournaments. Many had sought her out before the service and the reunions would begin with greetings and kisses, then the reminiscences: 'The last time we met, why, it must have been...'

Blanche felt stilted and unreal, quite unable to contribute anything to the nostalgic crowd. Her mind was on the fate of the daughter she had allowed to go off into enemy-occupied jungle and the loss of her dearest friends. After following the funeral cortege to the English section of the cemetery, she slipped away quietly, mentally apologising to her lost elegant, eloquent friends. She was aware of curious glances from other mourners, but could imagine Joan saying, 'Go on, darling, we totally understand.'

What she needed was to talk to George Harfield. She needed his adage-ridden reassurance, his strength.

'Aah!' the general sigh of relief when the gates were opened was audible. The Chinese glanced at her and hurried inside, anxious to be away from this spectrelike figure.

George was at his allotted table, rising immediately he saw her. 'I heard about the Wildons,' he said, catching her hands and lowering her into his visitor's chair. 'The bastards! God, it makes me feel so bloody hopeless!' He held on to her hands. 'Blanche, are you all right? You look terrible.'

'Thanks, George.' She gave his hand a squeeze as she added, 'That makes me feel much better.' And to her own chagrin tears began to run down her cheeks. 'I don't cry,' she told him.

'No, my love, I can see that.' He paused while she blotted her cheeks and eyes. 'You've come straight from the funeral. Are you alone?'

'I came in our car with the guard.'

'Liz?' he queried.

She did not answer.

'Liz didn't go with you?'

She shook her head slowly. He found the way she dropped her eyes at his last question quite out of character.

'So where is Liz?' She looked up at him then and he could only think her expression was agonised. He leaned forwards and demanded, 'Blanche! Tell me what's happened!'

She hesitated, wondering if this was why she had come—just to unburden herself to someone. She gazed at him silently, pondering the question of his specialness to her.

'For God's sake don't make me feel any more useless than I am here,' he pressed her to go on. 'At least I can listen—perhaps even advise.'

'I'm sorry, George, of course I must tell you...everything.'

He looked at her sharply. There was more than grief in this woman, more even than the after-effects of a double funeral.

She told her story simply, of letting Liz and Lee Guisan go off with the Sakai, then the news of the Wildons brought by the police. 'It felt like a punishment for being so stupid,' she said. 'Allowing her to go off like that.'

'No, no. I knew about the young guardsman being missing—and I did see him and Liz together once. I thought I interrupted a kiss, now I'm sure.'

The older man and woman exchanged glances almost as if exploring a possibility, or remembering long-lost intimacies with others. Their glances held so long it was as if each was wondering about the other in a new light. 'You let your heart rule your head, that's all,' he added.

'George, don't butter me with platitudes,' she began, then dropped her gaze and added quietly, with affection, 'Oh, I don't know, though, I miss your hackneyed phrases—damn you!'

'I've never been damned so nicely before,' he said. 'Come on, old lady—' He stopped and raised a hand to fend off her swift glance. 'No! Sorry! Know when I've gone too far. No, what I mean is, you would probably have had to lock Liz up to stop her going, and with a Sakai guide I would say they're...as safe as anyone in the jungle these days.'

'There's one more thing,' she confessed. 'This morning we heard distant shooting, real battle it sounded, and just before I left for Aubrey and Joan's funeral news came in that one of the tappers had found a dead jungle tribesman.'

'Not the one the girls went with?'

'No, the tapper was sure about that. He had seen that Sakai come to the gate for food.'

'Could have been coming back with a message I suppose. Makes me bloody mad—of all people, they're the innocents in this campaign. Heng Hou makes a sport

404

of shooting them as if they're just another kind of jungle game.' He sighed with deep distaste before going on, 'I'd have thought Heng Hou would have taken his men south fairly quickly, unless he's staying around for a definite purpose.' He pursed his lips. 'Look! As soon as you leave here, contact Robbo and tell him I said you've *got* to have a couple of Gurkhas at Rinsey. They put the fear of God into the CTs.' He stopped. 'Hell! I'd forgotten—he's gone after Liz.'

He looked across at Blanche Hammond. Not only was he powerless to help, he was now making useless suggestions.

'I'm in quite a fix, aren't I?' she said calmly.

'I'd give my right arm to be out and able to help—and I don't say *that* lightly.'

'No.' She accepted his sincerity and knew his mind went momentarily to Bukit Kinta and the mutilation and murder of Rasa.

'So you're at Rinsey just with your amah?'

'And the guard system you set up. It works very well.' He thought she seemed curiously unconcerned, as if her own safety meant little to her now.

'No way should two women be left alone like that, even with guards,' he insisted. 'Go to that Inspector Aba and tell him...'

He sought for a good reason. 'Tell him you believe his murder suspect is on the prowl.'

She did not add to George's concern by telling him she had a feeling Josef was around, that some evenings it was as if she could feel his enmity closing in on her.

George felt he was just floundering in a mass of feeble notions and looking at this woman he was full of admiration—and more. He wondered how she was keeping up at all. When one's husband and best friends had been murdered by the CTs, to also have one's daughter roaming around in the jungle... He sighed and muttered to himself.

'What did you say?'

'I said if I could see any way of escaping from this festering hole I would,' he repeated under his breath.

'George!' She gripped his forearm urgently. 'Don't ass about, don't do anything bloody silly. You're all I've got left.' She shook her arm fiercely. 'I need you. I need to know...to know that you at least are safe.'

He looked at her, swallowed hard and put his hand over hers as it rested on her arm. 'This is a fine time to tell you, but I love you, Blanche Hammond, have done ever since you took those coconut drinks from me on that train.'

She kept still, her eyes lowered, heart pounding. She gave no outward show of emotion as she wondered if this declaration was what she wanted to hear, what she had really hoped for.

'I've spoken when I shouldn't. I'm sorry. And if you don't come to visit me any more, well, perhaps I'll deserve that—but, my God, it'll finish me if you don't come!'

There was anxiety and hurt in his voice at his own suggestion. She looked across at him and shook her head.

'I'll never stop coming. Part of the reason I've not returned to England is that I could never abandon you to a series of casual visitors at long intervals. No, I would never do that, believe me.' She lifted her free hand and for a full three seconds laid it alongside his cheek. Something like an electric shock passed through both of them.

'My God,' he breathed as, taking her hand from his cheek, she placed it over his hand, 'I don't believe this. Could you wait for me, Blanche?'

'As long as it takes,' she told him.

'These youngsters don't know they're born,' he said gruffly.

They seemed from then on to be existing at two levels. They talked nonstop until the end of visiting time came. But it was to

407

both as if at a different, rather higher level their alter egos were silently wondering and staring at each other, quite overwhelmed by the discovery they had made.

Blanche told of her visit to the mine and seeing the girl. 'She knows I'm after her, but how to trap her?'

Both found release from their sufferings and help in the exchange of sympathies and ideas, while these invisible creatures looked on, waiting to be fully realised, however long it took.

'You'll get word to me as soon as there's news of Liz?' he asked urgently as the moment of parting came. 'And ask about those Gurkhas!'

'Keep cheerful, George. I'm sorry I came empty-handed, I'll make up next time.'

'As long as there's going to be a next time. I feel...I feel as if I could take this place apart with my bare hands.'

'But you won't.'

'No.' He was suddenly very solemn. 'I shall just live for the next sight of you.'

'Mem! Mem!' Anna's voice was full of concern as she came to meet Blanche.

Blanche threw her black-veiled hat on the hall table and hurried to meet her amah. 'Is there news?'

'The man they found this morning, army have been and taken away. He is Dyak tracker. Someone shoot and steal army shirt and shorts.'

'Not the tracker Sturgess took with him to go after the girls?' Blanche caught and held her breath in alarm.

'Mem!' The one word and Anna's look of despair confirmed the worst.

She sat down on a chair. 'So what's happened?' She asked about the shooting they had heard that morning. 'Has the area been searched? Have the police been?'

'All time you gone. The inspector want see you, but more trouble and he had to leave.'

'Let's both have a brandy, shall we?' Blanche nodded to the glasses and shivered. 'How is it possible to feel cold in this heat? I've been to see George Harfield in prison—after the funeral.' She patted the chair by her side for Anna to sit down. 'He thinks there are probably still quite a few terrorists in this area. Makes me wonder if Sturgess had been ambushed.' She stood up and paced the room. 'And if he's lost his tracker, no way is he going to find a Sakai village.'

'Sakai clever,' Anna said, sipping her brandy. 'Lee been living in jungle long time too. They be all right.'

'Yes. Positive thoughts, that's what we must have, or we'll go under.' She looked at Anna. 'We must be strong for each other now.'

Just as they were both striving to have positive, strong thoughts, the telephone rang and made them jump.

'Yes! Hello!' Blanche said, motioning Anna to stay where she was. 'Inspector Aba. Hello, I was going to be in touch with you...' Blanche turned towards Anna as she listened, her face becoming ever more grave. She put down the receiver after some time with just the briefest of thanks.

'The inspector was ringing to say he is planning to bring two guards to Rinsey. He'd hoped tonight, but they're fully stretched dealing with a workers' riot near Ipoh and another terrorist killing at Slim River. He also thinks there're still communists near Rinsey.' She went to Anna and caught her hand as the amah rose in alarm. 'We must make plans to defend ourselves as best we can. I shall double up the guards until the police can get here, and you and I will take turns resting during the night, keeping watch over Datuk.'

Anna put her unfinished brandy down. 'I go clean all guns.'

'I'll go and see Chemor. Thank God we've got him.' She silently also thanked God for George, for this new relationship

410

they had moved towards. Even banged up in prison he gave her the will to struggle on.

She did everything she could think of for their safety, moving beds out of the line of windows, making strict rules about lights. They would use only the dimmest of bulbs in the lounge, which had good shutters, and in the rest of the house, they would feel their way around. For all the precautions, she knew there was a last thing she had to do.

While Anna prepared their evening meal, Blanche took her rifle and went to sit by Neville's grave. There was something she had to tell him. It's a little like telling the bees, she thought. We used to have a gardener who went to the hives and told the bees all the births and deaths. This news is about both, Neville.

She shuffled her rifle butt in the dust. I'm not sure how much you lot know. Or how long it takes. I mean, are Aubrey and Joan there? There were a lot of reunions at the funeral. Voices from the past, Neville. I thought more about you and Liz, really. So are all your troubles over—or are you just all over?

That's the trouble, isn't it? How much should our consciences here be bothered about over there?

So I've told the death bit. The birth

bit is more difficult, but I shouldn't like to meet up with you under any false pretences. I mean, if we're attacked and wiped out tonight...

You know I was more enamoured of you than in love with you, Neville—all through. I was enamoured of your gaiety, your special capacity for enjoying life—you were a bit like the social grasshopper, and totally unbusinesslike. I suppose I was enamoured too with Pearling the house, the history. But if I married you for Pearling it got its own back—it became the millstone I had to carry around my neck all through the war on my own, with the girls.

About the girls... If you hadn't been killed, this new thing would never have happened. It certainly would not have occurred to me, and I'm sure George would never have spoken out. But Liz is all you—well, nearly all, occasionally I hear myself in her words, but the artistic bit—that girl worships you, always will. Wendy's more like me. She'll be a good businesswoman. She's coming out to Rinsey.

God, that gives me pause. We can't let Wendy come out for another funeral. Blanche broke off the internal monologue to pull her rifle nearer. I must do what I told George Harfield in prison this morning. I must stop assing about.

412

I find I love the man. She paused, then restated it plainly in her mind. I love George Harfield. He's everything I might have said I disliked ten years ago; bluff, blunt, earthy? Not sure about that last—more down-to-earth—whatever, the chemistry works between us. So that's it, really. I'll be staying at Rinsey. I was a bit surprised you'd left Rinsey and Pearling to me outright, no strings.

You were my springtime love, Neville, and it was a real crush, as that love should be. Perhaps the war ended that feeling. It was a kind of innocence, you know. But now I've found a man I love in a way I've never loved before—with all my mature heart. A love to sustain me in this bloody awful time. You're not missing much, my old love.

She sighed and looked up to see Anna standing a little way off, head bowed, hands clasped as if in prayer. The trouble is, Neville, now I've admitted to myself that I love him I want him out of that bloody prison even more.

They ate together early that evening, the three of them. Datuk was irrepressible, full of talk about a pet mongoose a boy had brought to school, which had found and killed a snake in the playground. 'It was poisonous, but it killed it!' He grabbed

413

his own throat, nearly knocking himself off his chair, demonstrating how the mongoose had lunged at the reptile.

'Useful to have around, a mongoose,' Blanche commented as Anna looked about to censor the boy.

'Wish *I'd* got one!'

'Your grandmother and I will think about it,' she told him, thinking he deserved some reward for bringing a touch of normality into their lives.

'Wow!' he said, eyes wide.

'Thank you,' Anna corrected.

'Oh! Thank you, Mrs Hammond. Thank you!'

'I seem to remember a boy who used to have his mongoose on a lead around the house, with a proper pen for it at nights. Does that sound a good idea?'

'Wow!' He caught his grandmother's eye. 'Yes, thank you Mrs Hammond. Wow!'

Anna raised her eyes and sent him off to do his homework.

'I'll just have a walk round to check on the guards,' Blanche said when he had gone. 'Don't want any slackness tonight. Then early bed, I think, I feel exhausted. Emotionally torn to shreds.'

She had noticed that when she sat near Neville's grave the guards tactfully moved away. She wanted now to be sure the patrol of the perimeter wire was being properly covered.

Thoughts of Wendy arriving made her determined to be much more assiduous about the defence of the plantation, and with two police guards coming soon it was perhaps just tonight that was the biggest danger time.

Starting at the back of the property she walked slowly around to the side, then to the front gates, where she spoke to Chemor. He reported that two of the men were just having their meal, but every post would be covered before nightfall. She walked on until she came to the spot where it was still possible to see the old path to the Guisans' bungalow, severed now and made a no-man's-land by the triple barbed wire. She could visualise the children running up and down, Lee always by Liz's side. She remembered Neville expressing a wish to see his grandchildren playing there—'green freedom', he had called it. Now she just prayed their daughter was safe—grandchildren seemed a dim and distant prospect.

Moving on, she passed the hut which contained the entrance to their escape route. Near the wire she walked circumspectly, anxious not to be seen by any of the Malay families, who would certainly press her to eat again with them, and it was considered very discourteous to refuse.

The guards at the back acknowledged her from a distance and, seeing her going back towards the area of Mr Hammond's grave, tactfully gave her space. She stood and watched as the falling sun gathered power and glory until it reached an intensity of brilliance only seen in the tropics. The evening sounds from the jungle were beginning, the crickets always first, then the others would follow.

Her hearing was acute and she found herself listening more intently as there came a different sound from the undergrowth. The wind lifted and let fall the foliage in a soughing sweep, but this was quite a different rhythm. She held her breath. This was the sound of something or someone pushing through the *beluka*. She looked both ways along the wire. The guards were out of her sight. She was about to move away when a soft voice spoke her name.

'No, don't move, Mrs Hammond. I have you covered. Don't make me shoot. Please stay and talk to me, Mrs Hammond. Listen to what I have to say.'

The voice sent a shiver of ice along her spine, echoed a boy's voice from ten or fifteen years ago. The same words. 'Mrs Hammond. Mrs Hammond. Please listen. I did not do it. I am not responsible.'

'I am all alone, Mrs Hammond.'

She heard him move nearer but still could not see him. She wanted to ask if Neville had been all alone when he shot him. She lifted her rifle to hold it in both hands.

'Don't do anything rash, Mrs Hammond. You've nothing to fear from me, Mrs Hammond.'

It had grated on her nerves even when he was a child, a deceitful, spiteful child, the way he repeated her name as if it was some special charm against punishment.

'You say you are alone. Let me see you.'

'You never did take just my word, did you?'

'And wasn't I wise?'

'Most times.' He laughed and she saw him emerge from just beyond the cleared jungle and steadily approach the wire. He held his rifle sighted on her, while she held hers loosely in front of herself.

She wanted him nearer.

'Josef Guisan,' she said as if she sought him a long time. 'So why should I trust you now?' She repeated the question and waited for the repeated pleas of innocence just the same as when he was a boy. Guilty as hell but prepared to argue that black guilt was white innocence until the last trump.

'Mrs Hammond, believe me, I mean you no harm—'

'You look threatening, Josef, your gun pointing straight at me.'

'Oh, it's habit,' he said and lifted the rifle in one hand, but she could see that his finger was still curled in the trigger. She just had this one chance...

'Bad habits die hard, Josef,' she said as she lifted her rifle a little and compressed the trigger on the upwards swing in one smooth, slick movement and shot him in the heart, '...like rogue dogs.'

The force of the impact knocked him backwards as if struck by a Titan's hammer blow. For a split second she saw his face registering surprise and fury, then as he fell he all but disappeared back into the undergrowth. He was undoubtedly dead and the smell of fresh blood was in the warm breeze.

The sound of the shot reverberated through the jungle and the hills and for a moment there was peace. She expelled the spent cartridge case while searching her soul for any sense of guilt. She looked up to where the sun emblazed the sky a deep blood red. 'I feel better for that, Joan darling,' she breathed, 'much, much better.'

The silence was shattered now by shouts and men coming running and the sound of a car horn blowing at the main gates.

Men came from their huts, the guards running along the wire. There was a babble of questions and many pointing fingers. Blanche led the way towards the front gate, meeting Inspector Aba, who had rushed from his riot at Ipoh bringing two guards for Rinsey.

'I've just shot Josef Guisan,' she told him, moving out and around the wire to where the body lay.

She had shot him in cold blood, she knew that. Murder, she supposed. She thought about George in prison. Lovers in prison, one for rape, one for murder. What about that? And what about Liz and Wendy? She watched Inspector Aba as he took over the lead; she doubted he would let the matter go without an inquiry.

They approached the fallen man with caution. But there was absolutely no doubt, the shot had hit the heart with pinpoint accuracy. The stain on the chest looked black now and the inspector ordered a man back for a lamp. Anna came too from the house and stood by Blanche, gripping her hand as the inspector raised the light.

'Aaah!' She greeted the sight of Josef's body with a cry that expressed justice done. By her side a small voice piped, 'that's a good thing! He hurt my grandmother many times.' He pushed himself between Anna and Blanche and took both their hands. Looking up at Blanche, he added, 'You like mongoose, kill bad things.'

Blanche regarded the inspector, whose officiousness seemed to waiver at Datuk's judgement. He went back to bend over the body. As he moved the rifle the hand was lifted too, and in death the finger was still curled in the trigger guard.

'It is fortunate thing he did not have time to fire first,' Inspector Aba concluded.

Chapter Twenty-Three

There was a feeling of extreme peace all around. There had been a voice before, but now blessed stillness. Alan felt on the very lip of heaven. He had only to bequeath his breath to the wind and be gone.

And yet...and yet...it felt like a dream, half remembered, something in life half yearned for even while not properly recalled.

There was a voice that came again and he remembered the same voice had called before. A siren voice, luring him away from this blankness that was oblivion. A siren voice, but it paused and he knew he could decide to go now.

420

The voice came again louder, as if it yearned for him. He wondered, wavered—siren voices invited disaster, sang sailors on to rocks.

He thought he heard another sound, as if he gasped—was he trying to swim away? Then there was much activity around him. Was this the final surge over treacherous reefs to the calm lagoon beyond?

Be still, leave me, leave me. His brain inside his skull felt too big, too much to be poured back in. 'Quarts into pint pots,' he heard his father say, adding with a familiar, weary acceptance, 'but you'll always try!'

'Alan, Alan,' the urgent voice said close by his ear, 'come back to me.'

How could he? He didn't know where he was.

Something like panic stirred at the base of his spine and ran like uneasy fingers up to his head. Sensation flooded back, awareness like all-over pins and needles assailed him and he felt as if his body was unbalanced, as if he swam or floated in some strange substance like...like the warm wobbly wallpaper glue his father's decorator used.

He remembered his father always had the firm's decorator at home. 'I like to see a good professional job,' he would say, than add as an aside just to Alan, 'and I don't want to have to do it.'

Memory came crushing back. His father was dead. The hurt of his death came sharp on the recollection. His father was dead; his mother? She had cried the last time he had seen her, cried about him, because of him. What had he done? It all seemed so sad.

Was it his mother speaking to him? It was a woman's voice, he thought. Like his mother, always asking him to do things. 'Take your father's lunch to him.' 'Go and tell your father the carpenter's not able to come today.' But his father was dead and his mother had cried because he had sailed far away, to the other side of the world.

He supposed he could open his eyes, though it seemed like quite an undertaking. Like someone shut up inside a difficult box of tricks with booby traps on all sides, he cautiously ordered his eyelids to go up a little. Nothing happened, only after a time the quality of colour seemed to have altered—black had become a kind of gingery brown.

It took him some time to realise that his eyes were parted a fraction and what he could see was hair—it could be a beard. He didn't know he had a beard. A small quaking laugh formed somewhere as he wondered if he was Rumpelstilskin.

Something moved across his vision, a hand, and he felt something being soothed on his lips, moist, sweet, nice. He was hungry, he realised, very hungry.

'Alan!' the voice was urgent. 'I thought your lips moved. Alan?' The fingers that had brought moisture before now played along his lips as if testing for some reverberation of life.

Then the moisture and the sweetness came on his lips again.

He could see no one.

Then another sensation blotted out all others. Someone was moving a finger along the line of his ribs. This had happened to him before—and this was a different memory. This was something he wanted. This was the voice. He wanted to see, and he forced his eyelids higher like a child reborn with an urgent instinct to view his world.

He could see a wall of bamboo, a high woven roof. Then he focused on someone very close to his side, someone—making free with his body. The face and the voice all came together. 'Liz!' he shouted. 'Liz!' The sound started in his mind like a triumphant shout, but came from his throat like the rasping of a rusty knife on an old dry brick.

'Alan? Alan!' This was the yearning voice! Now her anxious face peered down at him as if hope was some strange creature she was afraid to look for.

423

'Alan?' The word was all caution. He saw how she slowly allowed herself to recognise the light of rational life in his half-opened eyes. He saw her face transformed as finally she saw he knew her. 'Alan, my darling... Oh! I didn't think we'd ever really look at each other again.' She pressed her face close to his. 'Oh! Thank God, thank God! If there's no more than this, I thank God!'

He did not understand, remembering her finger along his ribcage. What was she saying? There was to be much more!

'I knew if I loved you enough you wouldn't go from me.'

He felt her tears hot on his cheeks and he tried to move a hand to touch her, but she rose too soon. 'I must tell the others.'

She ran to the doorway from the sleeping bench where he lay against one wall. He felt bereft as she left; turning his head to watch, he was alarmed when she seemed to drop out of sight from the door. Then he remembered native huts he had seen high on stilts. He had not realised that some might have such noble-seeming proportions inside. The room where he lay seemed enormous and airy, with pleasant filtered sunlight.

He heard her calling, 'Lee, Ch'ing, Pa Kasut! He's come round! He's come back!'

Then her head reappeared in the doorway. Alan felt his mind light up, and as she ran across to him he thought she was like a girl in an English buttercup field with the sun behind her—and he lying in the grass.

'Will you try a proper drink?' She took up a small cup and dipped it into a bowl. Then she was back by his side supporting his head, letting him sip from the cup. 'This is what the Sakais have brewed, it's kept you alive.'

He was aware of the strange sensation of hair all around his lips as he drank. After she had taken the cup away he tried to lift a hand to feel. He wondered at the slowness of the hand that came eventually from his side upwards. He wondered at the hand. Did those elongated, skeletal fingers belong to him?

Liz watched with a beaming smile and, as one after another climbed up into the room, she gestured to them, drew them over to the sleeping bench. 'He's moving,' she cried, 'he's moved his hand—and he knows me. He knows! Oh, Lee, thank you! Thank you, Ch'ing! Thank you, Pa Kasut!'

They came and peered at him. He peered solemnly back. He remembered the Chinese faces of Lee and her mother. There were many native faces, men wearing crossed bandoleers of tiny multi-coloured beads, women wearing colourful sarongs, some from the waist, some tied above their breasts. All were strangers—but all kind, all smiling.

'Pa Kasut.' Liz indicated the oldest of the men, who came forward nodding and smiling with great satisfaction.

'Good! Good!' he proclaimed and motioned with his fingers to his mouth. Alan nodded and Pa Kasut grinned broadly and ordered his women to go and prepare food, hurrying after them down the ladder like a fussy chef after his underlings.

When Alan had drunk, he tried her name again. 'Liz.'

It was better this time, recognisable. He looked at the other girl. 'Lee.'

They all laughed as if he had told them the funniest joke in the world.

They propped him up a little and gave him a different drink, goat's milk with a curious warm aftertaste like alcohol. It was so good, it warmed his stomach. He lifted a hand again and touched his beard. He remembered something of being in a raid, a jungle camp, the shooting, but it was vague, blurred as a misted window. 'How long?' he asked.

'Many weeks.'

'Where?' He queried his surroundings with his eyes.

'We're safe,' she told him. 'A Sakai hill camp. Lee says it's beautiful; I haven't looked around much.'

'You remember telling us to hide under our big bed?' Lee knelt by Liz's side at the bench. She nodded for him as she saw recollection in his eyes. 'Then when the communists came back and you were hurt...' She paused to draw her hand across the top of her head in the direction of the bullet that had scored Alan's skull. 'Then we hid you.'

With a great effort Alan brought his hands together in the Eastern manner of thanks. Lifting one hand to his head, he found and traced the smooth scar starting just right of centre and running back and across through his mass of hair. He was surprised that the sensitivity of the wound still bordered on pain.

Liz watched him realise the injury and the seriousness of it, how close he had come to death.

'Here's your food,' Lee said, going to help the women carry the cooking pots in. 'Pa Kasut will have prepared it. He has a wonderful knowledge of plant medicines. His mixture my mother is sure saved your life.'

As the days passed, Alan began to realise how much he owed to all these people, both the Guisans and the Sakais. He also began to feel that if there was such a place as heaven on earth, then this was probably it.

With Liz to help him first to drink and eat, then to sit and finally to take his first steps across to look out of the door, paradise indeed felt very close.

The hillside had sections of the ground cleared around it to allow the Sakais to grow their haphazardly broadcast crops of tapioca and maize, and the hut was built on stilts some ten feet from the ground. This gave a unique view of the jungle below. They could overlook the mass of variegated greens and the many trees blossoming in the canopy, never seen from the ground, only suspected by their perfume.

From above it was possible to realise how, with no winter to dictate their cycle, trees blossomed and fruited to their own individual rhythm. Each one in its own season produced flowers in masses of white, pink, scarlet or yellow. Yet more glorious Technicolor was poured from the outcrops of rock around the camp, where creepers in all the colours he last remembered seeing in nasturtium beds back in England vied for attention.

'How on earth did they get me up here?' Not just the steepness of the slopes but the ladder from the ground made him ask. The descent to ground level still looked formidable to him.

Liz laughed. 'They carried you, of course, all trussed up like a hammock, hung from poles.' She finished the sentence hardly aware what she said, for his expression had changed to one of complete anguish. He staggered as if some awful pain had stabbed him through, threatening to bring him to his knees, to fell him. Alarmed he might tumble, she pulled him away from the doorway.

'What is it?' she asked, grasping tight, almost shaking him in her alarm. He steadied himself again but held his head in his hands and groaned.

'I've just remembered Danny. Danny...' For a moment he had to search for his second name. 'Danny Veasey. He was killed on the op before I got this.' His hand went to his scalp. 'I...carried his body.' He looked at her now with urgent questioning. 'What happened to his body? God! It wasn't just left?'

'No.' She re-emphasised the word as he looked at her with some doubt. 'No. There was a military funeral; I read it in the *Straits Times*. One man missing, one man killed. Major Sturgess went to the funeral.'

'The major...and, I suppose, Sarge

Mackenzie and the lads, but I should have been there.' He went back to sit on his bed.

'I should have kept the newspaper, there was a full report. It was—' She broke off, reliving the trauma of that first evening she had believed Alan dead.

'I should have written to his mother.' His voice was low, thick with regret.

'You can still do that when we get back.' She moved to his side as he lay down, so slowly, like someone afflicted by a new wound.

'There was a photograph in the *Times*, I remember. I'm sure we'll be able to get a copy from somewhere. Joan may even still have hers, they never throw their newspapers out until the print's practically read off them.'

He did not answer and she saw he was asleep again. In the first few days she had been alarmed by these sudden lapses into sleep, fearing he might have slipped back into a coma. Now she saw it for the exhaustion it was, each new achievement tasking his strength to the limit.

Keeping watch by his bed, she was torn two ways. They did have to go back, but she felt that time here in this peaceful camp was what Alan needed. Once back they would undoubtedly be parted; she supposed he would be taken into a military hospital or sent on furlough somewhere like the army rest camp on Penang island—or even home to England. All she could be certain of was the time remaining to them in this jungle settlement—before the army in the shape of Major John Sturgess finally arrived.

It was a total mystery what had happened to the army unit he was supposed to have been bringing to recover Alan, travelling so quickly unhampered by *women*—that had proved a hollow boast! She had expected them within a day or two of Lee arriving.

She wondered if perhaps they had not even set out because she had disobeyed orders. But Sturgess had 'lost' Alan from a mission he was in charge of. Surely his duty would be to recover his man if the opportunity was given? Duty she would have thought to be a prime mover in the major's life—and giving orders.

Then she remembered Sturgess needed Lee to identify some of the communist suspects the police had rounded up. He would come, she decided grimly.

Ch'ing, Lee and Liz had become aware that there was a growing unease in the settlement. Lee had heard Heng Hou's name whispered fearfully among the women as they worked around the cooking fire. Their presence put the Sakais in extreme peril.

Liz's task must be to help get Alan fit enough to travel as soon as Pa Kasut thought it safe. In the meantime she decided to emulate her mother; if there was nothing to be done about a situation, then there was no point in worrying about it.

She went quietly to the door and waved to Lee, who sat with her mother helping some Sakai wives and girls dye bark cloths for new sarongs. Lee yearned for two things; to hear that Heng Hou was dead, and to be out of the jungle.

The women often sat and made extravagant plans for shopping trips, telling the Sakai women they must come to Rinsey after the troubles and they would give them pretty materials and cooking pots. Lee always became quite animated as she talked of things she would buy—but first she was going to the cinema at Ipoh. 'I'd like find boyfriend go with,' she confided. Then a trip to the shops of Kuala Lumpur.

Liz proposed they should all go to Singapore for a holiday. 'We'll shop until we just can't carry another thing and our feet are ready to drop off.'

'Then we go eat fancy cakes in restaurant,' Ch'ing had said, and a whole new topic opened up.

Alan stirred on the bed and she wondered how long it would be before they were all plunged back into their own lives. She realised that she had to treasure this time. What a place for a honeymoon! she thought.

Alan was still distressingly skinny, but already it was possible to see a difference. The bones in his shoulders no longer looked as if you could grasp them like handles.

The following morning she asked Sardin to come to help Alan down so he might walk about outside.

Alan hesitated on the top of the house ladder. As an interested crowd gathered, Bras and Sardin took his hesitation as an invitation to help and practically carried him down to ground level.

'Terra firma—I think,' Alan said, moving cautiously for the first time on real ground. 'Though it still feels as if it has a spring in it, like the house floor.'

'Afraid it's your knees.' Lee laughed.

'I should have done more exercise, some knee bends,' he said as he made a brave if unsteady attempt at just that.

'You need swimming,' Bras informed him.

The remark was greeted by the women putting their hands over their mouths to hide their smiles and Pa Kasut clearing his throat in the manner of all fathers mildly censoring their sons.

433

Alan thought of the last swim he'd had—in a river battling with a lethal packing case with Danny on the bank—and found nothing to laugh at.

'Is there a swimming place?' Liz asked.

'Oh, yes.' Bras pointed up between two high peaks of rock, then swooped his hand over and down.

'Between those peaks?' she asked. 'It looks a long walk.'

'No so far,' Bras said. Again the Sakais, male and female, seemed to find it a big joke.

'Is there something wrong with the place?' Liz demanded of Pa Kasut.

'No,' he replied at once and with complete conviction, 'very good place.'

'Then why is everyone grinning? Does everyone come to watch or something?'

Bras looked very solemn. 'No, very private.'

'Lee and I will go and look,' Liz decided. 'While Alan builds up his walking strength around the village.'

'Perhaps they're just pleased for us,' Liz pondered that afternoon as she and Lee headed up between the two sugar-cone peaks of rock.

'They do have a right to be,' Lee said, but then burst into laughter, 'and...'

Liz stopped. 'And what? Now you're doing it.'

Lee ran on ahead. 'I'll tell you when we get there. I want to see it.'

It really wasn't far. The path twisted almost back on itself and there between the high rocky peaks was a deep green miniature valley and in the middle a serene mountain pool. Its unruffled surface contained a perfect reproduction of the surrounding trees, the overhanging branches, the hills beyond.

The two young women walked towards the water feeling as if entranced. When they reached its edge, Liz turned to Lee for explanation.

'This pool has a legend,' she told her. 'Many, many years ago a beautiful Kedan princess ran away with her lover. They were chased by her father's men and he was killed. She escaped to this place but was so lonely and when she found she was with child she drowned herself in this pool. The folk story says that if any woman wants a child she has only to bathe in the waters, or just sip them.'

'So that's why they were all laughing.'

'That Bras is a bit of a lad, I think.'

Liz looked out across the pool and felt even the legend was no match for the beauty of the place. Then she realised that Lee was stripping off her sarong. 'You're going to—' She stopped; what a stupid question! She began to pull off her own slacks and shirt.

She launched herself into the cool, deep waters, swimming slowly, almost reverently. She felt as if the grime and the cares of all the world were washed away by the balminess of the water, by the green hills, the blue bowl of the sky tipped over and balanced on the tops of the peaks. She was indeed a stranger in paradise, she thought, and felt that tranquillity and insight were fleetingly hers. The whole mystic East held her thralled in its mountainous cup.

Turning on her back, she floated as high on the water as she could, so that she could feel the heat of the sun on her face, her breasts, her thighs, but could not look up into it because of its power. No wonder, she thought, the pool had a legend.

The next moment she gasped as a great smashing shower of water made her splutter. Lee had swum gently round and was now splashing her with her feet as hard as she could. Liz retaliated and the two played like the children they had been together. They thrashed around in the water as if suddenly making up for all the lost years during the war.

Once exhaustion had been reached, the two swam away from each other. The waves they had created became ripples and, as they finally climbed out and up to where they had left their clothes, they watched the waters became quite calm, and again reflect in stillness and serenity the surrounding scene: the near branches dipping in places to the surface; the green hills; the far peaks. 'As if we never were,' Liz whispered.

'You must bring Alan here soon,' Lee said equally quietly. There was a note in her voice that echoed Liz's knowledge that their time at this place was growing short.

'I will,' she said with meaningful certainty, then, catching her friend's hand the way they had done as children when either needed to elicit a favour from the other, 'but promise me you'll let me tell him the legend.'

The next day Liz persuaded Alan to walk towards the pool. Her enthusiasm for the place made him curious, yet disinclined to think he'd ever swim there.

'Why,' he asked, 'do I have the feeling that this place is...different? I keep thinking of those boys' adventure stories where such places are either kept for human sacrifice—or you come back married!'

'What a terrible idea!' She led him on slowly until they reached the mountain pool, then she sat down on the mound where she and Lee had undressed before and let him walk on alone, as enchanted as she had been with the first sighting.

Standing by the edge of the water, he felt the strangest sense of recognition for the place. *Déjà vu?* He wondered. Was this the very lagoon of peace he had been promised after death? He thought if his soul had left his body, as they say sometimes happens, then it had hovered above this place and now he saw it again.

Unlike all the churning brown rivers he had seen, this was clear, clearer even than the falls at Rinsey. Here the water had collected straight from the mountain rock.

Liz came quietly up behind him and slipped her arms around his waist. His hands came down over hers and held them there. Both kept their eyes on the view as she told him the legend.

'It's true, of course,' he said simply. Then he turned and took her into his arms. This was their first real embrace since his slow recovery had begun. Liz closed her eyes and felt she had come home.

He stooped to kiss her brow. 'You have a swim. I'll wait until I can walk the whole distance here without a stop, then I'll go in.'

She undressed before him, using none of the provocative movements that any women is capable of, but taking care to expose herself gracefully. She walked to the edge, stooped down and pushed off into the water, smoothly without a splash, so the ripples make even circles from her, out and out to the very edges.

At first he sat on the mound, rearranging her clothes neatly. Then he stood on the rock to watch as her body, weightless and pale in the clear aquamarine water, moved in graceful, long-reaching breaststrokes out across the pool, looking from above like a bird suspended in flight. He thought he had never seen anything so awe-inspiring, so beautiful.

'My siren,' he whispered, then, as she turned from the far side and swam to the middle and turned on her back, breasts and ribcage, thighs and feet lapping out of the water, he added, 'my brazen hussy.' He watched and willed her back to the shore, back to his arms. He would wait a few days more, he thought—then he would swim.

Chapter Twenty-Four

The inner fury Sturgess had felt for Blanche Hammond's stupidity in allowing Liz and his witness to go off into the jungle was somewhat tempered by the frustration of his own scout's unexplained disappearance. Entap had been difficult to control but

439

Sturgess was convinced he would never have deserted.

In the end Sturgess led his party off with the definite feeling that he was moving to some kind of climax, not only in this particular campaign but in his own life. It felt curiously like a last trial, last labour set by some gods—and if he fell down in this, he must be a complete failure.

He was thankful to have Sergeant Mackenzie with him. The rest of his group were unknown quantities, and the good and dapper doctor had made it clear he was not happy without a tracker. The doctor had unofficially 'mentioned' the matter to Chemor, but he still regarded himself as under instruction from his former employer. 'My job stay with the mem and Rinsey,' he insisted.

Sturgess had been incensed by the attempt at interference and had announced quite bluntly that the decision was his and they would go—time was of the essence—and Chemor would, as George Harfield had ordered, definitely stay put at Rinsey.

Briefing the doctor that his work harassing the Japs had equipped him with much jungle knowledge, he saw from his face that this statement had to be proved to be believed. The doctor made him feel very much like a patient being given good advice to which he was refusing to listen.

What he had not revealed, as they cut into the jungle towards the river named Sungei Woh, was that he had stayed with the Sakais on several occasions when trekking through their territory to blow up Japanese installations, to sever their lines of communications, or just hiding out.

But the best lead he had was personal knowledge of Heng Hou. Even in the war, John had not trusted this burly Chinese, who had, if not watched, taken more than his fair share of camp rations and had been disliked by many of his fellows. He had shot to leadership as the communists formed the jungle platoons after the war and, like many another communist leader, ruled by intimidation. His own men were frightened of him, and the civilian population, particularly the gentle and easily intimidated Sakais, were terrified of him.

John calculated that, deprived of his 'luxurious' jungle camp and his supplies, he would first take out his revenge and spleen locally. Anyone who stood in his path would be slaughtered as Aubrey and Joan Wildon had been. Even so, he guessed Hou would not yet have moved far. Josef had promised him his sister, and Hou could be as devious and persistent as any monkey hiding a banana in its armpit while holding

441

out a hand for more.

He would be looking for a hiding place not too far from paths to local kampongs which could be plundered for food, especially the dried fish and coffee which Hou had a particular taste for. Hou's appetites were his driving force.

John had hoped to take Hou quickly—and had wanted the Chinese girl, Lee, as bait. He had planned secretly to lay ambush around the Rinsey area, having leaked the information that the former jungle-camp girl was there.

Inwardly he brooded that he felt a bloody fool on three counts. He had seen the woman he had thought his devoted wife in Australia with another man's son on her hip. He had found a young woman he would have liked as a successor running off into the jungle after one of his own guardsmen, and now one of the best trackers he had ever known had somehow been lured away and most likely murdered.

Sturgess vengefully attacked the tree ferns and creepers growing up from the jungle floor like giant performing snakes. He had not expected to have the added task of trying to track and protect Elizabeth Hammond. He felt she had acted like a little fool; if Cresswell had survived and was with the Sakais, he had no doubt sooner or later news of him would filter out. It had a feeling of demotion to realise that Liz had fallen for a conscripted guardsman, while Blanche Hammond was motoring to Ipoh to visit George Harfield at every opportunity.

Sturgess severed a particularly sturdy liana stem. George was a good enough chap—the very best. He got on with life, stood no bloody nonsense; one of nature's gentlemen, you might say, but regarded few social niceties.

As the days passed, Sturgess's self-questioning and the tormented energy it gave him did not abate. Perhaps, he decided as he supervised the laying of tripwires around their resting area, he would do better to forswear women for ever, just pay for services. His father had said that was all marriage was—another way of paying for services.

The next morning, he smelled smoke. It was some distance away but he drew his party's attention to the sign. Soon he could discern the lingering smell of cooking. If this was a communist overnight camp, they were feeling fairly secure.

He followed his nose and soon they came to a small clearing, in the centre of which was a kicked-out campfire. This had been rather inadequately dealt with and wisps of smoke still came from the blackened circle.

The major knew he was not of the calibre of any native tracker, but it was impossible for men to use the jungle without leaving signs. He was sure he was on the track of the right group of communists. The very nature of their careless camp, and the haphazard way they had lain during the night, told of thugs on the make rather than campaigners for a cause.

The tracks he followed became confused as they traversed and sometimes followed better-defined tracks. Before dark overtook them again, they could all smell smoke and cooking odours, and soon they began to see traces of the smoke trapped beneath the dripping, dense canopy. John realised this was no meagre campfire; this much smoke must be from several fires—a largish Sakai settlement or even a Malay kampong near the river.

He called a halt and discussed with Sergeant Mackenzie and the doctor the way they would deal with it. 'We'll assume there are communists in the houses, perhaps even holding some of the villagers hostage. So cautious approach with men keeping ambush positions on the main paths.'

The sergeant nodded his approval. 'Want me to take a couple of men and circle to the far side?'

'We'll move off as soon as we can see, then, when we approach, you two men, and you, doc?' He questioned the other officer with a nod. The doctor nodded briskly back. 'You lot hare around to cover the far side. Shoot for their legs if they don't stop when challenged. Meantime we'll have grub up early and then move in a little closer tonight.'

They ate quickly, the men ravenous but quickly satisfied with the hard tack biscuits and chunks of corned beef, washed down with sterilised water from their canteens. They were tired, eager to move those last few hundred yards so they could rest up for the night.

As Sturgess led the way to what must be a good-sized jungle kampong, a worm of apprehension stirred deep in his stomach. This smoke was neither cooking fire nor bonfire, though it might be both. He found Mackenzie at his elbow, and they exchanged glances. 'Tell the men to stay here. We'll go forwards and look.'

They waited to see the men well concealed by the pathway, then moved cautiously forwards on their own. They had walked some hundred yards farther when both men froze. Someone was coming towards them along the same path. Instantly they stepped out of sight, watching and waiting.

445

A desolate-looking yellowy-brown village dog came hesitantly towards them, his nose pointing first to one, then the other. They waited a moment or two more, then, sure the dog was alone, stepped cautiously out.

'Come on, old chap,' John said softly. 'Let's go and see if we can find your master.' The dog very companionably fell in behind the two men, though when they reached the bank of the Sungei Woh where the village must lie, for they could see a row of fishing stakes in the river, it refused to follow them farther. Mackenzie urged it on with a wave of his hand but it lay down and put its head flat on its paws. It was at that moment Sturgess became sure they were going to find disaster ahead.

Walking farther along the river path, they could see what looked like an extension of the fishing stakes, but these poles were black. 'Bugger!' Sturgess breathed.

'Poor bastards.' Mackenzie echoed the sentiment as they went slowly forwards to the burned-out village where only the uprights of the houses had survived.

They looked all around. Some possessions the terrorists had no use for were scattered beyond the range of the fire, while in the ashes of the largest hut were burnt corpses. 'Five, perhaps six,' Mackenzie said, then corrected, 'Five and a child.'

446

They reconnoitred the area thoroughly.

'There'll be other villages farther along this river,' Sturgess mused, wondering about their fate. 'We'll move upriver quickly tomorrow, see if we can forestall the bastards.'

The sergeant took off his pack and extended the entrenching tool, half spade, half pick. It was part of the personal choice of equipment he carried, whereas Sturgess always brought along a Sten gun as well as his revolver. The sergeant began to dig at the edge of the clearing. 'You want to fetch the others up, sir?' he suggested, adding, 'Pity this is their first bit of action. Some of 'em are just wee bairns.'

The major order a brew up and an extra meal of bully-beef stew when the job was done. 'A bit more smoke's not going to make any difference,' he said as he handed his tin of cigarettes around.

It was a sober group of men who finally settled for that night. Sturgess rigged tripwires at both ends of the place he chose just beyond the village. Some of the young guardsmen had now seen the grotesque attitudes of violent death for the first time. The dog came slinking in and lay with its back against Sturgess's boot. He let it stay.

At first light they again moved forwards, Sturgess pushing them at speed for some four miles. Then he ordered caution; the riverbank was beginning to be more trodden, *beluka* rather than jungle edging the path. He went ahead and before long could see a Malay kampong. Its houses had been established a long time with platform and toilets built out over the river.

He moved away from the track and bellied forwards so he could see the centre of the houses. Pulling out his binoculars, he examined each house in detail.

Crossing the doorway of the largest hut he was sure he saw the shadowy figures of men who were not somehow right for this jungle village. He concentrated hard and at last caught the image he had half registered the first time: men with rifles on their shoulders, eating from plates as they strode about indoors.

'Got you, you buggers,' he mouthed, wishing he could glimpse that burly, square Chinese, just pin down exactly where Heng Hou was, but *his* style would be sitting down being waited on.

Nothing, Sturgess promised himself, would be allowed to go wrong on this operation. 'You or me,' he vowed.

He withdrew to his group, excitement and urgency in his voice as he detailed his plans. He would take four men and the sergeant and go to the far side of the village; the doctor would take charge of the remaining men.

'Allow us half an hour to be round the other side.' He paused and glanced at his watch. 'It is now eight forty-nine. We all move in at nine-thirty precisely. The largest hut in the middle, its facilities backing right over the river, is the main target. Shoot anyone with a rifle who doesn't surrender immediately. Don't let any of the bastards get away.'

Sturgess stationed himself nearest the village, two men strung out to left and right, with Mackenzie keeping watch at the rear so they would not be surprised by any CTs wandering into the kampong from their side. As he pushed his sleeve back to watch the final seconds—nine twenty-nine and—there was a noise behind him. He turned to see his sergeant standing in the middle of the path signalling to him. The signal was a cupped fist to the mouth and a bend forwards as if using a blowpipe. It meant Sakais were coming from their side. He signalled back, using the flat of his hand in a stopping motion. He glanced again at this watch; nine thirty. Nothing more he could do. Turning back to the sergeant, he stabbed a finger at his watch, then waved Mackenzie forwards.

They moved in towards the village and Sturgess was only too aware that he had deliberately placed the doctor and his men nearer the village so that the communists would be alarmed first from that side and run into him and his men's fire. Now he had one or more Sakais at his back.

He let his sergeant move ahead of him, wondering if he might warn this native arriving at the worst possible moment. Then, emerging from the jungle, he saw not just a Sakai but behind him a tall red-bearded figure. 'Christ! Cresswell!' he hissed—and the women must be with them. He fairly danced on the spot for one totally disconcerted moment, then, knowing his sergeant would go on and do his job, he ran towards the party, shouting, 'Cresswell, bandits ahead. Take cover, and stay down!'

Turning again, he ran back towards the kampong without any caution now, disregarding the communists' triplines which activated bundles of tins near the huts. There was shouting ahead, and then the shooting began, with the blood-chilling rattle of automatic fire.

A man with a gun of some kind came running towards him. Sturgess shot him between the eyes, jumped over his body and ran on, and suddenly he was on the edges of a battle. He dropped to the ground, for gunfire was coming from several of the huts. Mackenzie was obviously trying to edge his men in nearer to the main hut, but even as he did so, Sturgess from his position at ground level saw a burly figure jump from the latrine platform at the back into the river.

He thought it seemed a fitting outlet for Hou, but then began to fret as he realised his men were pinned down by at least two punishing automatics—one from Hou's escape hut and another from a man who must have been posted as lookout up a tree.

Raising his Sten gun, Sturgess aimed first at the man in the tree, who was not aware of this latecomer to the action. His burst of fire scattered the foliage and brought the man falling like a gigantic fruit from the boughs. The others could deal with the man in the hut doorway; he wanted the top man.

He fell back along the path a few yards and made for the river. There was no sign of the man or which way he had gone, but, knowing Hou, it would be away from the trouble. Unfortunately, that was towards where Liz Hammond was.

The major hoped Cresswell was still keeping everyone hidden, and he hoped the terrorist leader might stay on the far bank, but there were rocky outcrops on that side and Hou knew the area. Sten gun raised ready, the barrel constantly sweeping ahead and across the far side of the river, the major moved quickly.

Suddenly ahead he saw Cresswell leaping out of the jungle and running away from him, towards where he heard a cry for help, the scream of a girl.

Sturgess ran into the scene. Hou, hair still streaming from his emergence from the water, held Lee by the hair, her head pulled back, throat exposed. He had a long, thin knife poised at her jugular; in a second she could be dead. Liz Hammond supported an old woman, while two Sakais stood irresolute.

'Drop guns and go back,' Hou screamed at Cresswell and the major. 'Drop guns!' He pressed the knife. Lee made a strange, gurgling scream and a small trickle of blood ran down her neck. 'Next time!' Hou promised.

The two dropped their guns close to their feet, Sturgess lowering his to the ground by its strap. Hou snarled, 'Kick near! Near me!'

Sturgess looked at Cresswell, then at his own Sten gun. The two had understood each other before in the home of the Hammonds' old amah; Sturgess hoped his man understood now. Hoped he remembered a much publicised incident when a soldier had banged on a door with the butt of a Sten gun and the quick-reaction gun had gone off and shot the soldier behind.

He silently applauded the young man, who pretended to stagger as he went to kick his rifle forwards, giving Sturgess a further few seconds to calculate his move. Cresswell miskicked again; this, Sturgess knew, was as far as any delay could go. Hou growled again and lifted Lee off her feet, but now Cresswell got his foot behind the rifle properly and pushed it forwards towards the communist.

The animal-like growl was repeated and John knew he could delay no longer. He swung his foot back and kicked the metal butt of the Sten as hard as he could. The gun responded as he had hoped, and fired. In the split second of the shot he was diving forwards, as was Cresswell. The major pushed his hand up with all the calculation of a man trained in both assassination and defence, forcing the knife away from Lee's throat. He felt the girl pulled away, then Cresswell was on the other side, helping him pin the savage, screaming man down. Suddenly Liz was standing over all three men, holding the Sten gun pointing unwaveringly at Hou's forehead.

'You'd make a good regular soldier, Cresswell,' the major said across Hou's body as they each hung to one of Heng Hou's arms. 'Pleased to see you made it.'

Alan grinned. 'Thanks, sir, it is mutual. We'd have walked straight into this lad and his party.'

The pleasantries having been exchanged, they both realised that Lee was sobbing hysterically and shouting, 'Kill him! Kill him! I'll never be safe while he's alive.'

'He has only to move and I'll do just that,' Liz promised. 'Don't worry, Lee, he's going nowhere.'

Once the group had rounded up the communists left alive and Hou had been secured to Lee's partial satisfaction, there was quite a reunion.

Pa Kasut came forward and greeted John Sturgess like a returning prodigal son, and as recognition slowly dawned John stood shaking his head in disbelief.

'It can't be!' he exclaimed. 'The Japs never got you!' His eyes went then to Bras standing grinning broadly next to him. 'This is your boy! The young man who—'

'You saved from tank,' Pa Kasut said, and for a moment the joy of reunion was overlaid by the trauma of a remembered incident. 'Now we save this man for you.' He indicated Alan.

'Yes,' Sturgess said simply. He took stock of the tall, red-bearded young man with a long flash of white mixed in with his darker hair and he saw a man, old

454

in experience, pain—and love, he thought, looking from him to Liz, who stood close by his side. He could sense that their togetherness was unassailable. He held out his hand to Alan and wondered whether he deserved to have the younger man take it.

Alan did not smile but he did take the hand offered to him. 'Sir,' he said gently.

Sturgess shook it hard, then, turning, put his free hand on the old Sakai's shoulder and announced to the assembled group, 'Of course you know what Pa Kasut means—it's "Old Boot", tough as old boots! That's how this jungle hero got his name.'

Liz was surprised when, after they had all smoked together, the Sakais prepared to go back to their hill camp. She had not expected to part with their company so soon. They stood in line to shake hands and bid them goodbye. She felt a great affection for them and knew there was nothing she or Alan could ever do to repay them. They had nothing the Sakais needed. Sturgess gave them a tin of cigarettes, which Pa Kasut gave to Sardin—he of the trip to the cinema, Liz remembered.

As they set out again, Lee insisted on always walking behind the prisoners, so as to be sure Heng Hou was secure. She got a

455

little braver as they neared the main roads, pulling at his ropes to be sure they were still tight.

'His growl has gone now,' she said triumphantly, 'now he just...' She skipped in front of him, glowered and pulled faces at him to Ch'ing's consternation and disapproval.

'I'll feel happier when he's in gaol where he belongs,' Liz said grimly, wondering if the terrorist would be taken to the same gaol where George Harfield was incarcerated. It would be a strange irony.

Chapter Twenty-Five

'Mem.'

Blanche looked up from where she was writing to Wendy, communicating without giving away the fact that she was totally alone at Rinsey except for Anna. She recognised it as the same kind of letter she had written to the girls when they were at school and university during the previous war, concealing appalling anxiety.

'How well do you think Wendy would remember Joan and Aubrey?' she asked.

'Mem, it's the manager from the mine at Bukit Kinta.'

'George!' She rose, her heart thudding.

'No, mem.' Anna shook her head in swift correction. 'No, mem.' She consulted a card she now handed over. 'Mr Ira Cook.'

Of course the rather acned young man she had last encountered when she and Liz had fetched George's possessions. How ridiculous! she told herself. How could it possibly have been George? And what the hell did this individual want of her?

She scowled at Anna, who now shook her head at her as if she was a child and should behave herself. Blanche raised her eyebrows in irritated acquiescence and Anna hurried out.

'Come in, won't you?' Blanche called as he appeared in the doorway. 'Mr Cook.' She made a movement that could have been the beginning of a handshake or a gesture of general welcome.

Mr Cook kept hold of his stiff, white, tropical trilby with both hands. He was thinner, she thought, and his spots were somewhat improved. Knocked off, she wondered, for he put her in mind of a scrawny young cockerel who, in his white and ruffled feathers, looked as if he'd lost out to an older cock.

'Some tea?' she asked as he still did not speak and she began to feel impatient with this hat-spinning young man.

'Thank you.'

'Well, sit down, for God's sake, or we'll both be fidgety.'

'Thank you.'

Blanche waited, fascinated, as she perceived beads of sweat breaking out on the man's forehead. He appeared to be seething with inner agitations. He should never have come out here, she decided, he should be teaching juniors in some downtown school in New York.

'How're things?' she asked.

'Terrible, Mrs Hammond, terrible.' He squirmed in his chair as if incapable of finding a comfortable spot. 'I've come to ask for your help. I know you visit Mr Harfield.' He looked at her with such an intense, searching examination that she did not answer immediately when he asked, 'Is he well? Mr Harfield. Really well, I mean.'

As well as any innocent man can be, locked away.' She let her voice trail off into query and as he looked up at her she thought for a moment he was going to burst into tears.

'I'm being used, Mrs Hammond,' he burst out. 'I'm definitely being used!'

His almost girlish petulance made her want to reply that she was not surprised, but she was wondering whether in his paradoxical visit there could be some

458

further lead, some thread of information, that might help George. She could be very patient to that end.

'Tell me about it,' she said in as dulcet tones as she could feign.

'All the employees' records have been stolen.'

The prissiness of his way of speaking did not distract Blanche from appreciating the implications of this event.

'I have no accurate way of checking who actually works for me any more, and so many of them look alike to me.' He moved in small, negative jerks as he spoke. 'Odd men have arrived from time to time and I'm told tales about them having been on leave. Other families have left in the night—just gone.'

'Who tells you these tales and which families have gone?'

The prissiness almost became a pout as he admitted, 'The girl, Li Min. Then they have parties, drunken parties.'

Blanche was steely-eyed with attention now. Li Min! 'And the families that have gone?'

'I've been checking and it's all the relatives of Mr Harfield's former headman, Rasa—his sons and their families. All good workers at first.'

'Rasa's family,' she said slowly. 'George had great faith in them all. They would know who worked at the mine.'

Blanche waited; there was more than this, she was sure from his manner. He had some other humiliation locked up and battling to come out.

'George came to believe he had harboured some fanatical communists, the girl one of them—but proving it?' It was her turn to move a little uneasily as she went on, 'I have no proof of what I am about to say, but I never liked the cook at Bukit Kinta, Li Kim.' She paused to give an ironic laugh. 'It may be, of course, only because his name is so like the girl's, Li Min.'

'He above anyone would know my movements for the day,' Ira pondered. 'That could explain a lot. He also seems to know when to take messages—I mean, he seemed to know when I didn't wish to be disturbed.'

There was a curious change of tense there. So he didn't mind being disturbed now. What had he given up?

'I think, Mr Cook, if you want my help you had better tell me everything.'

He seemed to screw his hat and himself into a tense round ball, bending so low his forehead nearly touched his knees.

'When didn't you want to be disturbed?'

His shoulders gave a convulsive shudder.

'Ira!' she demanded. 'When didn't you want to be disturbed?'

He mumbled something.

'When?' she demanded.

'When I was with Li Min.'

Ah! Now we have it, she thought. So your gallantry and politeness have dug you in deep. What a baby you are!

'And I caught a full house!'

There was a moment's silence while Blanche recalled what the phrase meant: he had both syphilis and gonorrhoea.

She thought her first impression of him had been right—a very dishevelled cockerel indeed! She could have extracted some humour from this...if she had had anyone to share it with.

'You've been to—' She was going to say 'the hospital', but he interrupted.

'Rose Cottage—yes.'

'Yes,' she repeated, thinking he seemed to know all the right slang expressions but hadn't the sense to avoid the diseases.

'So you want me to ask George to make a list of all his former employees?'

'I do. I'm going to do my darnedest to root these commies out.' He looked up at her now. He had told all, kept the tears at bay, and there was a resolution in his tormented face which made her understand perhaps why he had been appointed manager at Bukit Kinta.

'Right.' She sat down opposite him,

461

businesslike, on his level, offering partner-
ship. 'But we have to be careful. We
mustn't do anything to make them suspicious. Above all, we want them to stay
at Bukit Kinta, make them feel secure until
we've organised a pounce.'

'OK,' he agreed. 'Shall I ring...?'

'No, I will. As soon as I have the list
I'll ring you just causally and you ask me
over for a meal. The day I'm coming, you
immediately send Li Kim to the market
with as long a list as you can think of.
I'll come over while Li Kim's out of the
way to tell you what has been arranged,
and I'll bring George's list.'

'OK, then we take it from there,' he
said, standing up, taller and shoulders
squarer than when he had entered. 'I
don't suppose you feel like shaking my
hand?'

'My dear boy,' Blanche exclaimed,
shooting out her hand, 'to err is human,
to tackle it takes courage.'

'I'd value your friendship,' he said.

'You have it,' she confirmed.

George was solemn when she told him.
Any glimmer of humour in the situation
would, she supposed, hardly be seen by
a man who was imprisoned at the hands
of the same girl. He was silent, brooding.
She thought of Joan with a sense of loss,

yearning for someone with whom she could share the joke.

'You don't suppose *not* having either syphilis or gonorrhoea would be considered grounds for an appeal?' he said after some time.

She laughed gratefully, wanting to throw her arms around his neck. 'My dear, dear man!'

'She must have just about eaten that boy alive. He came straight from the New York office, you know. Poor little sod! He's been to—'

'Rose Cottage,' she interrupted.

A twinkle showed in his eye as he asked, 'And what do you know about such expressions?'

'Neville often talked to me as if I was one of the boys when he was on leave from the navy. I knew all about "band in the box", "cold in the dong", "horse and trap".'

'Do you mind, woman! I'm beginning to feel either embarrassed or educated, not sure which.'

'Yes, all right, sorry!' But she rejoiced in the spark of real laughter that had come to his eyes. 'About Neville, promise me you'll never mind me talking about him. He was my first, but now my past love...' She paused and stretched out her hand to his. 'You are my love now.'

'And he loved her as he never loved before.' The spirit in the beginning of the sentence did not last until the end; his eyes slid away from her as he added bitterly, 'Of course, he may be too old to love at all by the time he gets out of here.'

'If that's how it is to be, OK, we'll take it. It's not so much longer than many women waited for their men through the war. At least I know you're safe in here!'

'Safe and sound.' His voice rang with deep irony.

'Having Ira Cook on our side might, just might, bring some kind of breakthrough. Do the list, George. I'll ask for special permission to come and collect it—not wait for the next visiting day. And if you can think of anything else we can do...'

'It can't be long before Robbo comes back,' he said.

'But the Dyak tracker we found murdered?'

'Not worried about that! Robbo's good in the jungle. If a message could be sent to him so he and the police could lay siege to Bukit Kinta before anyone knew he was back...' He bit his lip as he thought the idea through. 'If word gets out that he's back in the area, particularly with the girl Lee as a witness, every CT in the area will go to ground.'

She nodded solemn agreement.

'Robbo could be maintaining radio silence...' He looked across at her, his eyes full of speculation. 'But if there's any information about where he might be, Chemor could be sent in. He'll find them if anyone can, and divert them straight to Bukit Kinta—the whole shebang of them—that way there'll not be time for rumours to fly.'

George's face was grim now, the muscles in his cheeks flexing and unflexing as he clenched his teeth. 'If only I were out of this place so I could be some use!'

'You still don't realise, do you?' Blanche leaned forwards over the table.

'What've I missed?' His eyes searched her face for answers.

'Me!' she told him in a forceful whisper. 'Me!' She shook her head at him in exasperation. 'The use you've been to me!' Her voice rose high and wavered. 'For God's sake George, don't you see, you're all I've got to hang on to!'

'Don't upset yourself, love.'

'I want to upset myself!' She pulled a handkerchief from her dress pocket. 'And don't call me bloody love!'

'I shall call you love whether you're bloody to me or not,' he told her.

'Oh, George!' The tears came now and she fought them no longer. 'Don't ever let me try to change you,' she instructed, groping for another handkerchief.

'You can always try.' The tone did not match the words, but it stemmed her tears. They reached across and grasped each other's forearms as if in a mutual act of attempted rescue.

Their glances asked, shall we get through this ordeal? The answers lay only in his white knuckles and her convulsive gripping of his forearms.

'Go on, my lass,' George said after a bit. 'You've a lot to do.'

Blanche left in a strange state of vulnerability and resolve.

'Mem! Mem! Oh, Mem!' Anna came running out of the bungalow as Blanche stepped from the car and the guard-cum-driver took it to the cool of its *attap* roof.

Blanche stopped on the steps to the verandah, assessing the sound and the urgency of the call. But Anna was smiling. Looking overwrought but happy, she waved an envelope. 'Mem, the girls, they are safe. There is a message from the army.'

Blanche found herself kneeling on the steps. Pulling Anna down to sit beside her, she took the sealed envelope and asked, 'But how do you know?'

'The soldiers in the jeep. One said it was good news, and I made him tell me.'

Blanche tore open the envelope, praying the talk was truth. She read the brief message twice. 'They should be home in two days.' She opened her arms and the two women rocked and cried together.

'Things are coming right, Anna, I sense it. Find Chemor. I'm going straight to KL to see this senior officer.' She tapped the letter, glancing at the scrawled signature and its typed caption properly for the first time. 'Oh! I think I may know this man.'

She stopped halfway to the front door, seeing that Anna still stood there, hands cupped as if she contemplated a new problem lying within her palms.

'What is it?' she asked.

Anna looked out beyond the wire. 'What will you say to Lee and Mrs Guisan?' she asked.

Blanche made a swift and searching review of her conscience. 'I shall say it was quick and had to be done. As for the rest, I hope she'll agree with what we decided.' Both women made review of the burial next to Neville Hammond.

Blanche shook the communication again; this was not the moment for retrospection.

Anna nodded. 'I fetch Chemor.'

Driving from Rinsey with Chemor, Blanche studied the signature again. Unless there were two Edwin Neillands, this was a man she had known very well before the war. The second son of a local landowner at Pearling, he had made the army his career.

She raised her hands in thankful acknowledgement when a man of prodigious tallness, who had become more cadaverous with the years, rose to greet her with enthusiasm. 'Blanche, my dear girl, after all these ages! I've not long been here, y'know, or I'd have looked you up.'

'I know, Edwin,' she told him as they kissed on each cheek, 'but now I mean you to make up for lost time.'

'You never were one to lose minutes! Eh, Blanche?' He tried to engage her in his good humour.

'Eddie, I've no time for pleasantries even with such a dear old friend.'

'Get on then, m'dear,' he said briskly.

She told her story and he did not interrupt, though he made quite a few notes on a pad on his desk, spacing them around the page as if making a tactical map for a battle.

'Hmm! Right! Got the portrait. Tell you what we'll do. Major Sturgess is coming out at Milestone Thirteen, that's on the main road just north of Bukit Kinta.' He paused to consult his watch. 'Forty-two hours from now.'

'And they're all safe, my daughter, her friend...?'

'The whole caboodle, m'dear, all fine.'

'You don't know how much I need this news,' she said quietly.

'We'll have the police on the roads. I'll have an army unit melt into position round the village. Then we'll roll our survivors—that is, particularly your old manager's wife and her daughter—straight out of the jungle down to the old kampong and let them have a look round, see if they can see anyone they jolly well recognise. Won't take long.'

'Thank God for someone with some drive and some sense.'

'Come on, old lassie, don't you remember how I used to organise the hunts? No stragglers and no gossip when you were on picket duty alongside my spinneys!'

Blanche remembered and laughed. 'I do! You had the youngsters scared stiff.'

'Use the same methods! Never tinker with anything that still works.'

'You're a relief in all senses, dear Eddie. I was beginning to feel entitled to one bit of good luck. I believe you're it. So by Wednesday...'

'Wednesday evening should see you all home,' he confirmed.

She left him suddenly determined that whatever happened either before or on

469

Wednesday she was going to be at Bukit Kinta before the army, police and Liz and Lee arrived there. She had spent quite enough time waiting alone at Rinsey.

She would collect the list from George tomorrow, ring Ira in the evening, go to Bukit Kinta the next morning and stay there until it was all over. She'd use Chemor again, take him into her confidence. That would make at least two of them with their ears and eyes open on George's behalf.

Chapter Twenty-Six

Nothing happened the way Blanche had expected, once she had arrived at Bukit Kinta.

'I couldn't send Li Kim to the market, he seems to have disappeared,' Ira reported when they were both safely inside the bungalow.

This seemed ominous news to Blanche. 'Has anyone else gone? Anything else out of the ordinary?'

He shook his head, joining her to look down over the complex of lakes, dredgers, flat sunken areas of tin tailings, workshops of bamboo, *attap* and rusty corrugated-iron

470

sheeting, all closely edged by jungle. 'No. The men who've come in recently I've seen this morning shovelling ore near the dredgers...'

'And the girl?'

Ira drew her attention towards the neat vegetable plots to the right where the mine village lay behind the gardens. 'She's coming this way now,' he said, stepping away from the window.

'So she is.' Blanche watched her come nearer, noting the black cotton trousers and round-necked blouse the girl had on. She wanted to be sure she could pick the little communist out in any coming affray. 'We must be careful. Play it as if you're on her side, as if I'm just an interfering old bat.'

There was no time for more planning. 'Mr Cook!' the girl's voice came from the front door, full of knowledge that he was there and had a visitor. 'Are you in?'

'Come through, Li Min,' he called back.

'Please to come out. I wish private word.'

Ira glanced at Blanche, who acquiesced with half-lowered eyelids. He left the room and she heard them move across to George's old office. She slipped off her shoes and walked barefoot into the hall. The door to the study was not quite closed.

Ira was quoting her verbatim. 'No, no,' he said, 'she's just an interfering old bat. Come to see what's happening so she can report to old Harfield when she visits him.'

'Why her car gone?'

'She's sent the driver shopping. He's calling back for her.'

'Where she take Li Kim?'

'My cook? She's not taken him anywhere. *I* want to know where he is. Have you seen him?'

'I no see.'

'Do you know where he might have gone? Has he a girl?'

'No!' The tone was scoffing, but then she went on, 'You have girl...if you want.'

Blanche held her breath. Ira had got it right up to now, but this might be the greatest test.

'I want,' the young manager said gruffly, 'but I'll have to wait until—'

'Old bat gone!'

'Sure!' Ira said, sounding as if he moved in on the girl. 'Then I'll come. As soon as she's gone...'

'Ira! Baby! I miss you.'

The girl massaged the young man with her voice. Blanche turned and walked silently back to the lounge and her shoes. Standing at the window again, she closed her eyes and imagined the pleasure of shaking Li Min until her perfect white teeth rattled.

A few moments later Ira stood silently in the doorway. 'I feel nauseous.'

'You did well,' she assured him. 'Really—I listened.'

'My cook's disappearance seems to be a mystery to everyone.'

'Perhaps just some stupid coincidence. Let's pray it doesn't upset anything.'

'I'm uneasy about you staying, Blanche.' He joined her at the window. 'It all looks so peaceful but if there's to be a real showdown...'

'There is, I assure you, and when it happens I'm going to be here. I just hope it's not too much longer, or our mutual friend may become really suspicious about my prolonged presence or my car's prolonged absence.'

Ira glanced at her as if he too wondered about that.

'Chemor's just keeping himself and my car out of the way at one of the streetside cafes until he sees the army moving in. Then he'll follow in—I hope.'

Ira swore. 'I wish it'd get on and happen. What'll be the first sign, d'you reckon?'

They were speculating when Ira suddenly stopped talking, raised a stilling forefinger and listened intently. They could soon make out the sound of heavy lorries

473

grinding up the path into the mining complex. Army lorries, three-tonners, came quickly into view with soldiers sitting along the side seats beneath the obligatory protective netting. Ira and Blanche exchanged jubilant glances and hurried outside.

From the vantage point of the bungalow, they saw the soldiers jumping down from the lorries and running to encircle groups of workers or going towards the village. Following came police vehicles and Chemor in the Hammonds' Ford. There were already soldiers at all the gates, roads and paths around the mine, rifles at the ready. Edwin had been as good as his word; those men had certainly melted unobserved into their positions—but where were the survivors he had promised to roll into Bukit Kinta?

There was much shouting and Blanche saw that the men were being brought down from the dredgers and the workplaces and the women and children from the village, and all urged into lines. She saw the unmistakable black-trousered figure of Li Min in the gateway of the kampong, saw her turn and run back towards a hut. Two soldiers broke into a run after her but Chemor overtook them and caught the girl before she reached the hut's verandah. The soldiers went on while Chemor, gripping the struggling girl, brought her back to where the workers and villagers were being gathered. He released her, throwing her away from himself in the manner one releases a fighting cat.

So much was happening at once. Blanche recognised John Sturgess leading two men off towards the tin-roofed mine buildings, while one lorry still seemed to have a reserve of men just sitting still.

Where *were* her survivors?

She searched the milling throng and saw Inspector Aba strutting up and down the crowd of Malays and Chinese, shouting, 'Identity papers! Everyone have ready! Now!'

'In line! In line! Everyone in line,' someone else ordered.

The shouting both intimidated and created confusion, so the workers and the families shuffled and circled around raising dust, making it seem hotter than it already was, before they were finally sorted into some kind of line order.

Li Min and several men brought at gunpoint from the village were herded to the head of one line and kept under special guard. Sturgess was there, joined by the inspector. Sturgess lifted a hand towards the soldiers still in the lorry; Blanche followed the gesture, obviously some directive.

It was at this moment that Blanche

saw Liz. Her daughter emerged from the middle of the soldiers still seated in the lorry. Standing up totally exposed on the back, she looked all around. Blanche found herself shaking her head in delight and wonderment as she watched her daughter's glance sweep sky and hills. Otherworldly like her father, taking in the view first!

Blanche waved furiously as a young red-bearded man came from the front passenger seat to help her down.

Liz became suddenly aware of a woman near George's bungalow waving like a mad thing. She recognised her mother with a shock of combined love and guilt. 'Mother, what *are* you doing here?' She ran to greet her.

Blanche held her arms wide for her daughter and saw as Liz ran to her the set of Neville's head, the way the eyes focused on her now to the total exclusion of the screaming, shouting tension that was all around them—like her father, and because of that so very precious.

'Liz!' She clasped her daughter to her, registering the extra thinness of her body as she held her tight. 'Thank God! Thank God!'

'Mother!' Forgive me for going off like that! I must have put you through hell.' Liz saw new lines about her mother's mouth, etchings of determination, she thought, or worry she had caused.

'Hell, yes,' Blanche confirmed, 'but more because I watched you go.'

It took a moment for the implication to register. 'You watched...when Lee and I?'

Blanche nodded.

Liz threw herself into her mother's arms afresh. 'You really did understand.'

'I did,' she said and, thinking of George, added, 'I do.'

'I found him!'

Blanche grasped Liz's hand as she finally recognised Alan beneath the beard and gripped his hand too. 'We mustn't lose *anyone* again, I can't afford the heartache. So where is Lee and...?'

'Safe, but she must stay hidden for a bit longer,' Alan said beneath the hubbub going on so close to them. 'The major wants to make sure there are no hidden arms and have everything secure before he plays his trump card. If you come nearer to the lorry but don't look down to the floor...'

'I'll take Mr Harfield's list over to the inspector,' Ira decided, sounding as if he wanted no part of another intrigue. He walked purposefully towards the watchful lines of men, women and wide-eyed children.

'Mrs Guisan! Lee!' Blanche stage-whispered as she came close to the backboard of the lorry. The eight soldiers looked at her and some smiled, but none looked down at the blankets that lay on the floor between their feet.

'Mrs Hammond! I glad hear you after all these years.'

The small, smothered voice was husky, anxious. 'This is Mrs Carl Guisan speaking to you.'

From another age, Blanche thought.

'And Lee!' a lighter voice said. 'We have to wait to be called out. Tell us what is happening.'

'Thank God you are both safe,' Blanche said, standing as casually as she could, gripping the hands of her two young people and pretending she was talking to them.

'The major's got several men body-searching the lines of people,' Alan told the hidden women.

'You wouldn't think they could hide much,' Liz commented, looking at the women's sarongs and the thin cotton shorts and shirts most of the men were wearing.

One of the soldiers on the lorry clicked his tongue and commented, 'We found a bandoleer of ammunition wrapped around a baby at one village.'

'They're reaching the real suspects now,' Liz said, watching closely as the searchers moved in on Li Min and the men in her group. The guards raised their rifles at the suspects' chests, ready to fire at the least hint of trouble.

'There's some defiance,' Blanche confided to Lee and her mother. 'They want the men in the group to raise their hands higher.'

'Up! Up! Up!' The orders came louder and louder, men poked with their rifles to enforce the order—and then there was consternation and shouting.

'What's happened?' Liz's question was echoed all around. The lines of people craned forwards, some of the soldiers stood up and there were muffled enquiries from the floor of the lorry.

'No, it's all right!' Alan said as he saw Sturgess swoop down and pick up an object, examine it, then clip it on to his belt. 'One of the men had a hand grenade secreted under his armpit.'

There were other angry outbursts as the police found several more people in the lines without papers. One or two were taken back to their huts in the kampong to enable them to pick up identity cards left in their houses. Those unable to give a good explanation of themselves and their lack of papers were now handcuffed and circled with guards.

John Sturgess came striding towards them. Blanche noticed Liz kept tight hold of Alan's hand as John, nodding from one

479

woman to the other, said, 'Like mother, like daughter, neither of you do as you are told nor as expected!' His tone was sharp and military, but then he grinned, and both women let out relieved breaths. Liz glimpsed again the man behind the military mask. If only Robbo could let him show more often!

He tapped the back of the lorry. 'We'll start the show with Mrs Guisan and her daughter.'

The soldiers helped the two women out from their nest of blankets in the bottom of the lorry. There was time only for the briefest of greetings. Blanche had to disguise the shock she felt when she saw the stooped old Chinese. She would never have recognised this woman as the pert young thing who had captivated the heart of their outgoing, expansive manager, Carl.

Sturgess ushered them along the lines of people who had so far shown themselves to be genuine workers and families. Curiosity showed in all their faces but not guilt; it was obvious that the two women meant nothing to them.

It was a different matter as they approached the heavily guarded group. Most of them hung their heads so low it was impossible to see their features. Li Min, without seeming noticeably to move, managed to fade behind a bulky man.

'Heads up!' the police sergeant ordered and when this was not obeyed he detailed two constables, who went in and pulled the men's heads upwards and backwards by their hair, pushing a rifle barrel under their chins. Some still kept their eyes closed, while others stared insolently into the eyes of the women who had worked for them so many years in their main jungle headquarters.

Blanche went nearer, intending to stand behind Li Min where she had edged to the back of the circle. She also saw Chemor staring intensely at the girl, his black eyes reminding Blanche of those of a stoat she had watched hypnotise a full-grown rabbit before launching itself for the kill.

Lee stepped into the circle while her mother remained more remote, more intimated some yards outside. As each head was lifted, Lee not only spat 'Yes!' into their faces but named the terrorists. At last they came to Li Min.

Blanche held her breath as Lee looked at her long and hard. It looked like the meeting of arch-enemies. 'Oh! Yes!' Lee said at last as if savouring the moment. 'She came many times, she brought information about army and police raids. Fancied herself as partner to Heng Hou!'

Li Min seemed caught mid-reprisal as

she leaned forwards to vent her spite on Lee, but Chemor shouted in the same split second, 'Heng Hou, he told all about Li Min—he give away!'

The Chinese girl looked like a venomous black spider as she sprang round on Chemor and launched a tirade of abuse in her own language. One or two of her companions, in spite of their own peril, gave verbal approval of the sentiments she expressed and became more arrogant in their manner.

Blanche hated to see any initiative taken by the prisoners, futile though it might be, but she had reckoned without the deviousness and planning of a devoted employee and friend, for at that moment four soldiers went to the back of a police vehicle and hauled out another prisoner, whom they marched up to the group of suspects.

'See your leader, Li Min! He spoke out about you! He told!' Chemor pointed and danced about as if in ecstasy. Blanche watched in some amazement. He had seemed such a level-headed chap—devoted to George, but she had not expected this.

Heng Hou was pushed forwards until he stood before Li Min. At a nod from Sturgess he was pushed the final yard so the girl had to jump back to avoid contact with him. It seemed the final act that broke her control. With her hands tied behind her back, her avoidance had a writhing, sensual quality, as if she was squirming away from a sexual advance instead of from a man securely bound.

'Heng Hou! You said you *never* be caught,' she accused.

Chemor still capered like a mad monkey. 'He caught! He talk!'

Blanche glanced at John, expecting him to have George's old tracker removed, but he seemed to pay no regard.

'And I talk! I talk now!' Li Min came forward, facing Heng Hou again but at a safe distance as he growled and shouted at her. Her voice rose higher and he was silenced by the nudge of a rifle butt.

'He liar! He say he make me woman leader of communist republic, like wife of Mao Tse-tung. I say all right. Beat me and we trap "thorn in communists' side" George Harfield. He beat!' She nodded and Blanche felt a pang of sympathy for the girl as she saw the horror of the experience reflected in her eyes.

'He beat! He rape too!' Her voice rose to a scream full of tears. 'He rape like animal.' The pitch of her voice fell almost to a whisper as she added, 'Worse than animal. I hate...'

Blanche closed her eyes momentarily, letting a prayer of thankfulness swamp

483

her mind. George! She urged the message across the green jungles to Pudu Gaol. George, you're free!

On opening them again she saw Sturgess patting Chemor on the back. My God! she thought. It was all a put-up job between the two. Play-acting!

George had always said Robbo was his best friend.

Chapter Twenty-Seven

Blanche did not dare presume to take either Lee's or Ch'ing's arm or hand as they stood by Josef's grave. She had told of the encounter and the shooting and led the two of them outside. She felt poised on the knife edge of their judgement.

Ch'ing stood and looked for a long time, then she made a small gesture towards Neville's grave. 'He did not deserve,' she said quietly.

Blanche was not sure whether she meant Neville had not deserved his fate, or that Josef had not deserved her retribution. She relived the moments of their encounter and wondered yet again whether she had murdered Josef, or whether if she had not shot it would have been her grave alongside Neville's.

She started as Ch'ing linked an arm through hers and the two women went to sit on the seat overlooking the two graves.

'Better he died at Rinsey,' Lee said. 'We had happy times.' The girl's eyes softened while her head shook at the memory of the boy and the double-dealing terrorist he had become.

Liz came with Anna, as always practical, bringing iced tea. 'A bad boy,' Anna commented, looking down at the new grave, 'but in no more trouble now.'

'No,' his mother said, 'is blessing.'

'Oh, Ch'ing, I'm so sorry.' Blanche grieved for the truth of the mother's remark.

'It's strange,' Liz murmured, 'but already I seem to see him better as the boy he was.'

Lee came to her and linked arms. 'We'll bring flowers and gifts,' she said, and her mother nodded.

'We have lost so much.' Ch'ing included Blanche in the remark. 'Husbands...'

'Much time,' Blanche contributed, holding and patting the old lady's hand, though bringing herself up with a start as she remembered Ch'ing could only be her own age.

'Many years for us in the jungle,' Ch'ing added. 'Now we have to find work and place to live.'

'You'll stay here,' Blanche reassured her, 'for as long as ever you wish to.'

'If there is workman's house I would like,' Ch'ing said. As Blanche looked as if she would protest, she added, 'It's what I want.'

'Of course...'

'And work tapping,' Ch'ing added. 'Please.'

The politeness of the woman so fallen in her fortunes tore Blanche's heart. 'Whatever you want.'

'We can both tap.' Lee linked arms with her mother. 'This is freedom for us here at Rinsey—to earn dollars! Wow!' Lee raised her eyes to the sky at the thought, then, seeing Blanche still looking doubtful, she added, 'We need time to open wings gradually—perhaps fly later.'

'And we have a lot of shopping to do,' Liz reminded her.

'But first sleep to catch up,' Blanche said. 'Now the tension is over, I'm totally exhausted.'

'G and T in bed?' Liz asked. The offer seemed to tie another thread.

'Darling, when everyone's settled, marvellous!'

Later that night, Liz came and sat on

Blanche's bed. 'Like old times,' she began, then shook her head. 'No, not really. Everything's changed, hasn't it? You do like Alan?'

'I do,' her mother answered honestly. 'I think he has the right kind of practicality you need.'

'Really?' Liz was totally surprised. 'I never thought of him in that way.'

'Of course not, you're largely *im*practical,' Blanche said with a smile lest her daughter should take it as criticism.

'You can always surprise me, Mother.'

Blanche laughed and held out her arms. Liz hugged and held her tight, closing her eyes.

'Alan is being sent to the rest camp on Penang island,' Liz said as they released each other. 'I thought I might go up to stay in George Town so we could see something of each other.' She drew in her breath slowly through her mouth, preparing for a sigh, then added, 'He may be sent back to England quite soon.'

'His health is not in question, is it?' Blanche asked, anxious there should be no more heartache.

'The scar is very sensitive still. John Sturgess thinks he might be sent home with an earlier demob number than his own.'

'Then you must spend as much time as

you can together,' Blanche said. 'You have a lot to decide.'

Liz nodded soberly.

Once Blanche was alone, her thoughts moved from her daughter's future to wondering if George yet knew his prospects had so radically altered. Robbo had promised to consult his colonel, Edwin Neillands, as soon as he was back at base. He and Inspector Aba had promised everything would be done to speed George's release. But what about his job? And where would he live? She'd fit him in at Rinsey, however many seams she bulged was the decision which stilled the questions and allowed her to fall into sleep.

The next morning Anna took a call while Blanche was supervising the improving of the quarters for Ch'ing and Lee. She came running out to them. 'Major Sturgess, he say Mr George Harfield to be released at two o'clock. Can you pick up?'

Blanche felt the colour rising in her cheeks and in the instant of relief at the news she realised she hadn't blushed for years—couldn't remember the last time.

'Mother?' Liz queried. 'You knew he would be released.'

'Yes...it was just unexpected at that moment.' She put down the brush she

488

had been using. 'I'll probably leave you to organise the evening meal with Anna—for all of us. That OK?'

She turned away and left them, aware of the silence behind her. Not until she reached her room did she remember that they had been in the middle of a discussion about bedroom furnishings to be taken from the bungalow for Ch'ing and Lee. She grimaced at the realisation but hurried to pull a favourite green cotton dress from her wardrobe. She was behaving like a love-lorn creature. No! She stopped in the act of opening her underwear drawer. No, she was behaving exactly like her daughter—rushing off after her man.

She chose her fresh clothes feeling as if a mature woman was critically observing the young one as she flew about changing. Before she was quite ready, she broke off to go and find Chemor and tell him the news, and ask him once again to be her driver. She came back glowing. Chemor had wrung her hand heartily and imparted the information that it had been George who had taught him to drive.

She had not brushed her hair so vigorously since she was a teenager, thinking it added the imperative shine to make her a social success. Then, dissatisfied with her appearance, she rushed back to her wardrobe, held a pink check dress up over the green, discarded it and just left, regardless of time.

Inevitably, they were outside the prison early, and it was only as they arrived that she realised it was also one of the times visitors were allowed in. She recognised several of the people who had become familiar to her over the many visits she had made. They looked at her curiously when instead of joining the queue she went to stand on the far side of the prison gates.

Eventually a clock chimed two and a wicket gate set in the larger gates opened. She immediately saw George, carrying his small case, turning to shake hands with the warder who had unlocked the gate. Her heart went out to him; she felt both rejoicing and sorrow. 'Through the mill' were the words that came to her mind as he stepped over the prison portals into the public gaze.

His head went up and his lips parted in a smile as he saw her. She ran to him, caught his arm and kissed his cheek. There were 'Aah!'s of approval, nods and smiles from the many waiting women.

'So we're lucky,' she said. 'I might have still been queuing on that side.'

'I never thought—' He paused and frowned. 'I never thought of you out here, waiting with everyone else. Do you know what I feel like? I feel like having

490

what my mother would have called "a good blart".'

'You haven't time.' She nodded ahead to where Chemor stood beside the car, his grin so wide it looked impossible he should get all those teeth back behind his lips. 'But you do feel all right?'

'Better by the minute.' He gave her waist a quick squeeze before they reached Chemor.

George greeted his tracker with a hug, a handshake and a thump on the shoulder. There were tears in the Dyak's eyes. 'I glad see you, boss. Need you...' Words escaped him. '...all place.'

'Looks like I may be a bit of a wanderer, anyway,' he said, holding tight to Blanche's hand. 'Where do we go from here?'

'There's always room at Rinsey,' she told him, though the query in his voice reminded her of Ira Cook's message. 'Bukit Kinta is also available. Ira's been summoned to a meeting in Singapore. He rang specially to say to regard the bungalow as *your* home as always.'

George opted to go first to have a look at the mine. He was quiet as they drove. Leaning far back in the seat, he stared out at the countryside, but he was holding Blanche's hand tight. She accepted his need for silence.

'Not sure,' he began, as Chemor swept

491

the car triumphantly on to the track to the mine. 'I'll never feel quite the same about this place. Well, of course, it isn't my place to feel anything about, really...'

'Ira could opt for the New York office again, given a chance. And surely now you've been exonerated...?'

Any further speculation was cut short as Chemor blasted on the car horn: three short bursts, three long, three short. He drew the car to a rapid halt in a miniature dust storm before the bungalow, turned triumphantly and announced, 'V-sign, boss,' and repeated the performance on the horn.

Blanche took one look at George's face and burst into laughter. 'What a discreet arrival!'

There had been speculation among the staff about their former boss's return. The hooter blast swept away all doubts and as George stepped out of the vehicle he was immediately cheered by several of his workers. A cry went up and in less than a minute people were flocking from all directions to greet him, the men wanting to shake his hand or pat his back, the women and children beaming, clapping and calling, 'Welcome home! Welcome home, Mr Harfield, sir. Tuan! Tuan!'

He raised his arms high and wide, greeting them all with equal enthusiasm.

His colour too had risen, making him look much more himself; he was thinner, of course—but she could feed him up, Blanche found herself thinking.

'That feels right!' he said, beaming across at Blanche. 'I can't deny that feels right. I'll stay here tonight, anyway.'

He climbed on to the bungalow steps and raised a hand. 'Thanks, my friends. You've made me very happy. It does me good to see you all again. Let me have tonight to rest up and find myself again and I'll be round to see you all tomorrow.'

They waved and cheered him as they went off back to their duties and their homes. Standing at George's side, Blanche warmed to these self-effacing, warm-hearted people. She turned to find George watching her.

'What are you thinking?' he asked.

'I'm thinking how much I like these people and how bloody mad it makes me feel to think of them being exploited.'

'We're only at the beginning of it,' George said dourly. 'This country's got a long way to go before it stands up independent and rid of the scourge of gun-happy extremists.'

'And you'll stay and help?' She was aware that there was a lot of feeling out of opinions and intentions going on. Was Liz telling her she would go back to England?

493

Was she asking if George intended to stay in the Far East?

'I've given a lot of my life to this country.' He paused, looking out over the milky tin lakes where lilies proliferated. 'I think I may be too old to go back to frosts and snows.' He looked at her as if the real answer lay with her. 'If I'm wanted, I'll certainly stay.'

'Send Chemor back to Rinsey,' she said quietly, drawing him by the hand towards the bungalow. 'Tell him to say I'm staying over at Bukit Kinta for tonight.'

'I'll never let you go from me again if you do this,' he said in no more than a whisper.

'You can't be sure of that,' she said, still smiling brightly as if to the retreating crowd.

'I'm sure!' he breathed, and the tone of his voice brought a response she felt had been unused for as long as her capacity to blush.

He beckoned to Chemor and gave him the instructions. The Dyak glanced at Blanche and she added, 'You'll see all the guards are posted, everywhere well guarded?'

Chemor acknowledged with a salute.

'Fine!' George approved. 'See you to-morrow, my friend.'

They stood in the doorway and watched

494

him go as if he were the last guest at a prolonged party, watching until the Ford disappeared in the dust, so their solitude could be assured.

George dropped his case to the floor and, catching her hand, pulled her to him, slipping his arm around her waist. The contact of their two bodies was electrifying. She had thought him like a rugger player when she had first met him; now she knew his fitness exceeded her expectations. He held her close for a few more seconds almost as if confirming that first sensation. It was vibrant, she could have told him. It was sensational.

He lifted her and carried her to the bedroom, placed her back on her feet and began to take his own clothes off with a deliberation that had the most blatant sexuality she had ever known. She was so surprised and overwhelmed that she still stood fully clothed when he stood fully exposed.

Then, instead of taking a step towards her, he stepped away as if placing himself as audience and invited her to follow his lead. She did. Neither too slowly nor too quickly, but with the discipline of experience. Yet the knowledge was tight between them that in neither of their lives had there been anything quite like this before.

When she was naked she tossed up her chin and walked tall and proud towards him, feeling this was the most arousing thing she had ever done. If she had ever been ready to share love and sex with a man this was the moment.

George lifted her as she reached him and they stood united—only afterwards did they go to the bed.

Early the next morning there were movements in the kitchen, noises of china being moved and smells of bacon being fried. George went to investigate. He returned grinning.

'Li Kim's back. He looks a bit dishevelled. The police took him in before the raid, questioned him and only released him late last night.'

'Did they seriously suspect him?' Blanche asked, sitting up and letting the sheet fall around her like drapes around a classical torso.

'Possibly. His trouble is, like many another, he tries to be on the winning side, whichever it is,' George commented as he took off the shorts he had slipped into. 'Though, heaven help the Orientals, over the centuries many of them have had to be pretty inscrutable to survive at all. However—' he climbed back into bed and scooped her to him—'he's pretty sure he's

496

on our side at the moment.'

They breakfasted royally, and before Chemor arrived, Ira telephoned from Singapore with the news that he had the offer of a job in the firm's Singapore office, which he intended to take. 'But I'm to come back to Bukit Kinta as mine manager for the next two months so that you can have immediate leave, if you wish.'

'Yes, I'll take the leave,' George told him, 'and I'll go to Rinsey this morning.'

Chemor repeated his hooter performance as they arrived at the plantation gates. Blanche revelled in hearing George's belated protest and seeing the affection that radiated from everyone towards this man—hers! she thought.

Liz greeted George with genuine affection and enthusiasm—and her mother with a knowing nod and a drawn-out, 'hmm.'

'What do you mean by hmm?' Blanche asked.

'I think I mean I feel free to go off to Penang on the first train from Ipoh to Butterworth, ferry across to George Town—Alan will come and meet me there. I'll find a hotel...'

'On your own?' Blanche frowned. 'I'm not sure—'

'Look, Mother, the most dangerous bit will be from here to Ipoh. The trains are guarded. Penang island is safe—even the soldiers hand their rifles in when they get there.'

'It has to be safer than in the jungle among the CTs where she went chasing after him before.'

'Oh! It's nice to have an ally, George,' Liz said. 'It'll be great having you around—in the family?'

Blanche spluttered a little and made derogatory noises.

'Oh, come on, Mother! Don't be coy! I know the look of someone who's been bowled over. You looked suddenly ten years younger when the news came of George's release—*and* there had to be something or you'd have put this chap in his place way back.'

'You should have told us both,' George said. 'Saved a lot of time.'

'I don't reckon you've wasted much.' Liz stood watching the two of them, then pointed at her mother. 'That is the second time in my life I ever remember my mother blushing, and the other time was yesterday!'

'Don't labour it,' her mother warned.

'I reckon we should come clean,' George said.

'Actually she's quite wrong!' Blanche said airily. 'It felt more like twenty years—even thirty.'

'Which means,' Liz concluded, 'I definitely should not be here! I'm off to Penang!' She went to the door, put her hand on her heart and declaimed, 'You've got each other. And I'm just going to see if Anna's finished my ironing, so I can pack.' She waved, left the lounge, then peeped back. 'Be good!'

Blanche made a pretence of chasing her out but, reaching the door, closed it quietly. 'Elizabeth has quite amazed me. Not just by guessing what was going on, but I thought she might be upset because of her father.'

'It gives her freedom,' George said. 'Let's not grumble about the things that go right for us.'

The next day Liz crossed the channel to Penang on one of the ferries which cross and recross looking like nothing so much as a flotilla of gigantic water beetles straggling across the water.

She took a rickshaw to the small hotel agreed with Alan over the telephone, booked in and asked if there was a message for her. There was not. Just being in a hotel and waiting for news again gave her a strange and apprehensive feeling, but this time she knew she would not stir from the hotel until she heard from Alan.

Watching from her window she saw young

men strolling in twos and threes, obviously English soldiers though walking out from their camp in cheap cotton trousers and shirts they had bought locally. One of these groups paused outside and soon afterwards a letter was brought up to her room.

She tore it open, paused and laughed as she saw he had drawn matchstick men along the top all cheering. She went to sit by the window to read his message.

My darling Liz,

I am writing just in case you manage to come this early. I'm on duty until late afternoon—but great news. We have our own place!

I've rented a holiday bungalow. It is on Batu Feringgi beach—practically on the edge of the sea and just about four hundred yards around the headland from our camp. It is really a weekend bungalow used by a George Town barber, but we have full use of it for a month—and the regime in this camp is free and easy, the duties light.

I'll go to the bungalow tomorrow lunchtime and every afternoon until you come. There is everything there, except can you food shop on the way?

Come soon, my love.

Yours ever,
Alan

The taxi driver was amused as she stacked his vehicle with goods. She was less enchanted when as they drove he insisted on slowing down to point out places he obviously thought she should be interested in—or as she came to realise he thought he might earn more by taking her on detours. This went on until she told him that there would be two dollars extra if he could get her to Feringgi quickly. The difference was electrifying, even frightening, as they now careered along, disregarding not only the attractions but all other forms of life and traffic.

They were quickly across the island to the west coast, blazed a way through a sleepy fishing village and along the shore track, glimpsing blue ocean between palms as they sped along. The tropical growth on the land side was becoming denser and more encroaching, so Liz assumed few people used this road.

'Are you sure this is the right way?' she asked.

He turned and beamed. 'I bring Mr Khanti all time.'

She felt relieved when he turned back to look where he was going and only seconds later braked sharply before a small wooden building.

'If you would just put all my things near

the door,' she said, beginning to fumble in her handbag for his fee, Less he should try to find more reasons to earn himself a little more. Once the dollars had changed hands, he left with as much speed as she could have wished.

The bungalow was open and, though she called tentatively, she knew it was empty. She walked to the beach edge; palms behind, ocean in front, sky, it seemed, the deepest of blues, yet the sea deeper still. Everywhere appeared deserted. The beach bungalow was built on a wooden platform, level at the trackside but some feet above the beach where the sand sloped quickly into the lapping water. Although unprepossessing from the outside, no more than steep slant of attap roof running down beyond its walls to shade the platform it was built on, inside the house had been neatly divided into four parts. There were two bedrooms—Mr Khanti obviously had children, and she hoped they wouldn't miss their weekends at the beach too much. The lady of the house had kept most of the drapes in shades of white and cream with patterned brown cushions and rugs. On the tables were brown and white bowls and shells. It was altogether very pleasing.

The only things she was sure neither Mr nor Mrs Khanti owned were a thin blue cotton shirt and a pair of cotton trousers thrown on the double bed. These had to be Alan's, they were like those she had seen on the soldiers in George Town.

She sat on the bed, laying a gentle hand on them as if to divine where he was, when he would come. Then she was up and about the business of housekeeping, stowing away their groceries, leaning from the kitchen window and plucking brilliant red hibiscus, spoiling Mrs Khanti's colour scheme with bowls full in the kitchen and the lounge.

Everything done she could think of, even the wok oiled ready to cook in, she wandered out on to the beach. In both directions it was entirely deserted. To the right, no more than a quarter of a mile away, a heavily jungled headland tumbled small cast-off green islets into the sea. This was the way the camp lay.

She walked slowly, watching the sun sink down through a sky in deepening splendours of silver, bronze and, as it touched the horizon, pure liquid gold, seeming to resist being put out by the sea with a brazen display of pyrotechnics far across the sky. The last rim clung on and on, and when at last the whole circle had disappeared the sky still celebrated the passing.

She found to her astonishment tears running down her cheeks. This beautiful land, this land where she had thought all her dreams for the future lay...

'My Shangri-la!' she whispered to the fading glory. 'Still the same—but I've changed. You are the distant, brilliant land of my childhood.'

She turned to look from sea to land, dark now, menacing to the ignorant or the unwary. But westward, the sea seemed to hold its own light, as if having drowned in it the sun gave up light from below its waters. 'Ever more wonders!' Looking towards the headland, she was surprised to see how close its blackness loomed, how far she had walked. With a start, she saw a dark figure at the sea's edge outlined by the pale-green phosphorescence—a figure lifting an arm high in eager greeting. 'Ever more wonders,' she repeated.

They met running. He caught and swung her round so she felt on a carousel of pale sky and shining water.

They hugged and kissed and threw little remarks at each other, mere asides, banter to ride the excitement of reunion, the thrill of touching.

'You've shaved your beard.'

'I was on duty until five.'

'I had a mad taxi driver...'

'Today's duty sergeant thinks he's still at Caterham Barracks.'

'I think my mother will marry George.'

There was a pause, a kind of calming in this news. 'Good,' he said with gentle emphasis. 'Good, best thing that can happen.'

They were silent then, content to link arms and stand lifting their faces to the slight breeze coming from the sea. Its passage feigning coolness.

'It was getting late,' she said after a time. 'I thought you might not come.'

'I'll be here every night and most days,' he told her. 'The camp has steps down to this beach. There's a fence and a gate but...but I'm billeted with two good guys.'

She gave his arm a squeeze and immediately he folded her in his arms. 'Don't get into trouble,' she whispered.

'Do I care?' he asked, wrapping the words around her like a message of undying love.

'Don't want them sending you somewhere else. I would like the whole month here.' She laughed suddenly. 'You know honeymoons are going to mean nothing to us.'

'We'll just make it one long celebration,' he told her and they began walking slowly back towards the bungalow.

'I love you,' she said, 'for ever.'

'You'll be able to stay until my furlough is up?'

She nodded. 'And I'll travel with you when you go.'

'I hope,' he said, treading into the wet sand at the sea's edge, 'we're not talking metaphors, or some of George's proverbs here.'

She laughed. 'No, I'm talking planes and ships, or whatever will take us back to England.'

'You'd be happy to leave your mother behind? That is, if she stays.' It was easier to ask these questions as they walked.

'Oh, she'll stay, I know that. She may not know yet, but they'll marry and live at Rinsey and I'm sure eventually George will take over the plantation.' Predictions felt like certainties as they strolled, arms around each other. 'I feel closer to my mother than ever before in my life. It's like finding you had another best friend or older sister.'

'There is your sister.'

'Wendy? Wendy's like my mother, self-sufficient. She'll make her own decisions, no use trying to second-guess for Wendy. She'll make a life, and it'll never be dull.'

'At home either East or West,' Alan mused, then lifted his head. 'You know, I can smell rain coming just like you can in England—and the sky's darkening.'

'It won't be like English rain,' Liz had

hardly warned when the first spots began to crash down.

'Like being pelted with jellyfish,' Alan gasped as he caught her hand and they ran and leaped up on the bungalow's platform under the crude porch.

They were both soaked and the rain was already running from the roof in an unbroken sheet. 'Makes you feel shut off, doesn't it?' Alan said as he turned to her. 'The darkness, the rain.'

She thought how strange it was that rain, waterfalls, a lake with a legend, now an ocean featured in their love. 'There is a lot of water in Malaya,' she said while remembering there was also a trout stream running through the land of Pearling House.

'We should have taken our clothes off—like at the lake,' he said.

'Why not? Let's just stand out there.' She began to pull her saturated clothing off and stepped out into the downpour.

'Oh! lovely', she shouted above the din. 'Come on in—no, out!'

Alan pulled off his clothes and hung them on a chair which stood at the back of the verandah. He lifted his hands above his head and let the water stream over him, remembering the home-made shower at Rinsey when he had first dined in the house, first known Liz loved him.

They came together, letting the water stream over their entwined bodies. Liz had a mental picture of how they must look, how she could draw them. Art Nouveau style, sensual, with a background of wild Rousseau jungle. She would avert the faces so the picture could hang on the wall of their home, so only she and Alan would know the real significance.

All through the night their lovemaking was accompanied by the pounding beat of rain. But the morning dawned clear, gleaming with all the cleanness of a land new-scrubbed and polished by the storm. She felt him move from the bed, heard him go to the window, heard a faint gasp of amazement and, seeing her awake, he said in an awed voice, 'Come and look!'

She knew by the dancing of the light from the window what he was seeing and went to stand, her arm around him.

Raindrops still hung sparkling in huge prismatic drops from every leaf and over the streaming track hovered a myriad gaudy butterflies, like a curtain screening jungle from beach, screening them from the world.

'I wouldn't have believed it,' he whispered, 'if I had not seen...'

'It often happens after rain,' she told him.

He stood and admired them as long as

they remained, turning to her as the last few began to drift away, the wonder of it still in his eyes.

Four months later George and Blanche stood, arms linked, on the Jardine Steps of Keppel Harbour, looking up at His Majesty's Troop Ship *Lanshire*. Having loaded its returning troops, officers, wives, nurses, other personnel and Liz, the ship was preparing to leave for the month's journey home to England.

Both searched the ship's rail until Blanche squeezed George's hand. 'There they are! Together, look! Under the fourth lifeboat from the front.'

They waved energetically back to Alan and Liz, who had obviously spotted them some time ago.

'Goodbye, my love,' Blanche called. 'Goodbye! Give my love to Pearling. Let me know what's happening there. All the news.'

'They can't hear.' George shook his head at her efforts.

'I know, I know!' Blanche said, waving hectically.

The hawsers were slipped from the bollards, splashing down into the dock, and a tug moved in to nudge and nurse the troop ship out into the channel.

From the rail, pressed close by Alan's side,

Liz waved and waved, feeling unutterably separated from her mother as clear water appeared between boat and land.

Adrift. She felt she ought to try to explain to someone that life had somehow mixed up their journeys. She was the one who was supposed to stay and her mother to return.

Alan took her hand and held it very hard. It felt as if he brought her hovering heart finally aboard for the journey, anchored not to a place but to a person.

"What needest with thy tribe's black tents, who hast the red pavilion of my heart?"

Liz was never sure whether it was she who whispered the words.

This Large Print Book for the Partially sighted, who cannot read normal print, is published under the auspices of

THE ULVERSCROFT FOUNDATION

Miss Petrie was far from dull.

Edward Barraclough was not quite sure why. She dressed quietly enough, with no attempt to attract. If he had not seen those honey-gold curls that had tumbled about her shoulders at their first meeting he would never have known they existed. Miss Petrie wore her hair in a firmly disciplined knot, or even under a cap. She was not particularly tall, and her figure, from what he had seen of it, was slight. Apart from her forget-me-not-blue eyes, he would not have said there was anything interesting or attractive about her.

But Miss Petrie wasn't dull. She was quick-witted and amusing. And there was something about that small figure... Her carriage was graceful, her manner unassuming, but Miss Petrie was neither humble nor respectful, not underneath.

Edward Barraclough was intrigued. Perhaps he should spend more of the time he was forced to spend at Wychford in getting to know his nieces' governess!

Sylvia Andrew taught modern languages for a number of years, ultimately becoming Vice-Principal of a sixth-form college. She lives in Somerset with two cats, a dog, and a husband who has a very necessary sense of humour, and a stern approach to punctuation. Sylvia has one daughter living in London, and they share a lively interest in the theatre. She describes herself as an 'unrepentant romantic'.

Recent titles by the same author:

LORD CALTHORPE'S PROMISE*
LORD TRENCHARD'S CHOICE*
COLONEL ANCROFT'S LOVE*

*linked by character

And in the Regency series
The Steepwood Scandal:

AN UNREASONABLE MATCH
AN INESCAPABLE MATCH

A VERY UNUSUAL GOVERNESS

Sylvia Andrew

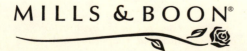

MILLS & BOON®

MILLS & BOON and MILLS & BOON with the Rose Device are registered trademarks of the publisher.

First published in Great Britain 2004
Large Print edition 2004
Harlequin Mills & Boon Limited,
Eton House, 18-24 Paradise Road, Richmond, Surrey TW9 1SR

ISBN 0 263 18195 2

Set in Times Roman 14½ on 16 pt.
42-0904-79327

Printed and bound in Great Britain
by Antony Rowe Ltd, Chippenham, Wiltshire

A VERY UNUSUAL GOVERNESS

Sylvia Andrew

Chapter One

Tall, with black hair, broad shoulders and a powerful stride, Edward Barraclough was an impressive sight as he walked through Green Park on his way back to North Audley Street. Though he was plainly dressed, his dark green superfine coat, silver-mounted cane, buckskins, and boots were all of a quality which indicated to the discerning that he was a man of wealth and distinction. The discerning might also have wondered what such an obvious member of the *ton* was doing in London, for this was the time of year when Society deserted the town for the pleasures of their country estates and the capital was very thin of company.

So, when Viscount Trenton saw Mr Barraclough emerge from the Park and prepare to cross Piccadilly, he hailed him with surprise and pleasure.

'Ned! What the devil are you doing in town?'

'The same as you, I imagine,' said Mr Barraclough. 'Business.'

'I didn't think the Foreign Office did any work till next month.'

'They don't. This was family business—bankers over here from Vienna.'

'Ah! What a bore, old chap!'

Mr Barraclough gave his companion an amused glance. 'Not at all! I enjoy talking to bankers.'

In Viscount Trenton's experience, interviews with bankers, or any men of business, were usually to be avoided at all costs, but he knew that Ned Barraclough did not suffer from the same reluctance. With good reason. The Barracloughs were enormously wealthy, with large estates in the West Indies and interests in banking and trade all over the world. And though you would never have guessed it, Edward Barraclough had a strange liking for work. Not only did he keep a personal eye on his own family fortunes, he also spent hours giving the Foreign Office the benefit of his considerable experience in the Americas. But, though it might seem odd, it did not prevent him from being a popular member of London society, and welcome wherever he chose to go. Jack Trenton liked him.

As they went up Clarges Street towards Grosvenor Square, he gave Ned a sly look and asked, 'Is Louise in town, too?'

'I wouldn't expect her to be anywhere else,' Mr Barraclough replied. 'She hates the country. Though she informs me that she wouldn't object to a trip to Brighton.'

'Are you going to take her there?'

'I might.'

'You want to keep a careful eye on that particular bird of paradise, Ned,' said Jack. 'If you hope to keep her, that is. Louise Kerrall is a damned handsome creature. You're a lucky dog to have such a prize. There's quite a few fellows in London who would soon take her over if you gave them half a chance.'

Mr Barraclough's teeth gleamed in a mocking smile. 'Are you one of 'em, Jack? I don't advise you to try. I've no intention of letting Louise go at the moment.'

'Oh, Lord, Ned! I didn't mean—! Y'needn't worry about me. I couldn't afford her! And I'm sure she's devoted to you—'

'Devoted?' Mr Barraclough's smile took on a cynical twist. 'Louise's devotion is in direct proportion to the value of the last trinket I happen to have given her. Particularly if it is diamonds. She's very fond of diamonds. But you needn't worry, Jack. It's not *devotion* I look for when I'm with Louise. Nothing so abstract.'

With a picture in his mind of Louise Kerrall's dark hair and languorous brown eyes, her creamy skin, red lips and generous curves, Jack said appreciatively, 'I dare say not!'

'So if you're not planning to take my mistress away from me, Jack, we'll forget her. Tell me instead why *you* are in town.'

Lord Trenton's expression grew gloomy. 'That's business of a sort, too. I've been seeing the lawyers.'

'Your father disinheriting you at long last?'

'No, no! Just the opposite. I've finally given in and made an offer for Cynthia Paston.'

'Have you, begad? Which one is that? The one with the teeth or the one with the nose?'

'The one with the teeth and a dowry of thirty thousand pounds.'

'And she accepted you?'

'Oh, yes. I may not be much myself, but the title is quite a draw, y'know. The Pastons like the idea of having a future Countess in the family.'

Mr Barraclough looked at the expression on Lord Trenton's face and burst out laughing. 'You're obviously the happiest of men! My congratulations!'

'It's all very well for you to laugh, Ned! Y'don't know how lucky you are! No one's putting any pressure on *you* to marry. No one's reminding you day after day that you're the only son and there's the damned title to consider. I'm not like you, with two brothers both older than me!'

'Only one now, Jack. My eldest brother was killed earlier this year. So was his wife. I thought you knew.'

'I'd forgotten. Sorry, Ned!'

'It's all right. Antigua is a long way away. Why should you remember?'

'All the same I ought to have. Carriage accident, wasn't it...? Is your other brother still out there in the West Indies?'

'Not at the moment. He and Julia are on their way here—they should arrive any day now.'

'Staying long?'

'Till next year's Season. They have my two nieces with them, daughters of the brother who was killed. Lisette, the elder one, is to be brought out next Spring. She's a lovely girl, I don't doubt she'll be a success. But I'm not looking forward to their arrival.'

'Oh?'

'I'm fond enough of my brother. And Lisette and Pip are delightful. But Julia, Henry's wife... Believe me, Jack, she's the best argument I've come across for a man to remain single!'

'I say, old chap, that's not very tactful!'

'Why? What's wrong?'

'It's downright unkind when you know I've just put my head in the noose!'

'If you feel that badly about it, why did you?'

'I've told you! *Noblesse oblige* and all that! Don't look at me so—you've no idea what it's like to have the family at your back all the time, rattling on about duty, preserving the line and all the rest. In the end I just gave in. It's enough to drive a man to drink.'

'Come and have one, then,' said Mr Barraclough sympathetically. 'The lawyers will wait.'

*　*　*

Lord Trenton met a few other cronies at White's, and after a while seemed to be drowning his sorrows so effectively that Mr Barraclough felt able to leave him. He resumed his walk back to his house in North Audley Street. The afternoon breeze was agreeably cool, and as he walked along he considered how very fortunate he was. At thirty, he was still free, rich and comparatively young. He had a mistress who was everything a man could want, beautiful, passionate and very willing—and, unlike a wife, she had no other claims on him. He was free to come and go as he pleased, and, when he tired of her, she would find someone else without any effort on his part.

Yes, his life was particularly well arranged. Unlike poor Trenton he was under no pressure to settle down. He could, and would, remain unencumbered for as long as he wished.

The only shadow on the horizon was the impending arrival of his sister-in-law. He frowned. It was an unfortunate truth that he and Julia cordially disliked one another. When to her chagrin he had inherited his uncle's fortune, she made no secret of the fact that she thought he should have stayed in the West Indies instead of choosing to travel the world as he had. His later decision to live in England was another source of displeasure. But he suspected that what really made her angry was the fact that, unlike his poor brother Henry, he took not the slightest notice of her.

This was as well, he thought as he crossed Berkeley Square and turned into Mount Street, for there really was no pleasing her. Far from neglecting his family responsibilities, he had allowed them to keep him out of England for a large part of last winter's hunting, and most of the London season this spring. What had started as a simple visit to Antigua had developed into a series of crises. Overnight his elder brother's two daughters had been made orphans, minors in the care of his brother Henry and himself. Making sure of their safety had been a major consideration, and he believed he had done more than his duty in that respect. It was now up to Henry and Julia to look after them.

Edward himself planned to make up for the last year's sacrifices as soon as he could leave London. He might spend a few days in Brighton with Louise, but afterwards he had various invitations from his friends to spend the later months of the year with them on their country estates. If and when that palled, he would return to London to enjoy town life again. A very attractive prospect, and one that he deserved, whatever Julia said!

Heartened by this thought, he leapt up the steps to his house, nodded cheerfully to his footman as he handed over his hat and cane, went into the hall, and started towards the stairs. But before he got to the first step he was stopped by his butler.

'Sir! Mr Barraclough!' Harbin looked as disturbed as Edward had ever seen him.

'What is it?'

'You have visitors, sir.' Harbin held out a salver on which was a card.

Edward read it. 'Lady Penkridge...? What does she want?'

'I don't know, sir. She has two young people with her.'

Edward frowned. 'I'd better see her, I suppose. Where are they?'

'In the library, sir.' Harbin went to the library door, opened it and announced Edward. Then he withdrew.

'Edward!' He was attacked by a small whirlwind. 'We've been waiting ages for you! Where've you been?'

Edward laughed, took the little girl into his arms and swung her round. 'I wasn't expecting you so soon, Pip! You should have warned me.' He put the child down and surveyed the room. Raising his eyebrow, he smiled at the other young person he saw, and went over to give her a hug. 'Lisette, I'll swear you're prettier than ever.' Then he turned and looked at the other occupants of the library. One was dressed in black, and stood ramrod straight. She had what looked like a permanent expression of disapproval on her face, with pursed lips and a nose like a hatchet. She was soberly dressed in rusty black, and what looked like the quills of a porcupine sticking out of an ugly bonnet. Not Lady Penkridge. He turned with relief to the other female, who was obviously waiting to speak to him. 'Lady Penkridge? I don't believe we've met?'

'No, indeed, Mr Barraclough. But I am very well acquainted with your brother and his wife.'

'Henry?'

'Yes. And dearest Julia. I have been a friend of hers for many years.'

'Indeed? Then I am pleased to make your acquaintance, Lady Penkridge. But…but I don't quite understand. Are my brother and his wife not here?'

'Julia is still in Antigua. And so is your brother.'

Edward looked at her in astonishment. Clearly enjoying the drama of the moment, Lady Penkridge nodded solemnly and added, 'They were unable to travel, Mr Barraclough. Julia broke her leg the day before we were all due to sail and Mr Henry Barraclough has stayed behind to look after her.'

'But…' Shocked, Edward demanded details of the accident. Lady Penkridge told him the tale, with frequent interruptions from his younger niece, who seemed to find the gory details of the accident more interesting than sad. But the conclusion was the same. It would be some time before Julia Barraclough could walk, and even longer before she could attempt the voyage to England.

At the end, somewhat bewildered, Edward said, 'But I still don't understand! Why, in that case, are my nieces here in London?'

'Edward! Don't say you don't want us here! We thought you'd be glad to see us!' This came from the small girl who had greeted him so rapturously a moment before.

Smiling reassuringly at her, Edward said, 'I am, midget, I am! I'm just a little puzzled, that's all. What are you going to do in England without your aunt?'

'It's all settled! We're to have Miss Froom as a governess. And you are to come with us to Wychford to look after us all.'

Edward's smile abruptly disappeared. *'What?'*

Lady Penkridge frowned at Pip. 'Philippa, I wish you would remember not to speak until you are spoken to! You must allow me to give your uncle the facts.'

'That would be helpful,' said Edward grimly. 'At the moment I don't believe what I've just heard!'

'First, may I present Miss Froom to you, Mr Barraclough?'

Edward loved his nieces, and the last thing he wanted was to upset them. But he had no intention of giving up his plans for the autumn in order to look after them, especially not in such an out of the way place as Wychford! So as he nodded to the dragon-like figure standing next to Lady Penkridge he said, 'Perhaps Miss Froom would take the girls into the saloon while you explain, ma'am? I'm sure Harbin could bring them some refreshments.'

Pip would have protested, but a look from her uncle silenced her, and she and Lisette followed Miss Froom meekly enough out of the room.

* * *

Edward waited until they had gone, then said, 'There's obviously some misunderstanding. I can't have heard properly. Would you oblige me by sitting down and telling me everything, Lady Penkridge? Slowly.'

His visitor settled herself, then began, 'You can imagine, Mr Barraclough, the confusion caused by Julia's accident—so unexpected and so immediately before the packet boat left Antigua. The Barracloughs were deeply worried. It was really impossible to change all their plans completely. So, since I was coming back to England on the same packet, I volunteered to bring the girls with me. It was a great relief to them, as you can imagine. Julia cannot possibly look after her nieces until she can walk. So, it was agreed that I should bring the girls and hand them over to you to look after until their aunt is able to travel.'

Edward considered this for a moment. Then he said carefully, 'You mean that *I* am to be responsible for my nieces? I alone? Without any help from my brother or his wife?'

'You will have Miss Froom.'

'Miss Froom!' There was a short silence during which Edward struggled to find some way of expressing his feelings which would be acceptable to the ears of a gently bred female. He failed.

Lady Penkridge went on in an encouraging tone, 'Julia is in good health. It shouldn't take long for her leg to heal. Perhaps only six or seven weeks.'

'Six or seven weeks! *Only* six or seven!' Edward's feelings got the better of him. 'This is a bachelor's establishment, Lady Penkridge. How the *devil* do you suppose I can keep Lisette and Pip here for six days, let alone six or seven weeks? I refuse! I damned well refuse!'

Lady Penkridge replied coldly, 'Your sister-in-law had the gravest doubts about your willingness to help her, Mr Barraclough, though she did not allow this to deter her. But I confess that your lack of sympathy surprises me. It is of course out of the question that Lisette and Philippa should remain here. I have taken a suite of rooms at the Poultney on Julia's behalf, and your nieces will stay there in Miss Froom's charge until you can arrange to transfer them to the house in the country where they were due to stay. The place is called Wychford, I believe.'

'Yes, yes, I know it. We had settled on a six months' tenure there some time ago. But it is in the heart of the countryside, over twenty miles out of London. I have other engagements, invitations I have accepted, commitments that would make it impossible for me to spend the autumn at Wychford. You must make other arrangements, Lady Penkridge.'

'I, sir? I'm afraid you are under a misapprehension. I brought the girls to England as a favour to your sister-in-law. But I now have to think of my own concerns. You will have to cancel these commitments of yours. I leave London in two days' time for the north.'

Edward gazed at her blankly. 'You can't!' he said.

'I can and will. I agreed to bring the girls to England, but my task ends there. As Julia said to me, they will now be entirely your responsibility.'

'My responsibility! Oh, yes, I can imagine Julia said that! This is all her confounded doing!'

'Mr Barraclough! Are you completely devoid of feeling? Your sister-in-law is at this moment lying on a bed of pain—'

'That is *nothing* compared with what she has done to me! And what was Henry doing all this time? Why hasn't he come up with a better solution? Dammit, *he's* the girls' guardian!'

'Your brother was naturally more concerned about his wife. And, as I understand it, you are also your nieces' guardian.'

'However, there is a substantial difference between us—Henry is married, and I am a bachelor!'

'That is why Miss Froom is here, Mr Barraclough. By a fortunate coincidence Julia had written to her some time ago to engage her services—'

'Fortunate! There is nothing fortunate about any part of this catastrophe!' muttered Edward.

Lady Penkridge ignored him. She went on, 'And I fetched her yesterday to join us. I am sure you may safely leave the girls in her hands. She comes with the highest possible recommendations. All that will be required of you is to take charge of the household at Wychford.'

'But I live in London, dammit!' Edward almost shouted the words. 'And I already have plans for the autumn! Why the devil did Henry agree to this cork-brained idea? Just wait till he gets here. If he wasn't my own brother, I swear I'd call him out!'

Lady Penkridge rose. 'I am sorry that your reception of my news has been so unfavourable, Mr Barraclough,' she said frigidly. 'Particularly as you express yourself in such immoderate terms. But there is nothing I can do about it. I leave London in two days. You have that time to make your arrangements. And now, if you don't mind, I shall collect the girls and return to the Poultney Hotel. Good afternoon.'

She gathered up her things and waited stiffly for him to send for Harbin to show her out. With a considerable effort Edward pulled himself together. It would do the girls no good at all if he antagonised this woman. Lisette was to come out in the spring, and for all he knew Lady Penkridge might have considerable influence among the London *ton*. He took a breath and gave her a charming smile.

'You are right, ma'am. It was quite wrong of me. It's just that...' He took another breath. 'It's just that I was a little upset at the notion that I would have to abandon all my friends, break the promises I have made, leave London and bury myself in the country for eight or nine weeks at least, with only my two nieces and their governess for company. And all within forty-eight hours. Absurd as it might seem to you, I was just a little shocked.'

He drew another breath and forced himself to smile again. 'But you have been very kind. I am sure Julia would wish me to show you our gratitude. May I call on you at the Poultney this evening? I should like to offer you and my nieces dinner there, if I may.'

Edward's charm was potent when he chose to exercise it, and Lady Penkridge was no more immune than many another lady in the past. Her manner was perceptibly warmer as she said, 'Thank you. Yes, the...the girls would enjoy that. And so should I. At what time?'

That evening Edward exerted himself to erase the unfavourable impression he had made on Lady Penkridge with such success that she began to wonder whether Julia had after all been mistaken in him. They parted on the best of terms, and after an exhausting two days of rearrangements, meetings, notes of apology and excuses, Edward saw Lady Penkridge safely launched on her journey north, then set out for Wychford accompanied by his nieces and Miss Froom.

As they left London behind them, he saw that something of his own gloom seemed to have affected the rest of the party. Lisette was gazing sadly out of the window, Miss Froom was sitting with a gimlet eye on Pip, and Pip herself was quite remarkably subdued. Edward roused himself. It was not his

nieces' fault that he had been forced into exile. The
poor girls had had a terrible time in the last year, first
with the upheaval caused by the accident and the loss
of their parents, and then the business with Lisette
and Arandez. And now this...

'I dare say you would like to hear a little about
Wychford,' he began.

'Has Aunt Julia bought it?' asked Pip.

'Don't be silly, Philippa,' said Miss Froom. 'Your
aunt will have leased it through an agent. It would
be unnecessary to buy it when you are to stay there
for such a short time.'

Edward regarded Miss Froom. This wasn't the first
time she had put the child down, quite unnecessarily.
He would have to keep an eye on her. Pip's lively
interest in everything she came across was one of her
main attractions, and he didn't want it suppressed.
He smiled warmly at his little niece as he said, 'I'm
afraid you're both wrong. There's more to it than
that.'

Pip's face brightened. 'A story, a story! Tell us,
Edward!'

'Well, when we first heard about Wychford it belonged to Thomas Carstairs. Thomas owned some
plantations in the West Indies, and he and his wife
became friends with your grandfather. Some years
later—just about the time you were born, Pip—Mrs
Carstairs came out to see us again after her husband
had died. She promised your father then that we

could all stay with her at Wychford when you and Lisette were old enough to come to England.'

'Like a good fairy at a christening!'

Edward smiled. 'Something like. Though she looked rather more like a witch than a good fairy.'

'Will she be there now?'

'No. She died not long ago—'

'And left the house to us!'

'Not quite.'

'Philippa, how many times do I have to tell you not to interrupt? And get back down on to the seat, if you please!'

Edward felt a spurt of irritation. Pip was standing on the seat, leaning half against him and half against the cushions at the side of the carriage. It wasn't safe, and Miss Froom had been perfectly right to object, but he had been pleased to see Pip once again her lively self. He ignored the governess and went on, 'That would have been quite wrong. Mrs Carstairs had no children, but she had other family. She left the house to her niece.'

'A niece? Like us?'

'Mrs Carstairs was about eighty, so a niece would be much older, wouldn't you say? Probably even older than I am!'

'Have you met her?'

'No, I've only dealt with her agent, a Mr Walters. But you must let me finish my story. I visited Mrs Carstairs several times at Wychford, and when I was last there, and told her you were all coming to

England this year, she remembered her promise to your father.'

'But she's dead!'

'That's true, but she stipulated in her will that Wychford was to be available to the Barracloughs for six months after your arrival.'

'That's a very strange condition, Edward,' said Lisette.

'Mrs Carstairs was a very strange lady. But I liked her.' He fell silent, remembering the last time he had seen the old woman.

She had been wrapped in shawls and huddled in her chair, obviously ill. But her gipsy-black eyes had been fiercely alive. She had looked at him hard, and then she appeared to make up her mind. She said, 'You'll do! The house likes you and so will she.'

Puzzled, he had asked, 'Who is "she", ma'am?'

Whereupon she had given one of her cackles and said, 'Never you mind! But she will. Eventually! Make sure you come back here! But there! I know you will.'

Edward had been tempted to dismiss her words as the wanderings of an old lady whose life was almost spent. But they had stuck in his mind, and now here he was, about to return to Wychford, just as she had said...

Chapter Two

Some thirty miles away, Mrs Carstairs and her house were also the subject of discussion between Rupert, fourth Earl of Warnham, and his daughter, the Lady Octavia Petrie. The day was cool, and Lord Warnham, who was in his seventies and felt the cold, pulled his shawl closer round his shoulders and gave his daughter a worried frown. In his gentle way he said, 'I wish your Aunt Carstairs had not left you Wychford, Octavia. It was most inconsiderate of her. I knew it would be a burden!'

'But, Papa, I assure you, I don't find it any sort of burden.'

'How can that be? You tell me that you must go to see it next week. All that way through the countryside to see a house that can be of no conceivable use to you! Of course it is a burden. She should not have done it. If she had consulted me in the matter I would have advised against it. She cannot have thought of the worry it would be to you to possess a house like that.'

'Papa, it is no worry at all! I am very *happy* to be the owner of Wychford.'

'But you cannot possibly keep it. You have no notion of what it means to look after a large house!'

'I look after this one, Papa.'

'That is quite a different matter, my dear. This is your home, and you have me to protect you.'

Octavia Petrie permitted herself a wry grin. It might be her home, but it was her father who needed protection. Even the most trivial of problems worried him. Much as she loved her elderly parent, she found shielding him from unnecessary distress far more demanding than looking after a house, however large it might be. She set about reassuring him.

'Wychford won't cause me any trouble, Papa! You know it won't. The Barracloughs are to rent it for six months, as Aunt Carstairs wished. The agreement is signed and sealed, and so far I have had nothing at all to do. Mr Walters has dealt with it all.'

'Walters is a good fellow. An excellent man of business! But he has done no more than he should. It would not be at all the thing for a lady to be concerned in property agreements and such matters. But I still cannot like it. Your Aunt Carstairs should have left her house to someone else. You would do much better to stay at home with me next Tuesday and let Walters get rid of it for you.'

Octavia smiled. Her father must be unique among parents. No other man would find it distressing that the youngest of his eight children, twenty-two and still single, had been left a large estate, including a house, by her godmother. But Lord Warnham's intense dislike of any threat to his unvarying routine quite blinded him to the advantages of such a handsome inheritance. Octavia hardened her heart and said firmly,

'I am not so very young, Papa. I shall be three and twenty next spring. And I really shan't find it a burden to make a simple visit to Wychford. I merely wish to see the house before the Barracloughs arrive. It will take less than a day.'

'A day! You must not be so foolhardy! It is all of ten miles.'

'Fifteen. But it is still quite light in the evenings and the roads are good—'

'You would subject yourself to travelling *thirty miles* in one day! I will not hear of it! Even with a closed carriage—'

'Oh, I would take the gig. I'd like to drive myself. Will Gifford would accompany me, of course.'

This suggestion so outraged the Earl that it took several minutes of Octavia's most skilful coaxing before he could be brought to resign himself to her absence. Eventually he said wistfully, 'I suppose you will have to go, but I shall miss you.'

'I hardly think so, Papa. Have you forgotten that Cousin Marjorie arrives tomorrow? You like her, don't you?'

'She is a very pleasant person, certainly, and plays whist and cribbage better than you do. You know you can be a little impatient, my dear. Yes, I like Marjorie.' He sighed and added, 'I can see you are quite set on this escapade, Octavia, so I shall say no more on the subject. But I do wish that Mrs Carstairs had not left you her house. I cannot understand why she did!'

'Nor can I, Papa. Though...she did say when she was last here that Wychford would like me.'

The shawl dropped off her father's shoulders as he sat up and stared. 'Wychford would *like* you? A house *liking* someone? What a very strange thing to say! But then, I was often puzzled by the things she said. She did not resemble your dear mama at all.'

'No, indeed! Harry and I were afraid of her when we were children. We used to call her the Witch of Wychford. But I got to know her better when she was here last spring, not long before she died. She...she seemed to understand...'

Octavia fell silent. It was true that there had been something witch-like about her mother's half-sister. Though nothing had been said, she, of all the family, had seemed to divine Octavia's growing restlessness, her boredom with life at Ashcombe. Octavia had found Mrs Carstairs's gypsy-black eyes resting on her more than once and had wondered what the old lady had been thinking. But it had certainly never occurred to her that her godmother would leave her Wychford.

'Understand? What is there to understand?'

'Nothing, Papa. Nothing at all.'

'A very odd person. Why should she leave you her house?' He was obviously still struggling to understand. 'What do you need a house for? Surely you're happy enough here?'

Octavia longed to say, 'I'm bored, Papa! I sometimes think I shall go mad with boredom!' But she was a kind-hearted girl and genuinely fond of her father, so she merely said, 'Of course. And I have no intention of living at Wychford, Papa. In any case I couldn't. The Barracloughs take possession in just a few weeks' time.'

'Who are these Barracloughs? Do I know them?'

'Old Mr Barraclough was a friend of Uncle Carstairs. They knew each other in Antigua. They are now both dead, of course, but the present Barracloughs have some daughters, who are to be presented next year.'

'That seems a very odd sort of arrangement. But the Barracloughs sound respectable enough.'

'They are extremely respectable, Papa. Mr Walters has had the highest reports of their standing in Antigua, and Mr Barraclough is at present in London working as a temporary adviser to the Foreign Office. I am very unlikely to meet them. Certainly not this time, for they won't be there.'

'Well, I suppose you must go. I shall do as well as I can with Marjorie.'

Octavia laughed at his tone of resignation. 'You'll do very well indeed, Papa!'

'You must see to it that she has the tapestry bed-room. She likes that.'

'Indeed, she does. She has used it every time she has paid us a visit for the past twenty years!' Octavia shook her head at her father in affectionate exasperation. 'Really, Papa! What do you think of me? The room has been ready for two days now. It only needs fresh flowers, and I shall put those in it tomorrow before she arrives.'

'And a warming pan for the bed, Octavia! Remind the housekeeper to make sure the bed is properly aired!'

'I shall do nothing of the sort! I have no wish to offend Mrs Dewey. If I know her, there's a hot brick in the bed already, and it will be renewed tomorrow. You may be easy.'

As soon as her father settled down for his afternoon nap, Octavia changed and made her escape to the stables. She collected her mare and Will Gifford, her groom, and set off over the fields. A good gallop might rid her of the feelings of impatience, boredom, weariness even, which were taking an ever-firmer hold of her spirits. Much as she loved her father, she sometimes felt an irresistible desire to get away. The fact that she had made her own trap, had chosen of her own free will to stay at Ashcombe, was little consolation now. How could she leave him? But she was looking forward to the following week when she would see Wychford for the first time. She began to feel more cheerful. Cousin Marjorie's visit was something to look forward to, too. She might belong to an older generation, but she was still young in spirit, and a very sympathetic listener.

Octavia's Cousin Marjorie, the Dowager Lady Dorney, was a widow, and lived some distance away in the Dower House of a great estate now owned by her son. She and Lord Warnham had always been good friends and since Lord Dorney's death a year or two before she had been a frequent visitor to Ashcombe. She spent a great deal of time gossiping about the family with him, or playing backgammon, whist, or the many other games he enjoyed. Lord Warnham liked her company and her visits had always been a success. Octavia had no qualms about leaving her father in her care.

When Lady Dorney arrived the next day, Lord Warnham was still having his afternoon nap, so, after greeting her warmly, Octavia took her off to her own little parlour. For a while they exchanged news of the two families, then Lady Dorney said,

'You're not looking as you should, Octavia. What's wrong? Is it this house your mother's sister has left you? Wychford?'

'Not you too!'

Lady Dorney raised an eyebrow at the exasperation in Octavia's voice, and Octavia went on, 'Papa wishes it had never been left to me. He thinks it too great a responsibility. Don't tell me you feel the same!'

Lady Dorney laughed. 'I am not as unworldly as your father, I'm afraid. No, I am glad for you. But if it isn't that, why are you looking so unlike yourself? You're obviously under some sort of strain.'

'I had hoped I wasn't showing it!'

'Perhaps not to others. But I know you too well. What exactly is wrong?'

Octavia hesitated. Then she said, 'You're right, it is the house. When I first heard about it, it seemed like a way of escape. But I soon realised that I couldn't possibly take it.'

'I'm not at all surprised at your wish to escape! The life you lead at Ashcombe is no life for a pretty young girl. You should have married years ago. I've never understood why.'

'That's soon explained. I never met anyone I wanted to marry!'

'You've never been in love?'

'Not really.'

'Never?'

Octavia gave a small smile. 'When I was younger I thought I was. With a very handsome young soldier, called Tom Payne—tall, blond, blue-eyed, and full of fun. He came down here on leave with my brother in the summer of 1812, and he and Stephen got up to such scrapes that I don't think I stopped laughing for the whole of that fortnight. I've never forgotten it.'

'That's hardly my idea of a great romance! Did he make love to you?'

'Of course not. I was only fourteen! I don't think it entered his head. But if he had lived...I might have met him again...'

'He was killed?'

Octavia nodded. 'At Waterloo. Both of them. He and Stephen together.' She paused then went on, 'I got over it, of course. Our acquaintance had been too short for real heartbreak. By the time I went to London for my come-out I was quite my old self. But...I never had an offer there that I wished to accept.'

'Oh, come now! That is absurd! You can't have been short of choice! You're not only a very pretty girl, you are rich and related to half the best families in England. You must have attracted any number of eligible young men!'

'Perhaps so. But not one of them attracted *me*!'

'You were surely not still pining for Tom Payne?'

'Oh, no! It wasn't that exactly, but...but he was always my ideal—blond, blue-eyed, and *fun*. And no one quite measured up to him. Compared with Tom they were so dull! I couldn't face spending the rest of my life with any one of them. And then London was noisy, and dirty...and full of scandal...'

'Then your mama died and you left town.'

'Quite without regret.'

'And you decided to stay at Ashcombe, to put off even considering marriage until your father could manage without you. I said at the time it was a mistake, if you remember.'

'But there wasn't anyone else! Harry couldn't stay—he was already in the Army—and the rest of the family were married and established elsewhere. Papa would have had to move in order to live with any of them, and you know how he hates change. He even refused to move to Warnham Castle when Grandpapa died.'

'So your brother Arthur took over the family seat. I must say, the Castle is more Arthur's style! How is he?'

'Much the same as ever. Pompous, opinionated and prosy! Sarah is expecting another child, and Arthur is full of hope that she will give him a son at last.'

'How many daughters has he?'

'Four.'

'And no son. His poor wife. She won't get much sympathy from Arthur if she fails him again. I can quite see why your father wouldn't wish to live in the Castle with Arthur! But I still don't see why you had to sacrifice yourself?'

'I assure you, ma'am, it was no sacrifice—at the time! But now...I feel trapped!' She gave a little laugh. 'Sometimes I feel quite desperate!'

'You need to get away for a while. Could you not visit one of your sisters?'

'What? To be a nursemaid to their children rather than to my f—' She stopped short. 'Rather than manage Ashcombe for my father? Here at least I only answer to him! But…with your help I shall have a brief holiday—all of eleven or twelve hours.' She got up and walked about the room. After a while she turned and said with an impatient gesture, 'Oh, pay no attention to me, ma'am! I wasn't forced into my life here—I chose it. Marriage would not be the way out. From what I have seen of my sisters' husbands, I would merely exchange one form of boredom for another.'

'You still haven't met the right man,' said Lady Dorney with a smile. 'He'll turn up, you'll see!'

'That is romantic nonsense! At fourteen I might have believed in fairy tales, but at twenty-two I've given them up. No, when I no longer have Papa to look after, I shall turn into a crotchety old maid living at Wychford with a pug and a downtrodden companion, and children will think me a witch, as I did Aunt Carstairs!'

'She had the air of one, certainly. She had a way of looking at people…I only met her once, but I felt she knew what I was thinking before I did myself! What is this Wychford like?'

'I've never seen it. My aunt never invited any of us there, she was something of a recluse. I shall see it for the first time next Tuesday. I'm so relieved you'll be here to look after Papa. I know how tedious it can be…'

Lady Dorney looked at Octavia in astonishment. 'My dear girl, you are quite wrong! I shall look forward to it!' She laughed at the expression on Octavia's face. 'You needn't look at me like that, Octavia. I am quite serious. I love looking after people, especially someone as sweet-natured and gentle as your Papa.'

'Really?'

Lady Dorney took Octavia's hand. 'Since Dorney died there's been such a...a hole in my life that I sometimes hardly know what to do with myself. Coming here might seem dull to you, but to me it's most enjoyable! Indeed, I'd be happy to keep your father company for longer than a day if you wished! Now, tell me how you intend to travel. How far did you say it was to Wychford? And what do you know about these Barracloughs? Might there be a charming young, blond, blue-eyed Mr Barraclough who will ''amuse'' you?'

Octavia laughed. 'If only there were, ma'am! But, according to Mr Walters, the Barracloughs are a sober, upright and highly respectable family. And since there are only two daughters, there are absolutely no prospects there for me, I'm afraid. In any case, I shan't meet any of them—the Barracloughs won't be there. They're not due at Wychford for another week at least.'

Meanwhile, some three miles from Wychford, the 'sober, upright and highly respectable' Mr Barraclough, grim-faced, got out of his carriage, which was leaning drunkenly to one side, examined

the broken wheel-pin and swore fluently and com-
prehensively. Three heads popped out of the window,
one interested, one nervous and the third dressed in
a black bonnet, its feathers quivering with outrage.

'Mr Barraclough! Sir! You forget yourself,' said
the black bonnet severely. 'Lisette! Philippa! Sit back
this minute and put your hands over your ears.'

'You'd do better to tell them to get out as quickly
as they damn well can, Miss Froom,' said Edward
brutally. 'I cannot promise that the whole lot won't
topple over any moment. Out with the lot of you!'

'But there's too much mud on the road!'

'Better muddy shoes than bruised bottoms! Out
with you! You first, Pip!' Ignoring Miss Froom's
gasp of outrage at his language, he lifted the youngest
of the three occupants out and swung her over to the
dry verge of the road. 'Now you, Lisette. Don't hang
back, you'll be perfectly safe with me.' Lisette was
lifted and deposited next to her sister. 'Miss Froom?'

'Thank you, Mr Barraclough, I'll get out by myself,' Miss Froom said with dignity.

'As you choose, ma'am,' said Edward with ironic
amusement. But when Miss Froom landed in the pool
of mud and would have slipped he caught her by the
waist and bundled her to the side to join the others,
where she stood, ramrod straight, bristling with in-
dignation.

He left her there while he went back to examine
the damage done to his carriage. Meanwhile, Pip took
advantage of the situation to scramble up the nearest

tree where she perched on one of the branches. When
Lisette looked up and saw her she gave her a very
sweet smile, but Miss Froom exclaimed loudly,
'What on earth do you think you are doing, miss?
Get *down* this instant! Get *down*, I say! Mr
Barraclough, tell that child to get off the tree. Look
at her! I must protest—'

'Protest all you wish, Miss Froom, it won't do you
any good,' he said impatiently. 'I have more urgent
things to do than listen to you at the moment. If you
can't control the child, then I suggest you leave her
up there. She's perfectly safe.' Then, turning his back
on her he shouted, 'Jem! Jem! Where the devil are
you? How bad is it?'

Scarlet-faced, Miss Froom drew a deep breath,
pursed her lips, and sat down on a nearby tree trunk.
'Sit here with me, Lisette,' she said coldly. 'And you
may take that silly smile off your face. I do not find
your sister's disobedience at all amusing.'

'She's not really disobedient, Miss Froom,' said
Lisette earnestly. 'Pip always looks for somewhere
to perch. She likes being high up. Papa used to call
her his little marmoset...' She bit her lip. 'She...she
used to make him laugh...'

'That may be, but if I am to be responsible for her
that child will have to behave like a young lady, not
a street entertainer's monkey! My previous charge,
the Lady Araminta, was younger than Philippa when
I first started to teach her. You would never have
found her up a tree, she was a model of good behav-

iour. But then so were all her sisters and brothers. The Marchioness, their mother…'

Both girls sighed. They had known Miss Froom for a mere three days but they had already heard more than they wished about the Marchioness of Ledbury and her perfect family.

After Miss Froom had finished on the subject of the Ledburys she turned her attention to Lisette. 'Try to act like a lady, Lisette! Put your feet together and sit up straight. That is better. Now! You may list for me the kings and queens of England in order of succession. We needn't waste time while we are waiting to continue our journey.'

'I…I don't know them.'

'You don't *know* them?'

'Not…not like that. In a list.'

'William the Conqueror,' shouted Pip. 'He shot an arrow into Harold's eye!'

Miss Froom ignored her. 'Then you will have to learn. What about the prophets of the Old Testament?'

'The prophets? Er…J…Jeremiah…'

'In order, if you please!'

'I…I can't do things like that, Miss Froom. It's not the way Mama taught us.'

'I see.' Miss Froom's tone suggested that she thought poorly of Mama's methods.

'Her lessons were fun, and we learned a lot!' said an aggressive voice from above.

'My methods of instruction are directed towards the acquisition of knowledge, not fun,' said Miss Froom coldly. 'Lady Ledbury fully approved of them. At the age of ten the Lady Araminta could recite all the...'

'The Lady Araminta sounds a dead bore to me,' muttered Pip rebelliously. 'And so does the Marchioness of Ledbury.'

'*What* was that, Philippa?'

'Look, Miss Froom! Edward is coming! I think the carriage is ready,' cried Lisette hastily. 'Come down, Pip, dear. We shall soon be on our way.'

Mr Barraclough reported that the pin had been re-placed, and they could now complete the last three miles of the journey to Wychford. 'So, we'll be off! Into the carriage with you! Miss Froom?'

They set off once again. But the silence was op-pressive. Mr Barraclough looked sharply at Miss Froom's pursed lips and pinched nostrils, and then at Pip. 'Is there something wrong?' he asked.

'Philippa is a very rude, undisciplined, ill-mannered little girl,' said Miss Froom sharply.

Pip sat upright, looking mutinous, and Lisette put a restraining hand on her arm. 'She didn't mean to be rude. She's tired, Edward. It's been a long day. I am sure she is sorry. Please forgive her, Miss Froom.'

There was silence. Mr Barraclough said, 'Miss Froom?'

'I do not mind so much for myself, though it is not what I am used to,' said Miss Froom stiffly. 'But when an ignorant little girl criticises the family of as great a nobleman as the Marquess of Ledbury, whose family goes back hundreds of years—'

Mr Barraclough, too, had heard his fill of the Ledburys. It was his private opinion that the Marchioness would have done better to pay less attention to her children and more to her husband. Ledbury's *amours* were the gossip of London. But he said, 'Yes, yes, it is absurd. You should not regard it, Miss Froom. In future you must try to guard that unruly tongue of yours, Philippa. Now, do you see the house?'

Chapter Three

They had just passed through some gates. Ahead of them was a long drive that wound round a lake. Pip leaned out dangerously and shouted with excitement, 'I can see it, I can see it! Edward, it's *lovely*! It's got funny little windows—and look! Barley-sugar chimneys and a tower! Can I have a room in the tower? Please let me have a room in the tower!'

Lisette peered round. 'What a beautiful colour it is in the evening sun,' she said. 'And just look at the trees! Green and scarlet, brown, gold—they're glorious! I think we shall like living here. What do you think, Miss Froom?'

Miss Froom had not recovered her humour. She threw a glance at the house. 'I doubt very much that I shall,' she said repressively. 'I know these old houses, though I have fortunately never had to live in one before. This one looks like all the rest—dark and damp. And those windows will let in the draughts.' She stared disapprovingly at Pip's lichen-stained skirt and tumbled curls, and surveyed Lisette with a frown. 'I can also see that I have a great deal of hard work before me before I achieve the standards I expect in my pupils.'

Mr Barraclough observed the excitement in Pip's face slowly die. He looked at the shadows in Lisette's eyes and said abruptly, 'I am sorry you find the prospect of teaching my nieces so repulsive, Miss Froom. They've had—we have *all* had—a difficult time of late. You were engaged to be responsible for their education, but until their aunt and uncle arrive from the West Indies I had hoped that you would see to their happiness and welfare as well.'

'Discipline and hard work bring happiness, sir,' said Miss Froom. 'That has always been my philosophy, and children are the better for it.'

Mr Barraclough regarded her with a thoughtful frown, but said nothing as the carriage came to a halt in front of shallow steps that led to a massive oak door. He ushered the girls and their governess into a large stone hall, where Mrs Dutton, the housekeeper, was waiting to welcome them.

She took Miss Froom and the girls on a tour of inspection while Edward went into the library, but after a short while the two girls came back alone and joined him there.

'That was quick!' he said. 'Where's Miss Froom?'

'She…she said she would lie down for a little,' said Lisette. 'She has the headache.'

Pip ran to her uncle and grasped his arm. 'Edward! Edward, please, please send her away. I don't like her! She's horrid!' she said fiercely.

'What's all this? Have you been rude to Miss Froom again?' asked Edward sternly.

'She deserved it! She said I had to sleep in a horridly poky room next to her so she would know what I was up to. But I wanted the little corner room! The one in the tower. Why couldn't I have the tower room?'

Their uncle looked harrassed. 'That's not my sphere, Pip, and it's a very poor reason for this tantrum! Or for being rude again.'

'It wasn't that! It wasn't that at all! She...she's cruel!' Pip threw herself on the sofa and burst into tears. Edward swore under his breath and looked on with a frown as Lisette took the child in her arms and comforted her. What the *devil* had he done to deserve this? He had always prided himself on the ease with which he could handle any woman in practically any situation. But this one tired, lost, little girl defeated him. Confound Julia! Why the *hell* did she have to break her leg just at this particular time! And what was Henry thinking of to send the girls over without her? He looked at his nieces and his mood softened. With a sigh of resignation he sat down beside them and said, 'What was it, Lisette? Tell me the whole. Is it true that Miss Froom was so disagreeable?'

Lisette said quietly, 'I'm afraid so. Miss Froom isn't at all a kind person. When she refused to let Pip have the tower room, Pip got angry and said that Mama would have wanted her to have it. Miss Froom said…she said she didn't doubt it. That Philippa was a spoiled little girl and the sooner she learned who was now in charge of her the better.'

'Miss Froom is tired after the journey. Pip can be confoundedly trying…'

'She said more than that, Edward. She said that our mama… She said that our mama was dead and wasn't coming back. And that if Pip carried on being such a naughty little girl she wouldn't go to heaven to see her mother again.'

'She said *what*?'

'That Mama was dead. It's true, of course.' Lisette looked down at the child in her arms. 'It was cruel of her, though.'

Edward Barraclough looked grimmer than ever and said with formidable calm, 'That settles it. Your aunt and I have made a mistake. Take Pip into the morning room, Lisette, and stay there with her. One of the maids will bring a drink for you both. You needn't concern yourselves any further with Miss Froom.' He strode to the door.

'What are you going to do?'

'The carriage is still harnessed up. It can take her to Kingston tonight, and she can take the London stage tomorrow.'

'No, Edward, you can't send her off into the night like that.'

'I can and will! I'll have that woman out of the house before she says another poisonous word to anyone.'

'No, you can't do that. It's too late. She mustn't be asked to stay alone in an inn. You must let her spend the night here. Send her away tomorrow.'

Edward scowled. 'You're just like your mother— too tender-hearted for your own good, girl.'

'Please, Edward! Miss Froom may be unkind, but we ought not to be the same.'

Edward was about to refuse, but he looked at Lisette's face and his expression softened. He said reluctantly, 'Very well. She can stay the night. Now off with you. I want to speak to Miss Froom.'

Miss Froom departed the next morning with pursed lips, a month's salary and a carefully worded letter for her agency. Pip was beside herself with glee, but her uncle was not so happy.

'Stop that war dance, Pip and try to think what on earth we're to do now! We're in a mess! Who the devil will look after you now that Miss Froom has gone? I can't leave you alone here, but I shall have to go to London occasionally.'

'To see that lady?'

Edward coloured angrily. There had been an unfortunate incident in the hectic rush of the past two days when Pip had accidentally seen him with

Louise. What was worse, she had overheard a footman's comment about her. It was not the sort of thing that should happen and he had been both furious and ashamed. He said now as sternly as he could, 'I've told you to forget that lady, Pip. You're not supposed to have seen her. If I hear you mention her again, there'll be serious consequences. Understood?'

'Yes. I didn't like the look of her much anyway. So why do you have to go to London?'

'I have business in London,' he said curtly.

Lisette, the peacemaker, saw that her uncle's patience was rapidly wearing thin. She said to Pip, 'Edward looks after our money, Pip. Not just his own but all the family's. And he has talks with important people at the Foreign Office in London. He really does have to go back sometimes.'

Pip was unabashed. 'All right, Edward. You'll have to send for another governess, then. But choose a young one! A pretty one.'

Edward shook his head and said with decision, 'On no account! You're too much of a handful, midget. I'll choose someone with her mind on her work, not some pretty flibberty-gibbet whose sole aim is to set her cap at the first eligible bachelor who happens along. She'd be more nuisance than she's worth.' He sighed and went on, 'I'll write off to the agency today, but it will be at least a week before we hear anything. And then there'll be interviews... It means I shall have to postpone some important meetings, but it can't be helped.'

Lisette followed him out of the room. 'Edward, I'm sorry we're such a burden to you,' she said. 'I'm sure we could manage without a governess for a while. I can look after Pip.'

Edward's habitually sardonic expression softened into a rare smile. Much as he chafed at the restraints that had been forced on him by the care of his two nieces, he was very fond of them both. Lisette's sadness worried him. She was too young to be so serious. 'Pip needs a firm hand and a lot of attention,' he said gently. 'And I want you to have fewer things to worry about, not more.'

'Pip will always listen to someone she likes. She still misses Mama and Papa. She needs kindness as well as firmness, Edward.'

'Leave it to me, Lisette. I'll make sure I find someone who will know how to deal with her. Not another Miss Froom, I promise.'

The following Tuesday, blissfully unaware that the Barracloughs had already taken up residence, Lady Octavia Petrie said goodbye to her father and Cousin Marjorie, took up her groom, and set off for Wychford with a sense of excitement out of all proportion to the event. Apart from one stop to rest the horses, she wasted no time, and when she arrived at the gates of the house the hour was still comparatively early. She looked up the drive, which led away curving and twisting through an avenue of trees. It was very strange. She felt a tug of recognition, a stirring of adventure. The place seemed to beckon to her...

'Take the gig back to the inn in the village, Will,' she said making up her mind. 'It isn't far to the house and it's a glorious day. I'll walk the rest of the way. You can fetch me in a couple of hours.'

When the groom demurred Octavia said impatiently, 'Don't be such an old woman! I shall be perfectly safe. Mr Walters has engaged a full staff for the house, including a housekeeper. I can't believe there'll be any villains among them, can you? Off you go!'

Octavia watched Will's familiar figure disappear down the road, then walked through the gates. The weariness of spirit that had dogged her for months slowly lifted as she walked up the drive, and she was filled with a sensation of release, a feeling that she was in an enchanted world. She smiled. Perhaps she was under the spell of the Witch of Wychford! On either side were magnificent old trees, some of them with branches hanging low, their foliage touched with gold, scarlet and brown with glimpses of a deep blue sky above. Here and there a bright midday sun flashed and sparkled through the leaves, dazzling her with fairy gold. She walked on towards the house, gazing about her with delight. It was as if she had drunk a glass of champagne, or been wafted off to a land of fairy tales... She nearly jumped out of her skin as a voice from above said,

'He won't have you!'

Octavia stopped and looked up. The sun blinded her and it was a moment or two before she could make out an elfin figure perched on one of the branches. 'I beg your pardon?'

'He won't have you. You're too young and pretty.'

'How very kind of you to say so!'

'He said you'd be more trouble than you're worth.'

'Did he, indeed? How was he to know that? Though I'm not sure I fully understa—'

'He's looking for another Miss Froom, but I wish he'd have you. You look far more interesting.'

'Er...thank you again. I think.' Octavia pulled herself together and made an effort to begin a more sensible conversation. She asked, 'Forgive me, but may I ask who you are?'

'I'm Pip. Philippa Barraclough.'

'What?'

'It's rude to say ''what''. Miss Froom got very cross with me for saying it.'

'But...but what are you doing here?' stammered Octavia. 'You're not supposed—'

'You mean I should be inside? On a glorious day like this?'

'Oh, no! That's not it. No sensible person would want to be inside on a day like today. That's not what I meant—'

'I'm exploring. We've only been here a few days, and yesterday I explored the other side of the house. It's a beautiful house. Have you seen its chimneys?'

Octavia gave up trying to be sensible. She was enjoying this bizarre conversation. It all seemed to be part of the madness of the day. 'No,' she said. 'Will you show them to me?'

A little girl dropped out of the tree. Black curls tumbled over a pointed face. The child was thin, but crackled with energy and spirits. Great grey eyes, sparkling with life, gazed at Octavia, examining her with critical interest. What she saw seemed to satisfy her. 'Come on!' she said, and set off.

Octavia laughed. 'Right!' she said and followed.

Pip suddenly stopped. 'Look!'

Octavia obediently looked, then gasped with pleasure. On the other side of a small lake lay Wychford, a rose-red house nestling among lawns and trees, its windows twinkling in the sun. Its somewhat crooked timbers and a small round tower to one side gave it a lop-sided, slightly quizzical look. A friendly house, an enticing house...a magic house. And on top... 'Barley-sugar sticks!' she cried.

Pip looked immensely pleased. 'I knew you'd recognise them,' she said. 'Oh, I *do* wish Edward would have you! He's at his wits' end, you know.'

'I'm sorry to hear it. Why is that?' asked Octavia.

'Because we've lost our governess. The last one. But I wouldn't be rude to you.'

'Is that why she went? Because you were rude?'

'No. Edward dismissed her. Sent her away without a character,' said Pip with relish. 'She was unkind.

Lisette didn't like her, either, and she usually likes everyone.'

'Lisette is your sister?'

'Yes. She's much older than I am. I'm ten. Do you believe in lists?'

'What kind of lists? Laundry? Shopping? Christmas presents?'

'No! Lists of facts to learn—the kings of England, for example.'

'Definitely not!' said Octavia firmly. 'That's a very boring way to learn anything.'

'I *knew* you were all right! I must go and find Edward. He simply *must* engage you!'

'As what?'

'As our governess, of course. That's why you're here, isn't it?'

'Oh, no! I—'

But Pip had darted off like a dragonfly.

'You mustn't be annoyed with Pip.'

Startled yet again, Octavia swung round, and began to wonder if she really was in a fairy tale, and this the enchanted princess. Standing behind her was a girl with one of the loveliest faces Octavia had ever seen. She had black hair like her sister, but her eyes were a deep purple-blue, the colour of violets. Every feature was perfect: a generous brow, a beautifully straight nose, delicately modelled cheekbones, rose-petal complexion, softly curving lips... The girl looked shy, and bore an indefinable air of sadness. The impulse to comfort her was almost overwhelming. A faint flush stained the girl's cheeks as Octavia stared.

'I...I didn't mean to startle you. I'm sorry. Only I'm sure Pip didn't mean to be rude. It's just that she sometimes forgets her manners when she is in a hurry. My name is Lisette. Lisette Barraclough.'

'I'm Octavia Petrie. How do you do.'

They exchanged curtsies. 'Won't you come in?' Lisette asked. 'I'm not sure it will do any good, Edward seems determined to have someone older, and he seldom changes his mind. But I'd like you to meet him.'

Octavia was not sure what stopped her from telling Lisette the truth about her visit to Wychford. Every canon of good manners demanded it, but she held back, intrigued by the situation, and highly interested in the two girls—the one so bright and spirited, the other so lovely, and so sad. So she said nothing as they set off up the drive.

'I expect you're wondering why we need another governess,' said Lisette. 'Edward engaged someone in London—someone who was very highly recommended to my aunt by the Marchioness of Ledbury.'

Octavia had met the Ledburys. No wonder Pip didn't like Miss Froom, she thought. No one who had the approval of such a self-satisfied windbag as Lady Ledbury and her awful children could hope to please a lively spirit like Philippa Barraclough!

Lisette went on, 'But hardly two days had passed before it was clear that Pip and Miss Froom would never get on, so Edward sent her away.'

'Without a character. I heard.'

'Is that what Pip told you? I'm afraid she was just romancing. Edward gave her a perfectly good reference.'

Octavia nodded. 'I rather thought that might be the case. But what did your aunt have to say about it?'

'She's not here. She broke her leg and is still in Antigua. She won't be able to travel for some time, so there's only Edward here to look after us at the moment, and he is a very busy man. That's why we need someone else so urgently.'

'I see. In that case, wasn't it rather hasty of your uncle to send Miss Froom away?'

'Perhaps. But once Edward makes up his mind about anything he does things right off. He would have sent Miss Froom away the first night we got here, even though it was very late. He can be quite ruthless when he chooses. But I persuaded him to wait till the morning.'

Octavia began to dislike 'Edward'. 'Poor Miss Froom! To be sent away so summarily—'

'Oh, no! She really wasn't at all kind, Miss Petrie. But he did give her a month's salary and saw to it that she was taken all the way to London.'

'I suppose that helped. But do tell me. Who is ''Edward''? Mr Barraclough?'

'Yes. He's our uncle, but he told us years ago to call him Edward. We are a great burden to him. At least for the next eight or nine weeks until our aunt arrives.'

'I see.'

Lisette fell silent and Octavia was left to her own thoughts. The situation was becoming clearer. The two girls were not the Barracloughs' daughters, but their nieces, and an accident had delayed Mrs Barraclough's return to England. A governess had been engaged, but Edward Barraclough had decided to get rid of her, and was now looking urgently for someone else until his wife arrived. For about two months... Just two months...

They had reached the lawn in front of the house.

'Miss Petrie, would you care to wait here for a moment? There's a seat in the shade over there. Or shall I take you inside? Edward asked me to deliver a message to our housekeeper, and I should really do it straight away. It will only take me a minute.'

'I think I should like to stay here,' said Octavia. 'This is all so beautiful...'

'You think so, too? Miss Froom said the house looked dark and damp.'

'Did she? Then the house didn't like her,' said Octavia without thinking. 'That's why she had to go.'

Lisette gave her a puzzled look, but didn't stay to ask what she had meant. She ran across the lawn and into the house, and Octavia was left to contemplate her inheritance... It was quite extraordinary—Wychford seemed to be smiling! How could a house smile? Of course it couldn't! It was just that the window-panes were twinkling in the sunlight.

She had a sudden vision of her aunt's gipsy-black eyes staring at her, then turning to rest thoughtfully first on her father, and then on Lady Dorney, last spring. What had been in Aunt Carstairs's mind? Here at Wychford Octavia suddenly saw what an excellent thing it would be if her father and his cousin decided to marry. They had always been close, and Lady Dorney was a caring, loving woman who needed companionship and someone to look after. Yes, it would be ideal. But it would never happen. Papa was too set in his ways—it simply wouldn't occur to him to ask.

The windows were still twinkling, still reminding her of those black eyes. What a strange house it was! Octavia's thoughts returned to her father. What if Lady Dorney could be persuaded to take her place for a while—two months, say? It might occur to her papa that his Cousin Marjorie was more comfortable to be with, more patient, easier to talk to, someone nearer to his own generation...

Two months. Would it be long enough? She was sorely tempted to try. She liked these Barraclough girls, and felt she could do something for them, especially as their uncle seemed to be something of a martinet. Should she go along with their assumption that she was a prospective governess?

Octavia jumped up and took a firm hold of herself. Twinkling windows, gipsy-black eyes, marriages, pretending to be a governess—where was her common sense? It was a mad idea! Her day of freedom had gone to her head! She would go inside to meet Edward Barraclough, and would inform him of her true identity before the mistake went any further. As Lisette approached her across the lawn the sun seemed to go in and Wychford's window-panes were dull. There was an air of reproach about the house and Octavia had an absurd feeling of guilt.

Lisette led her through the oak door and into the hall. Octavia kept a firm hold on her imagination as she looked about her. The house was not huge and the hall was of manageable size, with a large refectory table down the middle and a fireplace at each end. It had a superb plaster ceiling and two massive, symmetrically placed, brass chandeliers. A handsome oak staircase led to the upper storey, with a gallery leading to the bedchambers. But Lisette led her through the hall and on into a room at the far end. This was some kind of parlour or morning room, and it was reassuringly normal. A fire burned invitingly in the hearth, and the furniture was obviously meant for comfort rather than style. Octavia was invited to sit down.

'I...er...I don't think I will yet,' said Octavia. 'Not before I see your uncle.'

The door opened and Pip burst in. 'Here she is, Edward!' she cried. 'Please say she's suitable!'

A tall, broad-shouldered man followed her into the room. Though he was younger than she had imagined, he looked...dangerous, with an uncompromising chin and a hard mouth. He was quite handsome, though his nose looked as if it might have been broken in a fight. Black hair, clear grey eyes, and a tanned complexion. A small scar lifted the outer corner of one eyebrow and gave him a faintly devilish look. His expression was not welcoming. Oh, yes! thought Octavia. If this was a fairy tale, then here was the ogre!

Mr Barraclough stopped and gazed at her for a moment, coolly assessing her. Octavia became conscious that her person was slight, and not very tall, that her dress was unimpressive, that one or two of her honey-gold curls had escaped from her bonnet and were now tumbling over her shoulders. She flushed angrily under his gaze and wished she had taken time to tidy herself. As he came towards her his stride was arrogantly athletic, his air one of impatience.

'Edward Barraclough,' he said curtly. 'May I have your name?'

'Certainly, sir. I am Octavia Petrie.'

'Well, Miss Petrie, I don't know how you heard so quickly about the post of governess here, but I'm afraid you've had a wasted journey. You're not at all what I'm looking for.'

'You are quite wrong—'

'Am I? Whatever you may have said to charm my niece, give me one good reason why I should employ a woman who arrives on my doorstep—'

'I don't wish—'

Mr Barraclough swept on. 'Arrives on my doorstep without warning, hoping to be engaged on the spot.'

Octavia forgot her embarrassment. 'I should have thought that was exactly what you required, sir,' she said tartly. 'From what your nieces say, you need someone rather urgently. Or am I mistaken?'

Mr Barraclough stopped. He looked at her again, this time speculatively. 'No, it's true that we need someone...' After a pause he said slowly, 'Perhaps I *was* wrong. Perhaps you're not the pretty featherhead you look. You sound mighty sure of yourself.'

'*Featherhead!*' Octavia took a deep breath. 'Really, sir! I assure you I am far from being a featherhead. Nor, unlike others I have met, am I a *block*-head! Permit me to tell you—'

Mr Barraclough interrupted her yet again, but to Octavia's astonishment, instead of taking offence at her words, he laughed and nodded in approval as he said, 'That tone was fierce enough... And you're quick. There might be more to you than I thought.'

Octavia replied, 'I can be much fiercer than that, I assure you, sir! Not that I wish—'

'Edward, do say she may stay! *Please*!' called Pip from her perch on the window-sill. 'She doesn't believe in lists. She wouldn't need to be fierce with us.

I'm sure I could behave well if *she* was my governess.'

'It *is* only for two months, Edward.'

Lisette's intervention seemed to give Mr Barraclough pause. He looked at Lisette sharply. 'You'd like her to stay, too? It isn't just because you're sorry for her?'

Lisette shook her head and said emphatically, 'I think she would be absolutely right for us.'

Octavia could see that Mr Barraclough was impressed by Lisette's words, and decided that it was high time she said something. 'I'm sorry, but I must tell y—'

'What are your qualifications?' he asked. 'I suppose you have some?'

Octavia was once more annoyed by his tone. He could do with a lesson or two in good manners himself, she thought. 'I think I may say that I am qualified to teach the necessary skills,' she said coldly, remembering all the expensive tutors and governesses insisted on by her mother, her sojourn at a highly exclusive Seminary for Young Ladies. 'But that's not the point—'

'I suppose I'd be satisfied as long as you can keep them safe and happy, and under control. Can you do that? You wouldn't have to teach them very much. Lisette is to come out next year, but I expect her aunt will see that she knows how to behave in Society.'

'I do know something of that, too, but—'

'This would be the very highest society, Miss Petrie. I wouldn't expect or ask you to cope with that. I don't suppose Mrs Barraclough would want you to teach Lisette the manners of some Dame's School or other. She would want better.'

While Octavia was choking at hearing a Seminary that had been patronised by the cream of the English aristocracy described as 'some Dame's School,' he went on, 'Well, I suppose we could try you. If you'll come into the library I'll give you the terms and so on. You'll find the salary generous, but the appointment is only for a short time—eight or nine weeks at the most. You do know that, do you?'

'Your niece did say something of the kind. But I didn't come—'

'Good! Then it's settled. Come through to the library.'

Am I never to be allowed to finish a sentence? Octavia asked herself. This Mr Barraclough absolutely *deserves* to be deceived! She looked at the two Barraclough girls, Pip nodding her head and almost falling off her perch with excitement, Lisette smiling for the first time since they had met, her wonderful eyes glowing with pleasure. Gipsy-black eyes hovered at the back of her mind...sparkling window-panes... To her astonishment she found herself saying, 'Very well, sir,' and meekly followed 'the ogre' into the library.

Chapter Four

At the end of her interview with Mr Barraclough
Octavia fervently hoped that Lady Dorney had been
sincere in what she had said. She wasn't sure whether
she had succumbed to the force of Mr Barraclough's
powerful personality, or to the equally powerful force
of this strange house. But to her bewilderment she
found she had agreed to come back in four days'
time, complete with suitable references, to take up
duties as a governess companion to the Barraclough
girls. The 'ogre' had proved to be more accommodating than she would have imagined—or perhaps
more desperate. After she had explained that she
would like to keep an eye on an elderly relative who
lived some distance away, she was promised two
days a month, together with the use of the gig.

However, Mr Barraclough had made it all too clear
that he was still not convinced that she could manage.
This poor opinion of her abilities so annoyed Octavia
that, as she took her leave of the Barracloughs, she

swore to herself that she would prove him wrong if it was the last thing she did!

She refused the girls' offers to accompany her down the drive, and set off in good time to be at the gate when Will Gifford came to pick her up. Having committed herself to a totally mad impersonation, she wanted to make sure it was carried through without any hitches, and Will and the gig were a potential giveaway. Most chance-met governesses did not leave in a well-cared-for gig with a groom who treated them with the deferential familiarity of an old servant!

Perhaps 'impersonation' was not the word—escapade was more like it. After all, she was not impersonating anyone else, and she had given Mr Barraclough her real name, if not her proper title. And though she had never sought employment of any kind, she was fully competent to look after two girls for two months, whatever their uncle thought. She would earn the very generous salary he had promised her…

But she still couldn't understand why on earth she had agreed to do it! The house must have bewitched her. She stopped, turned and looked at it again. Wychford was once again sparkling and smiling in the sunlight. Perhaps there was more to the stories about the house than she had realised? Perhaps Aunt Carstairs *had* been the witch she and Harry had thought her! Why *had* she left her house to Octavia? Had she seen her goddaughter's restlessness, yet understood Octavia's reluctance to marry simply to escape from Ashcombe? It was possible.

But even the Witch of Wychford couldn't have foreseen the Barracloughs and their problem. Or... could she?

As Octavia walked on down the drive she was thinking of the last time she had seen Aunt Carstairs. They had said their farewells and the footmen were waiting to assist the old lady into her carriage. But just before she got in her aunt had turned round to take Octavia's hand and say, 'Be patient, child. Rescue is at hand.' Then, as the carriage prepared to drive off, she had put her head out of the window and added with a crow of laughter, 'There's even a hero in prospect, though you'll take time to recognise him.'

Octavia was turning these words over in her mind now as she drew near the gates of Wychford. A hero? Not among the Barracloughs, that was certain! Edward Barraclough was not only already married, he was the opposite of all her ideals. Dark, abrupt, discourteous, and not much gaiety about him... Anyone less like Tom Payne would be difficult to imagine! No blond prince among the Barracloughs, then. So where? Perhaps one of the local neighbours had a son... But how could she meet him if she was an employee, a governess at Wychford? Octavia gave a sigh. Surely Aunt Carstairs could have managed better than this! But as Will Gifford drove up she laughed out loud. She was beginning to believe her own nonsense!

Octavia got back to Ashcombe in daylight and, wasting no time before setting her plans in motion, invited Lady Dorney to have tea with her in private. 'It's an age since I saw Papa so happy, ma'am,' she began as they sat down in her parlour. 'You are so good for him.'

Lady Dorney looked at her with amusement. 'I'm glad to hear that. But I believe I know you too well to think it an idle remark,' she murmured. 'Tell me, what plans are you hatching in that pretty head of yours? I don't believe you invited me here just to pay me compliments. Incidentally, you, too, look happier—excited even. What happened today?'

Octavia hesitated, then launched into an account of her adventures. When she reached the point where Edward Barraclough said that she wasn't the featherhead he had thought, Lady Dorney was so amused that she nearly dropped her cup.

'So when did you tell him that, far from being an indigent governess in search of a post, you were the daughter of the Earl of Warnham, and the owner of the house he was renting?'

'I didn't. I haven't.'

'*What?* Why on earth not?'

Octavia took a breath and said defiantly, 'I've agreed to begin as their governess in four days' time.'

'But how can you possibly manage that? Rupert would never agree! To say nothing of pretending to be something you are not! No, no! You can't do it, Octavia!'

'I could. With a little help from you, ma'am.'

'Your papa will never consent.'

'I wouldn't ask him. I would tell him that it was as he feared—Wychford needs further attention than I thought, that I need to spend some time seeing to it. It's not quite a lie, ma'am!'

'It's not the truth, either! What do you think he would feel if he learned that his daughter was working as a governess?'

'I don't suppose he ever will. At the end of two months I'll come back here and take up my old life again. But I wish I could explain to you... Those children *need* me, ma'am.'

'So does your father. How will you persuade him to do without you?'

'Ah! That's where the favour comes in.'

'Tell me!'

'Well, you did say that you'd like to stay longer this time. And if you were here Papa wouldn't miss me nearly as much. Our housekeeper is perfectly competent, and the servants are all familiar with the routine of the house...'

'If you are suggesting what I think you're suggesting, the answer is no, Octavia! I won't do it! Take charge of this house? Certainly not!'

'You needn't take charge, exactly—just *be* here. I could come back regularly to see that everything is working, though I'm sure it won't be necessary. *Please* say you will, ma'am!'

Lady Dorney said somewhat coolly, 'You realise, I hope, what I would be risking? Rupert and I have always been good friends. He would hardly believe it if he found out that I had helped you to deceive him. He would certainly be distressed. It might well mean the end of our friendship!'

'It won't! I swear it won't. I just have a feeling... Cousin Marjorie, please do this! I know I am asking a lot. I can't even explain why it is so important to me. Perhaps it's the escape I've been looking for. Please help me!'

Lady Dorney hesitated, started to speak, then stopped again. Octavia waited in silence. At last her cousin said, 'I've tried to persuade you so often to escape that I suppose I can hardly refuse to help you now. And I haven't actually made any plans for the autumn, nor for the winter either. I don't imagine I'll be missed at Lutworth...' She sighed, then sat up and said with decision, 'Very well! I'll do it! I'll stay for two months. But I think I am as mad as you!'

With Lady Dorney's help Octavia was on her way back to Wychford less than a week after her first fateful visit there. Will Gifford was once again her companion on the journey, but this time he would return to Ashcombe without her. At the back of the gig was a small valise with a selection of Octavia's simplest dresses. Her hair was severely drawn back under an unadorned bonnet, her cape was of drab grey cloth plainly cut, and her gloves and boots serviceable rather than elegant. Lady Octavia Petrie, youngest child of one of the richest families in the south of England, and heiress in her own right of a handsome estate, had been replaced with simple Miss Petrie, newly engaged governess-companion to the Misses Barraclough.

A casual observer would not have known just how nervous she was. Her outward demeanour was composed and quietly confident. But the spirit of adventure had not disappeared. Inside Octavia was an unholy mixture of anticipation, apprehension, surprise at her own daring, and exhilaration at her escape. Two months. Two months to find out what she really wanted of life.

If anything, Wychford seemed more welcoming than ever. The day was overcast, but as the gig approached a fleeting ray of sunshine was reflected in those extraordinary windows. The house was smiling its quizzical smile. Lisette was hovering on the lawn, clearly waiting for her arrival. And as Octavia stepped out of the gig, Pip climbed down from the nearest tree. They took her over, Pip leading her to the door like a small tug in charge of a clipper, Lisette giving orders to the housekeeper.

'We've given you a room near mine,' said Pip. 'Not exactly in the tower but nearby. Did you know that the old lady who used to live here was a witch? Mrs Dutton wasn't here then, she lived in the next village, but she says all the villagers here were frightened of Mrs Carstairs.'

'Really?' As they went through the oak doors Octavia once again had the strange feeling that the house was enfolding her, welcoming her. 'I think she must have been a good witch, Pip,' she said, smiling. 'Wychford is a friendly house. Don't you agree?'

As a daughter of the Earl of Warnham Octavia had been accustomed all her life to the deference due to her rank and her wealth. But it was not difficult now for her to maintain her 'disguise'. She was neither arrogant nor conceited, and she had more than her fair share of charm. Her normal, easy, matter-of-fact manner served her very well with everyone at Wychford. Everyone, that is, except the master of the household. She was still very much on trial as far as he was concerned, and more than once Octavia found herself biting back an unbecoming response when he made one of his critical remarks.

Fortunately he was frequently away on short visits to London. She learned that there had been three Barraclough brothers. John, the eldest and father of Lisette and Pip, had inherited a wealthy plantation on Antigua. Henry, the second son, also had land in the West Indies and was still over there. But Edward

Barraclough, the youngest, had had little taste for plantation life, and when he had inherited a fortune made in banking by his uncle he had travelled the world. Now he apparently intended to settle permanently in England. At the moment he was attending meetings in the Foreign Office, advising the experts there on affairs in the Americas.

There had been some sort of plan for Lisette to marry the son of one of their neighbours in Antigua. But John Barraclough had suddenly changed his mind and decided to bring both girls over to England, where Lisette would be presented to London society. They had been busy with arrangements for the trip, when tragically both parents had been killed when their carriage had gone off the road, and the girls had been left orphaned. Their guardians, John's surviving brothers, had decided to carry out John's wishes, which was why they were now in England. But, the day before they left Antigua, Mrs Barraclough had slipped and broken her leg, and the girls had had to sail without their aunt. So the present plan was that the girls should live at Wychford in the care of a governess-companion until Mrs Barraclough could join them all there.

Octavia pieced this all together from what she learned in her first week at Wychford. Not from Lisette, who tended to be somewhat reserved, but from her sister. Discretion was not a word in Pip's vocabulary. Once she had decided that Miss Petrie was a friend, she confided everything she knew of her family's affairs quite freely.

One fine autumnal afternoon, after a morning's work in the schoolroom, Octavia and Pip were walking in the woods behind the house. Lisette had stayed behind to finish a book she was reading.

'You know, Miss Petrie, I think Uncle Henry was quite glad when Aunt Julia broke her leg,' announced Pip.

Shocked, Octavia stopped short and looked at her. '*What* was that?' she asked.

'I said that I think Uncle Henry was glad Aunt Julia had broken her leg,' Pip repeated patiently.

'But that's a dreadful thing to say, Pip! How could he be?'

'It meant that he had to stay behind to look after her. Uncle Henry didn't want to come to England, you know, and Aunt Julia's broken leg meant he had to stay in Antigua a bit longer.'

'But...I'm not sure I understand. If your Uncle Henry was so reluctant to leave the West Indies, why was it necessary for him to come at all? Surely your Aunt Julia and Uncle Edward would have been enough?'

'That's what Uncle Henry wanted. But Aunt Julia wouldn't hear of it. She said Edward couldn't be trusted to do the thing properly without the rest of the family to keep an eye on him.'

'Tell me, if you call your uncle ''Edward'', why don't you call your aunt ''Julia''?'

'Oh, we couldn't! She's *much* older than he is! She looks a bit like Miss Froom.'

'Really?' Octavia was surprised. Older than he was, and looking a bit like Miss Froom? It seemed a most unlikely wife for Edward Barraclough.

Pip went on, 'She and Edward don't like each other very much. It's easy to tell when people don't. They're always *extremely* polite to each other.'

Octavia pulled herself together and decided it was more than time for a proper governess to stem these confidences. 'Philippa, you should not tell me such things. What happens between husband and wife is not for the outside world to know.'

'What do you mean?' Pip looked puzzled at first, then bent over in a fit of giggles. 'Miss Petrie! You don't think... You don't think Aunt Julia is married to *Edward*, do you?'

'Of course I do! Isn't he?'

Pip went off into another paroxysm of giggles. 'He'd rather die! He said so! Aunt Julia is Uncle *Henry*'s wife! And I once heard Edward telling Papa that he would never know why Uncle Henry had married such a sour-faced prune!'

Octavia bit her lip and managed to say severely, 'Philippa! You must not, you really *must not*, repeat things like that, especially not to me! I'm sure your uncle would be very vexed to know that you had heard his words, and even angrier to know you were repeating them! Or even talking about him at all!'

'Would he?'

'Of course he would!'

'Then I won't say any more. I like Edward. But let me tell you this one thing. He isn't married, Miss Petrie. Lisette is sorry for him. She thinks he must have a broken heart, but I think that's rubbish. Some of the prettiest ladies in Antigua made a fuss of him, but he never paid them any attention. I was glad, I didn't like any of them much. I want him to marry someone nice.' She looked confidingly up at Octavia. 'You would do very well, Miss Petrie. I'd like Edward to marry you. You'll have to set your cap at him.'

Octavia gasped. What would the child say next? Choking back another urge to burst into laughter, she said sternly, 'That's enough! You must never let me hear you use such a vulgar expression again, Philippa! Where on earth did you pick it up?'

'What's wrong with it?'

'To accuse someone of setting her cap at someone is not at all the thing. It's not only vulgar, it's unkind. You mustn't use the expression.'

'Edward used it. When we were talking about governesses. He said he didn't want some pretty flibberty-gibbet whose sole aim was to set her cap at the first eligible bachelor who happened along. I don't think he meant himself, though he's very rich, you know. Lots of people have set their—' Pip caught sight of Octavia's frown and corrected herself. 'Have tried to make him like them. Why don't you want to?'

Repressing a mad impulse to tell the child that Edward Barraclough would be the last man she would ever consider, Octavia forced herself to think as a real governess would. The child's capacity for verbatim reporting was amazing, but she would have to be taught to keep such things to herself. 'I can see that you've been left to your own devices for too long, my girl!' she said firmly. 'You need a little discipline. Oh, don't look like that! I'm not a Miss Froom. But you'll have to learn to keep gossip and the things people say when they're not thinking strictly to yourself. It's called good manners.'

Pip sighed. 'I'll try to do as you say, but it's very hard. Lisette thinks Edward needs a wife, and you would be so suitable! I'd like you for my aunt— you're much nicer than Aunt Julia.'

'Philippa! What have I just said?'

'That I mustn't gossip. But that wasn't gossip, it was just an opinion! You would be good for Edward! You're prettier than any of the ladies in Antigua. And much prettier than the lady he visits in London. Though he must like her a lot. He gives her lots of presents.'

Octavia gasped. What else would the child come out with? And what had Edward Barraclough been thinking of to let her see him with someone who, from the sound of it, was quite possibly his mistress?

'I assure you, Philippa, that even if it were possible I would not consider marrying your uncle under any circumstances whatsoever!' she said emphatically.

'And we shall now finish this conversation and return to the house, where you will spend the rest of the afternoon improving your mind! Come!'

They turned to go back. Edward Barraclough was just walking towards them. He was only a few yards away, and looking more than usually sardonic. He could not have helped overhearing what she had just said.

'Mr Barraclough!' Octavia felt her face grow scarlet as she stammered, 'We didn't see you, sir…'

'Edward!' Pip launched herself at her uncle. 'We thought you were in London! What are you doing here?'

'Looking for Lisette. I have a letter from Antigua for her, but I couldn't find her in the house. I thought she would be with you, Miss Petrie.'

With a considerable effort Octavia mastered her confusion and said politely, 'Is she not in her room, sir? We left her there reading.'

'She isn't there now. I suggest you find her as speedily as you can. How long is it since you left her to her own devices?'

Octavia coloured again, this time with anger. But she said calmly and carefully, 'About an hour, sir. I left her, in her own room, with a book she said she wished to finish. It did not seem to me to be a very hazardous occupation.'

Mr Barraclough nodded. 'And if she had stayed there we should not now be looking for her. But she didn't. Nor did she answer when I called. Where do you suppose she is, Miss Petrie? While you have been…exchanging confidences with Philippa, my other niece has been unsupervised for over an hour.'

'Don't be angry with Miss Petrie, Edward. Lisette's safe. I expect she's sitting in the sun on the top of the tower. She likes it there.'

'On top of the…' Octavia picked up her skirts and began to hurry back to the house. Mr Barraclough overtook her after just a few paces. By the time she had reached the foot of the stairs to the tower he was already coming down, followed by Lisette.

'Why are you annoyed, Edward?' she was saying in a puzzled voice. 'It is perfectly safe up there! The parapet is high and the roof is sound.'

'I called you. Why didn't you answer?'

'I didn't hear you.' Lisette had reached Octavia. 'Miss Petrie, I'm sorry! I didn't mean to give you a fright.'

'It's all right, Lisette. I was anxious for a moment or two, but I should have known you are too sensible to do anything rash. Your uncle was worried when he couldn't find you. Did you finish your book?'

'Yes. And then I sat in the sun and fell asleep. That's why I didn't hear his call. Don't be angry with me, Edward!'

'I'm not angry,' he said abruptly. 'I was worried when I couldn't find you.'

Lisette shook her head at him. 'You needn't be,' she said. 'I'm quite safe here. Why were you looking for me?'

'I have some letters from Antigua for you, including one from your Aunt Julia. If you and Pip will come down in a few minutes I'll deliver them. I'd like a word with Miss Petrie first.'

Octavia looked at Mr Barraclough's frown. 'I think you'd both be better for a tidy up,' she said with a smile at the girls. 'The tower may be safe, Lisette, but it isn't very clean. And Pip's clothes always need attention! Tidy yourselves up before you come down.'

As she followed Edward Barraclough down the stairs, through the hall, and into the library she wondered what he would say. It would not be pleasant, she was sure. He had almost certainly overheard her words to Pip, and she steeled herself to be ready to apologise for them, though she was not at all clear what she could possibly say. But his attitude towards her supervision of Lisette was unreasonable, and if he were to accuse her again of neglecting her duties she would find that difficult to accept without protest.

She was surprised therefore when he invited her to sit down. He stared at her for a moment, then walked to the window. Without turning, he said abruptly, 'I suppose you think I was too hard on you.'

'About Lisette? Well…'

'You needn't hesitate, Miss Petrie. I believe I know what you think of me. But that is of no concern at the moment. I wish to explain why we are so careful of Lisette.'

'Sir?'

He came over and sat down at his desk. 'I'm not sure how much you've heard of our family history, though I imagine Pip has told you everything she knows by now. She seems to have taken a decided fancy to you.' Mr Barraclough's tone implied that he did not share Pip's feelings. 'She isn't too much for you?'

'I don't think so, sir. She is a delightful little girl. And a highly intelligent one.'

'Hmm! You seem to have her confidence at any rate. She's brighter than Lisette, of course.'

'More lively, certainly. But Lisette is utterly charming. She will be a great success in Society.'

'And what would you know of that?' he asked derisively.

Octavia bit her lip. She had spoken without thinking. Governesses would not normally be able to judge how Society would receive their pupils. But she recovered and said quietly, 'Her beauty, her gentleness and concern for others, must endear her to anyone who meets her, here or in the greater world.'

'You've read too many novels. I hope you're not stuffing Lisette's head with such nonsense. In my experience, gentleness and concern for others are not the qualities looked for in the ladies of society. Nor are they often found—' He stopped as Octavia drew a sharp breath. 'You wished to say something? No? Then I'll continue. Lisette's beauty will be a great asset, but she has a more reliable key to success, the most important one of all. Wealth, Miss Petrie.

Money. She is a considerable heiress. That is what will make her a success in Society.'

Octavia could not let this pass. 'I would not wish to stuff *anyone*'s head with romantic nonsense, sir. But neither would I wish to give any young person as cynical a view of the world as the one you have just expressed.'

'Yes, yes, I dare say. But your experience is somewhat limited. What if I were to tell you that, young as she is, Lisette has already been rescued from an unsuitable association?'

This was a surprise. Lisette had never mentioned anything of the sort. 'I suppose I would have to believe you,' Octavia said slowly. 'This was in Antigua, I take it?'

'Of course. The son of one of the neighbours thought that marrying my niece would be an easy way to make himself rich. Ricardo Arandez has a great deal of address, and Lisette, as you may have observed, is too ready to believe what people say, too ready to like them. Her father was the same. Arandez persuaded him to consent to a betrothal. Fortunately Lisette was still very young, so, though John agreed, he insisted it should not be official before she was sixteen. By that time his eyes had been opened to Arandez's true character.' He smiled grimly. 'I made sure of it. John withdrew his consent, and Lisette was saved from what would have been a disastrous marriage. Ricardo Arandez is a scoundrel.'

'Was she in love with this man?'

'Of course not! The girl was far too young to be in love.'

Octavia thought of Tom Payne and smiled. 'Is one ever?'

Mr Barraclough surveyed her. 'This is just what I feared. Miss Froom would have taken my point immediately, but you are still trailing clouds of romantic folly. Miss Petrie, let me make myself clear. Your task is to look after Lisette, and that includes guarding her from undesirable acquaintances until her aunt is able to take over from you. It is highly unlikely that Arandez will find his way to Wychford, but if he or any other potential fortune hunter appears on the scene, I wish to be told of it immediately.'

'The risk here is surely slight, but I will certainly promise you that. However, I hope that doesn't include acting as some sort of jailer, watching her twenty-four hours a day?'

'No, no. I admit I overreacted to her disappearance this afternoon. My excuse is that I had just heard from my sister-in-law, who is somewhat too protective of our nieces, and always ready to accuse me of not looking after them well enough. I suppose I was still under the influence of her letter.' He fell silent.

Octavia waited a moment, then said, 'Is that all, sir?'

'What? Oh, yes. Ask the girls to come in, will you?'

She went to the door. As she opened it he said, 'By the way, Miss Petrie!' She stopped and turned.

'I know it is almost impossible to silence Pip, but I should prefer you not to discuss my affairs with her. However...I am relieved to know that I am safe from your attentions—whatever the circumstances!' He sat back in his chair with a smile of satisfaction as she blushed and hurried out of the room.

Chapter Five

Still grinning, Edward reached out and pulled a letter towards him. It was from his sister-in-law. Just as he would have expected, it was full of the usual mixture of pointed remarks about his life style, instructions about the girls and dire warnings. What she would say when she learned that he had got rid of Miss Froom and replaced her with a green girl he hardly liked to think. But this time at least Julia had some justification for her fears. She had heard that Ricardo Arandez had left Antigua and was on his way to Europe. She was afraid he might have ideas about meeting Lisette again...

Edward Barraclough sighed. Life at Wychford was not as awful as he had feared. In fact it was occasionally quite pleasant. But, much as he loved his nieces, he wished to heaven he had not been called upon to fill the gap left by Julia's accident. Playing nursemaid to two vulnerable girls was no occupation for a grown man. There seemed to be no end to the problems, and meanwhile his personal life was suf-

fering a marked decline. Louise was not a woman to
tolerate neglect for long, and his most recent visit had
been something of a failure. He had found her bor-
ingly possessive. What concern was it of hers how
he spent his time away from her? He hadn't told her
how, of course, but she would never have believed
him if he had! That he was living in the depths of
the country with two young girls and a dowdily
dressed young woman! She would have found the
very idea ridiculous. And so did he! But that didn't
give his mistress—his *mistress*, for God's sake!—the
right to know where he went and what he did when
he wasn't with her! She was lovely enough, but her
voice could get unpleasantly shrill. He was starting
to lose patience with the old doddards at the Foreign
Office, too, and beginning to think he was wasting
his time on them. When would they learn to leave
eighteenth-century politics behind, and step into the
nineteenth century?

There was one bright spot in all this. Though he
didn't particularly want to admit it, Miss Petrie
seemed to be a success, for all her youth and pretti-
ness. Edward smiled again as he thought of her confusion when he had teased her a few minutes ago
about her remark to Pip. Her cheeks had been bright
red. Serve her right! No man liked to hear himself
spoken of with such scorn, even by a dab of a governess!

No, that was wrong. She might be small, but she
wasn't a dab of anything. An intriguing young

woman, Miss Petrie. The girls really liked her, and the servants all treated her with genuine respect. What was her background? She had brought a letter with her, but after a quick glance through he had put it away without bothering to study it more closely. He unlocked a drawer, took out a folder and opened it. The letter of reference was on top, and he picked it up and read it. It was from a Lady Dorney of Lutworth Court, who seemed to be a woman of intelligence and education. Edward remembered meeting Gerard Dorney a few years before. This was clearly his mother. Lady Dorney's letter recommended Octavia Petrie without reservation, praising her patience, her efficiency, her trustworthiness, her high standard of education... All the virtues. It made the girl sound so worthy! A Miss Froom without the sourness. So very dull.

And yet he had the distinct impression that Miss Petrie was far from dull. He was not quite sure why. She dressed quietly enough, with no attempt to attract. If he had not seen those honey-gold curls that had tumbled about her shoulders at their first meeting he would never have known they existed. Miss Petrie wore her hair in a firmly disciplined knot, or even under a cap. She was not particularly tall, and her figure, from what he had seen of it, was slight. Apart from her forget-me-not blue eyes, he would not have said there was anything interesting or attractive about her to a man whose taste ran to women like Louise Kerrall. For a moment he tried to think of Louise as he had last seen her, petulant but still seductively lovely...but the image of Miss Petrie kept getting in the way.

Miss Petrie wasn't dull. She was quick-witted and amusing. And there was something about that small figure: the imperious turn of the head, the straight back, the slender neck. Her carriage was graceful, her manner unassuming, but Miss Petrie was neither humble nor respectful, not underneath. Like Pip, she had a mind of her own, and though she was more skilled at disguising it, she was no more prepared than Pip to give way without argument.

Edward Barraclough was intrigued. Perhaps he should spend more of the time he was forced to spend at Wychford in getting to know his nieces' governess! He told himself with a grin that he would be perfectly safe. No risk of being caught. He had heard it from the lady's own mouth—Miss Petrie wouldn't consider him as material for a husband, not under any circumstances! What was more, she had sounded as if she meant it. For a moment Edward Barraclough was tempted to prove her wrong, but he rejected it instantly. It might well be an interesting exercise, but one did not seduce governesses—not if one were a gentleman.

As a result of these musings Mr Barraclough began to pay more attention to his nieces' progress at Wychford. He found Miss Petrie's methods of instruction unconventional—certainly by Miss Froom's standards. But to his surprise they were in fact quickly making up for lost ground. It was true that laughter was quite frequently heard coming from the room set aside for their morning lessons, but, when he stopped to listen, it always subsided after a moment and was followed by a period of eager discussion, then silence, or questions and answers. Sometimes Miss Petrie read aloud to them. Her voice was beautiful—warm, low in pitch and slightly husky.

When the weather was suitable the governess took her charges into the grounds in the afternoons, and Edward made an effort to join them occasionally. He discovered that lessons were not confined to the mornings in the schoolroom. The girls might not realise it, but they were learning a great deal more while they enjoyed themselves outdoors. Artists, music, scenes from history, a comparison of the plants to be found in the West Indies with those they found in the grounds of Wychford—these and many other topics were taken up to be discussed, dropped if they proved dull, or pursued the next day if they were interesting. At first Miss Petrie seemed inhibited by his presence, but as she grew more used to him he discovered that she used him quite ruthlessly to expand the scope of their discussions, and he was closely questioned by all three about his travels.

Each girl had a notebook for records. Lisette was their botanical recorder. Her exquisite line drawings of leaves, trees and late-blooming flowers were carefully dated and kept in a large folder. Some of them had been turned into delicate watercolours. Pip was more interested in animals and buildings. Her book was filled with bizarre sketches of birds, mice, insects, windows, gable corners, gargoyles and, of course, chimney pots. But the measurements and notes underneath were neatly kept, and checked by Miss Petrie.

And always, at some point in the walk, there would be a game, or some form of more energetic exercise. Pip needed no encouragement, but even Lisette was persuaded to run or skip.

Attracted by the sound of laughter and shouts, Edward came out one afternoon to find them behind the house, enjoying a particularly energetic ball game. All three, including Miss Petrie, were chasing about the lawn. Lisette was doing her best to dodge her governess and throw the ball to Pip. It was a lively, noisy scene, but when Miss Petrie saw him approaching, she left the girls to carry on by themselves and made frantic attempts to tidy herself up. She was still in the middle of twisting her hair into its usual knot when he joined her. Her cheeks were flushed and she was breathing quite fast. She looked about the same age as Lisette. He was amused at the air of challenge about her as she said,

'Good afternoon, sir. You've surprised us.'

He nodded a greeting. 'Miss Petrie. Allow me to congratulate you on your turn of speed. I doubt Miss Froom could have dodged about as nimbly.'

'I suppose you disapprove, Mr Barraclough?'

'Of what?'

'Of our unladylike behaviour.'

Edward looked at his two nieces and shook his head. 'I haven't seen them as happy as this since they came to England, especially not Lisette. No, I don't disapprove.' He laughed at her expression. 'Do I appear to you to be such an ogre, Miss Petrie?'

'Og...ogre! N...no, sir! Of... of course not!' she stammered. 'Excuse me, I must call the girls in. They must change before they get cold. Lisette! Pip!' She gave him a curiously embarrassed little nod and walked away to where Lisette and Pip were playing. He was impressed to see how they ran to her, took her by the arms, one on each side, and towed her in towards him. They greeted him with their usual affection, but when Miss Petrie ordered them into the house they obeyed her.

'You've done well, Miss Petrie,' he said as they followed the girls at a more sedate pace. 'I think I made the right choice of governess after all.'

'Choice, sir?' she said with a sceptical look. 'It was my impression that you thought me a last resort!'

'I thought you far too pretty. Tell me, why do you screw your hair into that hideous knot? Your honey-gold curls are far more becoming.'

Mr Barraclough had spoken without thought. The minute the words had left his mouth he regretted them. The girl was bound to be embarrassed by such a personal remark from her employer. But Miss Petrie did not flush in embarrassment or lose her composure. Her eyes were suddenly no longer forget-me-not, but ice-blue, and she froze him with the sort of look he would have expected to receive from a duchess in a London drawing room. 'Not, however, to a governess,' she said coldly. 'Excuse me.' She increased her pace towards the house.

He caught her up at the door. 'Forgive me,' he said. 'That was an unpardonable piece of impertinence. Please accept my apology.'

She hesitated, still with that film of ice around her, 'Very well, sir. But if you will excuse me I must see to your nieces.' She gave him a slight curtsy and started for the stairs.

Edward went to his library and flung himself into a chair. What a fool he was! Why the devil had he made such a stupid remark? Though…it wasn't as stupid as all that, said a small voice inside. Miss Petrie did look prettier with her hair loose. He dismissed the thought as irrelevant. Miss Petrie was a governess. A *governess*. One did not make such remarks to a governess. One reserved that sort of compliment for a flirtation with one of Society's beauties, or for one's mistress perhaps.

Confound it, why was he in such a state about it? He had apologised, hadn't he? The girl was not even the type he admired! Things had come to a pretty pass when a dab of a governess could make him feel presumptuous for passing a perfectly harmless comment about her hair. Who the devil did she think she was?

Edward got up and strode out of the room, shouting for his groom. He was in a thoroughly bad mood. Perhaps a good gallop through the fields would improve his temper.

From her window Octavia watched Mr Barraclough ride off. He looked displeased. She sighed. It was not surprising he was angry. Her response to his remark about her hair had been the conditioned reaction of Lady Octavia, daughter of the fourth Earl, not one to be expected of Miss Petrie, the governess. Miss Petrie might be embarrassed, but she would take more care not to offend, especially as her master acknowledged his fault almost immediately, and apologised. The truth was that she had been confused, surprised by her pleasure at what he had said. She had received many a compliment in her time and very few had affected her in the slightest. Why had Edward Barraclough's remark pleased her so? He was not at all the type she admired. His remark had not been particularly polished. Why had she been pleased? She had no idea. No idea at all! She turned away from the window and walked about the room impatiently.

She must take care. This situation was exactly what Edward Barraclough had feared when he had been reluctant to engage her. Too young and too pretty—that had been his objection to her. A featherhead! Well, she had proved she was no featherhead, but he probably now regretted having relaxed his guard, having complimented her on her work with his nieces. Octavia gave an impatient sigh. It had taken a lot to overcome this prejudice of his, and now it looked as if her efforts had been wasted. They would be back on their old footing when they next met.

She came back and sat down by the window. The past weeks had been so enjoyable. The Barraclough girls were everything she had thought, responsive, affectionate, and each in her own way imaginative. She loved teaching them. And recently she had seen a different side to Edward Barraclough. He no longer quite seemed the ogre she had thought him. Since he had taken to joining them on their afternoon walk he had seemed to be more human, with an unexpectedly strong sense of humour, often with a fine sense of irony behind it. Somewhat to her surprise she had enjoyed his company. Yes, Edward Barraclough was definitely more interesting than she had first thought him.

Had she shown him this too freely? Had he begun to think he might find a little extra amusement here to lighten the time he was forced to spend at Wychford until his sister-in-law could relieve him?

A gentle flirtation with the governess? Octavia stopped short and stood in the middle of the room. The thought was highly unwelcome. If that was the case, the sooner Mr Edward Barraclough was shown how wrong he was the better! A break was called for. She would speak to him the next day, and claim the free time he had promised her. And when she got back she would make sure she had her behaviour under better control.

Her suspicions increased when Mr Barraclough sent a request that she and Lisette would join him at dinner that night. Till now, if he was at home in the evening at Wychford, he had always dined by himself. Why had he decided on a change tonight? She was inclined to make some excuse, but Lisette begged her to give her her support.

'You *must* come, Miss Petrie! I wouldn't know what to say or do without you there to help me!'

'That is nonsense, Lisette, and you know it. We dine every night, you and Pip and I, and your manners are always perfect.'

'I'm sure to forget them if you're not there. I love Edward, but he's sometimes so intimidating, especially when he talks about politics and things. And this is the first time I've dined downstairs. I shall be so nervous I shan't be able to say a thing. No, you must come. Please don't send your excuses!'

So Octavia gave in, helped Lisette choose a dress, then went to her own room to see what she could find for herself. There wasn't a great deal of choice. Acceptably plain day dresses for Wychford had been comparatively easy to find, and the addition of a pretty shawl or scarf was enough to make them suitable for the evening meal with the girls. But most of her more formal dresses were either too frivolous, or too obviously rich. Not one was really the sort of thing a governess would wear. In the end she had brought a gown in dark grey mousseline, which she had worn during the period of mourning for her mother. It was cut comparatively high in the bodice with sleeves down to the elbow, and its train was small enough to escape notice. This she put on, together with a wide lace collar that had belonged to her mother. She had dressed her hair in its usual knot, and added a small cap of the same lace. Octavia would not admit even to herself what a temptation it had been to allow some of those famous curls to escape.

When the time was right she collected Lisette, and they went down the stairs together. Edward Barraclough was standing at the foot. For a moment he watched them without smiling. Octavia's first thought was how distinguished he looked in evening clothes. Her second was that however well the trappings of civilised society suited him, they could not disguise what he was. There could not be a greater contrast between the memory of her light-hearted, fair-haired, blue-eyed first love and this dark, powerful, successful man with his scarred eyebrow, and more than a touch of ruthlessness about him.

The top of the stairs was dimly lit, and Edward at first did not see Miss Petrie. She was standing half-hidden behind Lisette, wearing a dark dress that made her practically invisible. Then she moved and he saw the touch of white at her throat. Her hands came up to straighten the girl's shoulders, and give them an encouraging pat, then they started down the stairs together. Lisette was dressed in white, her dark blue eyes glowing like stars, her cheeks faintly flushed with excitement. Edward was filled with pride and pleasure. Apart from her amazing beauty Lisette looked like any normal, slightly nervous, sixteen-year-old girl. The air of sadness that had surrounded her ever since her parents' accident had almost gone.

His attention turned to Miss Petrie. She was wearing a grey dress with a white lace collar. Her hair was drawn back severely under a small cap. The effect was one of quaker-like modesty, but in spite of that she had such an indefinable air of distinction that anything less like a little dab of a governess could hardly be imagined. What *was* it about her?

Edward pulled himself together. The invitation to this dinner was for Lisette's benefit. He wanted to see how his niece's social education was faring under Miss Petrie before his exacting sister-in-law appeared. Julia would complain bitterly if Lisette's manners had fallen off. Besides, after this afternoon's contretemps, he was curious to see how Miss Petrie herself behaved in more formal situations.

'Lisette, that dress becomes you very well.'

'Miss Petrie chose it for me, Edward. And she helped me to choose what to put with it. I'm glad you like it.'

Edward turned to Miss Petrie. 'Shall we go in to dinner?' he said coolly.

It was not long before Edward realised that Lisette's manners could not be faulted. Moreover, he suspected that Miss Petrie's standards were every bit as high as those of his rigorous sister-in-law, if not higher. He could hardly believe that the two elegant creatures gracing his dinner table were the same two females who had been racing about the lawn that afternoon! At first Lisette was nervous in this new and formal situation and said little. But Edward noticed how Miss Petrie gradually drew her into the conversation, speaking of things the girl knew about, asking her about life on Antigua. After a while Lisette had regained her confidence and was talking quite naturally.

Edward turned his attention to the governess. She puzzled him more with every meeting. He was not surprised at her efforts to show Lisette in a good light, but the manner in which she had done it, the confident ease, her poise, were impressive. And though she was dressed modestly, a closer look had told him that the lace she was wearing had cost someone a pretty penny. What *was* her background? Lady Dorney's letter had been enthusiastic, but apart from the mention of care for an elderly relative it had not gone into any detail about Miss Petrie's family. It was time he tried to find out. Lisette was talking of the afternoon's game.

'You looked as if you were all enjoying it immensely. Who taught you, Lisette?'

'Miss Petrie. She knows a lot of games. She used to play them with her brothers and sisters.'

'Do you come from a large family, then, Miss Petrie?'

'Quite large, sir. But I was the youngest.'

'The eighth, perhaps? Since your given name is Octavia.'

'There were originally eight of us, yes. One of my brothers was killed at Waterloo.'

'Along with a great many others. That was a hard-won victory, indeed. What regiment was he in?'

'The Fifty-Second.'

'A crack regiment! You must be proud of him. Is yours an Army family, then?'

'I wouldn't say so. Stephen was the first of my brothers to join the Army,' she said briefly. But before he could ask any more she went on, 'From what you have told us, you were in India during the Waterloo campaign?'

'Yes, I spent some time in Madras.'

'That must have been an interesting experience. Is life there as hard as they tell us?'

With the unwitting aid of Lisette, who asked quite a lot of questions, Miss Petrie led the discussion away from herself and towards his account of life in India. He suspected this was not by chance, but if it had been deliberate the change of subject had been deftly done. However, he did not allow her to put him off for long. As soon as there was a break in the conversation he said, 'Tell me, Miss Petrie, how did you come to know Lady Dorney?'

There was a slight pause, then she replied, 'She is acquainted with someone for whom I have worked.'

'As a governess.'

'No, I believe I told you—I was looking after an elderly gentleman.

'And why did you decide to leave him?'

'I haven't left him altogether, Mr Barraclough. We both needed a change for a short while—that's why this position suits me so well. At the moment he has someone else to see to him.'

'I see. And Lady Dorney is a friend of his, perhaps?'

He saw how she shifted restlessly under his questions. 'She is a…a distant relative,' she replied after a pause.

'Is she a friend of yours, too?'

'I would like to think so. She…she is somewhat older than I am, and has lived a different sort of life.'

'How different?'

Miss Petrie gave him a straight look. 'Lady Dorney is a wealthy widow,' she said abruptly. 'And very well respected. She was the first person I thought of when you asked for a reference. Is it not satisfactory, Mr Barraclough? I could find others.'

'That will not be necessary. The letter is very complimentary. And I've heard of the Dorneys.'

'Good!'

There it was again, the touch of tartness, the hint of challenge! Most servants would be stammering with relief. But not Miss Petrie!

She went on, 'In fact, Mr Barraclough, I'd like you to release me for a day or two in the near future, in order to visit Ashcombe. I think we agreed that I could visit my family occasionally, and I haven't yet been back at all.'

Edward wished, he was not quite sure why, that he could think of a good reason to refuse, but there was none. 'Of course!' he said. 'I shall be in London tomorrow, but I think I can arrange to be here for a few days after that. Will the weekend suit you?'

'Miss Petrie! Why do you have to go? Pip and I will miss you!' cried Lisette.

'It won't be for long,' her governess said with a smile. 'Forty-eight hours at the most. The weekend will do very well, Mr Barraclough.'

'But—'

'Don't try to put Miss Petrie off, Lisette. She may have more than an elderly relative to see. A beau, perhaps?'

'Have you, Miss Petrie?'

'Governesses don't have beaux, Lisette. Those are for beautiful young ladies who are to make their début next spring.' This was said with an affectionate smile at Lisette. The smile faded as she turned to Edward. 'I hope Mrs Barraclough's injury will not prevent her from travelling to England for much longer. Is there any further news?'

Edward decided to concede victory for the moment. He would postpone further delving into Miss Petrie's background to another occasion. He said calmly, 'From what I've heard, matters are proceeding normally. My sister-in-law is reasonably strong, and very determined. She will come as soon as she can, I'm sure. Are you so anxious to be free of us, Miss Petrie?'

'Not at all, sir,' she replied politely. 'I have agreed to stay for two months, and I shall. After that—'

'We shall have to see.'

'As you say, we shall have to see. And now I think it is time for us to leave you to your cigars and port, sir. Lisette?'

'Are you not going to gossip in the drawing room till I join you?' he asked with a mocking smile.

'I think not.'

He found her quietly decisive air a challenge and asked, 'What if I insist?'

'Then we would have to agree, of course. But you wouldn't be so unreasonable! I'm sure you are pleased with Lisette's conduct tonight, but she isn't used to such late hours.'

Edward looked at Lisette and saw that she was having difficulty in keeping her eyes open. He laughed. 'You're right! And you're right about something else. I *am* pleased with Lisette. I congratulate you on your management of her, Miss Petrie. Miss Froom herself couldn't have done better. Goodnight.'

Lisette went to her uncle and put her arms round him. 'Goodnight, Edward,' she said sleepily. 'And thank you for a lovely evening.' She went towards the door. Her governess made to follow her.

'Miss Petrie!'

'Sir?'

'You must tell me more about your brother some time. Or shall I volunteer to take you to Ashcombe?'

Her eyes widened briefly, then she said composedly, 'That won't be necessary, Mr Barraclough. You've already promised me the use of your gig, and I can easily drive myself. I wouldn't dream of taking up your time. Goodnight. Thank you for a pleasant evening.'

He walked to the door with her to see her out. The top of her head barely reached his shoulder. But there was no shortage of spirit and pride in her carriage as she went gracefully up the stairs, the train of her dress trailing behind. A very unusual governess, Miss Petrie!

Chapter Six

Octavia had a hard time with her younger charge the next day. Pip was furious that she had not been included in Edward's invitation to dinner, and none of Octavia's attempts at consolation had any effect on her. When Lisette added to her sister's grievances by telling her that they were about to lose Octavia's company for two whole days, she took the news very badly indeed. She was rude during morning lessons, refused to eat her meal at midday, and later wandered out into the grounds in the afternoon before the others were ready.

Octavia decided not to pursue her immediately. Pip was basically sensible. She wouldn't come to much harm in the short time before they joined her, and a brief period in her own company might help to cure her of her megrims. So it was a few minutes before Octavia and Lisette set off round the lake to the woods at the other side. The leaves were turning fast, and their colours were more brilliant than ever. Lisette was enchanted and she and Octavia spent longer than they had intended gathering specimens to press in her notebook.

The afternoon had been fine when they left the house, but now clouds were gathering and the air was noticeably chillier. Their light jackets and thin muslin dresses were hardly enough to keep them warm, and after a while Octavia decided that Pip had been given long enough to recover her temper. It was time to seek her out and go back inside.

They knew better than to look for her along the paths or in the bushes. Pip would always choose to go upwards into a tree. But after a few minutes' scrutiny of all Pip's favourite trees, and increasingly loud appeals to her, it became clear that the child was deliberately hiding herself. Octavia was getting both angry and anxious. Large spots of rain were beginning to fall, and Lisette was shivering. She took off her own jacket, and, ignoring the girl's protests, put it round her shoulders. Then they went on, searching further and further away from the house. Eventually they caught a glimpse of bright red high up in one of the trees that overhung the far side of the lake.

Octavia was furious. The trees on the edge of the lake had been declared out of bounds, as were any but the lower branches of all the other trees. Pip had broken two of Octavia's cardinal rules. But this was no time to vent her anger. The rain was falling faster, and all three of them were getting very wet. Pip must not be made nervous or upset. The descent from the tree would be difficult enough in these conditions.

She kept her voice as calm and as matter-of-fact as she could manage.

'Good!' she called. 'I wondered where you had got to. Are you feeling better? Ready to come down? You must be getting very wet up there. I think it's time we all went in.'

'Aren't you cross with me for climbing this tree?' demanded Pip. 'I was sure you would be.'

'Then why did you do it?'

'I wanted to make you sorry! And I'm not coming down till you say you won't go away!' said Pip defiantly, adding, 'Miss Froom wouldn't have left us alone for two days, and I don't think you should.'

'Making me cross with you won't help matters. I might be tempted to stay away longer!' said Octavia.

'Besides, you won't be alone,' pleaded Lisette. 'Edward will be here. You like his company, don't you, Pip?'

'Edward doesn't like mine! He invites other people to dinner, but not me.'

'Edward *loves* your company! Look how much time he spends here at Wychford, even though he's such a busy man.'

Pip shook her head obstinately. 'No, he doesn't! He didn't want to bring us to Wychford at all.'

Putting more authority into her voice, Octavia said, 'Philippa, I'm too wet to be cross, and poor Lisette is cold. I'm getting a crick in my neck looking up at you. Let's talk about all this on *terra firma*.'

'I don't know where that is!'

'Yes, you do! It's the ground. Come down, Pip. We'll go back to the house and have toasted muffins in front of the fire. That's better than a boring dinner.'

Pip loved muffins. She hesitated, then got up and began to move along the branch. Her foot slipped on the wet surface, and Octavia, standing helplessly below, caught her breath. But Pip had hold of a nearby branch and had managed to steady herself again. Still clutching the branch she looked down. 'I...I can't!' she said uncertainly.

'Of course you can, Pip! You climbed up, didn't you? You can climb down again.'

Pip edged along a few more inches, then, just as she reached the trunk of the tree, she slipped again. For a heart-stopping moment it looked as if this time she really would fall. But she saved herself once again, and with what looked like a huge effort twisted round and sat down against the trunk. Her voice rose as she wailed, 'Miss Petrie! I...I can't! It's too slippy. I can't!'

Octavia's heart sank—this was what she had feared. Pip's fit of royal temper had taken her high up into the tree. But now she could see the dangers. She didn't lack courage and under normal conditions would have tackled the climb down with only the slightest of hesitations. Now, however, she was cold and wet, and probably hungry too. She was quite literally stiff with fright.

'Miss Petrie!' came a scared little voice from above. 'Miss Petrie, what am I to do? I'm afraid!'

Octavia turned to Lisette. 'Run to the house! Get help. I'll stay here. Quickly!'

Lisette threw a frightened glance up at her sister. 'Oughtn't I to stay?'

Octavia said forcefully, 'You can run more quickly than I can. *Go!*' To her relief Lisette obeyed the command, and ran off without more protest.

Octavia had already made up her own mind what she had to do. Lisette had to make her way all round the lake to get back to the house, and meanwhile Pip would only get colder and stiffer. If she was left by herself for too long she might even make another effort to climb down, and that could be disastrous. A quick examination of the tree showed Octavia that she had climbed many more difficult ones in her youth. Though she might be small, she was nimble. Her long skirts would get in the way, however... She took off her stockings and used them as a kind of sash to hitch her dress up above her knee. As she put her shoes on again, she called, 'Stay where you are, Pip! I'm coming up to join you!' Then she braced herself and set off up the tree. The rain ran down her face and into her eyes, but she ignored it, concentrating on finding her way through to the frightened child above her. It was an enormous relief when she found herself near enough and secure enough to take Pip into her arms and settle with her against the trunk. They were both cold and wet, but there they would have to wait for help. Getting Pip down by herself was completely beyond her.

Edward had returned unexpectedly early from London and was busy taking off his wet hat and cloak in the hall when Lisette dashed in. He took one look at her distraught face and her soaking dress and jacket and exclaimed, 'What's happened? Is it Pip? Where is she?'

Lisette began to sob out a somewhat incoherent story, but, the instant she managed to describe where Pip and her governess were, Edward turned to his groom and ordered him down to the lake. Then, stopping only to give orders to the housekeeper and deliver Lisette into her hands, he followed.

At first he thought Lisette had got the directions wrong. Except for Jem, there was no sign of anyone under the tree she had described. But then he heard a cry. Looking up, he saw what looked like a sodden bundle of clothing tucked into a hollow between the trunk of the tree and one of its main branches. It was Miss Petrie. In her arms he could just make out a red jacket and a tangle of black curls.

'Fetch a ladder,' he rapped out to the groom. 'And some men. And blankets, too!'

Before the groom had gone ten paces, Edward had taken off his coat and was scaling the tree. The rain was still streaming down, and the holds were treacherous. Even as he climbed he was wondering how the devil Miss Petrie had managed to get herself up there.

As he got near them he heard her say, 'Here's Edward, Pip! Isn't that nice?' Her calm voice held nothing but pleasure, but her face revealed the strain she was under as she held herself back into the curve of the tree, the child hugged tightly to her. The effort needed to balance them both must be enormous. They were soaked to the skin and Pip was shivering, her head buried against Miss Petrie's neck, with her hands clutching Miss Petrie's shoulders as if she would never let go. Pip was in such a state of panic that getting her to the ground could be something of a problem. His first job must be to reassure the child.

He paused, smiled up at them both, and said cheerfully, 'May I join you? Or shall I escort you down?' Then he swung himself up beside them.

Pip's face was hidden, and her hands only tightened their clasp. Miss Petrie said, 'I think you ought to make your peace with Pip first, Mr Barraclough.'

'What for?'

'You left her out of your dinner invitation last night.'

'Now, isn't that odd? I didn't think she'd mind it a bit! I thought she would much prefer a muffin tea in front of the fire this afternoon. That's why I've come home early. I was a little put out, I can tell you, when I couldn't find any of you about!'

Pip raised her head and said in a small voice, 'Did you, Edward? You came home early? Just for that? I'd like some muffins.'

'Well, you'd better come down, then, midget! Mrs Dutton won't like to be kept waiting. Hand her over, Miss Petrie, and we'll have her down in two shakes of a monkey's tail. That's right.' Edward's deep, re-assuring voice had its effect. Pip allowed herself to be transferred, and Edward gave Miss Petrie a sympathetic smile. 'You'll have to wait here, I'm afraid,' he said, as he moved along the branch. 'But I'll soon be back for you. Look, Pip! There's a ladder waiting, and it's only a little way down to it. Come on.'

Edward half-carried, half-guided Pip down to the ladder, which had been brought by Jem and one of the gardeners. He saw her to the ground and handed her over to his groom. 'Let Jem take you now, midget!' he said, giving her a hug as he wrapped her in one of the blankets. 'He'll take you to the house to get warm. Lisette is there. I have to rescue Miss Petrie.'

Jem set off and Edward turned his attention to the tree again. He had one foot on the bottom rung of the ladder before he saw that Miss Petrie was making her own way down!

'Don't be such a damned fool!' he exclaimed. 'Wait!' He climbed up the ladder and was just in time to see her slip on the last major branch before reaching the top rung. For a heart-stopping moment she hung above him, desperately clutching the branch over her head. He caught her just as her arms began to loosen their hold. With a grunt he hauled her against him and held her fast.

'I thought I told you to wait,' he growled.

'I th...thought your p...priority would be to see P...Pip safely indoors, Mr B...Barraclough, and as I was cold I didn't wish to wait for you to come back.' He could see the effort she was making to stop her teeth from chattering as she went on, 'I can't understand it. I would normally be p...perfectly capable of climbing d...down a tree like this by myself.'

'You're a fool! At the moment you're in no state for gymnastics—you're wet, stiff and cold. We must get you in as soon as possible. I don't want a bedridden governess on my hands. Come on!' He moved towards the top step of the ladder.

Miss Petrie looked down, swallowed, then shook her head. 'You'll have to give me a little t...time,' she said. 'I...I don't think I can at the moment. My arms and legs seem to have turned to j...jelly... It's absurd!'

He looked at her more carefully. Her face was pale and as wet as the rest of her. Her hair, loosened by Pip's clutching hands, was hanging down her back in a tangle of curls. She had a streak of dirt down one cheek and the neck of her gown had been pulled almost off her shoulder by Pip's frantic clasp. It didn't matter. The dress had been rendered practically transparent by the rain, anyway. He noted, without really thinking about it, that she had beautifully slen-

der ankles and a well-shaped leg... And then realised
with a shock that she had her dress pulled up to her
knees, and her legs were bare! Firmly telling himself
that this was no time to be distracted, he cleared his
throat and said, 'If I go first down the ladder, can
you follow me immediately after? I can quite easily
stop you falling if we stay close and go down together. It shouldn't be difficult. The sooner you're
indoors and in dry—' he cleared his throat again
'—in dry clothes, the better. Can you follow me, do
you think?'

She eyed the ground uneasily but nodded.

'Good!' he said.

He climbed down several rungs, then waited until
she was on the top steps in front of him, and they
slowly descended together. Edward's arms were either side of her hips, his face just above her waist.
She may be tiny, he thought, but she was beautifully
formed... An enticingly perfect bosom seen just a
moment before, a tiny waist immediately below his
eyes, the rounded contour of her hips between his
arms, those ankles... He hoped that Miss Petrie felt
safe, but if she had been able to read his mind at that
moment she would be seriously worried, and not
about negotiating her way to the ground! The sway
of those hips, the shift of her waist as first one foot
then the other came down the ladder, the brush of
her body against his, were having a surprisingly powerful effect on him! He fixed his mind firmly on the
job in hand, and managed to reach ground level with-

out doing anything he might later regret, such as letting the ladder go and putting his arms round the tempting curves in front of him!

He helped Miss Petrie off the last rung, where she stood in a daze, completely unconscious of the state of her clothing. When he turned round Seth, the gardener, was holding out a blanket, and grinning broadly as he eyed her.

Edward snatched the blanket from him and said sharply, 'Stop standing there like an ape, and take the ladder back to the shed! Off with you!' He turned back to Miss Petrie. 'You'd better put this round you. And pull your skirts down!' His tone was curt and she looked at him blankly, obviously not understanding his sudden anger. With an exclamation of impatience he pulled her towards him, undid her rag of a sash to release her skirts, then wrapped her in the blanket himself. She looked so lost and tired, that, before he could stop himself, his arms tightened and he kissed her.

For a moment she stood like a child accepting, even welcoming, his lips on hers. The feeling of her soft, responsive mouth under his was magical. Edward's lips moved, and the kiss deepened and changed in character. The blanket dropped as he shifted and held her more closely, more intimately, his body hard against her... She shivered, then clung to him, perhaps seeking his life-giving warmth.

'Octavia!' he said unevenly, and kissed her again.

The sound of his voice brought her out of her trance. She came to life immediately, pulling her arms free and pushing him away. 'No!' she cried, a mixture of shock and shame in her voice. 'No, you mustn't! I'm sorry if I seemed to be asking you to... Oh, what must you think of me? But I wasn't. I assure you. No!' She looked round frantically for the blanket, picked it up and pulled it round her again. 'You must believe me, Mr Barraclough!' she stammered. 'I'm not like that... Not at all...'

Edward was almost as shocked as she was. It was a long time since he had allowed his feelings to take over to such an extent. Whatever the temptation, he usually remained in complete control of what he was doing. He must put things right immediately. 'Miss Petrie, I didn't mean to...to... I'm the one who is sorry!' he stammered with a lack of self-possession that would have astounded his friends. 'I...I didn't think...and then I seemed to lose my head.... I apologise. Please believe me, it won't happen again, I assure you! Never!'

She gazed at him doubtfully, but what she saw in his face seemed to reassure her. After a moment she looked away and nodded. He went on, still feeling somewhat awkward, 'May I suggest we get back to the house as quickly as we can? You'll be ill if you don't change out of those wet garments soon. Do you...do you need my arm? Or shall I carry you?' He was shocked again as the thought of carrying her, of having her in his arms again, suddenly quickened his pulse. This was absurd! What was happening to him? He was behaving like a raw boy! It was almost a relief when she shook her head, and he could take a firmer grip of himself.

But then, when she had taken a few steps, she stopped. Without looking at him she said stiffly, 'I think I should like an arm to lean on, after all. I'm sorry.' She looked so worn, and so nervous, that he was overcome with remorse. Forgetting his own feelings, he offered her his arm.

The rain had stopped. Together they walked back towards the house. They were met halfway by Mrs Dutton, who had dealt with Lisette and Pip and was now coming to look for their governess. She offered to take over from Edward, but he refused. Miss Petrie's hand was only lightly resting on his arm, but he was proud she had trusted him enough to ask for his help. Besides, it felt strangely comfortable. He didn't wish to relinquish it.

As they drew up to the house a faint ray of sunshine caught the windows of Wychford. It seemed to Edward that they twinkled with surprising brightness in the watery light. The house looked somehow… pleased with itself.

The muffins were served in the small parlour in front of a roaring fire. By the time Octavia came down after changing, the others were gathered round a tea table laden with silver coffee pots, jugs of chocolate, lemonade and, of course, dishes of muffins. It was an attractive scene—firelight reflected on the silver, Pip sitting close to her uncle, Lisette, quite recovered from her anxiety, smiling at them affectionately across the table. Octavia hesitated on the threshold, but Edward Barraclough got up the instant he saw her and led her forward to her place.

Octavia found it impossible to meet his eyes. A short while before, when she had reached her bedchamber and removed the blanket, she had been shocked beyond measure at the state of her dress— torn, almost transparent, and, until Mr Barraclough had released it, she remembered, it had been held well above her knees by her stockings! No wonder he had taken such a liberty with her! Between the display of her person, and the way she had positively *asked* to be embraced, he might well have thought it discourteous to refuse! If he *had* been looking for a flirtation with the governess to while away the time at Wychford, she had just given him every encouragement! She stood in front of her mirror, holding her hands to hot cheeks, and feeling deeply ashamed.

He had been a true gentleman afterwards, she thought, taking the blame on himself, and apologising very convincingly. Perhaps he really thought he *had* been to blame, and wouldn't regard what had happened as encouragement. He had sounded sincere enough in his promise never to repeat it.

But that was no comfort. She knew that inside she had *wanted* him to hold her as he had, *wanted* him to kiss her. What did that say of her? She didn't even like the man!

But that wasn't true. Mr Barraclough might not be the blond hero of her dreams, but she liked him. His treatment of Pip that afternoon had been exactly right. One could do more than like such a man... Octavia drew herself up with a start, alarm bells ringing in her mind. She must not go further with this line of thought. Mr Barraclough might be everything that was admirable, but she had no intention of thinking of him as anything but her employer. In taking this job with the Barracloughs she had deliberately set herself in a different sphere from them, and the distance between Edward Barraclough and herself must be kept while she remained in his service.

She stared at herself in the mirror and wondered what would happen later, when her charade was over. If they met in London next year would she, *could* she attract him when he knew her for what she really was, the youngest daughter of the Earl of Warnham, and the owner of Wychford? He was a presentable and eligible male—there must be any number of ladies in society who would wish to claim him for themselves. Still, she could look quite pretty when her hair wasn't screwed into an unbecoming knot...and her family connections were impeccable.

She gazed at her mirror, but saw a man's dark face there. How strong he was! He had swung himself up that tree with no difficulty at all, and had afterwards saved her from falling. Then, when he had held her, kissed her, she had felt the strength in those arms, the power of his muscular body... Octavia passed her fingers slowly over her lips. He had seemed angry with her, but the kiss had not been at all rough. It had been gentle, tender, comforting. Not at all what she would have expected from a man like Edward Barraclough. Even when the kiss had changed, it had still in some strange way been tender. That kiss... It had aroused sensations inside her which were new and almost frightening. There was danger in such a kiss...

What would it be like if a man had a right to hold you like that? If you could let him take you even more closely into his arms without feeling you had to protest? For the first time in her life, Octavia considered what it must be like to be married—to a man like Edward Barraclough, say... This gave rise to such a feeling of longing that her eyes widened in shock, and she jumped up, away from the mirror and its dark, enticing images. What was she *thinking* of? One kiss and she was ready to abandon Tom Payne and his like, ready to let her blond hero vanish into the past, prepared to put a...a black-haired ogre in his place? Mr Barraclough was nothing to her! Nothing! How he would laugh if he could see her now, languishing over his image in her mirror! A man of experience like Edward Barraclough would take such kisses in his stride, hardly even notice them. Of course he would forget it!

Octavia pulled herself together with steely determination. The kiss had meant very little to him and it must mean nothing to her! She had been too long at Wychford, a break was definitely called for. And on her return she would make sure to remember who she was—Miss Petrie, a paid companion and governess, and definitely not someone for the master of the house to flirt with!

However, when Octavia went downstairs her meeting with Mr Barraclough went better than she had hoped, and she began to relax again. The muffin tea was in progress, and though he was civil, there was nothing in his manner to suggest that he regarded her as anything but his nieces' governess. She began to think that the episode in the woods could indeed be forgotten.

But after Lisette and Pip had gone early to bed, he asked her to stay behind, and she was in a panic again. When he saw this his face grew grim.

'I see you are nervous. Miss Petrie, what happened this afternoon was a mistake. I am deeply sorry for it, but I had hoped that we could put it behind us. Whatever you may have thought, I meant you no disrespect, and, if you are to continue to act as my nieces' governess, it must be forgotten. Anything less would give rise to an impossible situation. What do you say? Can you forgive and forget, or would you prefer not to return to Wychford after you leave to-

morrow? Much as I would regret it, I would understand if that were so.'

Octavia's heart gave a thump. Not to return? No!
She must! She must come back. She could not
leave…leave Lisette and Pip now! She pulled herself
together and said evenly, 'I'm sure I can put it behind
me, Mr Barraclough. We had both been under extreme tension, and I believe that we neither of us
behaved typically.'

A slight glint, quickly suppressed, came and went
in his eyes. 'Quite,' he said.

Octavia didn't like the glint. She went on coolly,
'Perhaps this break will make it easier for us both to
forget it altogether.'

'I hope so. Good! But this is not the only matter I
must discuss with you.' He paused, frowned, then
went on, 'You have done better than I hoped with
the girls. They appear to be well taught, and they are
certainly happier than they would have been with
Miss Froom. But this afternoon Pip was in some danger. The fact that you risked your own safety in order
to rescue her doesn't alter that.'

Octavia waited. She was aware that any other employer would have berated her before now. She tried
not to flinch as his voice changed and he went on,
'But tell me, Miss Petrie, what the *devil* you meant
by letting that child risk her life in such an irresponsible manner? Are there no rules, no precautions for
her safety?'

Octavia was miserably conscious that she was at fault. She had left Pip to her own devices for too long. It was no excuse that she had never imagined the child would be so disobedient. 'I...I am sorry—'

'Why do you allow Pip to climb when and where she pleases?'

'I don't! It's true that I haven't tried to stop her from climbing—she has so much energy, and she does seem to feel a need to be above the rest of us. It's a harmless enough habit, and I'm sure she will grow out of it—'

'Harmless!'

'But I *have* made some rules, Mr Barraclough. Certain trees are banned, and that tree is one of them. Any tree that overhangs the lake is forbidden. And so are branches that are as high as the one she got to today. Pip must have...must have forgotten.'

'Forgotten? Or was it defiance? I gather from Lisette that Pip has been in one of her black moods.'

'That's true. But she was ready to obey me when I found her. She would have come down if she hadn't lost her nerve.'

'If she hadn't fallen into the lake first.'

'Yes,' said Octavia. 'Yes, that's true. I'm sorry! I'll talk to Pip—'

'Don't bother. I had no wish to spoil this evening's muffin party, but I shall talk to her myself tomorrow and put my own absolute ban on high branches and trees near the lake. She won't do it again. But in future I'd like you to keep a closer eye on her when she's out of doors. Your task is to keep the girls safe as well as happy! When Pip is in one of her moods she can be very wilful. It's then she needs the firm hand.' He gave her a sharp look. 'Are you still sure you can control her?'

'Yes, I can! I'll be ready for her if it happens again. But please don't be too hard on her. I still feel that Pip is best governed by love, not threats.'

He looked exasperated. 'What do you imagine I'm going to do when we have our talk? Beat her into submission?'

'Of course not! But you can be more intimidating than you think to someone so much smaller.'

'I doubt very much I could intimidate you, Miss Petrie, tiny as you are.' He pulled a face and before she could say anything he put up his hand and went on, 'But, as you were no doubt about to remark, that's beside the point. I don't wish to intimidate Pip, merely to make sure she doesn't kill herself! For your information I love my nieces, both of them, and I shall do what I think necessary to keep them safe, without interference from you or anyone. Is that clear?'

This was the real Edward Barraclough, she thought. A hard man, with any softer feelings soon buried and forgotten! She said coolly, 'You make it perfectly clear, sir.'

'Good! In that case we'll forget it, along with all the rest. Now, when do you plan to leave? I'll make sure the gig and groom are available for you.'

'The gig will be enough, sir. I can drive myself.'
'As you wish. Goodnight, Miss Petrie.'

After she had gone Edward Barraclough sat staring at the papers on his desk, without seeing them. Though he would not for the world have admitted it, he was profoundly glad that Miss Petrie was going away for two days, and would indeed have given her a week if she had asked for it! It would give him time to recover. From what? What was there to recover from? After a moment's concentration he decided that he had no idea, only that it concerned his feelings towards Miss Petrie! They were, to say the least, inappropriate! Just now he had had to *force* himself to voice a perfectly justifiable criticism of the way she looked after his nieces. And when she had looked so stricken, he had had a hard job not to get up and reassure her! It was absurd! Ridiculous! Edward moved restlessly in his chair. What the devil was wrong with him? Why was he feeling so confused?

Perhaps it would be better if the damned governess decided not to return at all. No! He rejected that thought as soon as it occurred to him. No! That would never do—it would be most...most inconvenient. That was the word! If Miss Petrie were not to come back it would be inconvenient.

All the same, he was glad to have two days in which he could get over this curious fascination he felt for her. It was not at all reasonable!

Chapter Seven

But Octavia had to put off her visit to Ashcombe. At the muffin party Pip had been quieter than usual, and the next morning she woke up flushed, and complaining of a multitude of aches and pains.

Edward sent for the local doctor, who diagnosed a fever brought on by exposure. Careful nursing would be needed, and he recommended that his patient should be kept in bed for at least a week. When he offered to find a nurse, Octavia shook her head.

'I am well used to nursing,' she said. 'If you are prepared to trust me, I am perfectly confident I could manage.'

'There's no doubt that Pip would prefer someone she knows,' said Edward doubtfully. 'I should be easier in my mind if you were here with her. But aren't you just about to leave us for a while?'

'That can be postponed. I should prefer to stay until Pip is better.'

'That's settled then. But you must tell me if you need help.'

* * *

For the first three days Pip was quite ill. A truckle bed was put in the child's room, and one of the maids slept there at night, ready to call Octavia whenever Pip needed her. During the day either Lisette or Octavia sat with her, and Edward came in quite often, too.

But on the third evening Octavia looked up from her sewing to see that Pip's eyes were open and fully conscious. She got up and went over, taking the lamp with her.

'Hello,' she said putting the lamp down on the table by the bed. 'Welcome back. Would you like a drink?'

Pip was held up to sip from the beaker kept by the bed, 'I haven't been away,' she said slowly. 'I've had a headache. But I feel better now.'

'That's very good news.'

'Where's Lisette?'

'She's asleep, I think. She's been looking after you most of the day, and was quite tired. So I sent her to bed.'

'And Edward? Where's Edward?'

'He's been here a lot, too. I expect he'll come in later.'

'Can I get up?'

'Not yet. Perhaps tomorrow or the next day.'

'You're going away. You won't be here.'

Octavia sat on the bed and took Pip's hand in hers. The lamp enclosed them in a little circle of light, leaving the rest of the room in darkness. She said softly, 'I shall stay until you are better, Pip dear. Properly better.'

'I don't want you to go away at all,' said Pip fretfully. 'Mama and Papa said they would only be away for two days, but they never came back.'

'I shall come back, Pip. I promise.'

'But why do you have to go to this Ashcombe place? There's only some old man there!'

'It's not just ''some old man''!' Octavia hesitated, looked at Pip's flushed little face, and said gently, 'I wouldn't go if it was just any old man, Pip. He's my father and I love him. I have to see him, just to make sure that he's happy and well. He allowed me to come here to look after...to look after you and Lisette, but he'd be disappointed if I didn't visit him occasionally. You can understand that, can't you?'

'I suppose so... I didn't know it was your papa.'

'I haven't told anyone but you.'

'Couldn't he come here instead? I'd like to meet your papa.'

Octavia smiled. 'He's very old. He couldn't travel so far. I shall be back in two days, you'll see.'

'I suppose you have a lot of brothers and sisters at home, too.'

'Not one! I'm the youngest, and they're all married except one. And he's away in the Army.'

'What are they called?'

Pip was getting sleepy again. It wouldn't do any harm to talk about her family a little. It might send her off. 'Well, there's Arthur—he's the eldest. He has four daughters.'

'As old as me?'

'Two of them are older than you. Then after Arthur come my sisters Gussie, Eleanor and Charlotte. They're all three married with lots of children between them.'

'Are any of them my age?'

'All of Gussie's are older than you. And three of Eleanor and Charlotte's are. The rest are all younger.'

'Go on. Who comes next?'

'There's Elizabeth next. She was married but her husband died. She's been living in France, but I think she's coming back to England soon.'

'How many children has she got?'

'None.'

'Gussie, Eleanor, Charlotte, Elizabeth... Haven't you any more brothers?'

'Apart from Arthur? I did have two more, but Stephen, the elder one, was a soldier and died at Waterloo. Now I only have one other brother, beside Arthur.'

'Four sisters and two brothers. That's quite a lot,' said Pip sleepily. 'Will Edward come soon? I think I'd like to go to sleep.'

Octavia smiled and kissed her. 'He'll be here any minute,' she said.

'He's here now,' said a deep voice out of the dark.

'Mr Barraclough!' Octavia was startled.

'I didn't like to disturb you,' he said as he came further into the room. 'I was interested in your family, you see. Six brothers and sisters! No wonder you know so many games. How do you feel tonight, midget?'

'I'm better, I think. Miss Petrie says she won't go away till I'm properly better, though. And she's promised to come back.'

'Good!' Edward Barraclough's eyes rested on Octavia for a moment. 'I'm pleased she feels she can.'

Octavia felt her cheeks grow warm, and was thankful for the dim light. 'If you've come to sit with Pip, sir, I shall go to see that Lisette is asleep. She was very tired.' She leaned over the bed and kissed Pip. 'Goodnight, dearest Pip. Goodnight, sir.'

They followed much the same routine for the next couple of days, but, with the resilience of the young, Pip was soon full of her old spirit. Edward spent a lot of time with her, and Lisette was never far away. After a week Octavia felt she could safely leave them all for two days, and she set off for Ashcombe.

She need not have worried about her father. Lady Dorney's husband had suffered from a delicate constitution and Lord Warnham was having a most enjoyable time comparing a wealth of symptoms and their cures with his cousin. He had missed his daughter, of course, but not nearly as much as she had feared.

'Cousin Marjorie's collection of recipes for tisanes is bigger than my own,' he told his daughter. 'I do believe they have done my health a great deal of good. I hope you can persuade her to stay a little longer, Octavia. We have not yet tried the half of them.'

'She has agreed to stay for at least two months, Papa. She might even agree to stay longer if you wish. I don't believe she has any plans for the winter.'

'Excellent, excellent! We must make sure she stays till the spring. I was very cast down, you know, when I heard about poor Arthur's misfortune, but Cousin Marjorie was a great comfort.'

'What is wrong with Arthur, Papa?'

'His wife has had another daughter, my dear! I warned Arthur, before he married her—the Dawsons always have daughters. But he took no notice. Now the doctors have told him that Sarah cannot have any more children. Arthur has five daughters and no heir!'

Octavia did not particularly like her eldest brother, but this would have been a severe blow to his pride. 'That's very sad, Papa.'

'It is indeed! I feel for him.'

'It's Sarah I feel for,' said Octavia. 'Arthur won't forgive her for this.'

'You realise what it means, Octavia? It's now up to Harry to carry on after Arthur and I have gone! What do you think of that?'

The Honourable Harry Petrie, youngest of the Petrie boys and something of a daredevil, was Octavia's favourite brother. He was a Lieutenant in the Guards and as yet unmarried.

'Does it mean that Harry will have to sell out?'

'Of course! Arthur has already written to him. Arthur always takes such matters in hand, he is very obliging.' Octavia thought her eldest brother could be better described as officious, but she didn't say so.

'What did Arthur tell him?'

'That Harry must sell his commission and come home, of course. He can't waste any time in settling down and finding a bride.'

'Poor Harry!'

'Stephen shouldn't have gone into the Army. It's a very dangerous occupation. Harry wouldn't have had to sell out if Stephen had lived.'

'No, Papa. But then Harry would be at risk!'

Her father looked at her doubtfully, then decided to change the subject. 'You haven't told me how you are faring at Wychford, my dear. You look very well.'

'We are going along quite nicely, Papa. I think we are making progress at last, though much still needs to be done. I must go back tomorrow.'

'So soon?'

'I'm afraid so, Papa. I hope you don't mind?'

'Oh, you must not worry about me, my dear. I have Cousin Marjorie to talk to. We chat, you know, about our younger days. And she has promised to make me another tisane tomorrow.'

After more talk with her father, it was clear to Octavia that this stay of Lady Dorney's was being a huge success. Lord Warnham was as content as she had ever known him, and by the time she left Ashcombe she was no longer at all worried about leaving him.

In fact, Octavia was rather more concerned about what she would find waiting for her at Wychford, and asked herself if she was being foolhardy to return. She had pondered a lot over her behaviour on the day of Pip's accident, and how it would affect her relationship with Edward Barraclough. He had appeared to think the blame all his, and had seemed sincere in his apology, and in his desire to treat the kiss as a momentary madness, which was to be forgotten. There would be no repeat, of that she was certain. Mr Barraclough had meant what he had said. Certainly his attitude to her during the week that followed had been coolly correct.

No, it was not Edward Barraclough's attitude that worried her—it was her own! She would miss a lot if she were not to return to Wychford. She would miss Lisette's gentle charm and Pip's energetic liveliness. She would miss the quirky house and its funny windows, its lake and its ancient trees. But above all, and this was what dismayed her, she would miss Edward Barraclough's abrasive company. She had dismissed the importance of the kiss—it had been an accident, brought on by the exceptional situation, of that she was sure. She had always been the most sensible, level-headed member of all the family, not at all romantically inclined. Quickened heartbeats, panting breath, the torments of passion—these were for others, not Octavia Petrie. It was very unlikely that she would lose her head again. But this surprising enjoyment of Edward Barraclough's conversation was not so easy to ignore. Not one of the eligible young men she had met during her London season had intrigued her as much.

One other matter worried her. She and her brother Harry, the two youngest Petries, had always been close. If she was not at Ashcombe when he came back to England, he might well come to seek her out at Wychford. That *would* set the cat among the pigeons!

She consoled herself with the thought that it would take some time for Harry to find his way back to Ashcombe. If she was not already back home, she would make sure he got a message to tell him not to come to find her. In the past they had often been co-conspirators—he wouldn't let her down!

This settled, Octavia spent the rest of the journey disciplining her mind into a proper acceptance of her position. She was confident that her two-day absence had rid her of the unsuitable memories of how it had felt to have a man's warm body pressed against hers, of the images of a dark-haired man in her mirror. She was now once again the unromantic, down-to-earth person she had always been. Her duty was towards Lisette and Philippa Barraclough, not their uncle, and between them they would give her all the affection and interest that any reasonable governess could expect.

Edward Barraclough found to his annoyance that Miss Petrie's absence had not cured him. He was looking forward with unreasonable eagerness to her return, and not because the girls had been difficult to look after. The two days had been pleasant enough. But a certain spice had been lacking, and he had come to the conclusion that he missed Miss Petrie!

Though it wasn't easy, he had conscientiously tried to put the unexpected delight of the kiss right out of his mind, as he had promised. If she was to continue to live at Wychford, that was an area that must remain barred, he knew. But there was so much more to it than that...

It was strange. For such a little thing she had made quite an impression on him! He had always been attracted before to dark-haired, dark-eyed beauties, who were accomplished in the game of love. Neither their minds nor their powers of conversation had ever interested him. He would have said it was impossible that he should spend time really talking to a woman, enjoying her company, particularly the company of a *dab* of a woman, with scraped back hair, and features that were not at all striking. What was it about Miss Petrie...?

Was it the way her face changed when she laughed, the way her eyes narrowed when she concentrated, the way she raised one eyebrow to express scepticism, or irony? Was it her willingness to challenge him while somehow remaining perfectly respectful? Or was it the annoying habit she had of managing to make her views absolutely clear while saying nothing at all?

And she wasn't at all a dab of a woman. Her face had a delicate beauty, and though she was small she was perfectly made... Edward Barraclough sat up and shook his head. This was doing him no good at all. He must stop thinking of Miss Petrie and her perfect proportions, and do something to cure himself of this madness. Looking after his nieces was all very well, but the comparatively celibate life it brought with it was not good for any man. No wonder he had strange ideas about their governess! He must spend more time in London, and as soon as the governess returned he would. Though he had to give up the tempting invitations to join his friends' autumn house parties, there was plenty of entertainment still to be had in the capital. He would gamble in the clubs, drink with his friends, and enjoy Louise's considerable attractions. That would soon chase away these confoundedly unsuitable thoughts of Miss Petrie!

So Octavia Petrie was hardly back at Wychford before Edward Barraclough escaped to London, where he plunged into a determined round of pleasure.

It lasted a week. He had done what he had promised himself, sought pleasure wherever and whenever he could find it. He had gambled a great deal, drunk even more and whiled away many an hour with Louise, who seemed to have recovered her desire to please him. But, maddeningly, after just a couple of days, he grew restless. London began to seem stale and dirty, its set patterns of behaviour and conversation artificial and dull. He found himself longing for the freshness of the woods round Wychford, the sound of his nieces' young voices, their spontaneous laughter and games, the liveliness of their conversation, the sight of three figures as they wandered about the grounds, discussing and recording.

Even his hours with Louise began to pall. She was as lovely, as skilled as ever in her efforts to please, but once they had made love what else was there to amuse him in her company? *Her* eyes never sparkled with anger or challenge, only at appreciation of some bauble or other. The delicate arch of *her* eyebrow was never raised in disbelief or scepticism at something he said. She could pout prettily enough, but you never saw her laugh in sudden delight, or risk wrinkling her brow in a real frown. Furthermore—and he wondered why he had not seen it before—Louise was entirely devoid of any real sense of humour.

He came back on a blustery, cold day at the end of October, but even in the rain Wychford looked welcoming. The windows of the little parlour were lit up with the glow of a fire. He went up to the window and looked in. Three figures were gathered round a table, intent on a board with counters on it. As usual, Miss Petrie was plainly dressed with no attempt to flatter the shapely form beneath. Her hair was scraped back into its ugly knot, too, but the fire-light touched it with colour and life and he found himself smiling with pleasure at the sight. He watched how her face lit up with laughter as she passed a pile of buttons over to Lisette and threw up her arms in mock despair.

'Lisette! You wretch!' she cried. 'That was the last of my fortune. I am *ruined*!'

Lisette joined in the laughter, her lovely face quite transformed. But Pip got down and went round the table to give her governess a hug. 'You can have some of mine, Miss Petrie! I've got plenty.'

'You're a darling, Pip, but no, thank you. If you can't pay, don't play. My brothers taught me that from the first. Besides, you'll need all your wealth to beat Lisette. She's on the top of her form!'

'Who's that?' In getting down Pip had turned to face the window. She pointed at Edward. Then she

recognised him. With her usual shout of 'Edward!'
she raced to the door of the room and out into the
hall.

The sight of her employer made nonsense of Octavia's belief that she was a sensible, rational creature, with her feelings well under control. Her feelings when she saw his dark face at the window were
neither cool nor proper. Her heart had jumped, her
pulse had quickened, and she had caught her breath
at a sudden and vividly explicit memory of their kiss.
So much for level-headed discipline! However, she
still had some command of her emotions, and by the
time he came into the room, towed by an ecstatic
Pip, her manner was polite rather than warm.

'You've had a cold journey, I think, sir. Shall I
send for some tea, or other refreshment?'

'It can wait. Finish your game. I don't think I've
seen it before, have I?'

'Miss Petrie brought a lot from her home, Edward,' said Pip, dragging him over to the table. 'She
and her brothers and sisters used to play with them.
It's been too cold to go out today, so we got them
out. Look at Lisette's heap of winnings! She's ruined
Miss Petrie already!'

Edward picked one of the pieces up. It might be
old and battered, but it had originally been quite valuable. He put it down again and said, 'That's unfortunate. Let it be a lesson to you, midget! Now, let
me see you play!'

As the two girls got absorbed once again, he drew Octavia to one side and said in a low voice, 'How has Pip been? She seems well enough now.'

'I'm sure there's no lasting damage done. But she has the occasional nightmare when she wakes up crying with fright, convinced that she's falling.'

'Still? She had one while you were away at Ashcombe, but I thought they would disappear with time.'

'I think they will. It would be better if the weather improved and she could get out in the fresh air as she used to. Pip has so much energy—she needs to get rid of it, but I haven't dared to take her out for long. I've been trying to give her other things to think about. I've even been teaching her chess.'

He looked at his nieces. 'And backgammon. Are the chessmen as valuable as the backgammon pieces?'

Octavia stared at him. 'What do you mean?'

'Merely that I wonder about you. Those pieces are old, but they're not ordinary children's playthings—they're made of ivory, and I see some ebony and rosewood over there. Strange toys for the children of a poor parson.'

'Who told you my father was a parson? I certainly never have!'

'I think I just assumed it. You're obviously a woman of education, but you have to earn a living. You obviously like caring for others. A parson's daughter seemed to fit. Your family would appear to be eminently respectable.'

'Indeed they are, sir,' said Octavia.

'What is your father, if not a parson—a school-teacher?'

'No. He…he has been an invalid for years. Before that he…he looked after an estate.'

'Ah! A land agent.'

'Something of the sort. The…the toys were handed on from a family who lived in the local manor house.' Octavia felt very uncomfortable. She was getting deeper and deeper into a mesh of half-truths. She had brought the games with her from Ashcombe without thinking of their value, merely as a means of keeping the girls amused during the colder weather. Now Edward Barraclough was quizzing her, and his questions were getting too close to home! It was time to change the subject.

'Did you enjoy your stay in London, sir?' she asked.

'Not altogether,' he replied. 'Do you know the city?'

Here she went again! 'I…I stayed there for several months,' she said, 'but it was some time ago. I expect it has changed a lot. Have you heard recently from your sister-in-law?'

Edward frowned. He glanced at his nieces, who were intent on the game, and led her away to the other end of the room.

'I think Julia may well arrive in England earlier than expected,' he said quietly. 'She is very concerned about a former neighbour of ours—I think I told you about him. Ricardo Arandez. It seems he has followed us to Europe.'

'You think it is to see Lisette? Perhaps he loves your niece more sincerely than you thought?'

'It's her fortune he loves.'

'But what can he do? I thought you told me that her father had withdrawn his consent? He must surely know that Lisette would never act against authority! Pip might, but Lisette never!'

'I would agree with you, but the situation is not quite so simple. After my brother died, Arandez managed to convince Lisette that he had relented and wished her to marry him after all.'

'And this wasn't true?'

'Of course not! Once John had decided that Arandez wasn't suitable, that was it. He wouldn't change his mind.'

'Then…then why does Lisette believe differently?'

He sighed. 'I see I shall have to tell you the whole.' He threw a glance at the two girls. 'But not here. Come to the library.'

Once in the other room he invited her to sit, and began. 'Ricardo Arandez is plausible enough. My brother John saw that Lisette liked him, and eventually promised that if, when she was older, she liked the fellow well enough to marry him, he would give his consent. There were advantages to the match—

the Arandez estates border on ours. However, John soon came to realise that Arandez was not the sort of son-in-law he wanted, and withdrew his promise. Right?'

Octavia nodded.

'Then John and his wife were killed. Before the week was out Arandez was at the house, claiming that he had spoken to John the night before he died, and that John had regretted his change of mind. The promise of a match between Lisette and himself had been renewed. We didn't believe him. It was all too opportune. Henry and I sent him away, and told Lisette to forget him.'

'Wasn't that a little harsh? The poor girl was already in some distress. This Arandez might have been able to comfort her.'

'Comfort her! Hear me out before you judge, Miss Petrie! Arandez waited till I had left Antigua and then he approached Lisette in secret. From what Lisette told my sister-in-law, he showed her a letter from John saying that he wished her to marry Arandez as planned. We all think it was a forgery, though no one other than Lisette ever saw it. But it was enough to convince Lisette. She was prepared to defy her family and run off with him. Fortunately Henry saw them, and Arandez was sent packing.'

'Did it never occur to any of you that Lisette might be in love with this man?'

He uttered an exclamation of impatience. 'I've told you before, Miss Petrie! Lisette is far too young to be in love with anyone! Arandez used the fact that she was distraught and vulnerable after her parents' accident. She saw him as someone to cling to, that's all! She was *not* in love with him!' He saw her sceptical expression and went on more seriously, 'And it wouldn't matter if she was. Neither Henry nor I would ever allow her to marry Arandez!'

Octavia was not at all convinced of Lisette's indifference, and her heart ached for the girl. Her air of sadness might not be due solely to her parents' death. However, she saw little point in pursuing the subject for the moment. Instead she said, 'So you think your sister-in-law will be here earlier than expected?'

'She will if she can. I'm afraid Mrs Barraclough has no great opinion of my ability to look after our nieces, Miss Petrie. With some reason, I fear.'

'I disagree. She can't have seen you with them!'

He looked surprised, and said, 'I'm touched. Compliments from you are rare indeed!'

'I mean it. Look at the way you've just cut short your stay in London.'

'Er...yes. Yes, indeed! Though I have to confess that London is very boring in the winter months. I was not at all sorry to leave. Life at Wychford can be far more interesting.'

Edward had clearly spoken without thinking, but Octavia felt her face grow scarlet and looked at him accusingly. For a moment he looked blank then he smiled ruefully. 'I meant no harm, Octavia,' he murmured. 'I've done my best to forget as I promised. Don't make it difficult.'

'I...I don't know what you mean,' she said bravely.

'I meant, Miss Petrie, that we *both* need to keep a firm control of our memories. That is, if we are to continue to live under the same roof without the sort of scandal I would wish to avoid.'

Octavia's nerves were stretched to the limit. His sudden appearance, her efforts to counter his questions about her family, her sharp sympathy for Lisette, and now the discovery that the attraction between them was as strong as ever—it was almost too much! She called on all her reserves of pride and said coldly, 'You have no reason to fear scandal from any actions of mine, sir.' Then she turned away from him and went back to the table.

The game was finished, Lisette had won.

Octavia avoided Edward Barraclough for the next two days. It wasn't difficult. He took the girls to visit friends in Guildford the next day and readily accepted her excuses when she refused his invitation to accompany them. It was almost as if he was relieved. The day after that he was closeted in the library for most of the day, and eventually came into the parlour, frowning at some papers he had in his hand. The girls were playing chess, and Octavia sat by the fire, keeping an eye on their progress and sewing.

'Are you cross, Edward?' Lisette asked.

'No, I'm curious, that's all.'

'What about?'

'This house. I've been looking through every paper connected with our tenancy, but nowhere can I find the owner's name.'

'Isn't it Mr Walters?'

'No, he is merely the agent. The house was left to a niece of Mrs Carstairs, but I have no idea what she is called. All our dealings have been with Walters, and his signature is on every single document. I think Miss Carstairs, or whatever her name is, must be very shy. It's a pity. I should have liked to talk to her about her aunt. Perhaps I'll write to Walters to ask him if she would meet me.'

Octavia jumped. She knew that Walters would never divulge her name without her permission, but this sudden announcement had been a shock.

'Is something wrong, Miss Petrie?'

'Nothing, Mr Barraclough. I pricked my finger, that's all. It's nothing.' He regarded her closely, and Octavia was glad of the excuse to keep her head bent.

'Do you know anything about the house, Miss Petrie, or Mrs Carstairs's niece? Ashcombe is not that far away.'

Keeping her head bent, Octavia said carefully, 'Mrs Carstairs was something of a legend in the county. But...but we none of us knew she had any intention of leaving Wychford to her niece. The niece certainly never visited her here, as far as I know.'

'I see. Then I shall write to Walters. By the way, I'm taking the girls to Guildford again tomorrow. Mrs Allardyce has arranged dancing lessons for her own daughters and has suggested that Lisette and Pip share in them. Do you wish to come?'

'I think not. The girls' lessons have been a little neglected recently, and I should be glad of a chance to prepare some exercises for them.'

'As you wish,' he said, turning away. The girls protested, of course, but Octavia refused to change her mind. A day on her own, an opportunity to talk firmly to herself, seemed very desirable.

After Edward Barraclough and the girls had left for Guildford, Octavia spent some time preparing work for the next week. Her heart was heavy. Julia Barraclough might arrive quite soon, and from what had been said she was not the easiest of people to please. If the formidable Mrs Barraclough was not to be disappointed in the governess her brother-in-law had chosen, then they would all need to concentrate during the coming days. Otherwise her arrival might well betoken Octavia's departure. In any case, Octavia's time at Wychford would not last for very much longer. Two months was the original contract, and she had already been with the Barracloughs for well over half that time.

She worked steadily during the rest of the morning without any noticeable improvement in her mood. In the afternoon she dressed herself warmly and went out into the grounds. Perhaps a walk before the Barracloughs returned would clear her melancholy. The ground was wet and soft underfoot, though at least the rain had stopped, and the air was fresh. She walked briskly down the drive. When she turned the corner she saw a solitary rider coming towards her and recognised him with a shock.

Chapter Eight

'Harry!' cried Octavia. 'Oh, my goodness! What-ever are you doing here?'

The tall, fair-haired young man dismounted and enveloped her in a vast hug. His riding cape swung open to reveal the uniform of a Lieutenant in the Guards. 'What a way to greet your long-lost brother, Tavy! I expected better than this, I can tell you!'

'But…but where have you come from?'

'From Ashcombe, of course. I thought I'd stay a few days with you here, and have a look at your house. You're a lucky dog! From what I've seen so far it's a fine place! Fancy the Witch of Wychford leaving it to you!'

'B…but what did Papa tell you?'

Her brother looked puzzled. 'Why, that you were staying here putting the house in order. I didn't stay long to talk, I was too annoyed with him. Did you know that Arthur says I have to leave the Army?'

'I heard something of the sort, yes.'

'What I want to know is why the *devil* has Arthur any say in it?'

'I told Papa you'd take it badly. You're right, Arthur's too much of a busybody, but then he always has been, and now Papa has started leaving everything to him to do. It's the succession he's worried about, of course. You heard Sarah had another daughter?'

'Hang the succession! What do I care about the succession? I wouldn't do anything Arthur ordered me to, I can tell you. If it was just Arthur I'd stay put. But Father agrees with him. He wouldn't even listen to what I had to say, so I thought I'd come and find you. Although you don't seem as pleased to see me as you should!'

He sounded offended. Octavia gave him an affectionate hug and kiss. 'Harry, of course I'm glad, very glad to see you! How could you think otherwise? It's just... We have to talk. I have things I must tell you.' She pulled at his sleeve. 'Come away from the drive. They could be back at any moment.'

Her brother looked at her with suspicion, but didn't resist. 'Who are "they"? You look pretty worried, Tavy. What have you been up to?'

Octavia led Harry and the horse a short distance back from the drive along one of the rides that led into the wood. Fortunately, none of the groundsmen were about. As quickly as she could, she gave her brother the full story of her adventures at Wychford, omitting only certain personal and unnecessary details.

Harry had never been slow. In no time he was in full possession of the facts and highly amused.

Octavia gazed at him in exasperation and exclaimed, 'You're a dolt, Harry! Why are you laughing? Do you realise what would happen if they found out who I am?'

'Well, I can't answer for Barraclough, but if it were me I'd throw you out on your ear! Or can't he do that to his landlady?' Harry went into another paroxysm of laughter.

'Harry!' Octavia tried to stamp her foot, but failed in the soft ground.

'Well, what were you thinking of? It's a bit of a lark, perhaps, but I would have said you were past that kind of caper.'

'I've told you! I didn't mean it to be a caper! But the house…those girls… I was so tempted to stay here. You've no idea how I wanted to get away from Ashcombe!'

Octavia went on to tell him of her frustration, her boredom with her life at home. Harry was instantly sympathetic and said so. 'But all the same, there must have been some other way, Tavy. You've put yourself in a pretty impossible position with the Barracloughs. What are they like?'

Octavia stopped and listened. In the distance could be heard the sound of hooves, the crack of the coachman's whip and the crunch of wheels on gravel as a carriage turned in through Wychford's gates. She said nervously, 'If we're not very lucky you may find out sooner than you thought. That's Edward Barraclough's carriage arriving back from Guildford. Pull your cape around you. That scarlet uniform can be seen for miles. And keep quiet. They mustn't see us together. They mustn't see you at all!'

Octavia waited tensely, then breathed a sigh of relief as the carriage passed safely by. She turned to her brother. 'I'm sorry, Harry, but I'll have to go. If Pip can't find me in the house she'll come looking for me, or send Lisette.'

'But what am I to do? We haven't had any time at all together! There's much more to say. Dammit, we haven't seen each other for more than two years! Be reasonable, Tavy! Can't I come with you up to the house?'

'No! What could I tell Edward Barraclough? He's far too quick to be taken in by any story. He'd suspect something the minute he saw you.'

'We aren't very alike. I could pretend to be a friend.'

'You're not to come up to the house, Harry! In fact, I'd like you most of all to go back to Ashcombe and wait for me there.'

'What, hang about Ashcombe for another three or four weeks? There's no chance of that! I have to be back with the regiment well before then. Look, I'll go to Ashcombe for tonight, but only to leave my uniform behind, and collect some other things to wear. Tomorrow I'll get a room at the inn in the village here for two or three nights. We can see a little more of each other. Don't worry! I won't use my own name. I'll be Harry…Harry Smith.'

'That's not very imaginative.'

'Harry Smith is a great hero to anyone in the Army, my girl. He fought all through the Peninsular campaign, and at Waterloo.'

'I see…' said Octavia, her mind elsewhere. 'Harry, if you want to be a hero, *my* hero, you could do something absolutely vital for me. I have an urgent message for Mr Walters, and I've been racking my brains how I could get it safely to him. If you would agree to deliver it on your way it would solve my problem. Tomorrow if possible. His chambers are in Guildford.'

'Guildford! That's miles out of my way!'

'*Please*, Harry! It would take one worry off my mind if you would. I don't think for a minute that Mr Walters would do anything without consulting me first, but it's better to be sure. Mr Barraclough can be very forceful.'

'I suppose I could come back via Guildford… What's the message?'

'It's just that Mr Barraclough wants Mr Walters to arrange a meeting with Mrs Carstairs's niece. That's me, of course, and it's impossible. But tell Walters he must be sure *not* to give my name, or tell Mr Barraclough who I am. Understand? Walters is not to give in. Can you remember it? There isn't time to write it down.'

'My dear sister, I've carried longer messages than that, and more important ones, too.'

'Not to me they weren't. Harry, you're a darling! And now I *must* go! I'll see you the day after to-morrow. I teach the girls in the morning, but I'll meet you here at three. Don't come earlier, whatever you do! If the weather is good the girls may come out for a walk with me before that. If I see you when I am out with them, I shall ignore you.'

She hurried back to the house, suffering from a mixture of feelings. It was wonderful to see Harry again, but she was not at all sure she wanted him so close. Wychford village was small, and there was bound to be speculation about what such a handsome young man was doing there all alone. But, thanks to Harry, she had at least found a way of warning Mr Walters. Octavia sighed. Life at Wychford had started out so simply. Now it was getting more com-plicated by the minute!

The girls were full of excitement about their danc-ing lesson, and insisted on taking Octavia to the mu-sic room to show her the steps they had learned. Even Pip, who had been rather scornful, was enthusiastic. Days of confinement to the house had left her with a good deal of surplus energy, and she had enjoyed the activity, especially the more lively steps of the dances.

'Edward, you must help me to show Miss Petrie what we did!' she cried. 'Lisette, you play the piano!' Laughing, her uncle allowed himself to be dragged into the centre of the room, where he bowed and took Pip's hand, then set off round the room with her. They were an unevenly matched pair, to say the least, since Pip was not half her uncle's height, and danced with all the grace of a grasshopper. But her uncle treated her with the polish and courtesy due to a belle of the ball. This was Edward Barraclough at his best, thought Octavia, watching them both rather wistfully.

'Now you must try!' said Pip, after they were back. She led her uncle up to Octavia and put their hands together. 'Edward will show you how.'

'I...I think I know the steps, Pip. Your uncle has had enough, I'm sure.'

'Do dance with Edward, Miss Petrie!' called Lisette. 'Just a few steps—I'd like to see it done properly.'

'Miss Petrie?' asked Edward Barraclough, raising one eyebrow. 'May I have this dance?'

The contrast between that eyebrow and his excessively formal tone made Octavia laugh. She entered into the spirit of the thing. 'Why, thank you, sir,' she said with a graceful curtsy. 'Of course!'

He led her to the centre with a flourish, and bowed. Lisette struck up another country dance and they went twirling round, watched by a fascinated Pip.

Nothing could have been more closely chaperoned or more decorous. They were not dancing a quadrille or a waltz, but a harmless country dance with little close bodily contact. They did not even exchange a significant glance. But at none of the great balls she had attended in London had Octavia ever felt as she did in the music room at Wychford, dancing to Lisette's piano—exhilarated, in harmony with her partner, tinglingly aware of his touch, however slight. They went round twice, at the end of which she decided she had better stop. She curtsied and said, 'I think Lisette will be satisfied, sir.'

'Perhaps so, but I'm not,' he murmured as he bowed.

Octavia blushed, and looked at him reprovingly. It was a mistake. Mr Barraclough had such an engaging glint in his eye that she was strongly tempted to smile back at him. This would never do. She said severely, 'I think Pip looks as if she's had enough excitement for today, Mr Barraclough. Shall I see if Mrs Dutton has anything to suggest for supper?'

Octavia was unable to sleep that night. After tossing and turning for some time she sat up and stared at the circle of light cast by the small lamp by the door. It had been put there at the time of Pip's illness, and was now lit every night, in case Pip had another of her nightmares. But she didn't really see it. Instead she saw a dark face, the lift of a scarred eyebrow, the charm of a man's smile, the glint in his eye...

Octavia sighed deeply. The feeling she had for Edward Barraclough did not seem to be influenced by rational arguments. Just when she thought she had mastered it, it had sprung to life again at the mere touch of his hand in a country dance! She had seldom felt so alive, so aware of a man's presence. But it would not do! This was a passing phase, it must be! She must take a firmer grip of herself...

And now, just when she needed all her strength to master these new sensations, Harry had come to complicate matters even further. His presence in Wychford was bound to increase the danger of discovery. When she next saw him she must persuade him to go back to Ashcombe, even if it meant that she had to ask Mr Barraclough for another two days' leave of absence in order to meet him there. And she didn't wish to leave Wychford at all, even for two days. Time was getting so short...

Her anxious thoughts were cut short by a cry of fright from next door. It was followed by another, and another. Forgetting all her problems, Octavia leapt out of bed, and flung her wrapper round her. She snatched up her lamp and made her way to Pip's room. Pip was asleep, but was seriously disturbed, tossing in her bed, whimpering, her arms flailing about as she vainly tried to find something to hold. The child was having one of her nightmares. Octavia hastily set the lamp down, sat on the bed and took her in her arms.

'Hush, Pip, hush! I've got you. I'm here, my darling, I've got you safe.'

Pip's eyes opened, and she stared blindly at Octavia. Then recognition came and she buried her head against Octavia and wept, 'Miss Petrie! Oh, Miss Petrie, I was so frightened...'

'I know,' Octavia said, holding the child even more tightly. 'But you're safe now. It was only a dream, Pip. See? You're here in your little tower room, and I've come from next door to make sure you're all right. There's nothing at all to worry about, darling.'

Pip stayed still for a moment, then she lifted her head and gazed round. What she saw seemed to reassure her and she smiled. 'That's right. I'm safe in my tower room. And you're here. I'm so glad Edward chose you, Miss Petrie.' She nestled more closely into Octavia's arms, her eyelids drooped, and in less than a minute she was peacefully asleep again.

Octavia rested her cheek against Pip's hair. The child was so easy to love. What a wrench it was going to be for both of them when she left! She settled back against the pillows and her eyes closed....

Edward had not been fully asleep, either, but just dozing off when Pip cried out. His room was some distance away and at first he thought it was an owl or some little creature in the woods. But after a few minutes it occurred to him that the sound might have come from Pip's room. He lay there listening, but heard nothing. The house was in silence. All the same he decided that he would get no rest till he had made sure she was all right. Picking up his dressing gown and belting it round him, he strode swiftly along the landing to his niece's room. Here he stopped. The door was open, and through it he could see Pip's bed bathed in the light of a small lamp. Octavia Petrie was half-sitting, half-lying against the pillows, holding Pip in her arms. They were both asleep. Edward paused. He was in something of a dilemma. He had no wish to wake either of them, but though Pip was half under the blankets, Miss Petrie was on top, and lying very awkwardly. She would be cold and stiff when she woke.

He entered the room cautiously and stood by the bed. The ring of light shone on a face surrounded by loosely tied, honey-gold curls, resting lovingly on Pip's black mop. Miss Petrie was breathing gently, the rise and fall of her bosom clearly visible under her thin wrapper. It was one of the most touchingly, innocently seductive sights he had ever seen... Determinedly, he looked away, round the dark room for a blanket or something else to put over her to keep her warm. When he turned back to the bed he saw that her eyes were wide open and she was looking at him.

'Don't worry,' he whispered. 'I was merely fetching something to put over you. You'll get cold.'

She shook her head. 'Pip is sound asleep. I think I can leave her.' She twisted round, carefully pulled the covers up over Pip, then turned to stand up. She gave a cry of pain which was instantly suppressed.

'What's wrong?'

'My...my leg! It's gone to sleep...'

'Here, let me!' Edward gave her his hand and helped her to stand. 'You shouldn't have—'

'Don't talk here!' she said. 'We mustn't wake the child.' She took a step to the door and gasped, nearly falling as her leg gave way under her. Edward swept her up and carried her out of the room without saying a word. Then he set her down on the landing and carefully pulled Pip's door to.

'Can we talk here?' he asked in a low voice.

'I suppose. But there's nothing to say. Except to thank you for helping me. I would have been very stiff tomorrow.' She smiled up at him.

Edward could not help himself. His arms went round her and he held her very gently to him, one hand holding her head against his chest. 'My dear Octavia,' he said. 'What am I to do?'

She let her head stay for an instant, then moved to look up at him gravely. He was touched to see that there was no sign of fear in her eyes. The feel of her silken hair and her slenderness in his arms were sending his senses rocketing, yet he was determined to justify her trust in him.

'You have no idea how much I would like to take you with me back to my room—' he put a finger over her lips as she started to protest, and went on '—and yet I won't even try. That isn't for us.'

'That's good,' she whispered, 'because I would resist with all the strength I have. I won't be any man's mistress, however much—' She stopped.

'Go on!'

'No! I won't. I can't! This is wrong.' The instant she tried to remove herself from his arms he let her go, though the temptation to pull her back and kiss her was almost overwhelming. 'Goodnight, Mr Barraclough.'

'Octavia!'

'My name is Petrie, sir. Miss Petrie. I am a governess. Goodnight!' Before he could stop her she had gone into the next room and shut the door.

He went back to his room, but didn't even bother getting into his bed. Instead, he sat up and wrote some letters till morning came.

Edward went again to Guildford the next day, but this time he left the carriage behind and rode. He wished, he said, to discuss some matters with Mrs Carstairs's lawyer, who had his chambers there. In truth the ride through the countryside was almost more important to him than the meeting with Mr Walters. Edward was in a most unusual state of confusion, and he hoped that fresh air and exercise would help to clear his mind. But as he rode to Guildford, he was quite unaware of the glorious colours of the trees in their autumn foliage, the work going on in the fields to prepare them for the autumn ploughing.

He was struggling to come to terms with new and unwelcome thoughts. Before his nieces had come to England he had led the life of a wealthy bachelor, interested in his work, but always free to rove the world as he chose, to take up residence in London, Paris, Vienna, in the town or in the country, wherever he wished, without reference to any other person. It might be thought a selfish life—his sister-in-law certainly considered it so—but Edward had never cared for anyone else's opinion enough to let it interfere with his pleasures. He had counted himself fortunate to have reached the age of thirty without any of the usual entanglements—wife, children, obligations to others... His chief enemy was boredom.

And then because of Julia's accident he had been forced to accept responsibility for two young girls, orphans in a strange country. Though he had always been fond of his nieces, he had regarded their arrival as an imposition, an interference with his life of leisure. During the past weeks they had amused him, worried him, exasperated him, even occasionally annoyed him. But he had missed them when he had gone to London, and when the time came he would hand them over to Julia with real regret.

But they had brought with them Octavia Petrie, and this was now becoming a major problem, one that could not simply be handed over to someone else. The plain fact was that he could no longer persuade himself that his feelings were a temporary aberration. He suspected that they might well prove to be a real and permanent threat to his peace of mind. What was he to do about it?

Of one thing he was quite sure. Even if he had been ready to consider marrying—which he certainly was not—he would not think of marrying Octavia Petrie! He had never liked the Cinderella story. He had known men who had married women out of their sphere, and both partners had usually ended up very unhappily. Octavia Petrie was the last of a brood of children born to a respectable, probably not very wealthy, professional man. She had been brought up simply, quietly, in a remote country village. How could she possibly cope with life in London?

No, marriage to anyone was out of the question, but marriage to Octavia Petrie was especially so! He must not think of her as anyone other than his nieces' governess. Indeed, if the girls had not been so fond of her, and if the end of her time with them had not been so close, he would have sent her away immediately. But to do so without cause, merely because he feared temptation, would be unjust. He must be strong and fight it out till she went.

Satisfied that he had reached the only possible conclusion, Edward rode on with a heavy heart to Mr Walters's chambers. He arrived early and was kept waiting for a minute or two while the lawyer finished dealing with another client. When this client emerged, Edward was surprised to see he was a handsome young man, obviously from his bearing a soldier. A rare sight in the stuffy rooms of a country lawyer! But Edward's momentary interest in the young man was forgotten as soon as he entered the inner room.

Here he met with a setback. His confidence that he could persuade any lawyer to do anything he wanted proved to be misplaced. Mr Walters was everything that was amiable, but he absolutely refused to divulge the name of his principal.

'The lady's family are among my oldest clients, Mr Barraclough. They are very protective of the owner of Wychford, and indeed, I cannot myself see why you wish to approach her. I do not think she had a great deal to do with Mrs Carstairs during the latter's lifetime. So you must forgive me, but I very much regret that I am unable to oblige you.' He spread his hands apologetically and sat back.

Edward frowned, then shrugged his shoulders. 'I'm disappointed. It seemed such a small thing to ask. However, I suppose I have to accept what you say, though I think the family are being very unreasonable. One might almost be led to think the woman an imbecile.'

The lawyer gave a chuckle. 'I assure you that is far from being the case. She is eminently sane. But tell me, what do you think of Wychford? I've always thought it an odd sort of house.'

'It's delightful,' said Edward. 'My nieces love it. They will be sorry to leave it next spring. But I expect my sister-in-law will want to take them to

London soon after she arrives. They'll need a little town bronze.'

'Quite! Well, if there is nothing else...?'

'Nothing.' Edward's tone was abrupt. He added, 'If your client should relent, you know where to find me. Good day, Walters.'

He went out, feeling that, one way and another, the world was not on his side!

It was as well that Octavia did not know that Edward Barraclough had actually passed Harry in the lawyer's chambers, though neither had recognised the other. She had been on tenterhooks ever since that morning when her employer had announced his intention of seeking out Mr Walters in Guildford. It was difficult to concentrate on French grammar, or a review of the Counties of England together with the Seats of the Aristocracy to be found in them, when she was so anxious, and her lessons suffered as a consequence.

But this was not by any means the greatest of her worries. Her immediate concern might be the possible encounter in Guildford, but the turmoil in her mind had a deeper cause. In spite of her brave words the night before, it was Edward Barraclough's scruples, not her own, which had saved her. The impulse to put her arms round his neck, to draw his head down to hers had been almost overwhelming... Perhaps she ought to acknowledge the truth, at least to herself. Octavia Petrie had at last fallen in love. And with a most unsuitable man.

Moreover, by her impulsive and stupid actions on her arrival at Wychford, she had put herself into an entirely false position. What would happen if Edward Barraclough discovered how she had deceived him? Harry had said straight away that he would throw her out on her ear if he were Edward Barraclough, and she rather thought that Mr Barraclough would feel the same. Her only hope was to remain undetected until she left. Then perhaps she could join the Season next year and meet the Barracloughs on her own ground. And perhaps, just perhaps, Edward might forgive her.

That was, of course, only half the story. She had no idea of what he really felt about her, though she was aware of his resistance to the idea of marriage. But granted she could meet him on level terms, she was sure she had a chance. He did like her, and there was certainly a strong attraction between them...

Octavia saw the girls looking at her curiously, and returned to discussing the castles, courts and great houses of England's aristocracy.

Pip wanted to go out in the afternoon, and quite rightly said that the weather was perfectly suitable. Octavia had to agree, though she made Pip promise not to climb anything at all. The three of them wrapped up and set off round the back of the house, away from the main drive. Octavia wanted no encounters with Mr Barraclough on his return from Guildford! Pip was delighted to be in the open air again and ran about under Octavia's watchful eye for quite some time. But then she started to flag, and made no objection when Octavia suggested going back. Lisette, who had stayed to help entertain Pip, asked if she might just spend a few minutes by herself, looking for some specimens for her sketch book. Octavia hesitated, then gave in. There was still plenty of light, and, unlike Pip, Lisette was naturally cautious. She could hardly come to harm. So she made Lisette promise to follow them in after a quarter of an hour, and took Pip to get warm by the parlour fire.

Lisette was only slightly late, but came in with flushed cheeks and sparkling eyes, looking as if she had been running. Octavia wondered if the girl knew how stunningly beautiful she was. She thought not. Lisette was essentially a very modest young woman, and would have no idea of the impact her looks would have on the polite world. She might well find it difficult to cope with the admiration and attention that she would surely attract. Octavia made up her mind there and then, that, whatever happened between herself and Edward Barraclough, she would make certain she was in London during the next Season. The doors of Society's most exclusive hostesses were always open to Lady Octavia Petrie. After all, she was related to half of them! She must make sure that Lisette had the success and the support she deserved.

Chapter Nine

Lisette was even quieter than usual over tea, and Octavia asked her if there was something wrong.

'Oh, no, Miss Petrie! I was just thinking about...about this afternoon.'

'Did you find many specimens?'

'What? Er...no. Not many. The leaves are beginning to look faded, and I couldn't find anything else worth bringing in. I might find some more tomorrow.'

'We'll see. I hope you aren't sickening for something, Lisette. You look a little feverish.'

'Please don't worry about me. I feel very well, Miss Petrie.'

In fact, Lisette would have found it difficult to describe what she really was feeling! Guilty, nervous, excited, apprehensive... And all because of a chance ten minute encounter that afternoon with the handsomest young man she had ever seen. She fully intended to tell Miss Petrie all about it eventually, but just for the moment she wanted to keep it to herself. She gazed into the fire lost once again in the memory of that afternoon...

She had gone round to the front of the house and wandered off the drive up one of the paths through the wood. Suddenly she came face to face with a tall, blond young man. She was startled, but not really frightened. He looked harmless enough, though very handsome, and strangely, he seemed as shocked as she was. Lisette was quite reassured. After a moment during which he appeared to be trying to find his voice he stammered, 'I...I'm sorry. I didn't mean to frighten you. I...I was just w...walking in the woods. Where...where did you come from?'

It was such a ridiculous question that Lisette laughed. 'I live here,' she said.

'At...at Wychford?'

'Yes. I'm Lisette Barraclough. These are private woods, you know.'

'Are they? Yes, of course!' The young man appeared to be a little distrait, and Lisette began to wonder if she was wise to linger.

'I...I must go back,' she began. 'My governess is expecting me.'

'No! Don't go! You must forgive me if I seem a bit bowled over. It's just that I've never before met anyone as lovely as you.'

He blurted this out so straightforwardly, so simply, making no effort to come any nearer, that Lisette was both disarmed and deeply embarrassed. 'Please,' she said, holding her hands to her cheeks, 'you mustn't say such things. I don't know how to take them.' Then, feeling very shy, she went on, 'Tell me instead where you come from. Are you staying in the village? Or are you a neighbour?'

'I'm staying in the village for a few days. Visiting a...a friend. My name is Smith. Harry Smith.'

'Like the famous soldier?'

'You know of him?'

'Yes, I do! I've read a lot about him. How brave he was, and how he rescued a young Spanish girl, and then married her...it's such a romantic story! Oh, yes, I know quite a lot about Harry Smith—the other one, I mean.'

'That's wonderful!' The young man gazed at her in admiration. 'He's one of my own heroes. That's why—' He stopped short. 'Look, I'm not going to let you believe something that isn't true. Not you. My name isn't Smith at all, though it is Harry. There's a good reason for it, but I can't tell you at the moment. Please don't let it put you off me.'

Lisette gazed at him doubtfully, but he looked so anxious that she smiled. 'I believe you. But all the same, I can't stay. I have to go, really I do. I promised I wouldn't be long.'

'Meet me tomorrow!'

'I couldn't! It wouldn't be proper.'

'Oh, hang being proper! No, I don't mean that exactly...' He shook his head in exasperation. 'I don't know how to put it. You must think I'm an idiot!

You see, I've never been in this situation before. But I must see you again. Just a few minutes. Please!'

Lisette was strongly tempted. Her experience of young men was not wide, but this one seemed much nicer than any she had met before. 'I'll try,' she said at last. 'It'll have to be in the afternoon. I have lessons in the morning.'

'At two?'

'Here?'

'Here. You'll come? That's wonderful!'

'Lisette!' Lisette came back with a guilty start to the parlour. Miss Petrie was looking worried. 'You were miles away just then. I think you must have caught something,' she said and added decisively, 'No more walks for you until we're sure you're not sick.'

'No, no, I'm very well,' Lisette exclaimed in fright. 'Really I am!' And she set about convincing her governess that she was, with such success that there was no further talk of remaining indoors the next day.

The next afternoon Lisette begged to be allowed to look again for specimens for her notebook. Miss Petrie readily agreed and suggested that they all three of them set off straight away. 'I shall have to be back before a quarter to three,' she said. 'I have things I must do.'

'I could go alone if it is inconvenient,' said Lisette eagerly.

'Thank you, but I'm quite sure your uncle would not like me to leave you to look after Pip while I do other things,' said Miss Petrie with a smile. 'No, Lisette, we'll go now. There's plenty of time.'

Lisette was unused to subterfuge. The last thing she wanted was to have Pip on her hands when she went out to meet her exciting new acquaintance. It was only half past one. With luck, she thought, she could arrange to have a little time to herself, when she could slip away.

She was luckier than she deserved. Pip wanted to stay close to the house, where most of the leaves had already faded or even vanished, and when Miss Petrie saw Pip's sister looking longingly over to the other side she suggested that Lisette had ten minutes to herself again. 'No more, mind!'

Lisette sped off back to where she had met 'Mr Smith'. He was waiting for her. She was suddenly overcome with shyness.

'Hallo,' he said. 'I'm jolly glad to see you—I never really thought you'd come.'

'I...I...er...I shouldn't have. My governess would be so disappointed in me if she knew I was meeting you.'

'Rubbish! Tavy is a good sport. She wouldn't mind a bit!' he said heartily.

'Tavy? You mean Miss Petrie? You know her?'

'Oh! Er... Well, as a matter of fact, I do. In fact, she's the one I've come to Wychford to see. Only it's a touch difficult.'

'You're a friend of Miss Petrie's? Is that why you wanted me to meet you again—so that I would agree to give her a message or something?' Lisette was too young to hide her hurt.

'Oh, Lord, no!' Harry said hastily. 'Not at all. You mustn't believe—'

'What else am I to believe?'

Harry stared at her in dismay, and Lisette suddenly felt she wanted to get away. 'I think I'll go,' she said stiffly. 'They'll be looking for me.'

'No! Don't go like this! It's not what you think at all! Look, I'll tell you something, but you must promise to keep it a secret.'

'What is it?' said Lisette, still rather stiff.

'My real name is Petrie. Harry Petrie. Tavy is my sister.'

'Your *sister*?' Lisette felt a smile spreading over her face. 'Really? Are you the one in the Army?'

'She's talked about me?'

'Only a little. But why does it have to be a secret? I'm sure my uncle wouldn't mind your coming up to the house to visit her.'

'I'm sure he won't—when one or two things have been sorted out. But you'll have to take my word for it. It's got to stay a secret for the moment.'

'You're not in any kind of trouble, are you?'

'No! No, I promise you. It's more that Tavy doesn't want him to know about me. Yet. The situation is a touch delicate, take my word for it. Do you think you could do that? Keep it all a secret?'

'Oh, yes! I suppose it's really rather exciting. I'm so glad you told me—Miss Petrie is the nicest governess I've ever had.'

Harry started to chuckle. 'I'll tell her that, she'll be pleased. She's had enough experience of governesses herself.'

'What did you say?'

'Governess*ing*! I meant governess*ing*! She's had a lot of experience. Er…when can I see you again? Can you get away tomorrow? At the same time?'

'I'll try.'

He looked at her, hesitated, then said awkwardly, 'I'd like to know you a lot better, Lisette. I've not met anyone like you before.'

Lisette looked down. 'Thank you. I haven't known anyone like you. Perhaps, when Miss Petrie has told my uncle that you're her brother, we could meet properly. But I think I must warn you. Edward is very strict. He doesn't really wish me to make any new friends before I come out next year.'

'Then it's perhaps better he shouldn't know about me till next year. Then I'll come to London and we can be officially introduced.'

Lisette was doubtful. 'I shall be mixing with all sorts of people in Society,' she said awkwardly. 'I don't somehow think we'll visit the same places in London.'

Harry started to say something, then seemed to stop himself. 'We might,' he said with a mysterious look on his face. 'Meanwhile, we'll make do with what we've got, shall we?'

Lisette nodded. 'I'll come tomorrow at the same time,' she said. 'Goodbye, for now.'

'Goodbye, Lisette! You'd better leave it to me to tell Tavy that you know about her and me. She's going to be a little annoyed at first.'

Harry watched her as she sped through the trees back to his sister. He felt guilty at betraying Octavia's secret to her pupil, and his sister would have every right to be more than a little annoyed! But he couldn't have let Lisette carry on thinking he was interested in someone else! And she seemed to take it in her stride. She wouldn't tell. What a darling girl she was! If he could be sure of winning Lisette Barraclough, he might listen to his father and settle down after all! The temptation to tell her who he really was, the son of the Earl of Warnham and acceptable anywhere in London, had been very strong. But he had stopped himself just in time, and he was glad. He had betrayed enough of Octavia's secrets. Besides, it was a bit of a lark passing himself off as the brother of a poor governess! It hadn't seemed to make any difference to Lisette. He rather thought she quite liked him. For a moment Harry was lost in happy contemplation of a rosy future with Lisette Barraclough. Then he came back to the present. As soon as he saw her he would tell Octavia that Lisette knew they were brother and sister. He mustn't leave her in the dark. Harry went off to walk discreetly in the woods and wait for three o'clock.

But his honest intentions were foiled. Octavia didn't appear at three. Harry waited for an hour, then had to accept she had been prevented from coming and went back to the inn.

While Harry was waiting in the woods Octavia was in the library with her employer, who had taken her there to inform her that Mrs Barraclough would be arriving at Wychford the next day. She received this news with a sense of foreboding. Nothing she had heard of the lady encouraged her to think she would approve of Edward Barraclough's decision to dismiss Miss Froom and employ someone so much younger. Octavia was sure there would be changes, though she was not at all afraid that there was anything wrong with what she had taught the girls. In spite of Pip's illness they had done well. So much so, that when she saw how intrigued Pip had been with the dancing lesson, she had relaxed her academic routine, and had taught them some of the ways and manners of Society. This was, of course, in direct conflict with what Edward Barraclough had told her in their first interview. But he wasn't aware that no one could have had a more intensive, or more highly polished training than the Lady Octavia Petrie!

'I seem to have lost your attention, Miss Petrie.'

Octavia jumped and dropped Pip's jacket, which she had been carrying when Mr Barraclough had called her in. 'I'm...I'm sorry,' she said in confusion, picking it up. 'Please excuse me! This news has come as something of a surprise.'

'I did not know myself before an hour ago.'

'I was going over in my mind the differences Mrs Barraclough's arrival might make to my routine with your nieces. I imagine she would want to take over some of their training?'

'Training? What training? Do you mean their lessons? Mrs Barraclough would hardly wish to do any teaching!' His tone was cool. 'I have no idea of the state of her health. She was presumably well enough to travel, but I have no further information. Unless she is seriously incapacitated she will almost certainly wish to take over the running of the house and so on, and I shall hardly be needed. After the end of the week I shall expect to spend much less time at Wychford.'

Octavia looked down. It was better so, she told herself. It must be better for everyone!

His hard grey eyes rested on her hands, which had a painfully tight hold of Pip's jacket, and he echoed her thoughts. 'Though my sister-in-law's sudden arrival is inconvenient from many points of view, it has come at a good time for me. For us. I have decided that the less we see of each other the better, Octavia,' he said quietly.

She nodded. 'Of course. I know things can be...difficult between us. And I would not wish to embarrass you...'

'Embarrass!' He got up and stood gazing out of the window. 'It's not a question of embarrassment! Don't think I've dismissed what I feel for you so lightly! But I refuse to insult you by asking you to be my mistress, and, since I have no intention at the moment to marry, any other relationship is not possible. I intend to avoid you as much as I can. It is the only rational solution.'

Octavia felt a sudden surge of rage. *Any other relationship is not possible...I intend to avoid you...* Had she been the governess he thought her, this would have been cruel! No discussion, no regret, no attempt to comfort. Only a calm, rational decision, taken without reference to any feelings the poor creature might have herself. No options for governesses! The man was a monster!

For a moment she was strongly tempted to throw his 'rational solution' in his face, tell him who she really was, that she was more than his equal in rank, and probably more familiar than he was with the upper echelons of true Society! What was more, she owned the house he was living in! But two things stopped her. One was that though she was proud of her breeding, it was not in her nature to boast of it. But what moved her far more powerfully was the idea that he might misunderstand her motives for doing so. He might even think that she was pleading with him, hoping that, with the barrier of rank removed, he would declare his love for her on the spot. And that would be intolerable! She would not do it, not on any account! He could wait till he met her in London, and then he could *grovel*!

The thought of Edward Barraclough grovelling to anyone was so absurd that her lips twitched in an involuntary smile. He had turned round in time to see it.

'That amuses you?' he said.

'Not at all, sir. I think you are being very… sensible.' Try as she might, she could not help letting a touch of bitterness in her voice.

'My dear, I wish—'

'There is really no need for another word, sir. May I go?' she asked, standing up with determination.

He lifted his shoulders and let them drop. 'Of course,' he said sombrely.

Octavia was so angry and unhappy that she had difficulty in keeping her patience with the girls for the rest of the day. At dinner she sat quietly, carefully keeping strictly to what a governess might be expected to say and nothing more. It was not an easy occasion. Edward's face was like a thundercloud, and Lisette was not behaving normally, either. She was always quiet, but there was an air of abstraction about her that Octavia would have found strange if she had not been so preoccupied with her own thoughts. Pip had been allowed to join them, and she, too, was quieter than usual. The prospect of her aunt's arrival had subdued even her lively spirit. After dinner Octavia saw Pip to bed, then pleaded a headache and escaped with relief to her own room.

But not very long after there was a tap on the door and Lisette came in. 'I'm so sorry about your head,' she said. 'I asked Mrs Dutton to make up a tisane. It's here. It might help.'

Octavia was sitting in her chair by the window. She took the tray and put it down on the table. 'Thank you, dear,' she said, making an effort to smile. 'You're such a thoughtful girl, Lisette.'

'Miss Petrie, I must talk to you. I have a confession to make.'

Octavia shut her eyes. It probably wasn't anything serious, Lisette was too well behaved. But she had had enough of crises today.

'What is it?' she said, trying to sound sympathetic.

'I like your brother a lot,' said Lisette. 'Too much!'

Octavia's eyes flew open, her headache forgotten. *'What?'* she asked. 'Say that again, Lisette, I can't have heard you properly. You like…?'

'Your brother Harry. I like him. And I ought not to.'

Octavia shut her eyes again. It was too much! She really did not want this!

'Miss Petrie?' Lisette's voice was worried.

It was not going to go away by itself. Octavia pulled herself together and opened her eyes. 'My brother, Harry,' she said slowly. 'You've met him? When? How?'

'I thought you knew! He said he was going to tell you when he saw you this afternoon.'

'I didn't see him this afternoon. Lisette, are you telling me that you met my brother and didn't say a word to me about it?' said Octavia, beginning to get really angry. She had thought she had had enough for today. And now even Harry had let her down. She was surprised and disappointed. How dared he approach Lisette! And, having done so, how *could* he have betrayed his sister to her!

'I met him yesterday when I was gathering leaves in the drive. It was an accident. I didn't know then that he was your brother, of course, though he seemed very nice.'

'I'll have something to say to that brother of mine,' Octavia began ominously.

'No, don't blame him! He was polite and perfectly respectful. Though I don't suppose Edward would approve...'

'I am quite *certain* that Edward wouldn't approve!' said Octavia with complete conviction. 'What's more, nor do I, Lisette!'

Lisette gazed at her in astonishment. 'I thought you'd be pleased! Are you saying he's not good enough? I was afraid Edward might think so, but not you.'

'That has nothing to do with it! Even if...if Harry were the...the son of an earl, I still shouldn't approve of your meeting him like this. It is not right.'

'Well...that's just it, Miss Petrie. There's something I have to ask you about. Something I must confess.'

'You mean...*this* wasn't what you wanted to confess?' Octavia passed a hand over her brow. 'What else is there? What is it, Lisette?'

'Do you think it's very wrong of me to like Lieutenant Petrie? Or wicked of me to want to meet him again when I'm really betrothed to someone else?'

'Betrothed to someone else?' Octavia forgot her headache. 'What do you mean?'

'Before I came here I was promised to someone on Antigua, Miss Petrie. It was my father's last wish that I should marry him.'

'I...I don't understand,' Octavia said carefully. 'I thought your parents wanted you to come to England?'

'They did! I don't understand it either! But Ricardo assured me he had spoken to Papa the night before he died, and that Papa wished me to marry him straight away. He even showed me a letter from Papa. Do you think my father's last wishes ought to be sacred? Ricardo said they ought to be.'

'I...I think your father would want you to be happy, Lisette. Did he tell you himself that he wanted you to marry this Ricardo?'

'No. I thought he wanted me to come to England, as you said. That's what Edward and Uncle Henry say, and they're my guardians now. It was just the letter…'

Octavia paused. 'I don't think you should give too much importance to that letter,' she said slowly. 'You have only Ricardo's word for when it was written, or what was said that night. If he was desperately in love with you, he might have stretched the truth a little in order to persuade you to defy your uncles. He knew you wouldn't have done so otherwise. But…what about you? What do you want?'

Lisette shook her head. 'I don't know! I would have married Ricardo on Antigua. But now…. I don't know. It's different here. Do you think I'm betrothed?'

'That's easy to answer! I'm quite sure you aren't. You're in the care of your uncles until you are twenty-one, and you can't be betrothed without their consent!'

Lisette broke into a smile. 'So you don't think I'm wicked for wanting to see your brother again?'

'No, I don't. But I don't think you should meet him, all the same.' Octavia leaned forward. 'You've asked for my opinion, Lisette, and I shall give it to you. Your guardians are quite right. It would be very wrong to let you get too fond of *any*one, before you've had a chance to sample the world outside. I assure you, it's not a question of social sphere, or eligibility, or previous promises. Anyone who loved you would do all they could to save you from making such a mistake.'

Lisette nodded and looked down. 'I'm not to see Lieutenant Petrie again.'

'Not before you go to London. After you've been introduced to Society, it might be different. You might meet him then. It's only a few months away.'

'But...it isn't very likely, is it? We shan't move in the same circles.'

Octavia took Lisette's hands in hers. 'I'm *sure* you will meet my brother in London! Trust me. But until then I want your word that you will not try to see him here again. Do I have it?'

She waited until Lisette gave a reluctant nod, then went on, 'Thank you. And just think, Lisette. You told me once that when your uncle has made up his mind he doesn't usually change it. If he should catch you with Harry at the moment, I'm sure he would be so angry that he would banish Harry, and forbid you to see him ever again. Is that what you want?' She waited while this sank in, then continued, 'Of course you don't. But once you are out, after the beginning of the Season, he might be more prepared to listen to you. Be patient, Lisette. Things might turn out better than you can hope.'

'Can't I even say goodbye?'

'I'll see Harry and explain. It's really too risky, my dear. Your aunt could arrive at any time tomorrow, and you will be expected to be there to welcome her. Besides, there'll be more people about. I'll slip down to the inn tomorrow morning to see Harry and make sure he understands. Don't look like that, Lisette! Remember my promise!'

The next morning was full of disturbance and bustle. Mrs Dutton was seriously put out at Mrs Barraclough's sudden decision to come earlier than expected to Wychford, and spent all morning organising extra staff, discussing menus and making sure the best bedroom was ready for her new mistress. As she came out of her room, Octavia was surprised to find the housekeeper urging two of the men to take care with a large chair that was being carried up the narrow stairs to the room above Pip's.

'I believe it belonged to Mrs Carstairs, Miss Petrie,' explained the housekeeper. 'Mr Barraclough says it was in the top tower room when he first came to visit Mrs Carstairs, and he wants it taken back there. Apparently she spent most of her time up there when she was still well enough. The chair's an ugly old thing, but I'm told she loved it. She had it brought down to her bedchamber when she was ill. But it can't stay there. Mrs Barraclough is going to use that room, and the master doesn't think his sister-in-law would like it. So the chair is to go upstairs again.' From Mrs Dutton's expression she could well have done without the extra work!

So that room on the top floor of the tower had been a favourite of her aunt's? Octavia could well imagine it! She had only once taken a quick look inside it, and had been very intrigued. It was a strange room with a slanting ceiling and windows on nearly every side. The views were wonderful, and the tables and shelves were crammed with objects of all kinds— books, pictures, miniatures, ornaments, souvenirs... She had promised herself that she would go back one day to have a better look at it, but the room was normally locked, and Edward Barraclough kept the key. She had somehow never found a way of asking him for it. Today was obviously not the right time. Besides, she had things of her own to do, including a visit to the inn for her talk with Harry.

It was later than Octavia had hoped when she finally managed to slip away from the house to the inn, where she asked for Mr Smith. To her relief the inn was empty of company and she was alone as she waited for her brother in its small parlour. Harry had clearly not been expecting a visitor so early. He came downstairs, shrugging on his coat and, at the same time, making a vain effort to tie his cravat.

Octavia shook her head at him. 'Where's your man?' she demanded. 'He should be doing this!'

'Don't be a fool, Tavy! I'm in disguise, remember? I sent Crocker back to Ashcombe! What the devil are you doing here at this hour?'

'Here, you'd better let me do that,' she said, looking with a critical eye at his efforts. 'I can talk while I do it. I can't stay long. They're expecting Mrs Barraclough today, and I ought to be there. But I had to see you. Why did you have to tell Lisette that you were my brother?'

'She thought I was your lover, or something! I couldn't let her believe that, Tavy! She would have been put off before she'd even begun to know me! I was sure you'd understand.'

'You shouldn't have been speaking to her at all, Harry Petrie! But that's water under the bridge now. There are more important things to say. I've come to stop you from making a big mistake.'

'If you mean to warn me against Lisette, then I tell you you're wasting your time! She's the loveliest thing I've seen in my life, and I intend to marry her!' Harry said belligerently.

'And I wish you good luck in that, though you might have competition! But you'll still need her uncle's consent before you could—or do you intend to fly off to Gretna with her?'

'Of course not, dammit! What an improper suggestion!'

'Then you'd better listen to me. I know Edward Barraclough. He's very protective of Lisette, and would *never* consider you suitable if he found you were having clandestine meetings with her. And I wouldn't blame him! She's only sixteen years old, for goodness' sake! I'm surprised at you. What were you thinking of?'

'We met by chance the first time. And then... It was the only way I could get to know her, Tavy!'

'Rubbish! It would sink every hope you might have about the girl if her uncle were to find out. Harry, I mean what I say. You mustn't try to see Lisette again, not here in Wychford. She's too young and too innocent to know any better. But you— you're certainly old enough to know what you're doing, and it's wrong! What sort of man will Edward Barraclough think you are if he finds out that you're persuading his precious niece to misbehave like this?' Harry, looking slightly shame-faced, said he hadn't thought of it that way.

Octavia's voice softened. 'I know you haven't. But if you'll take my advice, you'll be patient. I've promised Lisette that I shall make sure she'll meet you in London, and you must wait till then. Once she has been presented to Society, then you can plead your case with her. Not before.'

'But she's so beautiful! Tavy, you don't know what it's like to be in love. I'd give up the Army and settle down like a shot if I could be sure it would be with Lisette Barraclough.'

This was a new Harry. Octavia was impressed in spite of herself. She said gently, 'Then you must bide your time and take your chance. You might well win. But don't spoil it by pursuing her now.'

'What will she think? I promised to meet her this afternoon.'

'I've made sure she understands the situation. She knows I'm talking to you. Trust me, Harry!'

'I suppose I'll have to,' her brother said glumly. 'It's clear you don't want me to meet her at the moment.'

'Much as I love you, I can't let you. I would stop you if you tried. And now I must hurry back. Leave here as soon as you can, Harry. I shall probably see you in a week or two at Ashcombe! Meanwhile, behave!' She hugged him. 'Smile! Three months isn't long! Think of what Papa will say!'

He grinned at her then. 'He'll be amazed! The last time I saw him I wouldn't hear of staying at home, and now...'

Octavia laughed and kissed him. 'Look after yourself, my dearest. Things will turn out right, you'll see. For you, at least. Goodbye!' She turned and hurried out of the inn.

She and Harry had been so absorbed in their conversation that they had failed to notice an important-looking carriage that had stopped briefly outside, long enough for the driver to ask for directions, and had then carried on. Julia Barraclough was arriving at Wychford.

Chapter Ten

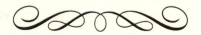

Julia Barraclough had sharp features, and narrow hands and feet of which she was inordinately proud. She thought it showed her breeding. She affected an aristocratic drawl, too, though her comments were usually as sharp as her nose. She was suspicious of everything her brother-in-law had done, including not only his choice of governess, but the freedom he had then granted her. She had not been very long in the house before she was making her views plain.

'Where is this Miss Petrie?' she demanded, after Edward and the girls had greeted her. 'I expected her to be here to give me an account of her work! Where is she?'

'I think Miss Petrie went out for a walk, Aunt Julia,' said Lisette, timidly.

'Out for a walk? What was she thinking of? Her employer is due at any time, and the governess goes out for a walk! Did you know about this, Edward?'

'Not exactly. But I don't find it a matter of concern, Julia. Miss Petrie is very conscientious. You arrived rather earlier than we expected, you know. She probably thought she would give you time to have a rest and a talk with the family, before you took up the reins. You can talk to her at dinner.'

'At dinner? Surely you do not allow the servants to dine with the family?'

There was a slight pause before Edward said in an even tone, 'Miss Petrie is hardly a servant. And the girls benefit considerably from her conversation at the table.'

'We shall have to make other arrangements now that I am here. I have no wish to be edified by the conversation of a country bumpkin!'

'That is a pity. I'm not quite sure how to arrange matters to satisfy you. As long as I am at Wychford, Miss Petrie will continue to dine with us,' said Edward courteously but firmly.

'Well, that won't be for very long, will it?' Julia said sweetly. 'But…did I hear you say 'girls'? Does that mean Lisette *and* Philippa? I do hope you haven't allowed Philippa to join you for dinner! She's far too young to be down in the evenings. She should be in the nursery with the governess. Miss Froom would have understood that, of course. A most superior woman, from all accounts. She was for many years governess to the Ledburys, you know. Dear Daisy Ledbury was quite upset when I told her you had let Miss Froom go.'

'Have you met Miss Froom?'

'Of course not! But I met Lady Ledbury in London while I was passing through, though I didn't meet her husband. He was staying with friends in the country.'

'You surprise me. However, Miss Froom was, in my opinion, completely unsuitable for my nieces. We were all glad to see the back of her.'

'That's right, Aunt Julia! Miss Froom was a horror!' cried Pip, unable to hold her tongue any longer. 'And you mustn't say things about Miss Petrie! Miss Petrie is the best governess you could want!'

'She has apparently failed to teach you to be quiet until you're spoken to, Philippa!'

'Miss Petrie likes to hear what I say!'

Lisette took Pip's hand. 'Shall I see if Miss Petrie is coming up the drive, Edward?'

'Do!' said her uncle with relief. 'Your Aunt Julia would probably like to have a rest. Tell me, Julia, are you completely cured?'

Lisette and Pip made their escape.

'It's going to be awful,' said Pip gloomily. 'I'd forgotten what Aunt Julia was like. She hasn't even brought Uncle Henry with her. He's not much but he's a lot better than her.'

'Uncle Henry wanted to stay in London for a few days longer,' said Lisette. 'He was going to look for a suitable house for us to rent there. And Aunt Julia was worried about us, so she said she would leave him and come down to Wychford alone.'

'If I were Uncle Henry I'd want to stay in London for *weeks*! I hope he does! Edward said he would leave as soon as Uncle Henry arrived, and I don't know what it will be like without Edward!'

'No,' sighed Lisette.

'Perhaps Miss Petrie would agree to stay a bit longer?'

'I wish she would, but I somehow don't think Aunt Julia will want her to. We shall have to see, Pip. I suppose it isn't too long before we all go to London.'

'Oh, why couldn't things stay as they were? We were so happy at Wychford with Edward and Miss Petrie! I don't want to go to London! I love this house!'

'So do I. Though I'd like to see London...and the people there. But wait! There's Miss Petrie coming up the drive. Pip, you're not to repeat the things Aunt Julia said about her, do you understand? They would hurt her.'

'Well, I won't! Miss Petrie! Miss Petrie!' and with her usual enthusiasm Pip ran off down the drive.

Octavia hugged Pip, then looked to where Lisette was waiting for her. Her heart gave a pang. It was so like the first time she had come to Wychford, and she had met Pip, then Lisette, almost at this very spot. She looked at Wychford. The house looked somehow closed...remote... It was astonishing how it changed with the weather!

'This is nice,' she said, as she came up, with Pip hanging on to her arm. 'I must go for a walk more often!'

'Did you enjoy it?' asked Lisette. It was clear to Octavia, at least, what she meant. Lisette could guess that she had been to see Harry.

'It was entirely successful, Lisette,' she said with a smile. 'It cleared the air completely.'

Pip looked slightly puzzled, but Lisette breathed an audible sigh of relief. She said, 'Aunt Julia arrived while you were out. Her leg seems to be not nearly as bad as we thought.'

'So your uncle will be leaving us soon?' said Octavia, trying to sound casual.

'Not yet. Uncle Henry has stayed in London and Aunt Julia can't manage on her own. He'll come down in a week or so, and Edward will leave then.'

Octavia didn't know whether to be glad or sorry at this news. Of course, things would not in any case be the same with Julia Barraclough there. 'I must hurry,' she said. 'Your aunt will be annoyed that I wasn't here when she arrived.'

'She was,' said Pip. 'Very.' Octavia saw Lisette frown and shake her head at her sister and she laughed.

'Don't worry,' she said. 'I deserve her disapproval. Come on! We mustn't keep Mrs Barraclough waiting any longer.' Octavia started to walk very fast, and, laughing and protesting, the girls tried to keep up with her.

* * *

Dinner that evening was once again rather strained. Mrs Barraclough made her disapproval of Octavia's presence at the table very plain by addressing her remarks exclusively to her elder niece and her brother-in-law. Lisette obviously felt her aunt's rudeness even more than Octavia, and was painfully embarrassed. She hardly said anything at all. Octavia remained calm, and responded to such remarks as came her way from Edward Barraclough with perfect self-possession, but did not feel inspired to expand on them. Even Pip was quiet. As they rose after the meal, Mrs Barraclough said coldly, 'I should like to see you in the library, Miss Petrie. In ten minutes, if you please. I should like a few minutes first to talk in *private* with my *family*.'

'Certainly, ma'am. In ten minutes.' Octavia left the room. If this was a foretaste of what life would be like under the new regime, she was not sorry it was to be short-lived! Mrs Barraclough was worse even than she had feared. An overbearing snob! But worse was to come.

In the library Mrs Barraclough gave her a merciless grilling, during which Octavia was forced to reply with less than complete candour. Some of the questions verged on the offensive, and Octavia dealt with these as she thought they deserved, with cool disdain—a reaction that did not endear her to her employer. But just when she had started to congratulate herself on avoiding the pitfalls in Mrs Barraclough's interrogation, her complacency was brought to an abrupt end when Mrs Barraclough suddenly said,

'I think I saw you at the inn in the village this morning. Who was the young man?'

Octavia did her best but she could not prevent the colour rising in her cheeks. 'Did you, ma'am?' she said, playing for time.

'I did, so don't try to fob me off, young woman! Who was he? Does Mr Barraclough know you have a follower in the neighbourhood? I can't imagine he does. It's something I have never allowed among the servants in my household!'

'Mr Barraclough has never asked me what I do in my free time, Mrs Barraclough. But you need have no further worry about the young man in question. I was there to bid him goodbye. He is leaving today.'

'And how long has your affair with him been going on?'

'There has been no affair,' said Octavia, suppressing her anger. 'He has been here for a mere three days. I assure you, Mrs Barraclough, you need not concern yourself with him any longer.'

'That is surely for me to decide, Miss Petrie! I insist on knowing his name, if you please!'

Octavia hesitated, then said, 'Smith. Mr Smith. He is an old friend of my family.'

'Really?' Mrs Barraclough's tone conveyed what she thought of this. 'Well, unlike Mr Barraclough, I do not permit mysterious walks, or secret assignations, Miss Petrie. For the remainder of your employment here, you will please inform me when you intend to leave the house.'

Octavia took a deep breath. 'Does that include my afternoon walks with the girls, ma'am?'

'Yes, of course it does! Well, I think I have made matters clear. I suppose, since my brother-in-law wishes it, you will continue to sit with us at dinner. At least when he is in residence at Wychford. Not otherwise. But I do not expect you to take part in any conversation. Your views are a matter of indifference, at least to me. Miss Froom would, of course, have appreciated that fact, but then Miss Froom is a well-trained servant and knows her place. That is all, Miss Petrie. I shall see you again tomorrow or the next day, after I've had an opportunity to judge what you have been doing with my nieces. You may go.'

Octavia came out of the library, quivering with suppressed rage. She had never in her life been spoken to in such a manner. What was more, she did not believe that her mother would ever have spoken to any of her governesses so. The woman was a viper, an ill-mannered, ill-bred viper!

Octavia thought she would explode if she didn't get some air. She walked rapidly up the stairs, fetched a thick shawl and slipped out of the side door on to the terrace. The sky was stormy, and a cold wind was blowing. Clouds raced across the face of the moon, sending eerie shadows over the terrace. Octavia hardly noticed any of it as she walked swiftly to and fro in an effort to master her fury, muttering imprecations, kicking a branch blown there by the wind quite unnecessarily out of the way. The branch was hard and her slippers thin. It hurt. She swore, stopped and nursed her foot.

By the time she put it to the ground again she had recovered enough of her equilibrium to start laughing at herself. She had always thought she had the least pride, the least self-consequence, of any of the Petries. She and Harry had always laughed at Arthur's air of self-importance. And here she was, giving way to a fit of fury just because some woman from the Colonies had dared to insult her. Lady Octavia Petrie at her most top lofty!

'If you stand still for very much longer you'll get cold.' The voice came from the shadows at the edge of the terrace. She peered in its direction and could just make out the figure of a man. Edward Barraclough. He went on, 'That was quite a fit of rage. I can guess what—or who, rather—caused it. She's a most unpleasant woman. Don't let her affect you, Octavia.'

'How can I not? She is in charge here.' She stopped and pulled herself together. 'And this is a most improper conversation. You should not be saying such things to me. Mrs Barraclough is your sister-in-law.'

'The history of my battles with Julia is a long one. She is aware of what I think of her.'

'You at least are in the fortunate position of being able to answer back!'

He came towards her. She could now see that he had been smoking a cigar. 'What's wrong? In the past you've quite often obviously disagreed with something I've said to you. I've even been amused at your efforts *not* to answer back. But I don't remember your ever being as angry as this.'

'That's because you have never made me feel like a servant! Mrs Barraclough does. I find it intolerable!'

He looked at her with a faint smile. 'That duchess air of yours is most intriguing, Octavia. Where did you pick it up?'

Octavia said woodenly, 'I don't know what you mean. Sir.'

He shrugged his shoulders and threw his cigar away. 'Julia has an unfortunate effect on a good many people. She is essentially a cold woman with very little imagination. I hope you'll stay with the girls as long as possible. They need you, they need your affection, your warmth.'

He was very close. His body was sheltering her from the wind. The temptation to lean against it was very strong... She made an effort and pulled herself away. 'I'm not sure...' she stammered. 'I'm not sure I can. The two months is very nearly up...' The moment of weakness had passed. 'No,' she said in a firmer voice. 'I can't stay longer. In fact, I somehow doubt I shall last even as long as that! I don't think your sister-in-law approves of me.'

'It's a damnable mess,' he said bitterly. Unconsciously he echoed Pip's sentiments of the afternoon. 'Why does everything have to change? Why the complications? It was so pleasant at first...' He turned again to her. 'I'm off to London tomorrow for two days. Don't let her get you down, Octavia. I expect to see you still here when I return. And now you must go in. Come!'

Julia had disliked Miss Petrie from the start. She disliked the obvious affection her nieces had for their governess. She disliked Miss Petrie's youth and charm. And she particularly disliked the manner in which she, Julia Barraclough, had been made to feel somehow impertinent during her interview with someone who was, after all, no more than a servant! It took a few minutes before she could feel composed enough to walk out of the library and go upstairs to her room. Once there she gazed critically round. What a dreadful place this house was! Old-fashioned furniture, dark rooms, musty passages... Impossible to keep clean! The sooner they could leave and go to London the better.

The maids had been careless. The curtains at the window overlooking the terrace were not quite pulled to, and with a frown Julia went over to close them. Her eye was caught by two figures down below, clearly visible in a patch of moonlight. Julia quietly opened the window in order to see better. Edward and Miss Petrie very close together...too close. Well,

well, well! *That* was how Edward had kept himself amused at Wychford! *That* was why he was so eager to have the governess at his dinner table! She leaned further out as they moved to go inside. Edward even had his arm round the woman. Julia's lip curled. Typical! Edward up to his tricks as usual! As for the young woman…!

She jumped back, gasping and spluttering as the rain spout over her window suddenly emptied the contents of its gutter on to her head. This *awful* house! She was drenched with foul-smelling water and spattered with dead leaves. Her cap sodden, her hair dripping down over her shoulders, she yelled angrily for her maid. The girl came running, but stopped, amazed, at the sight of her mistress. Her exclamations were soon cut short, however, and she was sent scurrying round to find more help, towels and hot water. After some minutes of furious activity accompanied by a stream of impatient commands, the maids had bathed Julia and put her to bed with a warm drink. Then they left, thankful to escape, and the room was quiet again.

Julia leaned back against her pillows with a sigh of relief. As she settled down for the night she was filled with a warm feeling of righteousness. Miss Petrie would have to go. Assignations at the inn with 'Mr Smith', an affair at home with her employer… For all her airs the girl was nothing but a light-skirt! Julia looked thoughtful. It wouldn't be easy to get rid of Octavia Petrie. Edward would probably deny

Julia's accusations, and he could be annoyingly obstinate. He might well demand proof if she tried to tell him about the episode with Mr Smith. Well, proof was what she would give him, and the inn was the place to start looking for it. She would send her maid down there tomorrow. She blew out her candle and composed herself for sleep.

The next day was a miserable one for Octavia. Edward Barraclough set off early for London, and Mrs Barraclough made excuse after excuse to keep the girls from her. Lessons were suspended, and to keep her occupied she was given set after set of laundry sheets and bills to check. When she offered to take the girls for their usual walk in the afternoon, Mrs Barraclough smiled coldly and said the weather was not at all suitable—she wished to keep them at her side. A fire was lit in the large salon, and the girls and their aunt spent the afternoon there, while Octavia sat alone in the small parlour. It was no consolation to her when the door to the salon was opened and she heard Pip's voice raised in protest. It was followed by an angry order from Mrs Barraclough, the sound of a scuffle, and then the door was slammed shut again. Octavia's heart ached for her charges, but she felt completely helpless. She was also very puzzled. She could tell that Mrs Barraclough had not liked her, but the woman was treating her as if she had the plague! What had gone wrong?

She and Pip had supper in the schoolroom. This was no hardship, but afterwards she spent most of the night lying awake, and got up feeling unrefreshed.

The day was no better than the one before. Mrs Barraclough announced at breakfast that she was taking her nieces to Guildford.

'Good!' said Pip. 'We can take Miss Petrie with us. I want her to meet my dancing teacher.'

'I think not,' said Mrs Barraclough. 'We shall be visiting friends afterwards, and I hardly think they would be interested in meeting your governess, Philippa.'

'But—'

'Be silent!' Mrs Barraclough turned to Octavia. 'I do wish you had managed to teach Philippa how to behave in company, Miss Petrie. She has always been a difficult child, but she seems to have got worse under your regime. We shall have to see what can be done before she becomes quite ungovernable. I have a good mind to leave her behind today!'

'Oh, would you? Please, Aunt Julia!' Pip's eyes were shining and she clasped her hands in supplication. 'Miss Petrie and I could have a day to ourselves, and you and Lisette could visit Mrs Allardyce in peace. Please say you will!'

This was not the response Mrs Barraclough had expected or desired. After a surprised pause she said,

'I prefer to keep an eye on you myself, Philippa. Finish your breakfast and get ready.'

Octavia followed Pip up to her room. 'Pip dearest, you must try to be good today. Your Aunt Julia is strict, but I'm sure she has your best interests at heart. Show her that I *have* managed to teach you something.'

'She doesn't like you. She wants to hurt you.'

'Pip!' Octavia sat down on the bed and held Pip before her. 'If I'm honest with you, will you be grown up enough to understand and not repeat what I say?' Pip nodded. 'You will? Good! I think your aunt disapproves of me, I'm not sure why. There's not much I can do about it. But that's not important. What is important is that she cares about *you*. She wants you to be a success, and she's right. You have to live with her after I've gone, remember, and you'll be much happier if you do your best to understand her point of view. Will you try? It would cheer me up no end if I heard when you all come back this evening that your aunt is pleased with you.' She gave Pip a kiss and pushed her away. 'Now, be off with you! Don't trip over your toes at the dancing lesson!'

Pip ran to the door, then came back to throw her arms round Octavia and hug her. 'Oh, Miss Petrie, I do love you! And I will try!'

'That's good!' said Octavia, and watched as Pip raced along the landing. 'Slowly, Pip! Slowly!' she called, smiling.

* * *

The sounds of departure died and Octavia was alone in the house. Even the servants seemed to be hiding. They were probably in the kitchen at the back. It was warm there, and the day was cold. It would soon be winter.

She wandered about the house like a lost spirit, until she found herself, she was not quite sure how, at the foot of the stairs leading to the room at the top of the tower. The room would be locked of course, it always was. She might just have a look... She slowly mounted the narrow stairs and found she had been right—the door was shut. And locked? She gave it a gentle push, and to her surprise it slowly opened. She went in.

A faint fragrance hung in the air, not sweet but herby, dry, intriguing. The chair she had seen being carried up was in front of the fireplace. There was even a fire in the hearth. It was almost out, but there was still a faint glow at its heart. Had it been lit by the servants who had brought the chair upstairs? Had Mrs Dutton ordered them to light it in order to air the room? It had lasted a long time, if that were so. It didn't matter. Whoever had lit it, she was grateful to them. They had probably left the door unlocked, too.

Octavia coaxed the fire into life again, and added one or two pieces of wood from the basket at the side. Then she wandered over to a table full of knick-knacks, and saw that there was a small framed drawing of herself among them. The picture of another little girl held pride of place. She read the writing below. *Theophania Carstairs, born 1770, died 1778.* So this had been Aunt Carstairs's daughter, her only child. Had she left Wychford to Octavia because she reminded the old lady of the daughter she had lost all those years before? A breath of air, like a sigh, wafted through the room. Octavia looked round. The windows looked firmly shut, but the room was high up. It wouldn't be surprising if there was a draught…

She sat down in the chair. So much sadness. With a heavy heart she thought once again about Julia Barraclough and what her arrival meant to Lisette and Pip. Pip was a very special sort of child, but Julia Barraclough was just the sort of person to rouse the worst in her: critical, overbearing, lacking in perception and full of ideas on discipline. Pip would have a hard time before she learned how to live with her aunt. And what would happen to all that lovely spontaneity while she did? Then there was Lisette… Lisette would never rouse her aunt's disapproval, she was always too anxious to avoid conflict, ready to believe the best of everyone. But the freshness, the charm of her gentle spirit, would be lost under Julia Barraclough's dominating personality. Lisette might well become a meek nonentity, even forced into Julia Barraclough's idea of a 'good' match. Harry just might save her if he was given the chance, but there was nothing Octavia could do about that at the moment. There wasn't much she could do at all.

She looked down in surprise when a tear fell on to her lap. She never cried! Octavia Petrie was famous for it—she never cried, not even when she was quite badly hurt. But the tears did not seem to know this piece of family lore. They came faster and faster, and were soon followed by a sob, and then another. Confused and ashamed, Octavia struggled to find her handkerchief. It wasn't there! It was a little scrap of a thing, it probably wouldn't have been much good anyway, but its loss was the last straw. Octavia hid her face in her hands, lay back in the chair and gave way to a storm of tears. It didn't matter that her hands were dusty, that her face would have streaks of dirt on it. Who was there to see?

She calmed down eventually, in some strange way feeling better...the scent of herbs in the room was even stronger... She closed her eyes. The image of a dark man floated in front of her. He was smiling that special smile of his, one eyebrow faintly raised, the glint in his eyes inviting her to share his amusement... Then he was serious again, telling her he loved her, that all would be well... Octavia felt happy again—and very sleepy.

Edward came back from London to find the house deserted. When one of the servants told him that the family had gone to Guildford for the day, he was quite annoyed, more with himself than anyone else. He should have ignored the strange urge to return that had attacked him in the middle of the morning. There had been no need to hurry back after all!

He wandered restlessly through the house, not quite sure what he was doing. There was an air of expectancy about the place that he could not understand. Eventually he came to the schoolroom. There was nothing of interest there. The schoolbooks were carefully stacked away, the papers on the desk in a neat pile. He turned them over. Laundry lists? Household bills? All noted and recorded in Octavia's handwriting. Edward dropped them back on the desk. What a spiteful woman Julia was! Octavia had offended her in some mysterious way, and she had taken her revenge by giving the governess a clerk's work to do!

How was Octavia being treated today? A visit to the Allardyces would give Julia numerous opportunities to humiliate her—Lavinia Allardyce was almost as great a snob as Julia! Edward stared into space. What the devil was he to do? It wasn't only Octavia who would suffer under Julia. Pip and Lisette would, too, especially when Octavia left. She had done so much for them. Pip was once again the merry little soul he had known in the old days, and the sad look in Lisette's eyes, which had so disturbed him, had almost vanished. For this he was sure he had Octavia to thank. As for himself... Edward swore violently. It seemed he couldn't stop himself from thinking about Octavia Petrie! He knew very well why he had come back early from London. It wasn't the first time it had happened. The truth was he couldn't keep away from Wychford for long while he knew Octavia Petrie was there. And now he had come back to find she was out for the day—what a waste of time!

A window banged shut, startling him out of his reverie. The house was empty, as far as he knew. Did they have an intruder? Edward came out of the schoolroom and looked around, but the house was silent about him. Something told him that it had come from the direction of the tower. High up. He went along the landing to the foot of the narrow staircase that led up to the top and listened. Nothing. All the same... Edward took out his bunch of keys and selected the one that fitted the door upstairs. Then he quietly mounted the stairs.

He found he didn't need his key. The door was slightly open, and through it he could see the light of a fire.

Chapter Eleven

Edward pushed the door further, and bunched his keys inside his fist. If there was an intruder he knew how to deal with him. He went softly in. The fire was glowing, but the room was empty. He stood at the door and the strong, sharp fragrance in the air brought back a vivid picture of Mrs Carstairs as she had been when he first visited her in this very room. She had been lying in that chair over by the fire, and he had hesitated, standing at the door like this. Her black eyes had twinkled at him.

'Come in, come in!' she had said. 'You needn't expect me to stand up for you. It's enough of an effort to get up here at all!' She was thin, but not yet wasted by illness, and her spirit was very much alive. 'Come over here! I want to have a look at you.'

He had advanced into the room. She had nodded. 'Yes. I thought you'd do. I was just thinking up someone like you. I'm pleased to see you again, Mr Barraclough. You're just what I need!' He hadn't quite known how to reply to this, and she had continued, 'You're not fair, of course, but that doesn't matter. I prefer dark men, myself. Do you still wish to rent Wychford when the rest of your family come over to England?'

Her conversation had always been somewhat odd, but never dull. He had enjoyed it. He had visited her several times after that, but each time she had seemed weaker, until she could no longer get up to the room in the tower, even with the help of the servants. That was when the chair had been taken down to her bedchamber. It had been brought back up here again just the other day.

Edward came further into the room. Then he saw that it wasn't empty after all. Octavia Petrie was lying back fast asleep in the chair. She was so tiny that she had been out of sight from the door. Why hadn't she woken up when the window had banged? He came nearer... She was in much the same position she had been in that night in Pip's bedroom. Then she had been in a nightgown and thin wrapper; today she was fully dressed in a plain blue stuff gown, buttoned to the throat. But the sight was as touchingly seductive now as it had been then. He knelt down beside her and saw the streaks of dried tears on her face. His heart melted and he put a gentle hand against her cheek. 'Octavia!' he whispered.

Her eyes opened, and widened as she saw him. Then she smiled and shook her head. 'I know you're not really here,' she said dreamily. 'It's just my imagination. You're in London. But it's nice to have your ghost to keep me company.'

Some bird outside—a rook or gull, perhaps—gave a cackle of laughter, but they didn't hear it.

'I'm here, all right,' said Edward. 'In the flesh. No ghost could possibly feel the way I do at this moment.' He bent forward and kissed her.

She was still half-asleep, but, after a brief hesitation, her lips softened and melted under his. He held her face in both hands and kissed her again, more demandingly, and this time fire ran along his veins as he felt her immediate, and passionate, response. He covered her cheeks, her eyes, the tip of her nose, her chin, with kisses, and, slowly undoing the buttons of her dress with trembling fingers, he kissed her throat, her shoulders, the shadow between her breasts… It wasn't enough. He lifted her bodily out of the chair and held her there in his arms. She felt so light, as if a breath of wind would blow her away, and he was suddenly afraid that he might hurt her, or frighten her with the intensity of his feelings. With great reluctance he gently set her down away from him.

For a moment she stared at him in shock and then smiled when she saw what was in his eyes. Lifting her arms, she wound them round his neck and fiercely pulled him back to her, holding her mouth to his. Not one of Louise's expert blandishments had ever made him feel half such a man, so electrically alive, so startlingly aware of every nerve in his body.

Never before had he felt such a desperate need to keep himself in control, as he knew he must. Never before had it been so difficult. His arms tightened round her and he pressed her to him, her yielding softness sending desire rocketing through his blood. Heaven forgive him, he must stop this, he must! It would soon be too late.

'Octavia,' he said, his throat dry.

'Don't talk,' she murmured, her lips still pressed to his. 'Talking will spoil it. Kiss me again, Edward! Please kiss me again!'

It was no use! He had to respond. Still locked in a kiss, they sank back in front of the leaping fire, lost to the world. He thrust her dress away from her shoulders, kissing the satin skin of her bared breasts....

A breath of air from one of the windows passed through the room, and Octavia shivered in the cool draught. It was the slightest of movements, but it was enough to bring Edward to his senses.

'I...I mustn't!' he said with a groan. 'God help me, I mustn't! You don't know what you're doing, Octavia. How difficult you're making it for me! This is where it must stop.' He unwound her arms from his neck, and drew her dress up over her shoulders again. Then he got up and pulled her to her feet, almost angrily. She stared at him, dazed. Then her face changed—it was as if she woke up. A look of shocked horror came into her eyes and she bent her

head with a sob. Turning away from him, she began
to fasten her dress.

'Octavia—' he said.

She shook her head, still not looking at him.

'Octavia!' he said again.

She put her hands to her ears in an effort to shut
him out. 'Don't! Don't say anything!' she said
hoarsely. 'It happened *again*! I don't know what
came over me, I don't *have* such feelings! Oh, God,
I'm so ashamed! What must you think of me? How
could I have let you...*begged* you to kiss me like
that? Allowed you to...to...touch me... Such wanton
behaviour... Don't look at me like that! I can't bear
it! I can't *bear* it!'

She whirled away from him and ran out of the door
and down the stairs as if she was being pursued by
demons. He heard the door of her room slam.

Edward looked around him. It all looked so innocent. Not at all like a scene for seduction. And yet it
had taken all the strength he had not to seduce
Octavia Petrie, here in this very room, even though
he was fully aware that it would be wrong. He felt
exhausted, battered by a maelstrom of conflicting
emotions...

It was some time before he felt ready to leave Mrs
Carstairs's room, and even then he still wasn't able
to think rationally about what had just happened.
Before checking the fire and locking the room, he
went round all the windows, examining them for
loose catches, or gaps in their frames. There was

nothing. The banging window must be somewhere else. He would get one of the handymen to take a look round the rest of the rooms. But...in that case, where had that sobering breath of air come from? Edward shook his head. Whatever its origin, they both had reason to be grateful to it.

It was no surprise when Miss Petrie sent a message to say that she had a bad head and would stay in her room for the rest of the day. Julia, of course, congratulated herself on winning the battle of attendance at dinner.

'These people are all the same, Edward,' she said. 'Give them a little leeway and they will waste no time in taking advantage of you. But they soon knuckle under if you are firm with them. Miss Petrie has had the day to consider her position, and has now realised that she cannot win. I dare say she will not come down to dinner again. Mrs Allardyce had some similar experiences to recount. Governesses always tend to think themselves a cut above the other servants. Did you know that Lavinia Allardyce is distantly related to the Ledburys?' She hesitated and threw a glance at her nieces. 'Lisette, since Miss Petrie tells us she has the headache and cannot, it seems, perform her duties, I should like you to take Philippa upstairs and see her to bed. She is tired after her day out, and I wish to talk to your uncle. You needn't bother to come downstairs again yourself.'

Edward roused himself. 'Not unless you wish to, Lisette. I should like to hear how your dancing lesson went.'

'Perhaps tomorrow, Edward?' Lisette's voice was subdued. 'I think I should prefer to stay with Pip till she goes to sleep. Aunt Julia is right, she is very tired.'

As the two left the dining room and went up the stairs Pip whispered, 'Can I see Miss Petrie, Lisette? I knew if I asked Aunt Julia she'd say no, so I didn't. But I'd like to tell her how well I behaved.'

'I'll see if she's well enough,' said Lisette with a smile. 'I was proud of you today, Pip, and I think it might do Miss Petrie some good to hear about it. Let me ask her first.'

Miss Petrie wasn't in bed, as they had half-expected. The lamp by the bed was lit, but she was sitting in a chair by the window, gazing out into the darkness. But she turned and smiled when she saw Lisette's head round her door.

'Come in,' she said. 'Where's Pip?'

'I'm here!' Lisette held Pip firmly back. 'We're sorry you have a headache again,' she said. 'Would we be too much for you?'

'Never!' said Miss Petrie. 'Come in.'

'Aunt Julia thought you weren't really ill,' said Pip, looking at her governess's pale cheeks and heavy eyes. 'But I think you look *very* ill, Miss Petrie. I think you should get Edward to send for the doctor.'

'I...I don't think that will be necessary, Pip. It...it's only a bad head. Tell me how you did today.'

'I was very good!' announced Pip. 'I was very good all day.'

'Was your aunt pleased with you?'

'She didn't say so. But she must have been. It was very boring at the Allardyces, though.'

'Poor Pip,' said Lisette with a smile. 'She tried so hard. I was really proud of her.'

'I'm glad. I think that deserves a cuddle, Pip darling.'

Pip needed no second invitation. She clambered on to her governess's lap and hugged her. Miss Petrie shut her eyes, and Lisette said quickly, 'I think that's enough, Pip. We've stayed long enough. You've told Miss Petrie about today, now we must let her rest. Come along.' Pip got down reluctantly and allowed herself to be led to the door. Here Lisette stopped. 'Can I fetch anything for you?'

'Thank you, but no. I shall go to bed very soon, and will be perfectly fit and ready to hear more about your day tomorrow. Goodnight, my dears.'

Pip was very quiet as they left to go to her room. Lisette kept her sister company while one of the maids undressed and washed her, then put her to bed. The maid went away, and Lisette came over to kiss her goodnight.

'Lisette,' said Pip in a troubled voice. 'Miss Petrie was crying.'

'I don't think so, Pip!'

'Yes, she was! It was too dark by the window for you to see, but her cheeks were wet. She was crying.'

Lisette hesitated. Then she said, 'I expect it was the headache. Remember how your head ached when you were ill? Let's hope she's better tomorrow. Goodnight, Pip.'

Lisette went out quietly. She hadn't wanted to worry Pip, but she very much feared that they were about to lose Miss Petrie sooner than they had expected.

Meanwhile, Julia was about to launch her campaign. 'Lavinia Allardyce tells me that Daisy Ledbury is a much wronged wife. Did you know? Ledbury is hardly ever at home, and usually in some very doubtful company. Female company.'

'Well, yes, I had heard something of the sort,' said Edward curtly. The last thing he wanted to hear was gossip repeated from the Allardyce woman. Julia was bound to find some reason to moralise somewhere, and he didn't think he could take it.

'Of course, morals are so slack in England,' she went on. 'Even among persons one might have thought would set an example. Especially to the young.'

'Really?' said Edward in his most repressive tone.

Julia took no notice. 'I had always expected governesses and the like would have a higher standard of behaviour than most,' she went on. 'But apparently it isn't so. Take Miss Petrie, for example.'

Edward stiffened. Julia could not possibly know of the scene in the tower room. Not possibly! Not even any of the servants had been around this afternoon, and Julia and the rest of the family had been in Guildford. So what did she mean? He said coldly, 'If you are about to be unpleasant about Miss Petrie, Julia, then you can save your breath. I know you don't approve of her, though heaven knows why. But I have always been very satisfied with her.'

'I'm sure you have, Edward,' said Julia significantly. 'But did you know she had a lover?'

'A lover? What nonsense is this?'

'No nonsense, my dear. I have made very careful enquiries. Miss Petrie's lover has been staying at the inn in the village. He left just as I arrived—only two days ago.'

Edward stood up. 'Be careful what you say, Julia! I won't have your poisonous tongue slandering a woman I hold in the highest esteem!'

'Yes, well, that's another story, isn't it? She has obviously caught you in her toils, too.'

By a very narrow margin Edward overcame his inclination to take his sister-in-law by the throat and choke her. The events of the afternoon had shaken him to the depths of his being and he was still very much off balance. He was no nearer to understanding what exactly had happened to him up there in the tower room, but to hear Julia, a woman he had always scorned and disliked, dragging Octavia's name

into the dirt like this was more than he would tolerate.

'I don't want to hear any more. I'll leave you to
wallow in your own filth, Julia. I don't want to hear
it.'

'I can prove it!' Julia's voice stopped him at the
door.

He turned round and said slowly, 'If this is one of
your fantasies, then by God, I swear I'll ruin you—
and your husband, too. It wouldn't be difficult. Your
finances are not as safe as you'd like them to be.'

'What an unpleasant thing to say! You sound very
fierce. I would be quite worried if I weren't so sure
of my facts.' She eyed her brother-in-law with interest. 'It seems you are even fonder of Miss Petrie than
I thought. But if that's the case, it's better you should
know the truth about her! That woman has been playing a double game, Edward. The day I arrived she
was not just out for a walk. She was at the inn, enjoying a little idyll with a certain Mr Smith. Smith!
You'd think she could find a better pseudonym for
him!'

'Go on,' said Edward grimly.

'I can answer for their meeting—I saw them myself, and she didn't try to deny it. They were alone
in the inn, enjoying a very intimate conversation,
when I saw them. But there's more to it than that.
When I made enquiries I found that others had seen
them kissing and hugging each other! She was even
seen helping him to dress!' Julia looked at him tri-

umphantly. 'Ask her! I challenge you—ask her who Mr Smith is! Let's see if she tells you.'

Edward stared at her, stunned. Then he shook his head and burst out, 'There's some explanation. There's got to be an explanation! I don't believe that Octavia…that Octavia would do this.' He shook his head. 'I must get out of here. I can't think…' He strode out of the room, through the hall and out into the grounds.

Julia followed him out and watched him striding down the path. She smiled complacently. She was sorry for Edward. Truly sorry! Always so sure of himself, always so ready to criticise others. And now the tables were well and truly turned. It must be quite distressing for him.

Still smiling, she turned to go back inside, but a sudden gust of wind blew the oak door shut in her face. She stared at it in disbelief. Where on earth had that gust of wind come from? *Inside* the house? Impossible! With an impatient exclamation she took the bell pull in her hand and gave it an angry tug. No response. Where were all the servants? Keeping warm in the kitchen, no doubt, and ignoring the needs of their betters! It was cold out here. She pulled the bell again, more vigorously, and the handle came away in her hand. With a cry of pure frustration she threw the thing away and, shivering in the cold wind that had sprung up, she set off round to the kitchen quarters at the side of the house. She would die of cold if she didn't find them soon! Someone would pay for this, she would see to it personally! As for this wretched house...anyone would think it was trying to get rid of her. Well, if it was, she had received the message. They would all leave this ruin as soon as they could, and find a decent place in London. She would deal with the Petrie woman and then set about arranging it... Where *was* the damned door to the kitchen quarters?

Edward walked about the grounds for a while, strenuously resisting any thought of duplicity on Octavia's part. Her honesty, her pride, her sweetness, her wit—all the qualities he treasured in her—were powerful arguments against Julia's accusations. His judgement could not, *could* not have been so wrong! But as his temper cooled, reason started to take over. He reminded himself that Julia would not have made these accusations without very good grounds. She was malicious, but not stupid. There must be, must be a mistake somewhere! He would have to go down to the inn himself, if only to scotch the story.

He set off for the village, convinced he would soon have an explanation. Then he would deal with his sister-in-law as she deserved!

It was getting late, but the inn was still open and the landlord was perfectly prepared to talk. Yes, he had had a young gentleman by the name of Smith staying with him, as nice a gentleman as you could find. And handsome with it. He'd wager the lad had been a soldier, he had the air of one about him. No, he couldn't answer for any visitors, not personally. But Maggie, one of the maids, had seen a young lady at the inn with him. Very affectionate they'd been. He thought she'd said it was the governess from the big house, but he could be mistaken, o' course. Did Mr Barraclough wish to question the girl himself?

Edward was still hoping for a misunderstanding. Octavia had apparently admitted meeting Mr Smith at the inn, but perhaps the maid had been mistaken in what she saw? When the landlord produced her, he put the question.

'Oh, no, sir!' said Maggie, giving him a dimpled smile. 'Most affectionate they were, huggin' and kissin'. They hadn't spent the night together, mind! But it was clear enough to anyone that they knew each other very well indeed—if you know what I mean. And it's true that he was not what you might call properly dressed when I first saw them. No, they was very fond of each other, of that I'm certain sure. Lovely to see them, it was. Him so handsome, and her so pretty, like.'

Edward left the inn and walked back to Wychford in a daze. He went straight to the library and poured himself a large brandy. And another. He couldn't understand it. Every instinct he possessed told him that there was something wrong. Octavia Petrie was honest. That he would swear to! But the evidence... How could she possibly have been so passionately responsive to him, if she was having an affair with another man? How could she have seemed so genuinely distressed, so movingly innocent when she realised how her behaviour must look?

Or was he being incredibly naïve? Had he forgotten that some of the most successful courtesans he had known had the art of projecting an appealing innocence that quickly disappeared once they were in the bedroom. But not Octavia! Dear God, no, not Octavia! He buried his head in his hands, trying not to remember the way she had pulled him to her, pressed herself against him, demanded his kisses. Were those the actions of an innocent? Before tonight he would have said yes, they were! They had been the reaction of an innocent who had till that moment been unaware of her own deeply passionate nature, someone who was experiencing for the first time the wildness, the temptation, of physical love. Surely her shame, her shocked modesty at the end, could not have been faked? But what if it had? What sort of a fool did that make of him?

His doubts grew. With the end of her time as a governess at Wychford fast approaching, had Octavia Petrie attempted to seduce the master into offering marriage? Had she really thought she could do it? If the truth were known, she had come damned close to succeeding, by God, she had!

Edward sat brooding the rest of the night. If this loss of judgement, this loss even of reason was what came of falling in love then he wanted none of it!

Innocent or not, Octavia Petrie would have to go. Immediately!

In the morning he asked Octavia to come to the library.

Octavia, too, had spent a sleepless night. It was torture to her to remember her behaviour the previous day. She had behaved like a trollop! It was as if she had turned into another person altogether in that room in the tower, one who had no modesty, no shame, no self-respect! How could she have? Edward Barraclough had always made his position perfectly clear. He had no intention of marrying—neither his nieces' governess, nor anyone else. And, knowing that fact, knowing that marriage played no part in his plans, she had allowed him to take such liberties with her! No, she had not *allowed* him, she had *asked* for them, *pleaded* for them. How could he possibly believe what she said, when she told him that she was not that kind of person? He probably remembered as well as she did that she had been just as wanton after he had helped her down from the tree. It was no use telling him, or herself, that she wasn't that sort of person. She *was*, where Edward Barraclough was involved.

It was quite clear to her that now, whoever she told him she was, however she presented herself, he would regard her as fair game, an easy prize for the taking. Governess or great lady, it was all the same, what man would respect her after such a display of...of mindless abandon! She knew what people thought of women who behaved as she had, and it wasn't flattering.

Worse than anything, she was afraid that, if Edward Barraclough kissed her again, there was no guarantee that she wouldn't behave in exactly the same way!

There was only one answer. She must remove herself from temptation, leave Wychford, leave Lisette and Pip, and go back to Ashcombe.

When Edward Barraclough's request to see her in the library was delivered she was tempted to leave the house there and then. The thought of facing him terrified her. But she set her jaw and went down, grimly determined to see it through. She *deserved* his poor opinion of her, his contempt. She even deserved any attempt he might make to persuade her to become his mistress. But she would not change her mind. Whatever he said, she would tell him that she was leaving Wychford the next day, as soon as she could arrange some manner of reaching Ashcombe. On one thing she was absolutely determined. She would *not* tell him what her real position in life was. Her family didn't deserve to have their reputation besmirched by her behaviour.

Edward was sitting behind his desk. He looked white and drawn, and her heart, her foolish heart, gave her a pang. He spoke without looking at her.

'Sit down, Miss Petrie.'

She sat, looking at her hands which were folded in her lap. There was a silence. When he spoke again she did not at first understand what he was saying. A complaint from Mrs Barraclough? Was that all? Why this fuss about a complaint against her from Mrs Barraclough? What was new about that?

But when he spoke again her heart gave a thump and she began to feel cold.

'Mrs Barraclough tells me you have had a friend staying at the inn. Is that right?' When Octavia nodded he went on, 'You didn't think to let me know? Or bring him to the house to be introduced? It *was* a man, I gather?'

'He...he was not supposed to come to Wychford. I didn't want him here. I told him to leave as soon as he arrived.'

'But he didn't leave immediately, did he? He stayed long enough for a very affecting little scene to take place.'

Octavia looked up. Had Edward heard about Harry's meeting with Lisette? Was that why he was so angry? She breathed an inward sigh of relief when he added, 'At the inn. You were being very...friendly with each other.'

How ironic! It wasn't Lisette he was angry about at all, but her own perfectly innocent meeting with her brother! Still cautious, she answered, 'I...I...er...we are very good friends.'

She jumped as Edward thumped his fist on the desk. 'Don't try to play with me! The maid at the inn thinks you are lovers!'

Octavia was astounded. 'That's not so!' she said angrily. 'How could you even *think* it? The girl's a liar!'

'Do you deny you were at the inn?'

'No.'

'Do you deny that you met a man there?'

'No.'

'Do you deny that he was only half-dressed when you met him the other day? That you embraced each other?'

'No. But that's because—' Octavia stopped short. Her own hopes of happiness were in ashes, but Harry's still had a chance. But not if Edward Barraclough learned about him while he was in this mood. She went on, 'That's because he had only just got up when I arrived. We were saying goodbye.'

'How very touching! I suppose you were missing him yesterday when you so charmingly invited my attentions. Or had you thought I would be a better prospect? Hoped for marriage, even? How disappointed you must have been when I managed to avoid actually seducing you.'

His voice was suddenly so harsh, his words so cruel, that Octavia could hardly breathe for a moment. This was the man who had held her so tenderly, breathed such words of affection, not twenty-four hours before! Her heart felt as if it was being squeezed by an iron fist. The fact that she had half-expected his contempt didn't make it any easier to bear.

'I understand your suspicions,' she managed to say at last. 'They're wrong, though I can hardly expect you to believe that. But for what it's worth, I give you my word that Harry Smith is not, and never has been, my lover. As for yester—' She choked and had to begin again. 'As for yesterday, I am more ashamed than I can say about my behaviour. You are quite wrong about my motives, but I don't blame you for thinking badly of me. You couldn't think worse of me than I do of myself.'

Edward regarded her in silence. 'You realise that I cannot possibly let you stay here after this?'

'If you are looking for an excuse to send me away, I can spare you the trouble. I could not possibly let *myself* stay here after what happened between us, Mr Barraclough. I...I had hoped to stay with your nieces to the end, but I'm afraid you must explain to them why I must leave as soon as it can be arranged. Try not to destroy their illusions about me.' Her voice wavered. 'I have grown very fond of them.'

He got up and walked to the window. Then he turned and said violently, 'Damn it, why did it have to happen like this, Octavia? For the first time in my life I—' He stopped. 'Never mind! What's done is done. You can go in the gig. Jem will take you. In an hour?'

She nodded and went to the door. He said abruptly, 'I'll explain as best I can to the girls. They'll miss you.'

Octavia couldn't speak. She nodded again and went out.

The windows of Wychford had a number of faces at them as Octavia Petrie left. Julia smiled as the gig went down the drive. She would have been failing in her duty to her nieces if she had allowed that...that harlot to stay on!

Lisette watched with a troubled face. She was old enough to wonder what lay behind Miss Petrie's sudden departure. It was more than her aunt's simple dislike of her, she was sure.

Pip was at the window of her tower room, but she could not see for tears. She hated her aunt! What was the use of being good when you lost one of the people you liked best in the world?

Edward's face was not at the window. He was bent over his papers in the library, determinedly *not* thinking of honey-gold hair, eyes alight with laughter or dark with desire, the feel of a woman's slender body in his arms... With a curse he threw his pen away and stared at his desk. He would master this. He had been perfectly happy with his way of life before he met Octavia Petrie, and he would be perfectly happy with it again. This terrible sense of loss was not to be borne!

* * *

There were only three of them at dinner that night. Pip had stayed upstairs. When the meal was nearly finished, Lisette regarded her uncle and said quietly,

'Why did you let Miss Petrie go, Edward?'

'I told you,' he said curtly. 'She found she had some urgent business at home.'

Lisette flinched at his tone, but went on bravely, 'I think that was an excuse. Neither Pip nor I can believe she would leave us so suddenly, not without explaining things to us herself.'

'Leave it alone, Lisette!' her uncle said.

'I think Lisette is old enough to know the truth,' said Julia. 'You should tell her. It will rid the girls of this admiration for a woman who doesn't deserve it.' Edward remained silent and after a pause Julia turned to Lisette. 'We did not consider Miss Petrie a fit person to have charge of you, Lisette. There! I've said it for you, Edward.'

The colour rose in Lisette's cheeks. 'I don't believe that!' she said. 'I think she had to go because you didn't like her, Aunt Julia!'

Edward gazed in astonishment at his gentle, well-behaved niece. Lisette never criticised, never argued with anyone!

Julia's face coloured, though not as prettily as Lisette's. 'Well!' she said. 'It's a fine thing when my own niece can say such things to me! I am more shocked than I can say at your rudeness, Lisette. But I know who is to blame! It is yet more proof of Miss Petrie's bad influence—if any proof were needed!

Miss Petrie left of her own accord, but if she had not, I confess freely, I would have dismissed her. It was as well that she did not have the impudence to ask for a reference, for I should not have been able to give her one!'

'Julia, I hardly think—'

'No, Edward, you heard what Lisette said. My own niece, a girl I have cherished like my own child, has accused me of spite. It is only fair that she knows the truth.' She turned to Lisette. 'Your precious Miss Petrie was having a clandestine relationship with a young man, Lisette, and that is something no responsible guardian could condone in a governess. She was even seen kissing him!'

The flush in Lisette's cheeks faded and she grew pale. She asked, 'The young man—who was he? What was his name?'

Edward's eyes narrowed at this strange question. What lay behind it?

'There's no need for you to know—' began Julia.

'Smith,' said Edward. 'Harry Smith.'

Lisette jumped up. 'And you sent Miss Petrie away because of that!' she exclaimed. 'How could you! Oh, how could you!'

'What's the matter, Lisette? What do you mean?'

'Edward! Harry Smith is Miss Petrie's *brother*! You've dismissed the kindest, nicest person Pip and I have ever known, someone we really loved, because she kissed her *brother*!'

Chapter Twelve

Lisette burst into tears and ran sobbing to the door, but Edward leapt up and fetched her back.

'Wait a minute, my girl,' he said sternly. 'You can't say something like that and then disappear. How do you know that Mr Smith is Miss Petrie's brother? Did she tell you?'

'No,' sobbed Lisette. 'He did. His name is Harry Petrie, not Smith at all.'

'This man told you himself? When? When did you meet him, Lisette?'

Julia started to say something, but Edward cut her off. 'I'll deal with this Julia,' he said brusquely. 'This has gone beyond the question of Miss Petrie's behaviour. Lisette has been in my care for very nearly the past two months, and, as her guardian, my concern at the moment is what has been happening to *her*.' He turned his attention to his niece, saw the state she was in, and made an effort to speak more gently.

'Sit down, Lisette, and try to calm down. Do you want a drink of water?' Lisette shook her head, but she did make an effort to compose herself. After a moment Edward went on, 'Tell me, where did you meet Harry Petrie?' He paused. 'At the inn? Did you...did you ever see him at the inn?' Lisette shook her head vigorously.

'Where, then?'

'We...we met in the woods. Here at Wychford.'

'Did Miss Petrie introduce you?' asked Julia.

'No! Harry and I met by accident.'

'Harry! You called him Harry, did you, when you met him in the woods? Fine goings-on!'

'Julia, I would like you to stop interrupting, and allow me to deal with this. Lisette will tell us the truth in her own time, I know she will. Please keep quiet. Now, Lisette, you said you met Harry Petrie in the woods, by accident.'

'Yes. Miss Petrie didn't know anything about it. I was collecting specimens for my notebook. It was after Pip was ill and we went out for an airing behind the house. Pip got tired and Miss Petrie decided to take her indoors, but she knew I wanted some leaves and things for my drawings. So she gave me a quarter of an hour to look by the drive. There are better ones there.' She threw a glance at her aunt. 'It was just a quarter of an hour!'

'Go on.'

'He was in the woods near the drive. He startled me. But his behaviour was very gentlemanly, and after a while I...I liked him.'

'What did Miss Petrie say when you told her you'd met her brother in the woods?'

'I didn't know that he was Miss Petrie's brother! He told me his name was Smith. Like the hero.'

'She knew, of course. She'd arranged it!' said Julia with a sniff.

'She didn't! I didn't tell her about it at all at first. I'm sorry, Edward, I really am. I knew you wouldn't approve, but I didn't mean any harm! He was perfectly polite and...and respectful.'

'When did you tell Miss Petrie about it?'

'After our second meeting. He told me then that he didn't want to lie to me. His name wasn't Smith, it was Petrie. He was Miss Petrie's brother.'

'Ha!'

'Julia!' warned Edward. He turned to Lisette again. 'What did Miss Petrie say?'

'She was very annoyed. With both of us. She said it was very wrong to meet her brother secretly, and that you would be angry if you knew. And that she would agree with you.' Lisette added sadly, 'She said I mustn't see him again—she wouldn't even let me say goodbye.'

Edward thought for a moment. 'So did you? See him again?'

'Oh, no!' said Lisette. 'Of course not, Edward! Miss Petrie said I wasn't to. She was quite clear about that.'

'Well, it seems to me that very little harm was done, though I am surprised you said nothing about it to me, or your aunt.'

'I was afraid you'd think he wasn't good enough for me,' said Lisette simply.

'You're quite right! Your governess's brother! What a fine match that would be!' said Julia sarcastically. 'Of course, it would be wonderful for him! One cannot blame Miss Petrie for wishing to promote such a windfall for her brother.'

'He was just a friend! And Miss Petrie had nothing to do with it! Why are you so unpleasant about her, Aunt Julia? What has she done to make you so unkind towards her? I don't believe for a minute that she would plan anything of the sort.'

'You will allow that I've been about the world a good bit more than you, my dear. I am considerably older and wiser. Miss Petrie's motives are perfectly comprehensible. It would be a negligent sister, indeed, who would fail to see the advantage to her brother in marrying a girl who is a considerable heiress!'

Lisette stood up twin flags of anger burning in her cheeks. 'Edward, I've told you everything now. I'm sorry for deceiving you. I'm even sorrier that my conduct has caused you to be so unfair to Miss Petrie.

But if you will excuse me, I should like to go to my room.'

Edward gave Julia an exasperated look, but merely said, 'Of course you may go, if you wish, Lisette. You've been very honest with us.' He hesitated, then said, 'Try not to blame yourself for Miss Petrie's departure. She had already planned to leave. Your behaviour wasn't the only cause.'

'Forget Miss Petrie and reflect instead on the possibility of other, more serious, consequences of your conduct, Lisette,' said Julia. 'We want no more dealings with unsuitable men. I would have thought you'd have learned your lesson from what happened on Antigua with the Arandez fellow!'

'Aunt Julia! This is nothing like what happened on Antigua! If you want to know the truth, I talked to Miss Petrie about that, too, and she helped me more than you or anyone else! You just forbade me to see Ricardo again, or even to talk about him, and that left me feeling that I was somehow betraying Papa. Miss Petrie helped me to understand what Papa had *really* wanted.'

'Marriage to her brother, I suppose?' said Julia nastily.

'No! Oh, I can't talk to you!'

'Tell us, Lisette,' said Edward quietly. 'What did Miss Petrie say?'

'That I wasn't to worry any more about what Ricardo had said. Papa would want me to be happy. To know the world, before I made any big decisions.

I still don't know what I feel about Ricardo, Edward, but I don't believe any more that we are betrothed. She at least did that for me. And now you've sent her away!' Lisette ran out of the room, and the door shut with a bang behind her.

'Was that really necessary, Julia?' asked Edward wearily. 'The child was already upset enough, without being reminded of Ricardo Arandez and what was probably the most distressing experience of her life.'

'Oh, I know where you stand, Edward!' snapped Julia. 'You're still so besotted with the Petrie woman, you'd see your niece marry her brother without doing a thing to prevent it. But I'll make sure she won't, if it's the last thing I do! In fact, I shall tell her so now!' Julia swept out and was halfway up the stairs before Edward could catch her.

'Julia!' he shouted.

She stopped and turned, her face contorted with spite. 'You won't stop me! That Petrie woman has turned Lisette against us all, and I'm not going to let her get away with it!'

She turned to carry on up the stairs, and screamed as one of the treads gave way with a large crack and she almost fell through the hole. She was still screaming as Edward leapt up the stairs and picked her up. He checked she hadn't seriously damaged herself, then carried her to her room. She was still kicking and screaming, swearing not to spend a moment longer in a house that showed every sign of wanting to finish her off.

Her maid arrived, but not all their efforts could calm her down, and in the end he slapped her, not too gently.

She stopped screaming and looked at him with loathing. 'I shall leave this house tomorrow, Edward! It isn't safe. It's tried three times to kill me and I won't wait for a fourth!'

'You've had a bad shock, Julia, but this is nonsense,' he said sharply.

'It isn't, it isn't! I refuse to live here! I want to go back to London tomorrow! I shall go mad if I don't.'

'In that case it might be wiser to go.' He thought for a moment. 'In fact, I think it would be better for all of us. You and the girls can leave tomorrow and I shall see that the house is properly shut down and follow you in a day or two. You'd better rest now. I'll leave you in the hands of your maid—she'll see to you. And I'll have a look at that stair. It will have to be put right straight away.'

He left the room and went to the head of the stairs. One of the estate handymen was examining the damage.

'I can't understand it,' he said, shaking his head. 'I've never known such a thing to happen before, Mr Barraclough. Never! Old Mrs Carstairs kept it all in such good repair!'

* * *

When Pip heard they were leaving she begged Edward to let her stay behind with him.

'I'll be good, Edward! I don't want to go to London, especially not with Aunt Julia.'

'I'm afraid you'll soon have to go to London. We're all leaving Wychford. But I'll see if I can persuade your aunt to let you travel with me. It will only be a day or two longer, mind!'

Julia, who was quite broken down by the latest accident, shuddered and readily agreed. 'My nerves won't take any more. The thought of being cooped up in a carriage with Philippa all the way to London appals me. By all means, let her wait for you! But Lisette must come with me.'

'Of course. Try to make friends again with Lisette, Julia. She's feeling very low. We don't want her to fall back into the melancholy state she was in last year. When you're feeling better you might think about dresses for her come-out. That should cheer her up.'

'Oh, I have great plans for that. I shall see if Madame Rosa will make some of her wardrobe. Daisy Ledbury was not at all sure she would. It seems Madame is in great demand, and can more or less choose her own clientèle. Perhaps I can persuade Lady Ledbury to put in a word for us.'

Edward saw them off with relief. Lisette was quiet, but she seemed to have repented of her outburst of the night before. The girl had been right, of course. There had been real animosity behind Julia's witch-hunt. Quite why, he wasn't sure. He wasn't sure, either, what he felt about Octavia himself. He had been less than impartial when listening to the story of her meetings with her supposed lover, of course. For a moment he had been beside himself with jealousy and murderous rage, unable to think clearly at all. The unaccustomed violence of his feelings had so shocked him that he had been glad to let her go. She posed too many problems, and he had decided long ago that what he wanted was a life without them. No wife, no one to remind him of his duty, no responsibilities. Above all, no one to make him feel as uncivilised as he had for a few minutes the day before. Never!

Except...he had a suspicion that, along with the problems, something else, something immensely important, had gone too, something he might regret.

Edward had no time for self-questioning during the next two days. He had a thousand things to do, the most important of which was to set in motion proper repairs to the staircase. Why *had* that stair cracked? The handyman couldn't explain it at all. He swore that the rest of the staircase was in excellent condition, with no sign of woodworm or decay. But what else could it have been? The idea that the house was trying to get rid of Julia was nonsense, of course! Hysterical rubbish!

There were other things to do. Wychford was a large house, and though there were still almost four of their six months' tenancy left, he doubted any of them would come back. Still, he wanted to leave it suitably prepared. Pip accompanied him everywhere, chatting, commenting, asking questions. Her talk was full of Miss Petrie and all the wonderful things they had done together.

'Of course, she did promise that she would see me in London. And I think she will, don't you, Edward? I hope she does. I wonder what she's doing now? I don't think she'll be a governess to anyone else. In fact, I don't think she's really a governess at all! She wasn't looking for a post when she first arrived, you know.'

Edward stopped in his tracks. 'What was that?'

'Well, she seemed surprised to find us here. And if she was hoping to be our governess she'd have known, wouldn't she? But she knew our name. It's funny, isn't it? I wish she could come back!'

On the last night, once Pip was in bed, Edward walked round the house checking that everything was in order. He came back to Pip's room to see that she was asleep, and as he came out he stopped by the narrow staircase up to the room in the tower. He had not been up there since…since that day. He couldn't avoid it any longer. It, too, should be checked. He went up the stairs, unlocked the door and entered the room.

It looked dim and ghostly in the faint light of his lamp. Ashes from the fire lit by Octavia lay in the fireplace. They could stay there. He walked to the chair and looked down. What a storm of feeling had filled this little room! For a short while the world had been on fire for him here... He turned, and a flicker from his lamp was reflected in the gilt of a picture frame on the table. He went over and picked it up. Mrs Carstairs's little daughter, Theophania. The child had been younger than Pip when she died, and there had never been any others.

The table was crowded with other pictures—miniatures, paintings, drawings... Obviously friends and family, people she knew. His eye was caught by one particular picture, a drawing of a young woman. It looked familiar. Picking it up, he held it close to the lamp. He had not been mistaken—it was a drawing of Octavia Petrie.

Edward studied the picture in his hand and wondered what Octavia Petrie's picture was doing on Mrs Carstairs's table, next to that of her beloved little daughter. He stood there for some minutes without moving. The room was cold, but he didn't feel it. Pip's words were going round in his mind...

She wasn't looking for a post when she first arrived...she seemed surprised to find us here...if she was hoping to be our governess she'd have known, wouldn't she?...but she knew our name...

Was this why Octavia Petrie had been so evasive about her background? He wouldn't have known anything about her family if he hadn't eavesdropped when she was talking to Pip. The keenly analytical mind that had made Edward such a success in the banking world was beginning to work. Was it possible that Octavia Petrie was Mrs Carstairs's mysterious niece? If Pip was right, she could well have come to Wychford merely to look it over, and their early arrival had taken her by surprise. But in that case why hadn't she simply explained? He now concentrated hard on that first interview. The more of it he remembered, the clearer it became that she had *not* come with the intention of working for him. No, by God, she wasn't any sort of governess! She had never said she was. The mistake had been his. But why had she not corrected him? Why had she embarked on such a mad escapade?

He shook his head. He had no idea. But one thing was clear even to an idiot like himself. She had pulled the wool over his eyes pretty neatly. Octavia Petrie had made a fool of Edward Barraclough, and had probably enjoyed doing it! What a fine joke it must have seemed to her—the prospect of being employed by her own tenant! No wonder he had seen irony in her eyes, had sensed challenge in her attitude, though none was ever openly expressed. How she must have laughed!

It must have been a shock to her when she found she was human, after all, when she had found herself caught in the end by something she *couldn't* control—little Miss Governess in the grip of straightforward, red-blooded passion. Of course she had fled! She was a fraud! Perhaps she *had* even introduced her brother to Lisette for her own purposes! He slammed her picture angrily down on the table, kicked the ashes so that they were properly spread, and left the room, locking it firmly behind him. He was finished with the whole business of his late governess! Miss Octavia Petrie was as dead to him as those ashes up there in the room. He had been saved from making one of the biggest mistakes in his life!

The next day he and Pip left Wychford. Pip made him pause at the bend for a last look. It was a dull day and the house had lost its quirky smile.

'What are you staring at, Pip? Wychford is empty.'

'But it isn't dead, Edward. I think it looks as if…as if it is waiting.'

'Come!' he said brusquely. 'I don't know what it could be waiting for. We're most unlikely to come back again.'

'Oh, look!'

'What is it now?' asked Edward a little testily.

'Didn't you see? The house smiled again!'

'Philippa, if you talk very much like that you will be thought mad. And your aunt will blame *me* for it! There are some stray patches of sunshine about. It was probably one of those hitting the windows. Now, no more talk of the house—it's London for us, midget.'

Edward decided he had one last duty before he finally put Octavia Petrie and her brother out of his mind. Lisette had clearly been very interested in Harry Petrie, and he owed it to her to learn a little more about the fellow, just in case he ever surfaced again. If he was the fortune-hunter Julia thought him, then he would certainly try to meet Lisette in London. The landlord had said he had the look of a soldier. So Edward selected one of the biggest gossips at the Horse Guards, a man for whom he had done a favour or two in the past, and went along to see him. Sir Charles said he would be delighted to assist. 'Petrie? Petrie... Let me think...'

'His brother Stephen was killed at Waterloo. Does that help?'

'Not much. Have you any idea how many were killed at Waterloo? But, wait! Petrie is the family name of the Warnhams. It's just possible that he's related to one of them... Leave it with me a day or two, old fellow. I'll do what I can.'

When Edward went back Sir Charles was triumphant. 'I was right! Lieutenant Harry Petrie of the Guards. That's probably the one you want. It fits together. He did have a brother who was killed at Waterloo.'

'Related to the Warnhams, you say?'

Sir Charles brayed with laughter. 'Related to them? I should say so! Indeed, I should! Young Harry will inherit the Warnham title one day, unless his brother Arthur can produce a son—which doesn't seem very likely now.'

'You mean…Harry Petrie is the son of an *earl*?'

'Exactly! The family is quite a large one—'

'Eight of them,' murmured Edward.

'What's that? Seven, dear chap. One of 'em died at Waterloo, remember. Now there are only two sons, the rest are daughters.'

'Respectable?'

'Highly! They're related to half the aristocracy in England. Their mother was a Cavendish, their paternal grandmother a Ponsonby, and, of the five daughters, one is married to the Duke of Monteith, another is the Marchioness of Rochford, a third married abroad—a French Count, I think… I forget the other, but it's equally respectable. Warnham's youngest daughter is the only one not married. She was one of the toasts of the Season a few years back, but she didn't fancy any of us. Pity. She was rich, pretty, well connected. She'd have been a prize for some lucky man. A cool customer, though. Hard to please.'

'Was she, indeed?' asked Edward.

'Oh, yes! Lady Octavia's heart would never rule her head! Her mother died just before the end of the Season, and she never came back to London, but I'd have heard if she had married. Of course, she's worth a good bit more now. Inherited a handsome estate from her godmother, I hear.'

Edward decided he had heard enough about Octavia for the moment. He said, 'Do you know anything about Harry Petrie himself? Is he wild? Does he gamble? Drink?'

'No more than the rest of them. Less than most, I'd say. Why are you so interested in young Harry? If you had a daughter I'd say you were pinning your sights on him, but you haven't. What's the interest?'

'One of my relatives came across him. I just wanted to check.'

'I hear Petrie is sending in his papers. If he enters the marriage market, you'd better get the girl's mother to work fast. He's bound to be one of next Season's matrimonial prizes!'

'Quite!' said Edward somewhat sourly. 'I'm very obliged to you, Stainforth. Let me know when I can do something for you.'

He went back to North Audley Street relieved, at least, that his niece had not fallen into the hands of a common adventurer. A match with young Harry Petrie ought to be approved by the stickiest of guardians. All the same, he sincerely hoped that Lisette would find someone else. The less he had to do with the Lady Octavia Petrie and her family the better it would suit him! Not just the owner of Wychford, but a star, the daughter of an earl, related to half the best families in the kingdom! What a clever little actress she was! How she must have resented his own and Julia's treatment of her—but never, not by a word, had she ever given a hint of her elevated rank. Why the devil had she done it? A cheap adventure? My Lady joining the ranks of the common people? Perhaps she had even done it for a wager!

Whatever it had been, he resented it. He resented the way she had deceived him, the fool she had made of him. He resented his own blindness. But most of all he resented the manner in which she still walked about his mind, taunting him with the memory of the way it had felt to hold her in his arms, filling him with unfulfilled desire. Damn the rich, beautiful, well-connected Lady Octavia Petrie! Why couldn't he forget her?

Octavia, too, was forced to postpone consideration of what had happened at Wychford. After taking the precaution of telling Jem put her down at the gates to Ashcombe and waiting till he had driven off again, she had asked the lodgekeeper to take her up to the main house. Here she was greeted with astonishment by Lady Dorney, and borne off straight up to her room, where she started to change.

'I should think so, too! Wherever did you get that shabby dress, Octavia? And what have you been doing with yourself? You don't look at all the thing!'

'I...I've had a difficult time during the past few days. Mrs Barraclough arrived, and there was really no reason why I should stay. So I came home.'

'What are your plans?'

'There are one or two things I have to do, promises I made, and then we shall see. Tell me what has been happening here. I know that Harry is back—he came to Wychford to find me.'

'So that's where he went! There was quite a scene here when he first arrived home. At the end of it Harry stormed out without telling anyone where he was going. Tell me, has Arthur always been as over-bearing as this?'

'Yes,' said Octavia briefly. 'Harry and I could never stand him. I don't expect Papa said much.'

'Well, no. But it was obvious that he really agreed with Arthur. Poor Rupert! He got quite agitated, es-pecially when Harry left in such a temper. I had to spend the whole of the next day calming him down.'

Octavia smiled. 'It was lucky you were at hand. You are so good for him.'

'I'm glad to hear you say that, Octavia. As a matter of fact, your father and I...'

Octavia took one look at her cousin's expression and laughed. 'Don't tell me!' she said. 'Let me guess—you and Papa have decided to get married!'

'Do you mind?'

'Not in the least—it's what I wanted!' Octavia put her arms round Lady Dorney and hugged her. 'I am so pleased for you both!'

'We decided that we enjoyed each other's com-pany so much that I might as well stay here all the time. It isn't what you'd call a great romance, Octavia. But at my age, I don't look for one.'

'Well, I think it very romantic! Papa is a lucky man!'

'Please don't think this will change things. I hope you will continue to consider this your home, my dear!'

'Thank you. But we shall have to see.'

After Lady Dorney had gone Octavia sat on the window-seat and stared out. She was truly delighted at this piece of news, but, in spite of what her cousin had said, there would be changes. The new Countess would take her stepdaughter's place as Ashcombe's chatelaine, and Octavia herself would at last be free to do as she pleased. Two months ago she would have been over the moon at the idea. But now... She sat for a while, then roused herself to go down and offer her congratulations to her father. Quite a number of things had to be done urgently before she could take time to think about her own future.

In accordance with her plans, Octavia drove over the next day to see her sister Gussie. Augusta, Duchess of Monteith, was now in her late thirties, but still had remnants of the charm and beauty that had taken London by storm twenty years before, and had enabled her to capture the Season's most eligible bachelor, the Duke of Monteith. Although the Duke was a large, lazy man with few pretensions to intellect, and Gussie a woman of energy and spirit, the marriage had been reasonably successful. She had presented her lord with four healthy children, the youngest of whom was about to go to Eton, and they now shared an easygoing tolerance towards each other, which satisfied them both. Octavia suspected that neither was wholly faithful, but if they did indulge in any affairs, they were very discreet ones. She had never heard any scandal about them. It was not the sort of marriage that had ever tempted Octavia, however.

The Duke was out shooting for the day, and the Duchess was at home and feeling bored. She was delighted to see her sister. They gossiped for a while, deciding that their father's proposed marriage to Lady Dorney was an excellent idea, deploring Arthur's manners, and exchanging news of other members of the family. Eventually Gussie sat back and said, 'I'm honoured by this visit of yours, Tavy, but why do I have the impression there's something behind it?'

Octavia's colour rose. She smiled and said, 'I never could hide things from you! Tell me, are you and Monteith planning to do the Season next year?'

'I expect we shall. We always do. Don't tell me you want to, too! I thought you'd given up on London? Or has the news about Papa's marriage changed your mind for you?'

'I—it's not that, exactly. But I should like to do the Season again, and I don't want to risk having an invitation from Arthur to stay in town with them.'

'Perfectly understandable. You will naturally stay with us. I should love your company, Tavy! Monteith spends most of his time in London at his clubs, and

I hardly see him. This is excellent news!' Gussie sat back and beamed at Octavia. 'That's settled then.'

'Actually, there's something more. I...I want you to recommend a governess to someone.' Gussie looked puzzled and Octavia hurried on, 'I'm very fond of a particular little girl. Her guardians will be looking for a new governess for her, and I want to make sure she has someone suitable, someone kind as well as efficient. Pip is a very special little girl. I remembered that your youngest is about to finish with the schoolroom, and thought of your Miss Cherrifield. Has she already found something else?'

'Not yet. I've hung on to her as long as I could! You could tell your friends about Cherry, if you wish. She would be ideal.'

'Er...that's not possible. I mustn't appear in the affair. You see, the woman who is most likely to choose a governess for Pip dislikes me. But a recommendation from a Duchess would impress her no end.'

Gussie looked at her sternly. 'You're not up to your tricks, are you? We're all very fond of Cherry here. I want her to find a good place. She is not to be made part of a game.'

'No, no! When you meet Pip, you'll see why I want to help. And when you meet her guardian's wife, you'd know why I couldn't do it personally! Please do this, Gussie. It's important to me.'

The Duchess looked at her youngest sister. 'I suspect there's more to this than meets the eye, little sister. Who is Pip? And what is your connection with her?'

'I... Gussie, don't tell Papa, but for the past two months *I* was Pip's governess! We were all at Wychford together.'

Gussie had never been easy to shock. She sat back and regarded her sister with amusement. 'A governess! So that's what you were doing there all that time! I did wonder. But...how on earth did you become a governess? And who is Pip?'

'Philippa Barraclough. There were two Barraclough girls—Pip and her sister Lisette.'

'Are they related to Edward Barraclough, the banker?'

'His nieces.'

Gussie put on a frown and said, 'Octavia Petrie, I am beginning to suspect the worst. Explain, if you please!'

'Wh...what do you mean?'

'Edward Barraclough is one of London's most eligible bachelors. *And* one of its most hardened. Are you telling me that you've been living down at Wychford with such a handsome brute for the past two months, teaching his nieces, and that is *all*? Impossible!'

'Well, it's true!'

'What? He employed Lady Octavia Petrie as a *governess*? Try telling that to the *ton*!'

'Er...not exactly. He didn't know who I was. He thought I was a parson's daughter.'

Gussie sat up and said, 'And to think I was feeling bored! 'Fess up, Tavy! I shan't rest till I've heard the lot.'

Chapter Thirteen

Octavia gave up and told her sister most of what had happened at Wychford. Not all. When she came to the end Gussie gazed at her sister in astonishment and said, 'Amazing! I would never have believed it!'

Then she put her head on one side and said, 'However, I think there's a little more to it, isn't there? I don't believe you spent all that time in Edward Barraclough's company without feeling just a tiny bit attracted.'

Octavia shrugged. 'You're right, of course,' she said a touch bitterly. 'I did what every governess is said to do. I fell in love with the master.'

'So this is why you want to do the Season? To try to win him? I'm sorry to have to say this, Tavy. You wouldn't be the first to attempt it, but you'd be the first if you got anywhere near him!'

'I wouldn't begin to try! For reasons which I refuse to go into, Mr Barraclough despises me.'

'He made love to you and you let him,' said Gussie, going unerringly to the heart of the matter.

Octavia nodded. 'And when he finds out who I really am he'll add deception to the list of my crimes. No, I don't think Edward Barraclough will fall for my charms. That's not the reason I want to do the Season.'

'Then what is it?'

Octavia leaned forward. 'I grew to love those girls, Gussie, and you will love them, too. I've told you about Pip, but there's Lisette as well. She's coming out next spring, and I want to help her, too. Julia Barraclough can't do nearly as much for the girl as I could. Could you use your influence with Sally Jersey to get vouchers for Almack's for the Barracloughs?'

'I should imagine Edward Barraclough has more influence with Sally Jersey than I have, my dear,' said Gussie drily. 'She has an eye for a fascinating man.'

'But it isn't the sort to get the patronesses to agree to vouchers! Gussie, Lisette is not quite seventeen, and she's the loveliest girl I think I've ever seen. And just as sweet-natured.'

Gussie blinked. 'That's praise indeed!'

'Harry thinks so, too.'

'Aha! Do I scent a plot, after all? Is poor Harry to be seduced into settling down and producing a family? You're the last person I'd have expected to find playing Arthur's game!'

'It would be a perfect match for him, I assure you, but I wouldn't try to force it. Lisette needs time.

There's a young man on Antigua and she has still to decide what she really thinks about him...'

Gussie surveyed her sister. 'I'm not sure I'm doing the right thing, helping you like this with the Barracloughs. You're too close to them, Tavy. You might do better to put them out of your mind. *All* of them.'

'Please, Gussie! The best I can now do for Lisette is to help her forget her problems and have a wonderful Season. Please help me!'

'Oh, very well, I'll do it. Sally Jersey will hand over the vouchers, she owes me a favour or two. But I warn you, little sister, I'm going to keep a careful eye on you when we're in London!'

Edward Barraclough was not mentioned again, and for the rest of the visit they discussed practical details. Octavia left her sister feeling that things were arranging themselves quite well.

Her next move was to London to pay a visit to Bruton Street. Madame Rosa was surprised, but very gracious. She had been dressing the Warnhams' daughters, all five of them, for many years, and Octavia was a firm favourite.

'Lady Octavia! Zis is indeed a pleasure,' she said, with one glance destroying any illusions Octavia might have about what she was wearing. 'I see you need my 'elp. Immediately. Are you planning to do ze Season next year?'

'I rather thought I might, *madame*.'

'You will need a new wardrobe, of course. 'ow many years since you were in London?'

'Too many,' said Octavia with a smile.

For a while they discussed trends, styles and materials. It was too early to make final decisions or arrange times for fittings, but Madame asked Octavia not to leave it too late. 'We are so busy, milady! You 'ave no idea! All ze world wants Madame Rosa to dress zare daughters. I do not, of course, accept most of zem. Indeed, I accept very few new clients now.'

'I wonder if you might make an exception?' said Octavia. 'I have a young friend who, I assure you, will make a sensation in Society when she comes out next year. She is very beautiful, Madame. She would be worth dressing. A Miss Lisette Barraclough.'

'It is not easy...I 'ave so many valued existing clients, Lady Octavia...'

'As a favour to me,' said Octavia, with a touch of firmness in her tone.

'Zen I will! Of course I will! If you would bring 'er to see me...?'

'I can't do that. In fact, I should be obliged to you if you do not mention my name at all, especially not to the person who will probably come with her—her aunt, Mrs Henry Barraclough.'

'*Alors*, am I to make dresses for zees Mrs Barraclough, too?' demanded Madame Rosa.

Octavia smiled again. 'Not if you are too busy, Madame,' she said sweetly. 'Just Miss Lisette.'

Satisfied that she had done everything she could to smooth the way for her girls, Octavia went back to Ashcombe. She was at last free to think about her own future.

In fact, the delay had given her turbulent emotions time to settle. After the scene in Mrs Carstairs's room, she had already decided she must leave Wychford, so Julia Barraclough's accusations had not made any difference to her plans. But Edward's readiness to believe them, his harshness, his cruel interpretation of her motives, had been a bitter blow. She had expected him to think less of her after her wanton behaviour in the tower room, but he had been even more contemptuous than she had imagined. Gussie need have no fear that she would throw herself at Edward Barraclough in London! She wouldn't risk any more of his contempt.

The events at Wychford were now in the past, and she was ready to pick herself up and start to rebuild her self-respect, without any interference from Edward Barraclough. She had been a fool. But foolishness was not a crime. And though nothing could excuse her wanton behaviour, she could see now that there had been reasons for it. Intense physical attraction had played no part in her experience of life, and she had been perilously unaware of its power. For a while in that tower room she had almost drowned in a sudden onslaught of desire, the irresistible excitement of a man's caresses. But now she was at least a wiser, if sadder, woman, with some sense of self-preservation. She would never risk such temptation again.

And what about the man who had brought about such a devastating change in calm, level-headed Octavia Petrie? What about her feelings for Edward Barraclough? It was truly ironic that the man whose opinion of her was so low had turned out to be the one man whose good opinion she wanted more than anything in the world, the one man she could love. It was unlikely that she would ever marry him, but it would be impossible to marry anyone else.

Octavia put this thought firmly behind her. Edward Barraclough was lost to her. But she had grown to love his nieces, and Harry was on the way to falling in love with Lisette. Knowing them both as well as she did, she truly believed they could be happy together. She had already done something towards smoothing the girls' way in London. Now she must deliver on her promise to make sure Harry and Lisette met again. Next year's Season was only a few months away.

The ache in Octavia's heart never quite went away in spite of all her famous self-discipline. But she was kept busy with her preparations for London, and time went by with surprising speed. Her father and his cousin were married in December. The occasion was a quiet but happy one, only marginally marred by Arthur's ponderous speech of congratulation. Christ-

mas came and went, and soon it was the end of
January and time to think of moving to London. By
the end of February Octavia was comfortably settled
in the Monteiths' mansion in St James's Square, and
the two sisters were busy with appointments with the
mantua maker, the milliner and all the other purvey-
ors of the fashionable image.

They went about London, renewing old acquaintances, seeing the sights, and completing their ward-
robes. Octavia breathed a sigh of relief when she
learned that the Barracloughs were staying with
friends in Gloucestershire, and were not expected
back before the middle of March. Her own visits to
Madame Rosa were more or less over, so there was
no risk of seeing any of the Barracloughs there.
Though she knew that they would all have to meet
sooner or later, she preferred to choose her own time
and place. It must not happen by accident, before
they were all prepared.

The moment came. It was announced in the *Ga-
zette*'s daily list of arrivals in London that Mr and
Mrs Henry Barraclough of Antigua, together with
their two nieces, had taken up residence in South
Audley Street. Miss Lisette Barraclough would be introduced to Society during the forthcoming Season.

There was no mention of Mr Edward Barraclough,
and Octavia could only assume that he had not yet
returned to the capital. It seemed a good time to reveal her true identity to the rest of the Barracloughs.

Though she had no liking for Julia, she had no desire to cause her a public loss of face. Their first meeting must take place in private. On the other hand, if she sent a note asking Julia to receive her, and signed it with her own name, it would certainly result in a refusal. So, two days later, she wrote a note to the house in South Audley Street, asking if she might call on Mrs Barraclough the following day, and signed it 'Mrs Carstairs's niece'. Julia ought to be sufficiently intrigued to agree to see her.

It went exactly as she had foreseen. Mrs Barraclough had expressed her pleasure to receive Mrs Carstairs's niece, but when Octavia walked into the room she stood up and exclaimed in a voice quivering with rage,

'Octavia Petrie! What are you doing here? Who let you in? How dare you present yourself in my house!' She went towards the bellrope to summon a servant, but before she could pull it Octavia said quickly,

'Mrs Barraclough, pray forgive me, but please don't do that! Give me a few moments, I beg you. I really am Mrs Carstairs's niece. I'm afraid I have been very unfair to you, and I've come to apologise. I'd like to make what amends I can.'

Julia looked at her suspiciously. 'You! Mrs Carstairs's niece? The owner of Wychford? What is this nonsense?'

'If you'll allow me to explain... Perhaps I ought to introduce myself properly.'

'I already know who you are! You're Octavia Petrie. Or is that a lie? Are you really Octavia *Smith*, perhaps?'

'No, my name is Petrie. I'm the youngest daughter of Lord Warnham.'

Julia sat down suddenly. 'But...but that's not possible! You were a governess!'

'That was a misunderstanding, a mistake made by your nieces and...and your brother-in-law. I should never have let it continue. I assure you, I am Lord Warnham's daughter.'

'The *Earl* of Warnham?' Octavia nodded. 'You're the Lady Octavia Petrie?'

Octavia nodded again and said, 'Please forgive me for deceiving you. It was very wrong of me. That's why I've come today. It was certain we should meet soon, and I wanted to explain it all beforehand.'

Julia sat for a moment, then said slowly, 'So your brother—Harry Smith—is the son of Lord Warnham?'

'Yes.' For the life of her Octavia could not prevent a touch of coolness in her voice at Julia's eye for essentials.

'I see...' After a brief pause Julia said more warmly, 'But what am I thinking of? Will you not sit down, Lady Octavia?'

'Thank you, but I hardly—'

'I'm sure Philippa would never forgive me if I let you go away without letting her have a word with you. Lisette is here, too.' Julia went to the bell rope again, and told the servant to find her nieces.

Octavia gave in and sat down. 'How are they?'

'They are both in excellent spirits. Pip has a new governess—' Julia grew red, and hesitated before going on rather hastily, 'Miss Froom was unfortunately not free, but Miss Cherrifield came with excellent recommendations. I believe she has worked with the Monteiths for the past ten years.'

'Does Pip like her?'

This was clearly of less interest to Pip's aunt. 'I believe so. The Monteiths were most enthusiastic about Miss Cherrifield. I think we were fortunate to get her.'

'That is quite a coincidence,' said Octavia innocently. 'The Duchess is my eldest sister. I am staying with her at present.'

'Really?'

The door opened before Julia could say any more, and Pip came sedately enough into the room, followed by Lisette. But when Pip saw Octavia she gave a kind of whoop and launched herself at her former governess. Ignoring Julia's scandalised objection, Octavia gathered the child up and hugged her. Lisette came over to join them. She was smiling, but Octavia saw with concern that the indefinable look of sadness was back in her eyes.

'Miss Petrie!' Lisette took Octavia's hand, then threw a puzzled glance at her aunt. 'We didn't expect to see you here. So soon, I mean.'

'Lisette, we have been…er…mistaken. Miss Petrie turns out not to have been a governess at all.'

'I knew! I knew! I said so to Edward!'

Ignoring Pip's outburst, Julia went on, 'This is Lady Octavia Petrie. She is the daughter of Lord Warnham, and the owner of Wychford.' Julia turned to Octavia with a smile. 'A charming house!'

'That's not what you said!' said Pip. 'You didn't like it. You said it was trying to kill you. That's why we all had to come away. But I liked it a lot. Do you really own Wychford, Miss Petrie? Really and truly? May I come and stay with you?'

'Don't listen to the child!' said Julia, looking slightly flustered. 'Philippa, behave yourself and stop interrupting! Lady Octavia is far too busy to entertain a little girl like you.'

'I shall be in London for some time, Pip. But, if it can be arranged, you shall pay me a visit at Wychford before long. Meanwhile, Mrs Barraclough, I wondered if you would permit me to take the girls out one afternoon?'

'Of course!' said Julia instantly. 'When are you free?'

'Tomorrow?'

'Certainly. How very kind!'

'But, Aunt Julia, you said we were to go with you tomorrow to see Mrs Allardyce—'

'The arrangement was by no means fixed,' said Julia firmly. 'I am sure Mrs Allardyce will understand perfectly. Is your brother in town, Lady Octavia?'

Lisette started and blushed, but sat back when Octavia said, 'Not yet. He is still sorting out his commitments to the Army, and is at present in France. But I believe he will be here in time for the Season.'

'We should be charmed to meet him,' said Julia.

'Charmed to meet whom?' asked a deep voice by the door. Edward Barraclough came in.

Octavia was profoundly grateful that Pip was still on her knee, that her face was half-hidden behind Pip's curls. This encounter had come somewhat sooner than she had planned—she had thought he was still out of London. She felt herself grow pale, then her cheeks were warm again as the colour surged back into them.

However, she had many times thought about their first meeting in London, and how she would deal with it. The feelings of humiliation and self-abasement following her flight from Wychford were now all behind her, and she was determined to be herself again—level-headed Lady Octavia Petrie, and no one's fool, least of all Edward Barraclough's!

So, by the time Mr Barraclough had come far enough into the room to see who their visitor was, she was quite composed—on the surface, at least.

'Edward, may I present Lady Octavia Petrie?' said Julia with a little laugh. 'What a distinguished governess you found for the girls! I hope it isn't too much of a shock for you.'

'It isn't a shock,' he said evenly. 'I discovered Lady Octavia's true identity not long after she left us.' He bowed to Octavia. 'I hope you are well?'

Octavia set Pip down, then got up and curtsied. 'Thank you, sir. But you could have saved yourself the trouble of finding out who I was. As you see, I've come to make my own apologies for deceiving you all.'

'It was no trouble, ma'am. It was incidental. I discovered your secret in the course of investigating your brother.' His tone was coolly businesslike.

'Really?' said Octavia, stiffly. 'May I ask why you found it necessary to investigate anyone at all?'

Edward's smile of apology was less than sincere. 'You must forgive me. I had to make sure that my ward had not fallen into the hands of some adventurer or other. At the time ''Harry Smith'' seemed a very dubious character.'

'Edward!' exclaimed Julia. 'Mr Petrie is the son of the Earl of Warnham!'

'That is what I found, along with the truth about Lady Octavia here. Has she told you she owns Wychford, as well? However, being the son of an Earl would not necessarily guarantee Mr Petrie's respectability,' said Edward drily. He turned to Octavia again. 'You will no doubt be relieved to hear that I heard nothing to his discredit.'

'Relieved?' asked Octavia coldly. 'What can you mean, sir? I know my brother. Whatever *you* may have heard about him is a matter of indifference to me.'

'Edward, does this mean I could meet Mr Petrie with your approval?' asked Lisette hesitantly.

'Once you are out, and have been suitably introduced, it would be difficult to object,' replied her uncle with a touch of impatience. 'But there are many other equally eligible young men who would be delighted to know you, Lisette. Don't set your mind too early on anyone in particular.'

'Of course not,' said Lisette in a subdued voice.

Julia decided to intervene. 'Lady Octavia has offered to take Lisette and Philippa out tomorrow, Edward. Isn't that kind? And what do you think? Her elder sister is Miss Cherrifield's former employer, the Duchess of Monteith!'

Edward shot a sharp glance at Octavia, but she met his eyes and said calmly, 'A surprising coincidence. I knew my sister had finished with Miss Cherrifield's services, but that she should end up with Pip... I believe she is an excellent governess.'

'No doubt,' he said drily. There was a short pause, then he asked, 'At what time do you intend to call for my nieces tomorrow? I might be here to accompany you.'

'Edward! That would be lovely! Just like our walks at Wychford!' cried Pip.

Octavia was not sure quite why Edward Barraclough wanted to join them in their walk and she was
not at all sure she ought to spend any time at all in
his company. But it was difficult to refuse in the face
of Pip's enthusiasm.

'That would be delightful, sir,' she said woodenly.
'Though I am surprised you have the time.'

'Not at all, ma'am,' he said smoothly. 'I shall
count it well spent.'

The next afternoon Gussie watched in amusement
as Octavia tried on one walking dress after another.

'Those two young girls must be very difficult to
please,' she said.

'Why do you say that?' asked Octavia, twisting
round to see how the latest attempt looked from the
back.

'I've seen you discard three of Madame Rosa's
best efforts, any one of which suits you perfectly.
Especially the one in zephyrine silk.'

'The blue one? You think that suits me best, do
you? Then I'll wear that,' said Octavia, nodding to
her maid to find it.

'Tavy, why don't you tell me what you're up to?
I refuse to believe that all this anxiety is in order to
impress the Misses Barraclough. Are you quite sure
that Edward Barraclough isn't accompanying you?
Or are you planning to meet some other young man
on your outing?'

'Of course not!' said Octavia indignantly. 'As if I would! The girls' uncle did say he might accompany us, yes. But I assure you, I have no desire to impress Edward Barraclough. I've told you, I'm now indifferent to him! Why this catechism?'

'Because you are behaving so unlike yourself! Martha has arranged that collar perfectly well, little sister, so stop fiddling with it. I wish to talk to you seriously.'

'I can't. I haven't time. Thank you for your advice, I think this blue outfit looks quite well on me. Goodbye, Gussie!' Octavia made her escape before her sister could probe any further.

Gussie looked thoughtful, then sent for her husband's secretary, who looked after her social arrangements. 'My rout party, James. I should like to add to the list of people to be invited...'

When Octavia arrived at the Barracloughs', she found another carriage already waiting outside. Pip was standing by it, and as soon as she saw Octavia she cried,

'Miss Petrie! We're going in Edward's carriage. He says it's better. And he says I can sit up with the coachman!'

'How kind!' said Octavia with something of a snap.

'You don't mind, do you? I'm sure you and he and Lisette will be more comfortable in the back.'

It was a sunny day, and Pip would be disappointed not to accept her uncle's offer. Octavia gave in gracefully, and prepared to descend. Edward Barraclough came out and took over from the groom who was helping her. Her hand jumped convulsively when he took it, but she controlled herself, and allowed him to lead her to his carriage and help her into it.

'Where had you intended to go?' he asked.

'I had thought we would take the carriage into the park, then walk for a while by the Serpentine,' said Octavia 'It's a poor substitute for the grounds at Wychford, but the girls might like to see the water fowl, and there are usually one or two small boats, too. But of course, if you have other plans, sir, you need not feel obliged to fall in with any of mine!'

He regarded her in silence. Then he turned, lifted Pip up next to his coachman, and seated himself opposite Lisette and Octavia. He surveyed them. 'What a very pretty sight! Hyde Park, it is!'

The carriage moved off and Octavia turned to Lisette. 'I never saw you riding at Wychford. I assume you do ride?'

'Oh, yes! I love riding.'

'Then you will enjoy seeing Rotten Row. We could perhaps go riding tomorrow or the next day.'

'Rotten Row. That's a funny name! What's rotten about it?' asked Pip, twisting round to talk.

'Nothing at all, Pip! In earlier times it was known as the *route du roi*—the king's road between

Kensington Palace and St James. I don't know how it came to be changed.'

Edward drawled, 'Instructive, as ever, I see. Old habits obviously die hard.'

'Some more quickly than others,' Octavia said coolly, and turned her attention back to Lisette. 'In the Season it is the thing to be seen riding or driving along Rotten Row between the hours of four and six. You will see most of the polite world there. But the best time to enjoy a ride is before the rest of the world is about—at eleven or twelve.'

They drew up just past the entrance to the park and looked at the scene along the Row. Though it was still early in the Season, it was already quite crowded.

'I don't call that riding!' said Edward. 'A tea party on horseback, more like! It's quite impossible to have a really good gallop.'

'Not only impossible, but frowned on, too! You mustn't do it, Lisette. Not if you wish to be approved of by the ladies of the *ton*.'

'Lady Jersey has been very kind already, Miss— Lady Octavia. Aunt Julia has received vouchers for Almack's.'

'That's good news!'

'I wonder what good fairy arranged for that,' murmured Edward. 'Sally Jersey isn't often so obliging to newcomers.'

'I believe it was Lady Octavia's sister, the Duchess of Monteith, Edward.'

'Was it, Lisette? Well, well, well! What a surprise!' Edward Barraclough was at his most sardonic. 'Shall we go on? Or do you wish to walk?'

'Let's walk, Edward!' said Pip, never content to stay inactive for long.

'Lady Octavia? Is this permitted to would-be leaders of fashion?'

Octavia ignored the irony in his voice and said, 'Certainly. Shall we walk to the Serpentine?'

As they walked along, Octavia was conscious that the polite greetings of her many acquaintances could not quite hide their curiosity. She nodded and smiled calmly enough, introduced the Barracloughs when necessary, and made sure that either Pip or Lisette was always between herself and Edward Barraclough. But after a while Pip could bear such a sedate pace no longer.

'Come on, Lisette!' she cried. 'Let's see the ducks!'

Octavia tried to protest, but Edward said, 'Let them go—we can keep them in sight. You're surely not afraid of being alone with me in broad daylight in the park, are you, Octavia? What do you think I could do?'

'Why, nothing, Mr Barraclough! Except to use my given name, when I don't believe you have my permission!'

'Oh, come! We are surely beyond that stage. In private.'

Octavia stopped and faced him. She spoke so calmly, in such a measured manner, that no one watching could have guessed the emotional turbulence behind her words.

'Mr Barraclough, I am no longer a governess in your employ. I know what you think of me, but what happened at Wychford is in the past. In the eyes of the world I am a member of an honourable family, and a lady of unimpeached reputation, who could hope to be treated with respect by someone who is no more than a casual acquaintance.'

'Casual acquaintance?' The mockery in his voice was evident. 'Is that what you would call it? Forgive me, Octavia! My memory is not quite so accommodating as yours, apparently.'

Octavia walked on, trying to control her anger. She had not expected this. For some reason she had thought he would be relieved to put Wychford and all that had happened there behind him. They were now beyond the crowds, though she could still see Pip and Lisette laughing at the antics of the birds round the lake. She had wanted to do so much for them, but if this man chose he could put an end to it all. Finally she said quietly, 'If you can't master that memory of yours, then I shall be forced to leave London. Is that what you wish?'

'Of course not! Why would you have to leave London?'

'There would be no point in my staying! I have no particular liking for town life. I only came this year because of my affection for your nieces. I thought I could use what influence I have in Society on their behalf.'

'Ah! The Duchess of Monteith. I thought as much. How very affecting!'

Octavia ignored this and went on, 'I believe I could do much more for them, but only if you stop reminding me of an episode I would rather forget. The gossips would quickly become suspicious if they heard you call me Octavia. Indeed, if you really wished, you could very easily destroy my credit in the world with a few well-chosen words. I could do nothing for anyone then.' She stopped again and looked up at him with lifted chin. 'So, which is it to be, Mr Barraclough? Can you forget the governess and her shameful behaviour, or shall I leave London and go back to Ashcombe?'

Edward Barraclough looked at her with a glint of admiration in his eyes, which disturbed her.

'What makes you so sure you know what I think of you?'

'You told me. I have not forgotten what you said on the last occasion we met.'

Edward paused, then said, 'I was angry. More angry than I've ever been in my life. I agree, I was mistaken. But why didn't you tell us that ''Harry Smith'' was your brother? Why did you leave me to believe the worst?'

'You wouldn't have listened. You thought you *knew* the sort of woman I was, and after my behaviour that afternoon I wasn't surprised.' She waved her hand in a gesture of impatience. 'But the sooner that's forgotten the better. The important thing is whether I can help Lisette and Pip. Am I to pack my bags? Or am I to stay and do my best for them? The decision is yours.'

There was a pause. Then, 'Lady Octavia,' he said at last. 'I concede defeat. I'll try to treat you with all the respect such a highly born lady deserves.' The words were placatory, but the tone was ironic. He went on, 'But I'm not quite sure how to proceed. How well am I supposed to know you?'

'As a good friend of your nieces. You needn't pretend anything more.'

'I'm not sure—' He stopped, then went on, 'Very well. But before we embark on this particular invention, I'd like you to tell me one thing.'

'Well?'

'What do *you* think of *me*?'

Octavia had not expected this. For a wild moment she was tempted to say, 'I don't know what I think of you, whether you're good or bad, kind or unkind. I only know I love you!' What a weapon that would give him! Would he be sorry for her, embarrassed, even? Or would he laugh? Perhaps he might feel he could tempt her to forget her vaunted respectability and have an affair with him, a rival for his mistress?

Octavia drew a breath and said, 'I admire your devotion to Lisette and Pip. But other than your nieces, we have little else in common. I certainly don't intend to pursue our acquaintance further than ordinary politeness would demand. Shall we join the girls? I think Pip is ready to move on.'

Chapter Fourteen

Octavia returned to her sister's house feeling as if her emotions had had enough buffeting for a while. For the next week she took care to visit Lisette and Pip when she thought their uncle would be out elsewhere. Plans for her sister's forthcoming rout party took up quite an amount of her time, too. She was annoyed, however, when Gussie showed her the guest list.

'What is Edward Barraclough's name doing here? I didn't ask you to include him! The invitation was meant for Mr and Mrs Henry Barraclough and Lisette! I thought you didn't want me to have anything to do with the other Barraclough brother!'

Gussie raised her brows. 'I could hardly invite one without the other, Tavy! Besides, brother Edward is much better *ton*, and twice as amusing as Henry and that awful wife of his. And, in the light of what you've told me, I want to see him again for myself. Why are you angry with me for including him?'

'I'm not angry! Who said I was angry? It was a surprise, that's all. There was no need for this!'

'Of course there was, Tavy dear! But don't look so annoyed with me. I think I have another beau for you, and we owe it all to Monteith's efforts. Now, there's a surprise for both of us!'

Octavia laughed in spite of herself. Gussie so seldom had a good word to say for her large, lazy husband. She asked, 'How did it happen, Gussie?'

'Oh, don't worry! Monteith didn't have to exert himself at all! The young man is the great-nephew of one of Monteith's numerous connections in Scotland, and he introduced himself the other day at Boodle's. Monteith liked him enough to give him an invitation to the rout party. I was delighted. It means that my dear husband has at least remembered that we are giving one!'

'Poor young man! He won't know a soul.'

'I shall invite him to dinner before the party. Harry will be there, too, and he can take Mr Aransay under his wing. I think they're about the same age, and Harry has any number of friends. Now, when am I to meet these Barracloughs of yours? Shall I call on them tomorrow with you? I wish to see beautiful Miss Lisette for myself. And Cherry tells me that Philippa Barraclough is just as bright and attractive as you said, too.'

Octavia was quite wrong about Edward Barraclough. Though he was not sure himself what he thought of her, he was certainly a long way from despising her. He might still be angry at the way she had deceived him, he might wish his harsh accusations unsaid, he might even still feel a lingering enchantment. All these and more he felt. But not contempt.

More often than he liked he found himself thinking about her, smiling at the memory of that imperious little figure by the Serpentine, chin lifted in defiance as she threw down her ultimatum. Treat her properly, or she would leave. He had started out full of suspicion, mistrusting her motives in coming round to meet Julia and the girls. He had invited himself on the excursion to Hyde Park with the intention of showing her how little her newly discovered status meant to him, prepared to cut her down to size with a few well-chosen reminders of their closer encounters if she adopted any airs.

But before long he had found he was enjoying their verbal fencing, had been unable to resist teasing her into defiance, delighting in the result. She had never been subservient, but now that she was free to talk to him as an equal, her directness, her readiness to take up his challenges intrigued and charmed him. Miss Petrie, the governess, had been like no other, and the Lady Octavia, youngest daughter of the Earl of Warnham, was equally rare a creature. He found her every bit as attractive.

Edward warned himself in vain against getting too interested in her. He reminded himself how she had deceived him, had probably laughed at him, had enticed him into near madness, but he found that he still wanted to know Lady Octavia Petrie better. He guessed she had been avoiding him, but was prepared to bide his time. She could hardly avoid him at the ball being held for Lisette.

Later it was generally agreed that the Barraclough ball was one of the Season's successes. Julia had done her work well, and, in a reversal of her previous attitude, had gladly accepted Lady Octavia's offers of help. As a result, most of the cream of London society was there, including a Royal Duke, two of Almack's patronesses, the Duke and Duchess of Monteith—even, briefly, the Duke of Wellington.

With her usual genius, Madame Rosa had produced a dress of masterly simplicity for Lisette's début. A touch of silver embroidery on the sleeves and hem of her floating white silk dress was all the decoration she had permitted. Lisette looked like the fairy princess Octavia had first thought her, her dark hair, violet eyes and delicate colouring enhanced by the silver and white dress and the posy of white roses tied with violet ribbons that she carried. She was a sensation. She was quickly surrounded by admirers, and the polite world was soon talking with enthusiasm of Lisette's beauty, her modesty, her charm. Some were so impressed that they even forgot to mention her considerable fortune.

* * *

Edward was proud of his niece, but regarded the crowd round her with a cynical eye. It wasn't often that wealth was combined with such beauty. No wonder she and Julia were under siege. He could see several well-known fortune hunters among her admirers, as well as quite a few sons of the impoverished aristocracy. Lisette was going to need all his help in the coming weeks to weed them out. He hadn't saved her from the clutches of Ricardo Arandez just to see her fall prey to an English counterpart!

After a while he relaxed and started to look round. Lisette was safe for the moment. His eye roved over the company, searching the crowd for one slight figure. When he finally saw Octavia he made his way through to her, and found her with her sister.

'Lady Octavia,' said Edward, bowing punctiliously.

The Duchess watched as Octavia said coolly, 'Mr Barraclough!' and curtsied to an exactly gauged depth. 'I believe you've met my sister, the Duchess of Monteith.'

'I've only once or twice had that privilege, but I've met your husband many times, Duchess,' said Edward, bowing again.

Eyes full of amused interest, Octavia's sister drawled, 'I must congratulate you on your niece, Mr Barraclough. She's the loveliest creature I've seen in years.'

Edward eyed Octavia's sister with appreciation. This was the sort of well-born lady he knew and understood. He could see traces of a family likeness, but, unlike Octavia, the sophisticated woman before him was very aware of her charm, and used it with a deliberation that was completely foreign to her younger sister. In other circumstances he would have spent an enjoyable hour or two's flirtation with the Duchess of Monteith. But not tonight! He said with a smile, 'Thank you. We are all very proud of her.'

'She has obviously been taught by an expert, wouldn't you say?' This time the amusement was even more evident.

Edward gave Octavia a sharp look, then said, 'Now, what *can* you mean by that, ma'am? I suspect your sister has been confiding in you. Am I right?'

'Tavy and I are good friends, as well as sisters. She has told me about Wychford.'

Edward raised an eyebrow, and Octavia said rather quickly, 'I've told my sister a lot about Pip and…and Lisette.'

'Ah! I see. Yes. Pip and Lisette. Duchess, the Barracloughs owe a lot to Lady Octavia, not least for her efforts on Lisette's behalf tonight.' He gazed round. 'A brilliant company. I doubt the Barracloughs could have managed it by themselves. My sister-in-law is delighted with its success.' He turned to Octavia. 'I wish you could have been here earlier. We had a hard time with Pip when she learned she was not allowed to come to Lisette's ball.

I had to promise to take her to see the deer and primroses at Richmond tomorrow before she was mollified. In fact, she wanted you to come, too, and I said I would ask you. Will you come? To please Pip?'

'I…er…I…'

'Of course you will, Tavy! A drive out to Richmond would be just the thing for you! You mustn't disappoint…' There was an infinitesimal pause before the Duchess went on, 'Mr Barraclough's niece.'

Octavia shot her sister a puzzled look, but said calmly, 'Thank you, sir. At what time?'

He grinned. 'May we discuss that during the next dance? Will you excuse us, Duchess?'

'Certainly.' He bowed and, before Octavia could object, took her hand and led her away.

Gussie watched them go. Edward Barraclough might have eyed her with appreciation, but she was far too experienced not to know when a man's serious attention was elsewhere. It seemed to her that, whatever Octavia thought, he was more attracted to her sister than he was willing to admit. If it were so, his intentions could hardly be anything but honorable, and she would do all she could to promote this interesting state of affairs. To see Edward Barraclough caught at last would be very satisfying, especially if he was caught by her own little sister! She smiled. Richmond Park to please Pip, indeed!

'I thought you promised to treat me with respect!' hissed Octavia as Edward escorted her on to the floor.

'What on earth can you object to now?' he asked in amazement. 'It's perfectly in order for me to ask one of my nieces' closest friends to dance, surely?'

'It was the way you did it! You didn't ask me, you simply dragged me away from my poor sister, who is now left alone!'

'My dear girl, half the gentlemen in this room have been waiting eagerly for an opportunity to ask your sister to dance with them! She won't be alone for long. She's a very fascinating woman, Oct—Lady Octavia!'

'She was always counted the beauty of the family.'

The movement of the dance took them away from each other. When they next came together Edward said, 'I've heard that *you* were one of the toasts of London when you came out. It doesn't surprise me. You look like spring itself in that pale green dress.'

'You shouldn't listen to gossip, Mr Barraclough. Nor should you try to flatter me. Casual acquaintances, remember? In fact, I'm not at all sure I ought to come with you tomorrow, in spite of my sister's intervention. It is almost certain to cause remarks.'

'Oh, no, you can't change your mind now! And I've been thinking about this casual acquaintances business. It won't work. Sooner or later London is going to hear about your "visit" to Wychford, and will wonder why we have pretended not to know each other. Let us say rather that we are distantly connected. That makes it respectable, surely?'

'Connected?'

'Through Mrs Carstairs! Have you forgotten that your aunt was a great friend of the Barracloughs? That I am still renting the house she left you?'

He watched as she absorbed this idea. 'You may be right,' she said doubtfully. 'London is bound to hear something sooner or later... Very well! We were about to settle on a time to meet tomorrow.'

'Richmond is a fair distance, and we shan't want to hurry. We'll call for you at eleven. Or is that too early?'

'Not at all. I'll be ready!'

The music came to an end and Octavia made to go.

'Not so fast,' said Edward, keeping hold of her hand. 'I want to take you to talk to Lisette.'

'But my sister—'

'Your sister is at present enchanting Charlie Stainforth. Look at her! She wouldn't welcome you. Come!'

He led her to where Lisette was standing surrounded by a bevy of young men. But when she saw Edward and Octavia she abandoned them all.

'You found her!' she said. 'Lady Octavia, I'm so glad I can talk to you at last! At the opening of the ball I hardly saw anyone, I was so nervous! Such a long line of people waiting to meet me! I want to thank you for this.' She touched her hair, which was held up with a delicate silver clasp.

Edward watched as Octavia smiled fondly at Lisette. He had never before realised quite how sweet her smile could be. Octavia's green silk dress was a perfect foil for her colouring, and its low cut, so very different from her Wychford dresses, revealed the lovely lines of her throat and bosom... He stood, not really listening to what they were saying, but watching the two of them talking animatedly to one another, the one so dark and the other so fair... He had been quite right about 'Miss Petrie's hair'. Tonight, of course, the loose knot on top of her head, the tendrils framing her face, had been artfully arranged by an experienced maid, and diamonds sparkled among the honey-gold curls. They were not hanging halfway down her back in the rain, or tumbled in disarray, reflecting the light of leaping flames... He drew a sharp breath as his body responded to the sudden memory. It was just as vivid, just as exciting, as it had been all those weeks ago...and he had thought he had mastered it!

Lisette had been claimed by someone else, and, with a smile of apology, she let herself be carried off.

Octavia turned to him, and said with determination, 'And now we shall return to my sister!'

Edward pulled himself together and shook his head. 'Wrong, Lady Octavia!' he said. 'Even the most critical tabby allows a young woman to have two dances with the same partner in an evening. I intend to have my second now!'

'But I promised Sir Richard...'

'What a pity. The poor fellow will have to wait.' Relying on Octavia's sense of propriety not to make a fuss at his high-handed behaviour, Edward took her firmly by the arm and led her back to the floor. This time it was a waltz. He took one of her hands in his, his other arm went round her waist, and they set off.

After a moment he said, 'Do you not find the ballroom remarkably chilly, Lady Octavia?'

She frowned at him. 'No.'

'Strange. I could have sworn there was an icy draught blowing down my spine. A Lady Octavia sort of chill.' An involuntary chuckle escaped her and he said, 'That's better! I had begun to think my fingers would drop off with the cold.'

'What do you expect, sir? I have pleaded with you to treat me as a casual acquaintance—'

'Distantly connected.'

'Distantly connected! But here you are singling me out! You may have stopped calling me by my given name, but you still treat me with a lack of ceremony, which will soon set tongues wagging if it continues.'

'That is nonsense! It's all in your imagination, Oct—Lady Octavia! What could be more unexceptionable than that Lisette's uncle should pay some polite attention to a friend who has done so much for his niece? His *nieces*! Pip would have been far easier to deal with if you had been there today. Julia has no idea how to handle her. Now, have you any more complaints, or are you ready to enjoy this waltz?'

They danced for a while in silence, and, whatever their differences might be, their steps were perfectly matched, their bodies moving as if by instinct in harmony with each other. Edward drew Octavia imperceptibly closer. She looked up and smiled. For a moment he forgot the music, forgot the other dancers, forgot everything but the enchantment of having her in his arms.

'Octavia,' he murmured, his eyes warm as he gazed down at her.

Octavia, too, had felt the magic, though she wanted none of it. Firmly suppressing her wayward feelings, she decided to open the subject of Lisette's secret worries. He might be receptive enough to listen sympathetically.

'Mr Barraclough,' she said, uncharacteristically nervous, 'I've been thinking about Lisette...'

Edward was disappointed. He had thought her smile was one of pleasure, shared pleasure. Apparently not. Suppressing a sigh, he said, 'What is it?'

'Before I left Wychford I had intended to talk to you about her, but...but there was no time. Has she told you that, after she had met my brother, she and I had a long talk?'

This time the disappointment was sharp. Had he been wrong about her after all? The English aristocracy spent half their lives looking for suitable matches, by which they meant rich matches, for their sons. Or in this case, brothers. Why had he believed that Octavia was different from the rest of her kind? He said with resignation, 'I suppose I ought to have expected this. Have you any idea how many other young men would like to marry into the Barraclough wealth, Lady Octavia? You might say your brother has a head start on all the others, but that doesn't mean I shall look with any greater degree of approval on him. I'd like Lisette to be happy, but I'm not at all sure she should throw herself away on a good-looking young soldier who has already persuaded her to meet him in secret!'

Octavia gasped and began, 'I didn't—'

He brushed this aside. His eyes were no longer warm as he continued, 'I'm disappointed in you. However beautiful you look tonight, you surely can't have thought you could charm me into changing my mind on such a serious matter as this!'

Angry colour flooded Octavia's cheeks, and she pulled away from him. 'I doubt I could charm you into doing anything at all!' she said, and started to walk off the floor. He pursued her to the end of the ballroom, where they had left her sister. She was not there. Here Octavia stopped and turned. She said in a low voice, 'For your information, sir, I wanted to talk to you about something quite different! I am as anxious as you that Lisette should be happy, whatever her choice. But she would not be ''throwing herself away'', if she married my brother!'

Irritated at the turn the conversation had taken, he said coolly, 'Unlike the rest of the world, ma'am, I do not believe a title immediately bestows virtue on its possessor, so please don't quote your brother's prospects of an earldom at me!'

'I was not about to! You are impossible, sir!' Eyes sparkling, twin flags of colour in her cheeks, Octavia faced him angrily.

Edward felt his own anger drain away. 'Octavia—' he began ruefully.

'And *don't* call me by my given name!'

'Ah! There you are!' They both looked round. Gussie was making her way towards them. She looked from one to the other, and raised an eyebrow.

'Have you arranged a time?' she asked. 'As far as I remember, Richmond is more than an hour's drive. You'll need to be up early, Octavia.'

Edward decided that discretion was the better part of valour. He had a feeling that Octavia was in such a temper that she would cry off their excursion if he gave her the slightest opportunity. He said briefly, 'Thank you for the dances, Lady Octavia. I shall call for you at eleven. Duchess, do you by some miracle have the next dance free? May I?'

He led Octavia's sister on to the floor, and afterwards stayed well clear of the Petrie family for the rest of the evening.

The next morning Edward collected Pip and drove to St James's Square. In spite of her anger the previous evening, he was reasonably sure that Octavia would accompany them to Richmond. Pip was a powerful draw. And he felt a spurt of pleased relief when he saw that she was dressed and ready for them. He wanted to talk to Octavia—their quarrel the previous evening had left unfinished business between them, and it needed to be cleared up.

Pip greeted Octavia with her usual enthusiasm, then settled down between her and Edward, eagerly watching the sights as they drove out down the Bath Road towards Brentford and the bridge at Kew.

Once at Richmond they left the carriage in charge of the grooms and walked. Pip was delighted. 'Miss Petrie! Look! Do you see the deer?'

'Lady Octavia will get annoyed with you, Pip, if you fail to call her by her correct name,' said Edward.

'No, I shan't, Pip! But I behaved very badly in pretending to be simply Miss Petrie. I shouldn't like the world to know about it all sooner than it has to.'

Pip fired up in her defence. 'You didn't behave badly at all! It was my fault. I told Edward you'd come to be our governess, and that was when it started. But I shall really try to remember to call you Lady Octavia now!' She added mournfully, 'It's just that ''Miss Petrie'' was friendlier, somehow.'

'I'm still your friend, Pip! I always shall be.'

Edward said wryly, 'You're a lucky girl, Pip. You should have heard the dressing down *I* got from Lady Octavia for forgetting her name. Now, why don't you go and take a look at those deer? Go quietly, mind— they'll run off if you startle them.'

'I'll go with her—' began Octavia.

'No! Wait! Off you go, Pip! I need to make my peace with Lady Octavia and I'd rather do it in private, if you don't mind. I don't want you to see my authority undermined.'

He said this so lightly that Pip laughed at the idea and went off quite happily, to begin stalking the deer. He looked at Octavia.

'I'm glad you came,' he said quietly. 'I was afraid you wouldn't.'

Octavia stared coldly back at him. 'I wouldn't have, if it hadn't been for Pip.'

'I guessed as much. I was sorry for last night. I was wrong to leap to conclusions—' Edward stopped and took a breath. 'Heavens above, I seem to do nothing but apologise! What is it about you? I would say I'm normally a very even-tempered man, but you bring out the worst in me!'

'That's easily explained. It's because you secretly despise me.'

'What?' For a moment Edward was so surprised he could hardly speak. Then he exclaimed, '*Despise* you? What for? Of course I don't despise you. What a damned stupid idea!'

'It's quite obvious you do! You must! After the shameless way I behaved that…that afternoon. And the lies I told. Of course you do!'

Edward was stunned. 'Octavia— No, I will call you Octavia for this, so don't scowl at me like a cockatrice.' He took her hands in his and said earnestly, 'Octavia, I swear, I have never, not for one moment, despised you. How could you think it? Scorn is perhaps the one emotion you have *not* roused in me! I seem to have suffered from most of the rest. Suspicion, annoyance, fury, delight. Disapproval, admiration, respect, and...and yes, desire. And, of course, jealousy.'

'*Jealousy?* When was there any cause for jealousy?'

'I was choking with jealousy when I spoke to you that last morning at Wychford. That's why the accusations I made were so bitter.'

Octavia tried to pull her hands away, but he wouldn't let them go. 'No, you must let me finish. You think I *despise* you for what happened between us? You couldn't be more wrong. Your vulnerability, your innocence were all that stopped me from taking you completely there and then in that tower room. Your instant response to me, the passion I had roused in you, went to my head. You can have no idea how hard it was to resist temptation. Yet I knew I had to—'

This time Octavia wrenched her hands out of his grasp and put them over her ears. 'No! Don't say another word! I don't want to hear! If you knew how ashamed I am every time I think of it...' She put her hands down again and faced him with proud desperation. 'I can't expect you to believe this, but I had never...*never* before given way to such a disgraceful display of emotion. I had never before experienced it. And I was sure you must despise me for it.'

'The shame would have been mine if I had betrayed you, Octavia. We were both in the grip of a very powerful force in that room. How could I condemn *you*?'

'But the next day—'

'The next day, after hearing Julia's accusations, and hearing what the maid at the inn had to say—' He shook his head in angry rejection of the memory, and went on, 'The thought that you might already have had a lover, that you were not the innocent I thought you, was driving me wild. I was furious with jealousy. And *that* is an emotion that *I* have never before experienced.'

He waited for a moment. When she stayed silent he said, 'I hope you can forgive me. I hope we can put it all behind us, and begin again, as if I had met you as Mrs Carstairs's niece, and the owner of the house I happen to be renting. But whether we can, or whether we can't, you must believe that I have never despised you.'

Octavia looked at him uncertainly. 'Begin again?' she said. 'Forget what happened? If I only could... Would it not be better to forget that we ever knew each other at all? Go our separate ways?'

Not in a thousand years, was the sudden thought that came unbidden into his mind. But he said quietly, 'Is that what you want?'

She hesitated, and he waited stiff with tension, watching her conflicting thoughts cross her face. When she said, 'I think it would be very difficult, if not impossible. What would Pip and Lisette say?' he let out a sigh of relief.

'Exactly. I don't think that's the solution at all. So, we'll begin again? This time as friends? At least, as something more than casual acquaintances?'

'I'll try. But not if you leap to false conclusions about me again.'

'I don't always seem to be rational when you are near, Octavia, so I won't make rash promises. But I'll certainly try not to! Now, what was it that you wanted to talk about last night? You sounded nervous.'

'I was afraid you'd tell me it wasn't my affair. I talked to Lisette about the man she knew in Antigua.'

'Ah! Ricardo Arandez. She said something of the kind. I gather you tried to help her.'

'The trouble was, I was working in the dark. You said once that Lisette's father found out something he didn't like about Arandez. That was why he withdrew his consent. Was it serious?'

Edward's face clouded over. 'Very.'

'So it's unlikely that your brother would ever have changed his mind again?'

'More than unlikely. Impossible!'

'Don't you think it would have been better to tell Lisette what was wrong?'

'Certainly not! She was a child.'

'But she's not a child now, and though she knows she is not betrothed, she is still half-convinced that Arandez was telling the truth when he said it was her father's last wish that she should marry him.'

'I thought we had scotched that!'

'No, your sister-in-law merely told Lisette she was never to mention Arandez again. She didn't say why.'

Edward was silent. At last he said, 'I see no necessity for bothering Lisette with the details of the story. She isn't in love with Arandez, and she has plenty to occupy her mind at the moment. If she hasn't yet forgotten him she soon will. Besides, in spite of Julia's fears, there hasn't been the slightest sign of him. No, I won't tell Lisette! It really isn't necessary.'

'I think you're wrong.'

'Then I'm sorry. But I won't change my mind.'

'Would you tell me instead?'

'Certainly not!'

'It's to protect Lisette! How can I help her when I don't know *why* her father wouldn't let her marry Arandez? You must tell me!'

Edward's expression darkened. He said stiffly, 'There's no question of it! I'd like you to leave this subject alone, Lady Octavia. Lisette is protected by those whose business it is! If Arandez ever dares show his face I'll know what to do, believe me!'

He sounded so fierce that Octavia saw any further effort would be wasted. She tried a different argument. 'But if he does, wouldn't it be wiser to let Lisette herself see him again? Isn't it better for her to face him, to discover what it is she really feels about him? She won't be happy until she does, you know.'

'Lady Octavia,' he said forcefully, 'you don't know what you're talking about! I would not willingly let that man anywhere near my niece!' Some demon made him add, 'Believe me, this is a much more serious matter than keeping at bay all those sprigs of the English aristocracy who simply have their eye on Lisette's inheritance.'

Octavia was already annoyed at his refusal to trust her. Now she was angry. 'I suppose you include my brother among those sprigs?'

'Yes, if you must know, I suppose I do!'

Octavia turned on him. 'That's *enough*! When will you realise, sir, that the Petries don't *need* anyone else's wealth. You do justice to no one—neither yourself nor my brother, nor Lisette—with such suspicions! I think I shall go to find Pip. I prefer her uncomplicated honesty to your pig-headed cynicism.'

Edward watched her broodingly as she walked angrily over the grass to where Pip was standing. He had done it again! Why did he always have to spoil things? He couldn't possibly have told her what Arandez had done, but with anyone else he would have managed to refuse more gracefully. As for that brother of hers... The trouble was, he had never come across anyone quite like Octavia Petrie before, and he wasn't sure how to deal with her. A lady of the highest society, yet she was as honest and straightforward as Pip, as gentle and caring as Lisette, a woman of courage and humour, and with a passion that could set him on fire in a way that Louise would never even begin to match. What was he to *do* about her?

'Marry her,' a voice inside him said. 'That's the only answer. Marry her before someone else does.'

Edward had started across the grass to join Octavia and Pip, but he now stopped short. *Marry* her? Give up his bachelor life? Join the ranks of those married men he had pitied in the past? Never! Look at the state she had got him into now, and he wasn't even engaged to her! Oh, no! Marriage was a trap he would never fall into. What a damned foolish idea!

Chapter Fifteen

The conversation during the return trip from Richmond was purely for Pip's benefit. Left to herself, Octavia would not have said a word to Edward Barraclough. She was angry and disappointed. One minute he was lifting her spirits by swearing, apparently sincerely, that he did not despise her, and two minutes later he was refusing to trust her with information about Arandez, and furthermore accusing her of promoting Harry's claims to Lisette's fortune! What was wrong with him? It was almost as if he deliberately picked a quarrel whenever they seemed to be getting closer. Octavia had no idea whether this was instinctive or deliberate, but to her mind it demonstrated even more clearly his reluctance to become involved. When they reached St James's Square she kissed Pip affectionately, and bade Mr Barraclough a very cool farewell.

Once in her room, she put Edward Barraclough firmly out of her mind and turned her attention to his niece. From what she had heard of the past year in

Lisette's life, it wasn't surprising that she was sad. Time would heal the pain of her parents' death, but it was obvious that Lisette would never be happy and at peace with herself until she knew what she really felt for Ricardo Arandez. Edward Barraclough had dismissed the idea that she had ever been in love with Arandez, and Octavia was now inclined to agree with him. Lisette had felt affection for a young man she had known since she was a child, and she had trusted him. Why else had she been so ready to believe his story about the letter? However, during the past six months away from Antigua Lisette had done some growing up. Her interest in Harry proved she was no longer in love with Arandez, if indeed she ever had been.

But, as long as Lisette still half-believed what Arandez had told her, she would never truly be free to think of anyone else. Octavia wished she knew what had caused John Barraclough's sudden refusal to let his daughter marry him. Did Lisette herself know why? John Barraclough must have given his daughter *some* reason for breaking off the relationship so abruptly.

So, when she called to congratulate Julia on the success of her ball, she took the opportunity to invite Lisette to come for a drive in the park. Miss Cherrifield had taken Pip with her to visit some of her former pupils, so the way was free for a confidential chat.

'I've been thinking about what you told me about Ricardo Arandez, Lisette,' she began as they drove along in the spring sunshine. 'What sort of person was he?'

'I'm not sure any more. When I was young I liked him a lot, though he was much older than I was. He always said he wanted to marry me, and I quite liked the idea, especially as it meant I would still be near my own home. His family lives on the next estate, you see. Mama and Papa seemed pleased, too, so I was very surprised when they changed their mind.'

'Do you know why that was?'

'Not really. But later I thought it must be because of some disagreement about boundaries. Edward thought the Arandez family had taken some land that belonged to us. Papa wouldn't talk about it, but that was the only reason I could find.'

'Were you unhappy? Did you badly want to marry Ricardo?'

'I thought I did at first, but not afterwards.'

'Why was that?'

'When Mama and Papa were killed and he told me that Papa had wanted me to marry him straight away, I wasn't sure I wanted to. So I told him I needed time.'

'My poor girl, of course you needed time! Your parents' accident must have been a terrible shock! Surely he understood that?'

'No. He said that Papa's last wishes ought to be a ''sacred duty''. He got angry when I still wouldn't do as he wished, and called me a stupid little girl. But then Edward and Uncle Henry saw him and sent him away. When they said I wasn't to see him again, I was almost relieved. But then, after Edward had left for England, Ricardo came back again and wanted me to go away with him. He was more like he had been in the past. He said he was sorry he had frightened me, it was because he loved me so much, and had promised Papa he would always look after me.'

'But you had your uncles to look after you! They were your guardians.'

'That's what I told him. I said I was quite sure Papa wouldn't have wanted me to run away with anyone. Then he showed me Papa's letter. We were just leaving when Uncle Henry saw us and called his men. That was the last time I saw Ricardo. I can't seem to forget it. The men were dragging him away and he was shouting that I must wait for him, that he loved me and would come for me. I...I think sooner or later he will.'

They were silent for a moment. Then Octavia said, 'And what will you say if he does?'

'I don't know! I once thought I was in love with him, but I'm not sure any more that he was telling the truth about Papa. And...and I met your brother and I found that I liked him much better! *Much* better! Lady Octavia, I just don't know *what* I would say!'

'I suppose in the end it comes down to one simple question, Lisette. If you think you're still in love with him, then you must persuade him to be honourable and wait till you have your guardians' proper consent. No running away again. After all, if it was just a matter of a boundary dispute, they may well come round if they see you're serious. But, if you are *not* in love with Mr Arandez, then you will have to tell him so. It's as simple as that.'

Lisette sighed. 'It does sound simple when *you* say it. I'll try to do it. Thank you for talking to me, Lady Octavia!'

After chatting with Lisette on less fraught matters for a while, Octavia thought she could safely take her back to South Audley Street. She was surprised at Edward Barraclough. The quarrel over the boundary must have been very bitter indeed to cause so much trouble in the family. But when she thought more about it, she decided that the delay it had caused hadn't actually done Lisette any harm. Without that dispute, Lisette might well have married Arandez and only afterwards discovered that what she had felt was affection for a childhood hero, not love for the grown man. She could have been very unhappy. As it was, she had a chance now to find out what she really wanted of life.

On the evening of Gussie's rout party her husband came in late to the salon just as Gussie was about to give him up and start dinner without him. He was accompanied by a tall, very presentable young man with blond hair and clear blue eyes. Introductions were of necessity rather hasty, but the Duke smiled blithely at his wife and in his rumbling voice presented his protégé as 'Billie Farquhar's great-nephew, m'dear, Richard Aransay.'

'You're very welcome, sir,' said Gussie. 'You must forgive our lack of ceremony this evening. The house has been made ready for later, and we are dining in the morning room. Perhaps you would take my sister, Lady Octavia Petrie, in to dine? And this is my brother, Lieutenant Petrie. I expect you two young men about town will find a lot to say to each other! Shall we go?'

Octavia found Mr Aransay an entertaining dinner companion. She gathered that he had just spent several weeks with his great-uncle, and his irreverent account of the activities of that eccentric peer reminded her strongly of Tom Payne. For a while her anxieties about Lisette, her sense of injury at Edward Barraclough's lack of trust, were forgotten as she laughed at Mr Aransay's stories, supplemented by those of the Duke, who had his own tales to tell of Lord Farquhar. The time passed very agreeably, and it was a surprise when Gussie rose from the table and announced that their other guests would soon be arriving. It was time to get ready to receive them.

The reception rooms of Monteith House were impressive, and tonight they were beautifully laid out for Gussie's guests. A table of refreshments surrounding a large bowl of fruit punch had been put out in the ornate dining room, and liveried footmen circled the rooms with trays of champagne and wine. There was no dancing, but a group of musicians provided a pleasing background of music. The salon was gleaming in the light of several hundred candles in its huge chandeliers, reflected over and over in the mirrors that lined the walls. Soon the rooms were filled with the hum of conversation interspersed with laughter, a sure sign of the evening's success.

The Duke had taken Mr Aransay off after dinner, presumably to exchange some further reminiscences, so Harry, who had been told by Octavia that Lisette would be present, was free to go through the rooms busily greeting old friends and members of the family, and remaining constantly on the watch for the arrival of the Barracloughs. As was Octavia. This time there would be no informal, accidental meetings, such as the one at Wychford. This evening Harry would be properly introduced to Lisette's family as Lieutenant the Honourable Harry Petrie, son of the Earl of Warnham, and, with one notable exception, she was fairly certain they would regard him with complaisance.

The Henry Barracloughs arrived with Lisette, who was looking exquisite in jonquil yellow. When Octavia introduced her brother, Julia almost simpered at him.

'We've heard about you, of course, Lieutenant Petrie. Your sister has told us you've recently left the Army. The Guards, I believe?'

Harry tore his eyes off Lisette and turned with one of his most charming smiles. 'Yes, Mrs Barraclough. My father wishes to see more of me. I hear you are from Antigua? I believe it's a beautiful island...'

Octavia waited till she saw that Harry had the situation well in hand, busily charming Lisette's guardians, then moved away. She wandered through the rooms, finally acknowledging to herself that she was waiting for Edward Barraclough to appear, though what she would say to him when he did she had no idea!

'Exquisite! Truly exquisite!' Octavia turned round. Richard Aransay was behind her, his eyes fixed on Lisette.

'Indeed she is. And one of the Season's greatest successes.'

'I see your brother is with her at the moment?'

'Lisette has many admirers, sir. Would you like me to introduce you?'

Richard Aransay smiled. Octavia wondered why it made her uneasy. 'I hardly think that is necessary, Lady Octavia. Lisetta and I know one another quite well. You might say very well.'

'I beg your pardon, Mr Aransay?'

'Forgive me, ma'am, my name is Arandez. Richard Arandez. I'm afraid my host's vagueness misled you when he introduced me tonight.'

Octavia was looking at him in shock. 'You are Richard Arandez? *Ricardo* Arandez?'

'I see you've heard of me. Has Lisetta been telling you about us? I hear she thinks a great deal of you.'

'Mr Arandez, I'm sorry, but I don't think you should be here! The Barracloughs—'

'Have for some reason best known to themselves warned me off Lisetta. Is that what you wanted to say? But I am here by invitation, Lady Octavia. Since when have the Barracloughs decided who should be invited, or not invited, to Monteith House? My great-uncle was a very old friend of the present Duke's father.'

Octavia gave him a straight look. 'Did you know Lisette would be here tonight, sir?'

'Let us say that I hoped so. I have to talk to her.' He glanced at Lisette, flanked on either side by Harry and her Aunt Julia. Henry Barraclough was close by. 'But not at the moment. Is there somewhere where you and I can have a talk?'

Octavia eyed him for a moment, then, without speaking, she led the way through the press of people to the winter garden, which opened out from the last of the suite of rooms. 'I think this is private enough, sir. But I warn you, I'm not exactly prejudiced in your favour.'

'Of course you aren't! The Barracloughs have almost certainly poisoned your mind against me. I hear you're quite close to them. But do you think you're being fair, Lady Octavia? I love Lisetta. For many years I watched her growing up and, encouraged by her parents I may say, I looked forward to the day when she would be old enough to marry me. Her parents' death was a tragedy for me as well as those poor children. I not only lost two of my dearest friends, but the promise of future happiness with the girl I loved.'

Octavia was impressed in spite of herself, but she asked bluntly, 'Why don't Lisette's uncles like you?'

'They see me as a threat to their control of the Barraclough fortune.'

'I believe there was more to it than that, sir.'

Arandez stiffened and he frowned. 'I...I'm sorry. I don't understand,' he said somewhat warily.

Octavia went on, 'Wasn't there a quarrel? A dispute about some boundary?'

The frown lifted. He shrugged his shoulders and with a rueful smile said, 'Ah, yes! That boundary. It caused a great deal of trouble. Much more than it was worth. Lisetta's father realised it was not a problem in the end.' He gave Octavia a direct look out of clear blue eyes. 'Now that you've met me, Lady Octavia, do you think I'm the villain the Barracloughs claim? Lisetta and I love each other. She will never be happy without me, and I...I want more than anything in the world to have the right to look after her, as her father wished. If only I could talk to her!'

Octavia was torn. She had some sympathy for Richard Arandez. He seemed sincere enough. Again she thought of how much he reminded her of Tom Payne, and Tom had been as open as the day. On the other hand, Edward Barraclough had made it more than clear that he wished Lisette to have no contact of any kind with Arandez. What should she do? Ricardo Arandez was an apparently perfectly respectable young man, sponsored in Society by her sister's husband. He would be accepted everywhere, and in the end he and Lisette were bound to meet *somewhere*—if not here, then certainly somewhere else. Surely it was better that they meet here tonight where she herself could keep a careful eye on them? She was risking Edward Barraclough's severe displeasure, but she was, after all, used to that!

'Very well, sir,' she said. 'I shall take you to Lisette. But I need hardly remind you she is one of my sister's guests tonight. She mustn't be upset, or put under any pressure. As far as London society is concerned, Lisette has *no obligation* to anyone other than her guardians. Do you understand what I mean?'

'Thank you! And, yes, I promise to be discreet. But I assure you, she will be delighted to see me! There will be no pressure, Lady Octavia, only relief.'

Octavia preceded him out of the winter garden full of misgiving, not at all sure she was doing the right thing. As they went through to the salon, she turned to Arandez and said, 'I shall stay with you, Mr Arandez. Lisette is very dear to me.'

'Of course, ma'am,' he said with a confident grin. 'But you will soon see how very dear she is to me, too!'

* * *

Henry and Julia Barraclough had left Lisette in Harry's care and were being ushered towards the dining room by the Duke, presumably for some refreshments. Lisette looked happy enough, though she was rather pale. The salon was quite warm, and several other admirers surrounded her, all pressing for her attention. Octavia quickened her pace to join her. Lisette was basically shy, and her success, far from going to her head, was causing her some distress.

When she saw Richard Arandez with Octavia she went even paler. She said uncertainly, 'Ricardo? What a surprise! I...I didn't know you were in London!'

'Lisetta!' He bent towards her as if to kiss her cheek, but she drew back nervously.

'Not...not here!' She gave him her hand, then turned to Harry, who was standing behind her. 'Lieutenant Petrie! Let me introduce an old friend—Ricardo Arandez.'

Harry shook his head. 'Miss Barraclough obviously knows you, Aransay, but why does she give you a Spanish name? I thought you were a Scotsman!'

'I come from Antigua,' said Arandez briefly. 'Lisetta and I are very old friends, indeed, more than that—' Lisette went even paler and drew in her breath.

Octavia stepped in before he could go any further. 'Mr Arandez!' she said with a smile. 'You'll find you have quite a deal of explaining to do, I'm afraid. My sister's husband is notoriously absentminded. You're probably known all over London as Richard Aransay from Scotland!' She paused, then added with a significance meant for him alone, 'I did warn you.'

He nodded and said easily, 'Lisetta and I were children together, Lieutenant, but we haven't seen each other for some time. May I take her away from you for a minute or two? I have news of her friends on Antigua.'

Harry gave Lisette a look of inquiry. She said hesitantly, 'I...I think I should like to talk to Mr Arandez, Lieutenant Petrie. For a short while. Will you excuse me?'

'Harry, you may take me to the dining room,' Octavia said before her brother could object. 'I'm so thirsty, and I know Gussie ordered some deliciously refreshing drinks. Let's go to find them. We won't be long, Lisette.'

Octavia led Harry away. 'What does all this mean, Tavy? Why are you encouraging that fellow? You know I like Lisette!'

'Don't worry, brother. There's no real competition there. My guess is that Lisette has grown up a little since she last saw Mr Arandez. Just give her time to find it out for herself. How did you get on with the Barracloughs?'

'I must say, I don't know what you have against Mrs Barraclough. She was very pleasant to me. A bit too gushy, perhaps, but quite easy to talk to.'

'Face it, Harry! You're quite a catch!' said Octavia, thinking she sounded every bit as cynical as Edward Barraclough.

'What about Lisette's Uncle Edward?' asked Harry echoing her thoughts. 'Has he forgiven you yet?'

'I'm not sure what the situation is at the moment. I suspect we shall fall out again quite badly as soon as he sees Ricardo Arandez with Lisette. He disapproves of Mr Arandez even more than he does of you!'

'Good! But why should he fall out with you? It's not your fault that Arandez is here.'

'Try telling that to Mr Barraclough! In fact, you can tell him now—he has just come into the room. I don't think he can have seen Arandez yet, though. He doesn't look angry enough.'

Harry looked towards the door. 'So that's Barraclough! He's a good-looking chap, Tavy. Powerful, too. I shouldn't like to fall foul of him!'

Edward Barraclough made his way over to them, hesitated fractionally while he eyed Harry, then bowed and said, 'Good evening, Lady Octavia.'

Octavia returned his bow and said in a neutral voice, 'Mr Barraclough. My brother, Lieutenant Harry Petrie.'

'Ah! Lieutenant!'

'Not for much longer, I'm afraid, sir. I've already sent in my papers.'

'Ah, yes.' There was a short silence during which the two men examined each other. Then Edward said, 'You know my niece, I believe.'

'I was introduced to her tonight, sir. In the company of your brother and his wife.'

Edward gave him a grim smile. 'Come, Lieutenant! You're surely not trying to tell me it was for the first time!'

'No, sir. I've met Lisette twice before at Wychford. And if you will permit me, I should like to meet her many more times still!'

Octavia drew in her breath, but Harry's audacity had done him no harm. Edward laughed and said more naturally, 'We'll have to see about that! You have a good advocate in your sister, at all events.'

'Tavy is the best of sisters, sir.'

'Tavy? What a pity to reduce a beautiful name like "Octavia" to "Tavy"!' He turned round and surveyed the room. 'But where is my niece at present?'

'Did...did you not see her as you came through? I...I think she is in the saloon, sir,' said Octavia swallowing hard. 'W...with an old friend.'

'Would you show me, ma'am? Excuse us, Lieutenant Petrie.'

Octavia cast a last despairing glance at Harry and took Edward's proffered arm. As she led him back towards the saloon she took a deep breath and began, 'I could have prevaricated, Mr Barraclough. But I choose not to. I hope you will give me credit for that at least. Your niece is with Mr Ricardo Arandez.'

Edward stopped. He said very quietly, 'What did you say?'

Octavia swallowed again and repeated, 'Your niece is with Ricardo Arandez.'

They had reached the wide doors to the saloon. Lisette was with Arandez in an alcove formed by one of the tall window embrasures. Arandez was leaning towards her, talking urgently. She was listening, but not particularly attentively, her eye wandering over the crowd, apparently in search of someone else.

Edward Barraclough drew in his breath with an audible hiss. 'Is this your doing?' he asked, his lips barely moving.

Octavia hesitated. 'Not exactly,' she said. 'My brother-in-law—'

As if the mention of his name had conjured him up, the Duke of Monteith clapped Edward on the shoulder. 'Barraclough!' he exclaimed. 'The very chap! I've got a young fella here from your part of the world. Jamaica, what? Come and meet him. You come too, Octavia!''

He steered Edward over to the alcove and gave a loud laugh. 'He doesn't waste time, I see! Already got the prettiest girl in the room with him! What a lad! Your niece, ain't she?'

'I thought my niece was with her aunt,' Edward said ominously.

The Duke brayed with laughter. 'Got to make allowances, Barraclough!' he roared. 'A pretty gel and a handsome fella—o'course they'll meet! She's perfectly safe, though. Good chap, Aransay. Know his uncle. Splendid fella!'

'You must excuse me, Duke! I need no introduction to Mr Arandez. But I should like to see my niece restored to her aunt and uncle.' They had reached the alcove. Ignoring Arandez, Edward simply said, 'Lisette?'

The Duke looked briefly surprised, then gave another laugh. 'Never knew you were such a stickler, Barraclough! Never mind, Aransay! I'll take y'to meet Puffy Rogers. Great chap, Puffy. Lost fifteen thousand last night. Didn't turn a hair. Come on!' He set off towards the card room.

Arandez looked uncertain, but Lisette said, 'Yes, do go, Ricardo! I want to find Lieutenant Petrie. I promised to introduce him to Edward. Edward, you stay here!' She disappeared in the direction of the dining room before anyone could stop her.

Edward said pleasantly, 'You'd better follow Monteith to the card room, Arandez. I have no desire to make a scene, but I'm not sure I can keep my hands off you for very much longer. Furthermore you'd better stay away from Lisette in future. As we both know, I could make London very uncomfortable for you if I chose.'

For a moment Arandez looked as if he might argue, but then he shrugged his shoulders and went. Edward turned to Octavia. 'You arranged this,' he said flatly.

'I didn't, but I would have, if I had known that Mr Arandez was going to be here tonight,' Octavia said defiantly.

'You don't fool me, Octavia! You arranged it with your brother-in-law, though you knew very well that I would stop it if I had known. How the devil did you get Lisette away from Julia and Henry?'

'I didn't have to. They had left her in Harry's hands.'

'I don't believe it! Julia wouldn't do such a thing! Especially not with Arandez in the house.'

'Mrs Barraclough didn't know Mr Arandez was here. But Harry is a very eligible *parti*, Mr Barraclough, and your sister-in-law sees no reason to discourage him! So she left them together. I was the one who brought Arandez over here to them. He wanted to talk to Lisette, so I...I let him.'

Edward's face darkened. 'If anything happens to Lisette because of what you've done,' he said harshly, 'I'll make you wish you had never been born!'

Octavia felt a pang of fear, but she faced him bravely. 'Don't be so blindly pig-headed! It is exactly as I said. Lisette has grown up a lot since she left Antigua. A few minutes in Arandez's company have been enough to convince her that she has outgrown him! Instead of berating me, look at her now! Does she look like a girl in danger of falling into his power again?'

Edward looked over to the other side of the room where Lisette was coming towards them, escorted by Harry. They were both laughing as they approached. He hadn't seen his niece so carefree in a long time.

'Edward! Lieutenant Petrie tells me he's already met you! And I was so looking forward to introducing him myself.' Her voice faded. 'Why are you looking so angry? Aunt Julia likes him. She left us together…'

'What were you saying to Arandez?'

Lisette's face cleared and she came close and took his hand. 'You needn't worry any more about Ricardo, Edward. I shan't do anything foolish. I found out tonight that I'm quite cured. As soon as I can, I shall tell him so.'

Edward frowned even more heavily. 'You are not to talk to him at all, Lisette! Don't go near him!'

Octavia cleared her throat, and he turned to glare at her. Undeterred, she said quietly, 'Don't you think you're being a little draconian, sir? Since Mr Arandez is my brother-in-law's protégé, he is bound to be seen everywhere. It would be difficult for Lisette to ignore him completely.'

Edward set his jaw and turned to Harry. 'Lietenant Petrie, I must have a word with your sister. Do you think you could look after my niece for a few minutes?'

Harry looked doubtful. 'It depends on Tavy, sir. Does she wish to hear what you have to say? It doesn't sound as if it's about the weather.'

'The temptation might be considerable, but I promise not to strangle her, if that's what you're worried about.'

Octavia said, 'Take Lisette, Harry. And you needn't look so anxious, either of you! I'm not afraid of Mr Barraclough.'

Harry's face lit up. 'In that case, there's nothing I'd like better! Miss Barraclough, shall we go to find something to eat and drink?'

After they had gone Edward said, 'You should be.'

'Afraid? Of you? Never!'

A small smile flickered in his eyes, then disappeared. Then his expression changed and he said heavily, 'The fact that Arandez has appeared, and in such distinguished company, means that the situation is different. You seem so determined to refuse to do anything I ask that you force me to tell you more about him.'

'I would like you to.'

'Is there somewhere where we can talk?'

'My brother-in-law's library? We'll be undisturbed there.'

'You're not afraid of the gossips if we're seen? I seem to remember you were morbidly anxious about them a short while ago.'

'That is a trivial matter compared with this business of Lisette. Will you follow me?'

Chapter Sixteen

Once in the library—a room which was hardly ever used and certainly never by the Duke—Octavia turned and faced him, a challenge in her eye.

'Now, Mr Barraclough. I'm listening. But I warn you, I shall continue to do what I think best, whatever your prejudices about Mr Arandez. Indeed, I'm not sure why you are so worried. Lisette has told you she no longer thinks she is in love with him, just as I said she would. Once she has met him again to make that clear to him, I doubt you will be troubled any further by the man.'

'*Prejudices!*' He walked about the room, his every movement expressing anger and frustration. Finally he came to a stop in front of her and said abruptly, 'I simply don't know how to tell you this. Not even Julia knows the whole truth. But I can see that, unless I do, you will go your own headstrong way to disaster, and take Lisette with you.'

'Oh, come! Surely no dispute over boundaries can be as serious as this!'

'Is that what you think it is?'

'It's what Lisette thinks.'

'She must never know anything different. I want your word on that.'

Octavia hesitated, then said, 'Very well.'

He looked at her for a moment, as if he was still not sure. Then he made up his mind and said, 'Two years ago Ricardo Arandez abused and raped a girl of sixteen on the island of Jamaica. The girl died.'

Octavia stared at him, horrified, then sat down. 'I don't believe it!' she said.

'I assure you it's true. He has always been known for his harsh treatment of the slaves on the Arandez plantation, but on Antigua cruelty to slaves is not regarded as a crime. It's one reason why I left the place and became a banker. But this was different. This girl was not a slave. He ought to have been punished and disgraced, of course, but the girl's family was far from wealthy and Arandez's father was able to pay them off.' He watched her for a moment while she took it all in. Then he said, '*Now* do you see why I want Lisette to have nothing to do with him?'

'Yes, I...I... Are you *sure*?'

'Of course I'm sure,' he said impatiently. 'Do you think I'd make a statement such as that unless I was absolutely certain? I saw the girl's parents myself. I spoke to some of the authorities on the island.'

'But he looks so...so *decent*!'

'It's his chief asset.'

'Oh, God! And I encouraged Lisette to talk to him...' Octavia put her face in her hands.

'Quite!' He regarded her for a moment, then said, 'I would have spared you this, but—'

Octavia lifted her head and looked at him steadily. 'I wouldn't have listened to you otherwise. You are right to be so angry. I...I beg your pardon.'

His frown faded and a rueful smile appeared. Taking her hands in his, he drew her up from the chair and said, 'You've done it again, Octavia. It's very strange. I do get angry with you, you infuriate me. But I can never sustain it. Why the devil is it so?'

Octavia was finding it difficult to breathe. 'I...I don't know,' she croaked.

His eyes on her mouth, he said, 'I still fantasise about you, you know. I still have sudden memories of that tower room...'

'So do I,' she whispered.

He pulled her slowly towards him. 'Octavia!' he murmured, and bent his head to kiss her.

For a moment they were lost, locked in each other's arms, back in that room in the tower, passion mounting between them... But then they slowly came back to earth, unable this time to forget for long who and where they were. Octavia stared at him.

'What is it?' she asked, bewildered. 'It's still there, that magic. I've tried so hard to forget. You say you don't despise me, but—'

'Don't!' he said harshly. 'You mustn't say such things, not even think them. I don't despise you, Octavia. It's myself I despise for being so weak.'

'But it isn't *weakness* to love someone.'

His arms tightened round her. For a moment it looked as if he would kiss her again. Then almost violently he said, 'It is for me!' and turned away from her. 'No, Octavia! I've felt more for you than for any other woman. Some would call it love, perhaps. But it isn't *enough*. I have no wish to marry. I doubt I ever shall. I've no desire to tie myself down, to drown in a sea of domesticity, not even with you. And I respect you too much to offer anything else.'

He was as determined as ever. It was the end of hope. For a moment Octavia wanted to argue, to shout, to tell him what a fool he was to reject all that they could offer each other for so trivial a reason. But pride stopped her. She would beg for no man's love. Calling on all her training, all her pride, she managed to say coldly,

'It's as well you do. I would find any such offer very difficult to forgive.' She paused, then went on, 'As for marriage... You've been very frank, Mr Barraclough, so let me be equally frank. Since you don't intend to ask me, you'll never find out whether I would have accepted you or not. But, like you, I have always avoided marriage, and it would now take a great deal for me to give up my own independence, more perhaps than you have to offer. I am sure this feeling we have, however powerful, is transitory. It will die when we see less of each other—as we undoubtedly shall.'

'Octavia!'

She went on as if he had not spoken. 'It's time to go back to the salon and join Lisette and the others. Thank you for trusting me with the facts about Arandez. I shall do what I can to protect Lisette until something can be done about him. Do you wish me to say anything to my sister or brother-in-law?'

Her voice was polite, but still very cold. He frowned, and looked for a moment as if he wanted to say more, then gave up and followed her lead. 'I think not,' he replied. 'You can't tell them everything, so better not to say anything at all. I'll find a way of dealing with Arandez.'

Octavia nodded and they went out. She had to work hard to appear normal as they joined the crowds. She was still shattered at what she had heard about Arandez, at how easily she could have encouraged Lisette into danger. And a cold weight lay on her heart. However strongly Edward Barraclough might be attracted to her, it was now more than clear that Gussie had been right. He would never commit himself to marriage. Her only recourse was to rid herself of her own absurd weakness.

Edward's face was grim as they searched the rooms for Lisette and Harry, but could find neither. His frown grew even heavier. 'I thought I could trust that brother of yours to look after her properly,' he said impatiently. 'Where the devil are they?'

Octavia caught a glimpse of jonquil yellow among the leaves of the winter garden. She closed her eyes. A scene between her brother and Edward Barraclough on top of everything else would be too much to bear. She said wearily, 'I think they're down this way.'

Edward looked and swore. 'That damned puppy! I should never have left Lisette with him! Come!' He set off at such a pace that Octavia almost had to run as he shouldered his way through the crowd.

But Harry and Lisette were not enjoying a quiet tête-à-tête in the winter garden. Arandez was with them, and they were just in time to hear Harry say in a voice which was quiet but full of warning, 'I've told you, Arandez! Let Miss Barraclough go!'

'Damn you, she's betrothed to me!' snarled Arandez.

'I'm not, Ricardo! I told you! Why won't you listen to me? I'm sorry, but I don't want to marry you. Leave me alone!' Lisette sounded distraught.

Arandez jerked her to him. 'Never!'

There was a sudden howl of pain as Harry chopped Arandez on the arm with the side of his hand, then pushed him aside. He moved Lisette out of the way, then told her gently to go back to her aunt while he dealt with her tormentor.

'I'll take care of him, Petrie,' said Edward as he moved forward. 'Oblige me by looking after Lisette and your sister. Take them out of here.'

'Come this way, Lisette,' said Octavia. 'We needn't go back through the crowds. You can recover in my room. Are you coming with us, Harry?'

Harry's face was flushed with anger. 'I think I'll stay, if you don't mind,' he said abruptly. 'Just in case the fellow tries any more tricks. But take Lisette to safety.'

Octavia didn't stop to question. She simply nodded and took Lisette away.

Some time later she heard a tap at her door. Harry was there.

'I've come to see how Miss Barraclough is,' he said.

'She's having a rest. I was just going to come down to look for her aunt. I think she should go home. Where is Arandez?'

'Gone,' said Harry briefly. 'You won't see him again tonight. Barraclough made it more than clear that he wasn't wanted. In fact, I doubt we'll ever hear any more of the fellow. It would take a braver man then Arandez to ignore Barraclough, I can tell you.'

'Good. Could you find Mrs Barraclough for me, while I stay here with Lisette?'

But Lisette joined them at the door. 'I'd rather you didn't. Aunt Julia will only make a fuss. If Ricardo has gone I should like to come down again, if I may.'

She smiled at Harry. 'I'd like to thank Lieutenant Petrie for looking after me. And... I still haven't had any of those lovely looking refreshments.'

Octavia looked on in amazement as Lisette, who had seemed on the point of collapse just a few minutes before, smiled even more widely at Harry and said, 'Will you wait for me? I need to tidy myself a little first.'

Harry nodded, and she disappeared.

Octavia raised both her eyebrows at her brother, then shut the door and went to help Lisette.

'Are you sure you're well enough?'

'Oh, yes. I'm not nervous when Harry—Lieutenant Petrie is with me.'

'You can call him Harry to me, my dear,' said Octavia with amusement. 'But don't let your uncle hear you! I have to say you're looking a lot better than you did.'

'It's as you said, Lady Octavia. Now I've told Ricardo, I feel happier than I've been for a long time. I'm free of him at last!' She paused, then said shyly, 'And Harry is even nicer than I remembered.'

'I'm glad you think so—I'm quite fond of him myself. But you must still go carefully with your uncle. There's no reason why Harry shouldn't have his approval, but there does seem to be a certain reluctance about him!'

'He'll come round. As you say, there's no reason why he shouldn't, and Aunt Julia approves. Shall we go down?'

Lisette opened the door, took Harry's arm and started off down the stairs. The difference in Lisette, her composure, her air of serene confidence was almost unbelievable! Was this all it had taken? To confess to Ricardo Arandez that she no longer loved him? Octavia's expression was wistful as she watched the two go down to join the company. It looked as if for them at least there would be a happy ending.

She went back into her own room, shut the door and leaned against it. Solitude at last! The pain in her heart was getting worse. Edward Barraclough had admitted that he loved her, and in the same breath had taken away all hope that he could ever think of marrying her. What a stupid, stupid man he was! A sob escaped her, though her eyes were dry. What was she to do? Certainly not join the crowds downstairs again—Gussie's guests must do without her. This feeling of hurt was like a physical injury, which no balm could reach, nothing could alleviate. And to disguise the pain, to pretend that she felt nothing, was beyond her just for the moment. She needed time to overcome it....

Some one else was filled with pain and anger, and was less willing to suffer without taking revenge. Arandez was no longer able to convince himself that Lisette loved him, but he had by no means given her up. The prize was too rich and too lovely to be given up without a struggle. For the moment she was too well protected for him to get near her, but while she remained unmarried there was hope. His chance would come, he was sure.

But as time went on he found that the word had gone round. Fewer and fewer drawing rooms were open to him, and he was tempted more and more to seek his amusements in the sub-world of London society, a world that catered for the more depraved appetites. But the deeper he sank, the more he craved revenge. He began to promise himself that Lisette would be sorry for what she had done to him, sorrier than she realised. He had tried to deal honourably with her, but she had thrown his honour back in his face. The more gentle approach—persuasion, reproaches, his affecting stories about her father—had proved useless. Force was the only answer—as it was with all women in the end. His chance would come, and then she would pay... He went back to his underworld and bided his time, and urged his servants meanwhile to keep a vigilant watch on her movements.

After that evening Octavia had little or no contact with Edward Barraclough—no more confidences, no more arguments, not even about Harry. It was not difficult to avoid him. There were plenty of gentlemen only too willing to escort Lady Octavia, dance with Lady Octavia, talk to Lady Octavia, and in her own way she was having almost as great a success as Lisette. She showed the world a brave face, and no one suspected that Lady Octavia's heart was slowly breaking.

But as the Season wore on, and London got warmer and dustier, she began to think of Wychford, its greenery, its lake, the cool shadows among its trees and longed to go back there. The Barracloughs' six-month tenure was over and the house was now available to her. Her task in London was finished. Pip had her governess, Lisette had been launched as successfully as anyone could have wished, and it was now generally acknowledged that she and Harry Petrie would probably make a match of it.

Everyone, it seemed, was happy except herself. Life in London was just as stale, her admirers just as predictable, as they had been five years before, and this time the effort of keeping up appearances was proving harder with every day that passed. In the end she could bear it no longer; when the excuse to leave London came her way, she seized it eagerly.

It came during a visit to the Barracloughs in South Audley Street. Harry was as usual deep in conversation with Lisette, and Octavia was left talking to Julia. Her fortitude was sorely tested as Julia went into a long diatribe about Edward Barraclough's behaviour.

'He has never taken his responsibilities as seriously as I should have liked, but I have never known him as bad as this! He is the talk of London! I cannot imagine what has happened to him. Anyone would think he was deliberately trying to let the family down. He drinks and gambles to excess, and from what Henry tells me he is spending a fortune on that...that harpy of his!' Then, probably realising that she had been indiscreet, Julia said hastily, 'Not that I know about that sort of thing, of course. No decent woman would!'

At last, to Octavia's profound relief, Julia left the subject of Edward Barraclough's misdemeanours and turned to the rest of the family. But what she had to say was not much more comforting. She was worried about Pip.

'What's wrong?' asked Octavia. 'I thought she looked a little pale the last time I saw her! Is she ill?'

'Not exactly, but I'm afraid London doesn't suit her at all. She is forever talking of Wychford. Her governess has been very good—she has taken the child to all the sights she can think of, but you know Philippa. She has so much energy, and yet the heat and dust are sometimes too much even for her. London is not the best place for a child of her age and inclination. I don't know how we shall deal with her when Miss Cherrifield goes away.'

'Goes away? I thought she would stay as long as you needed her?'

'Oh, she will return. But it was arranged before she came to us that we would release her for three weeks at the beginning of May. What Philippa will do without her I cannot imagine! I have no time to spend on her. My time is taken up with looking after

Lisette. That scoundrel Arandez is still in London, and Edward and Henry insist that she must be chaperoned wherever she goes. Your brother is very good, of course. He spends a great deal of time with her.' She threw a fond glance at Lisette and Harry, sitting on the other side of the room. 'I think there'll be a match there, don't you? But I can't even leave them unchaperoned for too long. Which means I have very little time for Philippa.'

Octavia thought for a moment, then said, 'May *I* look after Pip while Miss Cherrifield is away? I am thinking of going down to Wychford and would be delighted if she could come with me.'

Julia regarded her with surprise. 'You want to leave London? Before the end of the Season?'

Octavia nodded her head. 'Shocking, isn't it? But I would love to leave London, in fact. Pip's company would be an additional attraction. Would she come to Wychford?'

'I am very sure she would—she never stops talking of the place.' Julia's tone conveyed her own opinion of Wychford.

'Well, then, shall we consider it settled? In a week's time, you said? Perfect! And...Pip can stay as long as you can spare her. Miss Cherrifield could even join us down there when she comes back. I doubt I shall return to London once I leave.'

'Lady Octavia, it would be a godsend! I cannot say how grateful we should be! Are you sure?'

'Quite!'

'Let me send for Philippa so that you can tell her yourself.'

Octavia was concerned when she saw Pip. The air of crackling energy that had so attracted her was considerably diminished, and Pip's welcome, though enthusiastic, was less exuberant than it usually was. But when she heard of Octavia's invitation she went pale with excitement.

'You mean it? You really mean it? Oh, Miss Petrie, I mean, Lady Octavia, how good you are! Lisette, did you hear? I'm to go back to Wychford!'

Many were considerably surprised, of course, at Lady Octavia Petrie's decision. Gussie was extremely put out, and Octavia had a hard time reconciling her to the idea, but she remained firm. She was tired of London, and had no desire to hear any more gossip about Edward Barraclough. She suspected that he was doing his best to forget her, and she had no desire to be there when he succeeded and the secret, silken bond that had held him to her was finally broken.

So, after a busy week, Octavia, Pip and a small retinue of servants travelled down to Wychford. As they drove up the drive Pip could hardly restrain her excitement.

'Look, Miss Petrie, look! It's laughing!' She turned round. 'I'm sorry, I mean, Lady Octavia.'

Octavia laughed and put her arm round Pip. 'Call me what you wish, Pip. I shan't mind.' She looked out. 'I do believe you're right!'

It was sunny, but there was a slight breeze and the leafy branches along the way were swaying and dancing in the air. Their shadows, reflected in the windows of Wychford, gave the house an air of merriment, and Octavia felt a lift of heart. There would always be Wychford.

Mrs Dutton was waiting, and took the news that the owner of Wychford was 'Miss Petrie' with a comfortable smile and the comment, 'I always suspected there was something about you, my lady! We all hope you'll be happy with what we've done to the house. The repairs to the staircase went very well, though the men still don't understand what happened. It seems to be quite safe now, though. I've put Miss Philippa in the tower room, but I wasn't sure which room you would prefer. I've prepared both the main bedroom and your old one, as well.'

Octavia looked at Pip's pleading eyes and said, 'I'll sleep in my old room, Mrs Dutton, thank you.'

Soon they had both settled in and busied themselves exploring their domain, and if Octavia was less deliriously happy than her little guest, she found a measure of peace. But she never suggested that they should go up the stairs to the room at the top of the tower. When Pip asked about it, she said vaguely that she thought the key had been lost.

* * *

In London, meanwhile, Edward Barraclough was fighting a losing battle. He had seen very little of Octavia after the scene in the Monteiths' library, and whenever they did meet her manner was so different that she hardly seemed the same person. It was as if an invisible wall of ice separated them. She had clearly drawn a line under their long and curiously close relationship, and he was now seeing the Lady Octavia Petrie the world knew. Charming, well-mannered, and indifferent. A cool customer, as Stainforth had said. He ought to have been happy it was so, but in fact he could hardly bear it.

When he heard that Octavia was intending to leave London it took considerable strength of will not to hurry round to the Monteiths' house to see her, but he had resisted the temptation. What could he say to her? Beg her to stay, to smile at him, to talk to him in her old way, to be his Octavia once more? Not while he was as determined as ever to avoid the trap of marriage. No, she had the right idea. Better that she should go, better that he should no longer be reminded of how it had been between them, better that he shouldn't catch sight of the proud lift of her head, her honey-gold curls on the other side of a room, and be seduced all over again. Better by far to let her go. Once she was out of sight he would forget her, he was sure. That was all it needed—her absence, and a little time.

But time proved him wrong. London was a desert without her, and life hardly worth living. Louise was no comfort, and after something of a scene he parted company with her. It wasn't long before she found someone else. Gambling lost its fascination, too, and even the cut and thrust of banking seemed a joyless affair. He lost patience with the Foreign Office, and after offending several important gentlemen there he left them to their own devices.

He viewed Lisette's evident happiness with Harry with a jaundiced eye, but could find nothing to object to in it, and decided after an uncomfortable search of his conscience that he was chiefly envious. When Harry asked for permission to pay his addresses to Lisette, Edward was just able to pull himself together and give his consent with reasonably good grace.

That same evening he went back to his house in North Audley Street and, as the fire died down and the house grew silent, he sat steadily drinking brandy and contemplating the wreck of his well-planned, well-organised life. What had happened? Just last September he had walked through Berkeley Square, pitying poor Trenton for having to marry, and congratulating himself on his own untrammelled, carefree existence. What had gone wrong? Why did it no longer seem sufficient?

After a while his mind turned to another problem that was occupying him, namely the behaviour of Ricardo Arandez. The fellow was being seen less and less in Society's drawing rooms, though he was still in London. After the warning he had been given in the Monteiths' winter garden, this was hardly surprising. But where was he spending his time? And why was he still in England, now that it was clear he had lost Lisette for good? Ricardo Arandez was not a man to give up lightly, nor would he forget anything he saw as an insult. Until it was absolutely certain that Arandez had gone back to the West Indies, Lisette must be guarded all the time.

This decided, Edward found it impossible not to go back to the other, all-important question. What could he do about his own, deep dissatisfaction? He eventually fell asleep, still reluctant to accept the answer. But just a day or two later, he found that his mind was suddenly made up.

Lisette missed Pip. And she missed Octavia. The thought that neither of them knew of her engagement, however unofficial, worried her, too. But her request to visit them at Wychford did not find favour with her aunt.

'Really, Lisette, that is most inconsiderate! You know I would have to accompany you, and the thought of that house makes me shudder. Besides, the Season will end quite soon, and I don't want to miss any part of it, especially not the Marchants' ball! You can surely wait till then.'

But when Harry saw Lisette's disappointment he hit on the happy idea of escorting Lisette to Wychford himself. But though Julia was tempted she vetoed it. 'It can't be done! Not before you are officially engaged, and even then I should be reluctant.

No, Lieutenant Petrie, it's kind of you to offer, but it won't do.'

Julia had been made to feel guilty, and she was so annoyed that the next time she met Edward she expressed her feelings to him.

'I have devoted myself to that girl, got her engaged to one of the town's most eligible bachelors, and what is her response? She wants to drag me back to a house she knows I can't stand, merely to see her little sister! It's not as if they are missing anything, Edward. There's nothing official. The proper engagement celebration will come later when Lord Warnham has given his consent. Really, I wish you would speak to the girl! Instead of being grateful, she walks around looking as if I have committed a crime! But I can't allow her to go with only Lieutenant Petrie to accompany her. Apart from the proprieties, it isn't safe. Not with Arandez about.'

'I'll escort them.'

Edward's offer came quite spontaneously, and it astonished both of them. After a moment's pause Julia accepted with delight, and called Lisette to tell her so. Edward found himself making the necessary arrangements with them in a sort of daze, still not sure what had caused him to make the offer and wondering if he had gone quite mad.

Only later, when he was alone, did he finally acknowledge that to take Lisette and Harry to Wychford meant that he would see Octavia again, and that this was what he wanted most in the world. He had no idea how she would receive him, nor what he would do about it, but for better or for worse he had to know once and for all what it was that made life so impossible without her.

The decision made, life suddenly acquired a brighter hue, and the world seemed a better place.

Chapter Seventeen

The morning they left London was sunny and the countryside looked especially lovely as they bowled along. As they turned into the familiar drive Harry made them laugh with his account of how he had hidden among the trees the first time he had come, and they were still laughing as they turned the corner and the house came into view. Edward felt a surge of happiness. Wychford with its crooked gables, its sparkling windows and its odd little tower, looked welcoming and...expectant. That was the only word. Expectant.

Lisette had sent a message ahead, and Pip was waiting for them. When she saw the carriage she dropped out of her tree and raced up to the house, shouting, 'They're here, they're here, Octavia!'

Octavia stood framed in the massive oak doorway. She looked thinner, paler, than she had, but as the three visitors got out of the carriage her cheeks flooded with colour. For a few moments all was confusion and excitement as the younger Barracloughs greeted one another.

'I didn't expect you,' said Octavia distantly, looking at Edward. 'Lisette only mentioned herself and Harry.'

'I suppose you'd call me a kind of chaperon,' he said. He would have been astonished at how cool he sounded to her. At the sight of Octavia his heart had melted within him. He had forgotten everything but how much she meant to him, had wanted to snatch her into his arms and kiss away the look of unhappiness in her eyes... And he hadn't dared. For the first time in his life he was uncertain about his reception. He was paralysed by the sudden thought that Octavia might have found the cure that had eluded him, that she might no longer welcome his touch. But to restrain himself from taking her into his arms, to make himself sound anything like normal, had taken every ounce of his self-control.

He had been right. Octavia gave a little laugh, but the wall of ice was still firmly in place as she said, 'Of course. Julia wouldn't willingly come near Wychford again! She regards the house as dangerous.' There was a slight pause, then she went on, 'You must forgive me. I don't quite know what to say. The situation seems so odd. The last time we met here you were the master and I the governess, and now...' She shook her head, then began again. 'Will you come in, sir?' she said formally. 'I've arranged for some refreshments. They're in the little parlour—I wasn't expecting you, you see.'

'Don't treat me as a stranger, Octavia! Please!'

She gave a painful smile. 'I really don't know how to treat you at all. There were no classes for this sort of situation in my Ladies' Seminary. But come in. The others are waiting.'

As Edward stepped into the hall he looked around him. The hall looked the same as ever with no sign of damage to the staircase. The massive brass chandeliers gleamed in the sunlight shining through the long windows.

'Pip looks a great deal better,' said Edward, striving for normality.

'She loves Wychford,' said Octavia. 'We've had such fun together.'

'You spoil her.'

'Oh, no! I truly believe that Pip could not be spoiled. I shall miss her a lot when she finally has to go back to her aunt.' She bit her lip, then said brightly, 'Lisette has surprised me. I always thought that she and Harry would suit, but never that she would bloom as she has. Can I take it that Harry now has your approval?'

'Wait a minute or two longer and they will tell you themselves.'

Octavia led the way into the small parlour. On the table was a tray with glasses and an array of Mrs Dutton's delicacies. Beside it stood a wine cooler with a bottle in it. She hesitated, then turned to Edward. 'Would you...?'

Edward opened the bottle and poured its sparkling contents into the glasses. Octavia handed them out one by one, even passing a small one to Pip. She raised her glass.

'First of all, welcome back to Wychford,' she said. And waited, a small smile on her lips as she looked at her brother and Lisette.

Harry cleared his throat. 'Tavy, we've come today to ask you to wish us happy. Lisette and I... That's to say...Lisette has agreed to marry me,' he said. 'And her guardians have given their consent.'

Pip gave a cheer, and Octavia's smile widened. 'My darlings! This is wonderful news!' She put her glass down and embraced Lisette. 'Harry, you always did have all the luck in the family, but this is the best of the lot! I can't think of anyone I'd like more as a sister.'

Edward said, 'With your permission, Lady Octavia... To Harry and Lisette! Long life and happiness!'

They all drank. Pip was so excited she hardly tasted her wine before she begged them all to excuse her. She had something in her room for Lisette. She disappeared, having made them promise not to talk about their plans till she was back.

There was a silence. Harry drew Lisette aside. Edward looked at Octavia. For a moment they were both lost in each other, lost in memory... Then Octavia shook her head and turned away.

'This...this won't do! I won't...I can't...' She stopped and took a breath. 'I wonder what Pip is up to,' she said with determined cheerfulness. 'I think we ought to go to see.'

They went into the hall and came to an abrupt halt. Mrs Dutton was there, looking terrified; surrounding her was a gang of men armed with pistols.

'I'm...I'm sorry, my lady. They burst in when I opened the door. I couldn't stop—' She gave a little scream as one of the men bundled her out of the door to the servants' quarters and locked it. He turned round and looked at his leader, still holding his pistol at the ready.

Harry took an impulsive step forward and the pistol was instantly turned in his direction.

'Don't move, any one of you!' said Ricardo Arandez. 'My...friends are all ready to shoot. Stop where you are!' The men spread out and faced the end of the hall where Octavia and the rest were standing. It could be seen that there were four of them, not counting their leader, though to Edward's experienced eye they looked a poor lot. Still, men with guns were always dangerous.

His eyes fixed on Arandez, Edward said abruptly, 'Better do as he says, Petrie. There's no place for a dead hero here.'

Arandez circled round and stood at the other end of the hall, behind his men. Octavia was horrified at the change she saw in him. Any resemblance to Tom Payne had vanished from this emaciated creature.

The fresh complexion was blotched and pale, the blue eyes bloodshot. He looked on the verge of a collapse—and all the more dangerous because of it.

Arandez noticed how Edward and Harry were measuring their chances as his men approached, and he said quickly, 'Don't get too close to them, you fools! Can't you see they'll leap on you if you get too near. Keep the guns pointed at the beautiful young lady in the yellow dress. My future wife. If anyone moves, fire. But no one would dare, would they, Barraclough? Not if it meant Lisetta would die. She's my safeguard.'

'What do you think you can do here?' asked Edward harshly. 'You're mad, Arandez!'

'Perhaps I am. But I'll have Lisetta, even if I have to kill the lot of you first. I might even begin with you, Edward Barraclough. You're the one who has caused all my troubles! Your damned brother was happy enough for me to marry Lisetta till you told him about my activities in Jamaica! Yes! I might just begin with you!' He lifted his gun and pointed it at Edward. 'Beg for your life, Barraclough, or you'll die here and now!'

In this moment of tension when the eyes of everyone else were fixed on Arandez and Edward, Octavia saw a slight movement on the gallery immediately above Arandez. Pip was quietly climbing on to the balustrade. Arandez and his men, who were all facing away from her, were unaware of it.

Octavia caught her breath and looked fleetingly at Edward. It was clear that he too had seen Pip. He cast a quick glance at Harry, then raised his voice and asked loudly,

'What do you wish me to say, Arandez? That I'm sorry? I might say something of the kind—but only if you tell your men to take their guns off Lisette first. They don't look very reliable to me. Do you really want *her* killed, too?'

Pip was now on top of the balustrade. Arandez said, 'Very well. I would really enjoy hearing you crawl, Barraclough. Do as he says!'

His men lowered their pistols, and at the same time there was a bloodcurdling yell and Pip landed with a thump on Arandez's shoulders. He staggered, and his pistol went off somewhere into the ceiling. With a roar of rage he threw the useless weapon away and dragged Pip down, fighting to release himself. The moment of distraction had given Edward and Harry their chance. Kicking and punching, they soon had all four of Arandez's accomplices on the floor, and were relieving them of their weapons.

Arandez was still fighting Pip. To her horror, Octavia saw him take out a knife, with the clear intention of using it to free himself from the child's leech-like grasp, and she hurled herself at him, screaming, 'NO! No, you mustn't!'

She took hold of the hand with the knife and hung on to it, dragging it down and away from Pip with all her strength. He pulled his hand free with a curse and flung Octavia from him so violently that she hit the ground several feet away, and lay in an inert heap, her head against the edge of the fireplace.

Edward had finished with his man. He looked up just in time to see Octavia fall, and leapt over to her. Pip was already there, kneeling beside her and desperately calling her name.

'She's dead!' wailed Pip. 'Octavia's dead!'

Edward cradled Octavia in his arms. 'Don't be a little fool,' he said roughly. 'She isn't dead! She can't be! She mustn't be!' He put his fingers against the side of Octavia's neck...

A sudden howling gust of wind swept through the hall and set the huge chandeliers swinging wildly. Arandez took a couple of paces towards Lisette.

'Lisetta—' he began uncertainly, stretching out a hand in appeal.

The fixings of the chandelier over his head suddenly gave way with a groan, and it crashed down on top of him, followed by a mass of plaster and dust. The noise was deafening. Arandez crumpled and fell. The silence that followed was uncanny.

It was broken by Edward. 'Thank God! Oh, thank God! There's a pulse there. She's alive.' For the first time he looked round and saw the chaos in the centre of the hall. 'My God!' he said in an appalled voice. He looked round at the servants who had broken their way in, and were standing at the end of the hall wide-eyed. 'See if you can help that poor devil under the chandelier. Come on! Step to it! And fetch a doctor. Immediately!'

Harry had been comforting Lisette, but now they came over. 'Octavia ought to be in bed. Let me take her,' said Harry, bending over his sister.

'Leave her alone!' said Edward fiercely, pushing him away. 'She's mine! I love her and she's mine! I'll take her!' Harry looked at him in astonishment, but didn't argue. Edward picked Octavia up in his arms, and, as he walked to the stairs, he said over his shoulder, 'Get Lisette to look after Pip. Her knee is bleeding. And Harry—see what's has happened to Arandez. I doubt we can do much for him, but you'd better take a look. Don't let the girls anywhere near! Bring the doctor to Octavia's room as soon as he arrives.'

Edward carried Octavia slowly up the stairs. He laid her on the bed, covered her, and knelt down beside her. For a moment he buried his head in the covers, then he said in a broken voice, 'Dear God, Octavia, don't leave me now! Not when I've only just found out how much you mean to me!'

Octavia's eyelids fluttered. But then she was once again still. He looked at her white face, the blue bruise on her temple, and said even more desperately,

'Dammit, you mustn't die, Octavia! Without you there's no happiness, no joy. You've *got* to live! You've got to give me time to tell you what you mean to me! I want to marry you, take care of you, live with you forever! I love you so much! I don't think I could face life without you! Please wake up!'

Octavia opened her eyes. 'Edward!' she said contentedly. 'Was that you I heard? Saying you wanted to marry me?'

He started to tell her how much, but stopped and looked more carefully at her. After a short silence he said slowly, 'You devil, Octavia! You heard it all!'

'Most of it,' she said.

'You mean, you let me carry on believing you were badly hurt, perhaps dying, when all the time…'

'I think you owed me that much. I *was* badly hurt. But by you, not Arandez.' She sat up. 'Where is he? What happened to Pip?'

He pushed her back against the pillows. 'Pip is perfectly sound apart from a few grazes. Lisette is with Harry. And Arandez is dead.'

'Dead! Did you…?'

'No, I didn't, though given the chance I might well have killed him. I'll tell you about it later. I expect you'll say that the house did it. But now you must rest till the surgeon comes.'

She would have protested, but Mrs Dutton came in at that point with the surgeon, and Edward was dismissed.

Octavia's questions had reminded him that he had some clearing up to do and he went downstairs. The servants told him that the men Arandez had brought with him had recovered and vanished while no one was looking, presumably back to their haunts in London. The surgeon had seen Arandez's body and it had been taken away. The chandelier, too, had been lifted away, though most of the dust and plaster was still there. Edward looked at it, then up at the ceiling.

'I don't know how it could have happened, sir,' said Mrs Dutton tearfully. 'After what happened to Mrs Barraclough the men went over everything, including that chandelier. It should never have fallen the way it did. They're saying in the kitchen that it was all a judgement. He was a wicked man, sir. He could have killed Lady Octavia. Do you think it was old Mrs Carstairs…?'

Edward shook his head. 'No, Mrs Dutton,' he said firmly. 'There's nothing supernatural about it. Look at this.' In the rubble on the floor was a broken piece of the chandelier's supports. Something had cut a neat hole right in its centre. 'That's a bullet hole,' said Edward. 'When Arandez fired his pistol into the ceiling that's where it went. Chance, perhaps. But nothing supernatural.'

He went towards the stairs, but heard Mrs Dutton say, 'Well, you may call it chance, if you wish, Mr Barraclough, but it was a very funny chance, and I know what *I* think it was!'

Edward smiled and went upstairs. Lisette and Pip, with Harry in close attendance, were already with Octavia, who was sitting up looking pale but fully conscious. The surgeon was on the point of coming to look for him. Octavia, he said, had had a narrow escape. She was shaken, but he had not found any serious damage. Rest and quiet for a few days ought to cure her. He departed after promising to call in two days' time to see how she did.

Edward came to the bedside, and said calmly, 'Now that everyone has seen you're not dead, Octavia, I expect you would like Lisette and Pip to show Harry the house. I want to talk to you.'

She sat up even straighter. 'No!' she said in some agitation. 'I don't want... Pip could stay...'

'No, she can't,' Edward said firmly. 'I promised to tell you what happened, and I intend to do so. Without an audience.'

Harry grinned at Lisette. 'I think your uncle means it,' he said. 'And after having seen him in action this afternoon I would hate to fall out with him.'

'Good man,' said Edward. 'You're not too bad in a fight yourself. You can call me Edward if you wish. Goodbye.'

Pip cast a knowledgeable glance at her uncle. 'I know why you want to get rid of us,' she said. 'I heard what you said when we thought she was dead. And I don't mind going if it means you're going to marry her. I always said you ought to.' Lisette laughed and dragged her away.

When they were gone Edward sat on the bed and said softly, 'Now, my love, we shall have a little chat.'

'Rest and quiet. That's what I'm to have,' said Octavia.

'You shall have all the rest and quiet you could wish for,' said Edward.

Octavia's face fell. 'Oh!'

'But not before you've told me two things. The first is why you pretended you were unconscious.'

'I was unconscious for a while. And then when I came to you were saying such wonderful things…I wanted to hear you say more.'

'Such as?'

'That you loved me. That you wanted to marry me. In fact, I'd quite like to hear it again…?'

Edward said firmly, 'Not before you tell me the second thing I want to know.'

'What is it?'

He put his hand on her cheek and said very seriously, 'That you forgive me for being such a fool. That you love me in spite of it.'

'You *are* a fool, Edward!' she said softly. 'Of course I love you! I couldn't have behaved so…so shamelessly with anyone else.'

He laughed triumphantly and took her into his arms. 'My dearest, sweetest Octavia! I can't possibly tell you what your shameless behaviour did to me! But now I want so much more. I want you to share your life with me, let me look after you, grow old with you, have children, *your* children.'

'But Edward! You said—'

'I know what I said, all the things I swore I would never even consider. And there's only one woman in the world who could have changed my mind for me.

You. Only you. I adore you.' He took her hand and kissed it. 'Marry me, Octavia, and I'll swear I'll do everything I can to make you happy.'

Octavia's pale cheeks were suffused with colour. 'Of course I will, dearest Edward! With all my heart.' She leant forward and kissed him, then drew back and smiled. 'Indeed, I hardly dare say no! Aunt Carstairs brought you here. Think what Wychford might do to me if I refused you!'

Gently, carefully, Edward leaned forward and gave her a long, lingering kiss. A sigh, a faint breath, soft as a summer zephyr, and perfumed with the dry scent of herbs, passed through the house and out into the summer air. Wychford was content.

*   *   *   *   *

HISTORICAL ROMANCE™

LARGE PRINT

BELHAVEN BRIDE

Helen Dickson

When Anna Preston was introduced to her estranged family at their Belhaven estate, London's glamorous set became her new milieu, with never-before-dreamt-of trips to Paris and the French Riviera. There was now even a chance of a place at Oxford.

Thrown headlong into this exciting new world, she needed a solid rock to cling to, and this she found in Alex Kent. Having escaped the revolution in Russia as a boy, Alex was an impressive – if enigmatic – man. He sought to protect Anna from the perils of her new life, but even he couldn't keep her from the dangers that come with falling in love…

THE HEMINGFORD SCANDAL

Mary Nichols

Jane had broken her engagement to Harry Hemingford and sent him packing after his scandalous behaviour. So why was he back now, just when Mr Allworthy had proposed? Her suitor was undoubtedly a good match, but had she ever really fallen out of love with Harry?

Was safety really more important than the joyous happiness she found in Harry's arms? Perhaps Society's opinion should just go hang!

Regency

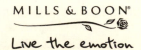

MILLS & BOON®

Live the emotion

HISTORICAL ROMANCE™

LARGE PRINT

THE NOTORIOUS LORD
Nicola Cornick

To sensible Rachel Odell, Cory, Lord Newlyn, has always been her friend and now, suddenly, she's aware of him as a man – an exceedingly handsome man. But he is her complete opposite, an adventure-seeker…and a rogue. It dawns on Rachel that throughout the summer Cory has been waging a slow, deliberate campaign to seduce her – but why? Is it because Cory has a secret agenda, or is it simply that he wants to claim his best friend as his bride…?

BLUESTOCKING BRIDES

The ladies of the Midwinter villages are about to be shocked, scandalised and…seduced!

FALLEN ANGEL
Sophia James

Nicholas Pencarrow, Duke of Westbourne, is intrigued by the woman who saves his life and then vanishes. Every attempt to make contact with this beautiful mystery lady is politely rebuffed.

Brenna has a dark secret she must keep buried, so she has built a respectable, uncomplicated world about herself where she avoids all male advances. Although, against her better judgement, the determined man keeps breaking through. Could she risk harming Nicholas's reputation by lowering her guard just once?

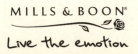
MILLS & BOON®

Live the emotion

HIST1204 LP